Woodwind Ensemble Music Guide.

compiled by

Himie Voxman & Lyle Merriman

The Instrumentalist Co.
1418 Lake St., Evanston, IL 60204

PREFACE

The present work is the first in a series of bibliographies of the literature in print for wind and percussion instruments. A second series will deal with the solo and instructional repertoire.

The prime source of information has been catalogs received from some 262 publishers. A number of foreign music information centers have supplied supplementary material. We are grateful to the many publishers and agencies who have so courteously responded to our inquiries.

The last quarter-century has witnessed a dramatic increase in the wind instrument repertory. Voluminous publication of new compositions, reissues of out-of-print items, and first editions of material previously existing in manuscript only has made it very difficult if not impossible to keep abreast of available literature. It is our hope that these bibliographies will widen the repertoire used in instruction and public performance.

In the past few years numerous changes in the publishing field have occured. Music dealers are therefore often uncertain as to the continuing availability of certain items, especially when a single catalog is divided among more than one new owner. Transfer of firms has in some instances been accompanied by drastic deletions from catalogs. While some change is inevitable and often desirable, one regrets the disappearance of many compositions pruned by new owners more strongly influenced by sales records than musical merit.

The lack of a central convenient source of information as to music currently in print has resulted in the inadvertent publication of the same piece of music either from an early print or from manuscript by more than one publisher — to the detriment of each in many instances.

It would be highly presumptious to assume that *Woodwind Ensemble Music Guide* can solve all these problems. Lack of response by some publishers, a certain degree of confusion in some catalogs as to instrumentation, authorship, and perhaps our own oversights preclude any claim to completeness or total accuracy. Our hope is that subsequent revisions will correct errors, add comprehensiveness, and reflect the suggestions which we welcome from the book's users. We are grateful to Mr. Traugott Rohner, President of *The Instrumentalist Co.*, for providing the incentive and opportunity to present this volume to our colleagues in the wind instrument fraternity and to the music publishing industry.

Lyle Merriman
Himie Voxman
Iowa City, Iowa U.S.A.
November 1973

ABBREVIATIONS

a	alto	nar	narrator
A	Alto voice	no(s)	number(s)
arr	arranger	ob	oboe
b	bass	opt	optional
B	Bass voice	org	organ
bar	baritone	perc	percussion
Bar	Baritone voice	pf	pianoforte
bc	*basso continuo	pic	piccolo
bk	book	rec	recorder
br	brass	rev	revised
bsn	bassoon	S	Soprano voice
c	contra	sax	saxophone
cel	celeste	sdr	snare drum
cemb	cembalo	str	string(s)
cl	clarinet	T	Tenor voice
comp	compiler	tamb	tambourine
ct	cornet	ten	tenor
db	double bass	timp	timpani
dr	drum	tpt	trumpet
ed	editor	tr	transcriber
ehn	English horn	trb	trombone
eu	euphonium	tri	triangle
fl	flute	tu	tuba
go	gong	V	Voice
guit	guitar	va	viola
hn	French horn	vc	violoncello
hp	harp	vib	vibraphone
hpcd	harpsichord	vn	violin
instr	instrument(s)	vol	volume
mar	marimba	ww	woodwind
MS	Mezzo Soprano voice	xyl	xylophone

* see General Information

SYMBOLS

Instrumentation inside parentheses indicates alternate part:
  fl(ob) - flute or oboe

Slash between two instruments indicates doubling by one player:
  ob/ehn - oboe and English horn

Key signatures: (1) Upper case letter(s) indicate major key(s);
  (2) Lower case letter(s) indicate minor key(s).

iv

GENERAL INFORMATION

Basso continuo
Since catalogs do not usually indicate whether or not a basso continuo part includes separate bass and keyboard parts, we have arbitrarily considered it to be a single keyboard part. Thus, a trio sonata for flute, violin, and basso continuo will be listed in the "Three Instruments" section, in the "Woodwind, String, Keyboard" category. When looking for trio sonatas, however, the reader should also check the "Four Instruments" section, "Woodwind, String, Keyboard" category.

ad libitum
Instruments designated as *ad libitum* are not counted in classifying a category. E.g., a work for three clarinets and piano *ad lib* is classified as a clarinet trio only.

Collections
The "Collections" category includes those publications containing a group of pieces by more than one composer.

French horn
In the Two, Three, and Four Instruments sections, the French horn is classified as a brass instrument. Beginning with Five Instruments, the French horn is regarded as a woodwind instrument to minimize the number of categories.

Percussion
The number of percussionists required is based on the number of percussion instruments indicated in the catalog. E.g., vibraphone, xylophone, cow bell would be counted as three players, although it is possible that one performer could cover all three parts.

Guitar, Harp, Percussion, Recorder, Tape
In order to be helpful to those devotees of the guitar, harp, etc., we have made separate categories for them. Any compositions using one of these instruments, however, is cross-referenced; i.e., a work that includes both guitar and percussion will be found in the "Instruments including Guitar" category and the "Instruments including Percussion" category.

BIBLIOGRAPHIC INFORMATION

Composer-Arranger, (Editor)   Publisher
    Title, Opus no., date of composition when given, key, no. of volumes, Instrumentation

Titles are abbreviated as follows:

a. Catalog: Concerto in D Major, Op. 14, No. 3
   Bibliography: Concerto, D, op. 14/3

b. Catalog: Largo from Symphony No. 4
   Bibliography: Largo (Symphony No. 4)

CONTENTS

TWO INSTRUMENTS

TWO FLUTES

Ambrosius, H.	Sonata	S&C
Arma, P.	3 résonances	B&V
Arnell, R.	5 Inventions	HE
Arrieu, C.	Duo in 4 Movements	Amp
Babell, W.	Bourrée	FrC
Bach, C.P.E.	10 Easy Duets (Wq. 81, 82, 193)	WZ
Bach, J.S.,	15 Two-Part Inventions	CF
Bach, J.S.-Schönicke	2-Part Inventions	WZ
Bach W.F.-Maganini	Canon (Sonata, f)	CF
Bach, W.F.	Duo Sonata	EdM
Bach, W.F.-Walther	6 Duette, 2 vol.	BrH
Bach, W.F.-Wummer	6 Duets, 2 vol.	Int
Bach, W.F.-Schittler	Sonata	Leu
Bach, W.F.-Gloeder	Sonate E♭	B&N
Bach, W.F.-Gloeder	Sonata E♭	Int
Bach, W.F.	3 Sonatas	CF
Bach, W.F.-Rodemann	2 Sonatas, e, f	B&N
Barge, W. (ed)	Heiteres aus alter Zeit	WZ
Barre, M. de la-Scheck & Ruf	Suite, G	Ric
Barre, M. de la-Zöller	Suite, e, op. 4	HSM
Beck, C.	Sonatine	SS
Beck, F.	A Conversation for Two Solo Flutes	AMC
Beckwith, J.	5 Pieces (1951)	AMP
Beethoven, L. van	Allegro and Minuet	EdM
Beethoven, L. van-Wummer	Allegro and Minuet	Int
Beethoven, L. van-Walther	Allegro and Minuet	WZ
Beethoven, L. van-Brodszky	Sonata	EMB
Bennett, Richard	Conversations	UE
Berbiguier, T.	7 Duets, op. 28	Int
Berbiguier, T.	6 Duets, op. 59	Int
Berbiguier, T.	6 Easy Duets	EdM
Berbiguier, T.	3 Duos Concertantes	EdM
Berbiguier, T.	3 Duos, op. 4	EdH
Berbiguier, T.	3 Duos, op. 22	Sim
Berbiguier, T.	3 Duos, op. 46/1	EdH
Berbiguier, T.	3 Grands Duos brillans, op. 38/1	EdH
Berbiguier, T.	3 Grands Duos brillans, op. 38/2	EdH
Berbiguier, T.	3 Grands Duos brillans, op. 38/3	EdH
Bialas, G.	Kanonische Etüden	B&N
Blank, A.	2 Simple Canons	B&H
Blavet, M.	Duette	Hei
Blavet, M.-Mann	French Duets	M&M
Blavet, M.	6 Sonaten, op. 1/1-3	Ric
Blavet, M.-Ruf & Zöller	Sonata, G, op. 1/4	HSM
Blavet, M.-Ruf	2 Duets, op. 1/5,6	SS
Bodinus, S.-Birkner	Sonata, E	HMo

Two Flutes

Bodinus, S.-Havelaar	Sonata, e	B&V
Boehm, T.-Pellerite	3 Duets	SM
Boismortier, J.-Döflein	55 leichte Stücke, op. 22	SS
Boismortier, J.	6 Duetti, op. 1	WIN
Boismortier, J.-Ruf	6 Easy Duets, op. 17, 2 vols.	SS
Boismortier, J.-Frötscher	6 Sonatas, op. 1	B&N
Boismortier, J.	6 Sonatas, op. 1	Pet
Boismortier, J.-Frötscher	6 Sonatas, op. 6	B&N
Boismortier, J.	6 Sonatas, op. 6	Pet
Boismortier, J.-Raugel	Sonata, b	B&N
Boismortier, J.	2 Sonatas	Int
Boismortier, J.-Schlenger	2 Sonatas, C, g	WZ
Borris, S.	Duettino, op. 116/2	B&N
Bossler, K.	Sonatine	HG
Bousquet, N.	Favorite Flute Duets (Two Sonatas)	CF
Briccialdi, G.	Duo Concertant No. 2, op. 100	Int
Briccialdi, G.-Wummer	16 Duets, op. 132, 2 vols.	Int
Briccialdi, G.	16 Flute Duets "Dialogues," op. 132	B-M
Bucquet, P.	First Suite	EdM
Bucquet, P.	Second Suite	EdM
Bucquet, P.-Bouvet	Suite No. 2	EME
Butterworth	3 Dialogues	Pet
Cage, J.	3 Pieces (1935)	Pet
Cambini, G.-Lebermann	Duo, A, op. 11/5	SS
Cambini, G.-Lebermann	Duo, e, op. 11/4	SS
Cambini, G.-Lebermann	Duo, G, Op. 11/6	SS
Cardon, J.	3 Duo Concertans	EDh
Carles, M.	5 études concertantes	ALe
Castelnuovo-Tedesco, M.	Divertimento	TP
Cecconi, M.	Jeux	E-V
Chagrin, F.	6 Duets	Nov
Charlton, F.	Harlequin	CF
Chédeville, N.-Taylor	Pastoral Sonata "L'Allemande"	Ric
Chédeville, E.-Arx	6 galante Duos	B&N
Chédeville, N.-Upmeyer	2 Pastoralsonaten, op. 8	B&N
Chédeville, N.-Upmeyer-Wummer	2 Sonatas	Int
Cherubini, L.-Godfrey	2 Fugues	PrA
Childs, B.	Music	TP
Corrette, M.	Sonate I, op. 21a	B&V
Couperin, F.-Schmitz	Concerto, G	B&N
Couperin, F.-Ruf	Duo, G	SS
Couperin, F.-Schmitz	Musik für Flöte	B&N
Couperin, F.	Suite 1	TP
Croft, W.-Hunt	Sonata, d	S&C
Davenport, L.	3 Duets	SF
Devienne, F.-Moyse	Air with Variations	Int
Devienne, F.	Duos, op. 75, 2 vols.	B&V
Devienne, F.-Kalmar	18 Kleine Flötenduette	SS
Devienne, F.-Wienandt	Siciliano	SM
Devienne, F.	6 Celebrated Sonatas	EdM

Two Flutes

Devienne, F.	6 Duos Concertants, op. 83	Pet
Devienne, F.	6 Easy Duets, op. 82	Int
Devienne, F.-Wienandt	Sonata No. 1, G	SM
Devienne, F.-Wienandt	Sonata No. 2, C	SM
Devienne, F.-Wienandt	Sonata No. 3, D	SM
Devienne, F.-Wienandt	Sonata No. 4, F	SM
Devienne, F.-Wienandt	Sonata No. 5, A	SM
Devienne, F.-Wienandt	Sonata No. 6	SM
Devienne, F.	Sonatina No. 1, D	Pet
Devienne, .F.	Sonatina No. 2, F	Pet
Devienne, F.	Sonatina No. 3, G	Pet
Devienne, F.	Sonatina No. 4, d	Pet
Devienne, F.	Sonatines Nos. 1, 2 and 3. 2 *fl, bass ad lib*	E-V
Devienne, F.-Wienandt	38 Duos	SM
Devienne, F.-Nagel	3 Duets, op. 18/4-6	Hei
Dexter, H.	Au clair de la lune	Pet
Dexter, H.	Country Dialogues	Pet
Döflein (ed)	Bicinien. 20 fantasies.	SS
Doppelbauer, J.	7 Little Duets	LDo
Doran, M.	Sonatina	Wes
Drouet, L.	Grands Duos Brillans & Faciles, op. 74/1	EdH
Drouet, L.	Grands Duos Brillans & Faciles, op. 74/2	EdH
Drouet, L.	Grands Duos Brillans & Faciles, op. 74/3	EdH
Drouet, L.-Quakernaat	2 Airs	B&V
Dubois, P.	Berceuse et Rondo capricioso	ALe
Ehrlich, A.	Testimony (1962)	Isr
Eriksson, G.	Flöjtduetter	Nor
Escher, R.	Sonata (1955), op. 8	B&V
Excoffier	Fantasia-Gracioso	E-V
Fesch, W.de-Ruf	6 Sonatas, op. 9	B&N
Fesch, W. de	Sonatas, op. 9	Pet
Fesch, W. de	30 Duets	WIN
Fesch, W. de-Döflein	3 leichte Sonaten	SS
Filas, T.	Interval Duets	Cha
Filippi, A. de	7 Modes	Gen
Finger, G.-Bergmann	Sonata, C.	S&C
Finger, G.-Hunt	Sonata, G, op. 2/6	S&C
Finger, G.-Rodemann	2 Sonatas	HMo
Fischer, J.C.-Ruf	3 Divertimenti	Ric
Fox, F.	BEC-3	See
Freundlich, R.	An Endless Round	FrC
Freundlich, R. (arr.)	4 Old Dances	Ric
Fuerstenau, A.	6 Duets, Op. 137, 2 vols.	Int
Fuerstenau, A.	3 Grands Duos concertant, op. 36/1-3; Published separately	EdH
Fuerstenau, C.	6 Duets	B&V
Fuerstenau, C.	6 Duets	EdH
Fuerstenau, C.	3 Duos, op. 2	EdH

3

Two Flutes

Gariboldi, G.	Duos grandués, op. 145	ALe
Gariboldi, G.	6 Little Duets, op. 145/B	CF
Gariboldi, G.	6 Melodic Duets, op. 145/C	CF
Genin, P.	Grand Duo Concertant, op. 51	Bil
Genzmer, H.	Sonata, f$^\sharp$	SS
Geraedts, J.	4 Inventies (1943)	SD
Geraedts, J.	6 Studies in Euler's toongeslachten (1962) 1 & 2 fl	SD
Geuss-Birkner	8 Duets	HMo
Gibbons, O.	6 Fantasias, 2 vols.	Pet
Giesbert, F. (ed)	Duos of English Masters	NV
Goeb, R.	2 Divertimenti	CoF
Grenser, K.-Wienandt	Grand Duo	PrA
Grieg, E.-Thaulow	Butterflies	MCA
Handel, G.	Allegro (Sonata No. 2)	CF
Handel, G.-Dart	Duo	S&C
Handel, G.-Laidlaw	Sonata, e	Spr
Hart, F.	Sonatina	Wes
Hasse, J.-Nagel	Duette	Hei
Haubenstock-Ramati, R.	Interpolation	UE
Haydn, F.-Walther	Echo	WZ
Haydn, F.-Wienandt	Minuet in D	SM
Haydn, F.-Wienandt	3 Duos	PrA
Haydn, F.-Wienandt	3 Duos (Op. 101), Vol. 2	PrA
Hermann, R.	Flute Willow	CF
Hindemith, P.	Kanonische Sonatine, op. 31/3	SS
Hosmer, J.	4 Duos	M&M
Hotteterre, J.-Ruf & Zöller	Suite, b	HSM
Hugot, A.-Wienandt	Polonaise	SM
Hugues, L.-Veggetti	La Scuola del Flauto, op. 51, 3 vols.	Ric
Jelinek, H.	4 Kanons, Op. 15, No. 6 (1950)	UE
Kellner, D.-Wienandt	Gavotte Ancienne	SM
Ketting, P.	Partita (1936)	SD
Koechlin, C.	Sonate, op. 75	EdS
Köehler, E.	40 Progressive Duets, op. 55, 2 vols.	CF
Köehler, E.	Progressive Duets, op. 55, 2 vols.	WZ
Köehler, E.-Drouet	6 Sonatines, 3 Duos Concertants	SM
Kölz, E. (ed)	Galante Menuette	LDo
Konietzny, H.	Pas de deux (1968)	B&N
Krakamp, E.	Concert Suite, op. 139	EdM
Krebs, S.	Contemplation	See
Kuhlau, F.-Veggetti	3 Brilliant Duets, op. 80	FrC
Kuhlau, F.-Veggetti	3 Brilliant Duets, op. 102	FrC
Kuhlau, F.	3 Duets, op. 80	CF
Kuhlau, F.	3 Duets, op. 80	Int
Kuhlau, F.-Veggetti	3 Duets, op. 10	FrC
Kuhlau, F.	3 Duets, op. 10	Int
Kuhlau, F.	3 Duos, op. 10	Bil

4

Two Flutes

Kuhlau, F.	3 Duos, op. 57 bis Published separately	Bil
Kuhlau, F.	3 Duos, op. 80	Bil
Kuhlau, F.	3 Duos, op. 80	Pet
Kuhlau, F.	3 Duos, op. 81	Bil
Kuhlau, F.	3 Duos, op. 81	Pet
Kuhlau, F.	3 Duos Brillants, op. 13 bis	Bil
Kuhlau, F.	3 Duos Brillants, op. 81	CF
Kuhlau, F.	3 Duos Brillants, op. 81	Int
Kuhlau, F.	3 Duos Brillants, op. 102	Bil
Kuhlau, F.	3 Duos Brillants, op. 102	CF
Kuhlau, F.	3 Duos Brillants, op. 102	Int
Kuhlau, F.	3 Duos Concertants, op. 10	CF
Kuhlau, F.	Duos Concertants, op. 10	Pet
Kuhlau, F.	3 Duos Concertants, op. 87	Int
Kuhlau, F.	3 Grand Duets, op. 39	CF
Kuhlau, F.	3 Grand Duets Concertant, op. 87	CF
Kuhlau, F.	3 Grands Duos, op. 39 Published separately	Bil
Kuhlau, F.	3 Grand Duos, op. 39	Int
Kuhlau, F.	3 Grands Duos Concertants, op. 87 Published separately	Bil
Kummer, G. (K)	Sonatina, Op. 36/3	EdM
Kummer, G. (K)	3 Duets, op. 132	Int
Kummer, G. (K)	3 Duos Concertants, op. 9	EdH
Kummer, G.	3 Duos Faciles, op. 74	Bil
Kummer, G.	3 Petits Duos, op. 20	Bil
Lang, I.	Duo (1963)	EMB
Lax	Twilight Carol Polka, op. 112. 2 picc	FisC
LeClerc, J.	6 Sonates, op. 1	WIN
Lendvay, K.	4 Duetti	EMB
Letnan, J.	Styri Skice (1963)	SHF
Licht, D.	3 Pieces	M&M
Lincke, P.-Walters	The Glowworm	Rub
List-Pretsch (eds)	Old and New Duets, 2 vols.	FrH
Locatelli, P.-Ruf	6 Sonatas, op. 4, Vol. 1 (1-3)	Ric
Locatelli, P.-Wummer	Sonata, e	Int
Locatelli, P.-Ruf & Zöller	Sonata, D, op. 1/6	HSM
Locatelli, P.-Schlenger	Sonata, e	WZ
Locatelli, P.-Ruf	2 Duets, Op. 4/4&5	SS
Loebner, R.	Windvögel über Oklahoma	HG
Loeillet, J.-Ruf	6 Duets, op. 5, 2 vols.	SS
Loeillet, J.	Sonata, d	Gal
Loeillet, J.-Hanson	Sonata, d	Pet
Loeillet, J.	Sonate, e (No. 942)	EV
Loeillet, J.	Sonate, g (No. 943)	E-V
Loeillet, J.-Ruf	3 Duets	SS
Lorenzo, L. De	Suite Moderna, op 83	Pet
Maganini, Q.	Couperin Suite	EdM
Maganini, Q.	In the Beginning	EdM
Maganini, Q.	Petite Suite Classique	EdM

Two Flutes

Maganini, Q.	2 Humming Birds	EdM
Mahaut, A.-Heuwekemeijer	6 Sonate da Camera, 2 vols.	EdH
Martinu, B	Divertimento	EME
Mattheson, J.-Hunt	Sonata, a, op. 1/12	S&C
Mattheson, J.-Hunt	Sonata, B♭, op. 1/11	S&C
Mattheson, J.-Hunt	Sonata, d, Op. 1/1	S&C
Mattheson, J.-Hunt	Sonata, F, op. 1/2	S&C
Michael, F.	Ginko	BrH
Migot, G.	6 petits préludes, 2 vols.	ALe
Mills, C.	Suite for Two Flutes Soli	CoF
Monteclair, M. de	Concerto No. 1, D	Pet
Monteclair, M. de	Concerto No. 2, G	Pet
Monteclair, M. de-Viollier	Concerto No. 3	Hei
Monteclair, M. de	Concerto No. 3	Pet
Monteclair, M. de-Frötscher	6 Konzerte, 2 vols.	WMS
Mouret, J.-Aubanel	12 Airs a chanter et a danser	GaM
Mozart, W.-Barge	Duets, op. 74/1, D	Pet
Mozart, W.-Barge	Duets, op. 74/2, e	Pet
Mozart, W.-Barge	Duets, op. 74/3, D	Pet
Mozart, W.	6 Duets, op. 75, 2 vols.	CF
Mozart, W.-Barge	6 Duette, K.V. 156 (1-3)	WZ
Mozart, W.-Wehsener	6 Duette, K.V. 157 (4-6)	WZ
Mulot, A.	Suite dans le style ancien, op. 13	Dur
Naudot, J.-Ruf	Babioles, op. 10, 2 vols.	SS
Naudot, J.-Höckner, W&H	6 Sonatas, 2 vols.	Sim
Naudot, J.-Taylor	Sonata	Ric
Paisible, J.-Ruf	6 Duets, op. 1, 2 vols.	SS
Paisible, J.-Hunt	Sonata, d, op. 1/1	S&C
Paisible, J.-Hunt	Sonata, F, op. 1/2	S&C
Paisible, J.-Hunt	Sonata, g, op. 1/4	S&C
Paisible, J.-Hunt	Sonata, C, op. 1/5	S&C
Passmore, J.	Adagio and Allegro, op. 2	CF
Pelz, W.	Minuet Petite	B-M
Petrassi, G.	Dialogo Angelico (1948)	ESZ
Petyrek, F.	3 Tänze (1924)	UE
Pisk, P.	Suite, Op. 80	Pet
Pla, J.-Lebermann	6 Sonatas	SS
Pleyel, I.-Steinbeck	12 Duets, 4 vols.	LDo
Popp, W.-Soussmann, H.	Easy Duets	CF
Popp, W.	Melodic Suite	EdM
Porret, J.	12 Easy Duos, op. 648	HEI
Porta, B.-Wienandt	Duo for Equal Instruments	TP
Porta, B.-Wienandt	2 Duos for Equal Instruments	TP
Quantz, J.-Nagel	6 Duets, op. 5, 2 vols.	Hei
Quantz, J.-Mueller	6 Duets, op. 2, 2 vols.	BrH
Quantz, J.-Wittgenstein	6 Duets, op. 2	Sch
Quantz, J.-Ruf & Zöller	Sonata, a, op. 2/2	HSM
Raphael, G.	Kanonische Suite, op. 47/5	B&N
Raphling, S.	Variations	EdM
Reicha, A.	Variations, op. 20	JB
Reicha, A.-Polnauer	Variations, op. 20	Pet
Reicha, A.-Polnauer	3 Romanzen, op. 21	SS

Two Flutes

Reicha, A.-Moyse	3 Romances, op. 21	Int
Reidt, F.-Sonntag	Duett, F	Pet
Rossi, M.-Moyse	Andantino & Allegro	Int
Rowe, P. (arr)	Fun for Flutes. *2 fl, opt pf*	PrA
Ruf, H. (ed)	2 Duos alter englischer Meister	S&C
Sacco, P.	Andante and Cantabile	Wes
Saro, H.	Studies in Canon Form	CF
Saunders, R.	Clock Duets	Nov
Schade, W.	20 Easy and Progressive Duets	CF
Schickele, P.	A Small World (1962)	Can
Schneider, W.	Sonata	MV
Segerhammer	Little Cascade Waltz	PrA
Sollberger, H.	2 Pieces	M&M
Soussmann, H.-Tillmetz	12 Duets, op. 53	Int
Soussmann, H.	12 Light Pieces, op. 47	EdM
Soussmann, H.-Doeppler	12 Pieces, op. 47	Int
Stamitz, K.-Bormann	6 Duets, Op. 27, 2 vols.	NV
Stamitz, C. (K)	3 Duets, op. 27	Int
Strongin, T.	4 Duos	TP
Stutschewsky, J.	3 Miniatures	See
Szervánszky, E.	Suite (1956)	EMB
Telemann, G.	Dresden Duets, e, A, E	B&N
Telemann, G.	Dresden Duets, G, a, b	B&N
Telemann, G.	Marburg Duets, B♭, c, E♭	B&N
Telemann, G.	Marburg Duets, f, B♭, E	B&N
Telemann, G.-Davenport	Partita, e	M&M
Telemann, G.-Loewer	6 Duets	B&V
Telemann, G.-Budde	6 Duets	MV
Telemann, G.	Sonatas in Canon Form, op. 5	Int
Telemann, G.-Richert	6 Sonatas in Canon, op. 5	SS
Telemann, G.-Rikko	6 Sonatas, Vol 1 (Sonatas 1-3)	TP
Telemann, G.-Rikko	6 Sonatas, Vol. 2 (Sonatas 4-6)	TP
Telemann, G.-Bergmann	Sonata, B♭	S&C
Telemann, G.-Bergmann	Sonata, C	S&C
Telemann, G.-Bergmann	Sonata, d	S&C
Telemann, G.-Ruf & Zöller	Sonata, e, op. 2/5	HSM
Telemann, G.-Hunt	Sonata, F	S&C
Telemann, G.-Champion	Sonata, g	S&C
Telemann, G.-Bergmann	Sonata, G	S&C
Telemann, G.	Sonatas, op. 5, 2 vols.	B&N
Telemann, G.	Sonatas in Canon Form, op. 5	Pet
Telemann, G.	Sonatas, op. 2, 2 vols.	B&N
Terschak, A.	Duos Progressifs, op. 70	CF
Terschak, A.	12 Characteristic Pieces	EdM
Tillmetz, R.	12 Exercises in Modern Rhythm, op. 54	WZ
Toeschi, C.-Lebermann	6 Duets, op. 11, 2 vols.	SS
Tremblot de la Croix	10 Inventions	ALe
Tulou, J.	6 Duet Etudes	EdM
Tulou, J.	3 Duos, op. 14	EdH
Tulou, J.	3 Easy Duets, op. 102	Int
Tulou, J.	3 Easy Duets, op. 103	Int

Two Flutes

Tulou, J.	3 Easy Duets, op. 104	Int
Tulou, J.	3 Easy Duets, op. 193	E-V
Twinn, S. (ed)	12 Old English Songs	Gal
Ulrich, J.	5 Duets (1966)	WH
Valentine, R.-Ruf	4 Duets, op. 6/1-4	SS
Valentine, R.-Glazer	4 Sonatas	CF
Valentine, R.-Peter	6 Sonatas	MRL
Valentine, R.-Nagel	3 Sonatas, op. 14	Hei
Vigne, P. de la-Ruf	3 leichte Suiten	Ric
Walckiers, E.	3 Duos Concertans, op. 1/1-3	EdH
Weber-Ostling	Duets, 2 vols.	B-M
Wendling, J.	Duets, op. 4/4-6	EdH
Wendling, J.-Heuwekemeijer	Duetto, Op 4/1-3	EdH
Wienandt, E.	Minuet and Gavotte	SM
Wraniczky, P.-Wienandt	Siciliano	SM
Yuasa, J.	Interpenetration	TP
Zachert, W.	6 Suiten im alten Stil	WZ
Zehm, F.	6 Capricen	SS
Zirnbauer, H. (ed)	Bicinien	SS

TWO FLUTES - COLLECTIONS

Carey	Flute Duet Album	B-M
Fleury, L.	Oeuvres originales des XVII et XVIII Siècles	ALe
Gearhart, L.	Flute Sessions	Sha
Guenther, F.	Masterworks for Two Flutes, 2 vol.	B-M
Hodgson (arr)	Flute Album, 2 vols.	Pet
Johen, K. & G. Wierzejewski (arr)	Tänze aus Bachs Zeit	FrH
Kaplan, D. (arr)	Gotham Collection of Duets	Spr
Moyse, L.	Album of Flute Duets	Sch
Moyse, L.	30 Easy Duets	M&M
Moyse, M.	Album of 30 Classical Duets	Int
Schaeffer, D. (arr)	Duets are Fun	PrA
Schaeffer, D. (arr)	21 Rhythmic Duets	PrA
Stouffer, P.	Album of 10 Baroque Compositions	HEI
Voxman, H.	Selected Duets, 2 vols.	Rub
Wienandt, E. (ed)	11 Duets	PrA

TWO OBOES

Arnell, R.	5 Inventions	HE
Babell	Bourée	FrC
Bach-Maganini	Canon (Sonata, f)	CF
Bach W.F.	Duo Sonata	EdM
Bacon, E.	The Cock Fight	BB

Two Oboes

Beethoven, L. van	Allegro and Minuet	EdM
Bergt, C.-Degen	Duet No. 2, F.	Hei
Bergt, C.-Degen	Duet No. 3, B♭	Hei
Bergt, C.-Degen	Duetto No. 1, C	Hei
Blavet, M.-Ruf	2 Duets, op. 1/5&6	SS
Blavet, M.-Ruf	6 Sonatas, op. 1, vol. 1 (1-3)	Ric
Boismortier, J.-Ruf	6 Easy Duets, op. 17, 2 vols.	SS
Bonvalet	La Clairière - La Pinède	E-V
Boutry, R.	Toccata, Saraband and Jig	ALe
Bucquet, P.	Suite No. 1	EdM
Bucquet, P.	Suite No. 2	EdM
Butterworth	3 Dialogues	Pet
Chagrin, F.	6 Duets	Nov
Chédeville, N.-Upmeyer	2 Pastoralsonaten, c, C	NV
Clodomir, P.	12 Duos	HeE
Davenport, L.	3 Duets	SF
Devienne, F.	6 Celebrated Sonatas	EdM
Dexter, H.	Au Clair de la lune	Pet
Dexter, H.	Country Dialogues	Pet
Freundlich, R.	An Endless Round	FrC
Freundlich, R.	4 Old Dances	FrC
Garnier, F.-Gerlach	Anfänger-Duette (Methode)	FrH
Haydn, F.	3 Duos	Bil
Kaplan, D. (arr)	Gotham Collection of Oboe Duets	Spr
Lacour, G.	Suite en duo	Bil
Lancen, S.	The Twins	Pet
Loeillet, J.-Ruf	6 Duets, op. 5, 2 vols.	SS
Loeillet, J.-Ruf	3 Duets	SS
Luft, H.	24 Etudes in Duet Form	CF
Luft, J.-Steins	12 Etudes, op. 11	B&B
Luft, J.	24 Studies, op. 11	MR
Migot, G.	Pastorale	ALe
Montéclair, M. de	6 Concerti, 2 vols.	Pet
Mozart, L.	4 Short Pieces	HeE
Naudot, J.-Ruf	Babioles, op. 10, 2 vols.	SS
Owen, D. (arr)	21 Duets	Ken
Paisible, J.-Ruf	6 Duets, op. 1, 2 vols.	SS
Pla, J.-Lebermann	6 Sonatas	SS
Porret, J.	12 Easy Duos, op. 648	HeE
Porta, B.-Wienandt	Duo	TP
Porta, B.-Wienandt	2 Duos	TP
Raphling, S.	Duograms	EdM
Rhys, S.	6 Inventions	OxU
Ruf, H. (ed)	2 Duos alter englischer Meister	S&C
Saro. H.	Studies in Canon Form	CF
Schaeffer, D. (arr)	Duets are Fun	PrA
Schaeffer, D. (arr)	21 Rhythmic Duets	PrA
Sellner, J.	12 Duos, 3 vols.	E-V
Sollberger, H.	2 Oboes Troping	CoF
Stoker, R.	Little Suite	Pet
Stouffer, P.	Album of 10 Baroque Compositions	HeE
Takahashi	Operation Euler	Pet

Two Oboes

Ulrich, J.	5 Duets (1966)	WH
Vigne, de la-Ruf	2 Little Suites	Ric
Wuorinen, C.	Bicinium	CoF

TWO CLARINETS

	Clarinet Album No. 1	Pet
	Clarinet Album No. 2	Pet
Arnell, R.	5 Inventions	HE
Bach, C.P.E.-McGinnis	Duet	Int
Bach, C.P.E.-Stephan	Duet, C	B&N
Bach, C.P.E.	2 Duets	TP
Bach, J.S.-Luisetti	Bach Inventions	SF
Bach, J.S.-Langenus	Clarinet Duos	CF
Bach, W.F.-Maganini	Canon (Sonata, f)	CF
Bach, W.F.	Duo Sonata	EdM
Bacon, E	The Cock Fight	BB
Balbatre, L.	Air with Variations	EdM
Barret, A.-Toll	12 Duets	CF
Bartok, B.-Suchoff	23 Progressive Duets	B&H
Bassett, L.	Clarinet Duets	Uni
Bavicchi, J.	5 Dialogues	JB
Beethoven, J.	6 Easy Duets	HeE
Beethoven, L. van	Allegro and Minuet	EdM
Beethoven, L. van-Berlinski	Clarinet Duets	TP
Beethoven, L. van-Grisez	1st Symphony	ALe
Beethoven, L. van-Grisez	1st Trio, B$\flat$	ALe
Beethoven, L. van-Toll	Rondo (Pathetique Sonata)	CF
Beethoven, L. van	3 Duos	Spr
Beethoven, L. van-Grisez	Trio, op. 11	CF
Bellini, V.	Duet (Norma)	CF
Bender, H.-Cochrane	4 Clarinet Duos, op. 30	CF
Benjamin, T.	After-Dinner Pieces	SM
Bennett, R.	Crosstalk	TP
Berbiguier, T.	6 Easy Duets	EdM
Berkes, K. (ed)	Clarinet Duos, 3 vols.	EMB
Berr, F.	20 Petits Duos	Bil
Berr, F.	26 Progressive Lessons	B&H
Berry, W.	2 Canons	E-V
Blazevich, V.-Beeler	Concert Music	SF
Boehm, F.	12 Petits Duos, op. 5	Bil
Borghi, L.-Wienandt	Divertimento	TP
Borghi, L.-Wienandt	5 Clarinet Duos	SM
Brahms, J.-Langenus	Sonata No. 1	B&H
Brahms, J.-Langenus	Sonata No. 2	B&H
Brepsant, E.	15 Duets, 3 vols.	CF
Bucquet, P.	First Suite	EdM
Bucquet, P.	Second Suite	EdM
Buschmann, R.	Miniatures für Zwillinge (1969)	B-N
Butterworth	3 Dialogues	Pet
Cadow, P.	Elegie und Rondo	PG

Two Clarinets

Cavallini, E.	3 Grand Artistic Duets	CF
	Published separately	
Cavallini, E.	2 Grand Duets	CF
	Published separately	
Cazden, N.	10 Conversations, op. 34	Spr
Chagrin, F.	6 Duets	Nov
Chedeville-Den Arend	L'Aine	HeE
Clergue, J.	Melodie - En Balancelle	E-V
Clodomir, P.	12 Duos	MM
Cockshott	Variations on a Passepied	SF
	of Handel	
Cori, C.	Bach Literature Duets	SF
Cori, C. (arr)	Melody Duets, Bk. 2	KPM
Couperin, F.	Suite I	TP
Cragun, J.	8 Concert Duets	Rub
Crazioli-Rocereto	Minuetto (Sonata, G)	Vol
Crusell, B.-Michaels	Duo I, d	HSM
Crusell, B.-Michaels	Duo II, C	HSM
Crusell, B.-Chapman	Progressive Duet No. 1, F	Pet
Crusell, B.-Chapman	Progressive Duet No. 2, d	Pet
Crusell, B.-Chapman	Progressive Duet No. 3, C	Pet
Crusell, B.	3 Duos	MT
Cunningham, M	Sonatina	CoA
Da-Oz, R.	10 Miniaturen	Hei
Davenport, L.	3 Duets	SF
Davidson, J.	Two Part Invention	PMP
Delguidice, M.	20 Duos Faciles	Bil
Depelsenaire, J.	Pastourelle - L'Argyrometre	E-V
Devienne, F.-Steinbeck	Duo Concertant No. 1	LDo
Devienne, F.-Lebermann	Duos, op. 69/1&2	SS
Devienne, F.-Lebermann	Duos, op. 69/3	SS
Devienne, F.	6 Celebrated Sonatas	EdM
Dexter, H.	Au clair de la lune	Pet
Dexter, H.	Country Dialogues	Pet
Diemente, E.	3 Pieces	See
Domazlicky, F.	3 Duets, op. 3	HU
Donizetti, G.	Sonata	Pet
Elton, A.	Short Sonata	Che
Fesch, W. de	Andante and Menuet	HeE
Franck, C.	To Little Children	HeE
Frank, A.	Suite	OxU
Gebauer, E.	Duo No. 5	Heu
Gebauer, F.-Wojciechowski	6 Duos, op. 2	HSM
Glazounov, A.	10 Duets	MR
Grundman, C.	Puppets	B&H
Hajdu, M.	Clarinet Duets (1951)	EMB
Handel, G.	Allegro (Sonata No. 2)	CF
Harvey, P.	Graded Study Duets, Book 1	B&H
Harvey, P.	Graded Study Duets, Book 2	B&H
Haydn, F.-Grisez	Fifth and Sixth Sonatas	CF
Haydn, F.	Sonata, D	EdM
Haydn, F.-Skolnik	The Witches' Canon	EdM

11

Two Clarinets

Hess, W.	5 Duos, op. 64	Pet
Heussenstamm, G.	8 Short Duets	Wes
Hook, J.-Curwin	Guida di Musica	Cha
Huffnagle, H.	Streamlined Duets	KPM
Hyams, A.	7 Micro-Organisms	SM
Kaufmann, A.	Concertino No. 2, op. 86	LDo
Kietzer, R.	Duette, op. 94, 3 vols.	WZ
Klerk, J. de	Kleine Partita	MM
Klosé, H.	3 Concert Duets	EdM
Klotzman, A.	Fun	MCA
Klug, E.	Divertimento ticinese	Hei
Koechlin, C.	Idylle	ChM
Kolman, P.	Sonata canonica. *cl, bcl*	SHF
Kraft, L.	Little Suite	TP
Kraft, L.	Two's Company (1954)	B&H
Krejci, M.	Momentky	Art
Kreutzer, K.-Michaels	Duo, C.	HSM
Kroepsch, F.	5 Duets	CF
Kroepsch, F.	5 Duos	EBM
Kroepsch, F.	5 Duos	SM
Kueffner, J.-Drucker	24 Easy Duets	Int
Kuffner, J.	50 Progressive Duets	CF
Kuhlau, F.	3 Duets, op. 81	CF
Kunz, A.	Fun for Two (1964). *2bcl*	Can
Kurtz, S.	3 Impressions	SF
Lacour, G.	Suite en Duo	Bil
Lancen, S.	The Twins	Pet
Lanese, T.	Elementary Duets	Leb
La Violette, W.	Duet Album	B-M
Lazarus, H.	3 Concert Duets Published separately	CF
Lazarus, H.	3 Grand Artistic Duets	CF
Lazarus, H.-DeVille	3 Grand Concert Duets	CF
Lazarus, H.	20 Easy Progressive Duets	CF
Lazarus, H.	24 Easy and Progressive Duets on Operatic Melodies	CF
Lefevre, X.	6 Petits Duos Faciles	Bil
Lester, L.	Clarinet Twosome	CF
Lewin, G.	Two of a Kind	B&H
Lijnschoten, V.	4 Canons	T-M
Maganini, Q.	Canonico Espressivo	EdM
Maganini, Q.	Couperin Suite	EdM
Maganini, Q.	In the Beginning	EdM
Magnani, A.	6 Duetti Concertant	CF
Magnani, A.	Sonata	CF
Malige, F.	7 Duos	FrH
Mamlok, U.	8 Easy Duets	CoF
Mamlok, U.	Sonatina	CoF
Maschayeki, A.	9 Expressionen. *cl, bcl*	UE
Mazas, J.	Duets	SF
Mazas, J.	Duo	HeE
Mazas, J.	Petit Duos Nos. 1, 2, 3, 5	MM

Two Clarinets

McCabe, J.	Bagatelles	Nov
McLuckie, I. (ed)	12 Below B	B&H
Mendelssohn, F.-Grisez	Duo Concertant, op. 114	ALe
Miaskovsky, N.-Lester	Fugue in a Classic Style. *cl, bcl*	Wes
Minor-Farnsworth	Fun Duets	Sha
Mirandolle, L.	3 Duos	ALe
Moser, C.	Variazioni diatonique	GZ
Mozart, L.	4 Short Pieces	HeE
Mozart, L.	16 Duets	EMB
Mozart, W.-Freeman	Clarinet Duet No. 4	SF
Mozart, W.	Die Kegelduette	MV
Mozart, W.-Hodgson	Duets, op. 70/7, 8	Pet
Mozart, W.-Hodgson	Duets, op. 70/9, 10	Pet
Mozart, W.-Hodgson	Duets, op. 70/11, 12	Pet
Mozart, W.	Duo, K. 487	MM
Mozart, W.-Gee	Excerpts from the Clarinet Concerto, K. 622	SM
Mozart, W.-Toll	Piano Sonata No. 4, Excerpt	CF
Mozart, W.-Tenney	6 Duets, op. 70, 2 vols.	CF
Mozart, W.-Magnani	6 Duets, op. 77, 2 vols.	CF
Mozart, W.-Drucker	6 Duets, 2 vols.	Int
Mozart, W.	Sonate No. 1	MM
Mozart, W.-Langenus	3 Duos	CF
Mozart, W.-Dahm	3 Sonatas	Vol
Mozart, W.-Haskins	12 Duets	OxU
Mozart, W.-Bellison	12 Duets, K. 487	FrC
Mozart, W.	Trio No. 7 (K. 498)	CF
Mueller, I.-Simon	6 Easy Duets, op. 41	Int
Mueller, I.	6 Easy Duos, op. 41	EBM
Naumann	Petit Duo	MM
Nevin, M.-Holzman	Inventions	AMP
Ortolani, O.	More (Theme from Mondo Cane)	EBM
Ostrander, A.	First Pals	EdM
Owen, D. (arr)	21 Duets	Ken
Paisner, B.	Swing Duets	KPM
Patachich, I.	Petite Suite	ALe
Pelz, W.	Candlelight Waltz	B-M
Pelz, W.	Fireside Reveries	B-M
Pelz, W.	Graduation Waltz	PrA
Persichetti, V.	Serenade No. 13	E-V
Pleyel, I.-Glazer	Duets 1 and 2	OxU
Pleyel, I.-Gebauer-Wienandt	Duo in C	SM
Pleyel, I.-Gebauer-Wienandt	Duo in d	SM
Pleyel, I.-Gebauer-Wienandt	Duo in F	SM
Pleyel, I.-Simon	Duos, op. 14/1-3	EBM
Pleyel, I.	6 Duets, op. 8	CF
Pleyel, I.	6 Little Duets	CF
Porret, J.	Duo de Concours No. 8	MM
Porret, J.	12 Easy Duos	MM
Porret, J.	12 Progressive Duets, op. 254	MM
Porret, J.	7th Contest Duo	MM
Porret, J.-LaVoisier	12th Contest Duo	MM

13

Two Clarinets

Porret, J.-Marivaux	13th Contest Duo	MM
Porret, J.-Nelson	14th Contest Duo	MM
Porta, B.-Wienandt	Duo	TP
Porta, B.-Wienandt	2 Duos	TP
Poulenc, F.	Sonata. *A & B♭ cl*	Che
Pranzer, J.	Duo No. 1 (3 Duos concertants)	EMT
Pranzer, J.	Duo No. 2 (3 Duos concertants)	EMT
Pranzer, J.	Duo No. 3 (3 Duos Concertants)	EMT
Purcell, H.-Wright	Prelude	PrA
Rainer, G.	Miniaturen für Zwillinge	B&N
Raphling, S.	Sonatina	EdM
Rathburn, E.	Conversation (1956)	Can
Rimsky-Korsakov, N.-Gnesin	Canzonetta; Tarantella	MR
Roe, C.	3 Bagatelles	B&H
Rolla, A.	Virtuoso Study	EdM
Russell, R.	Abstract No. 1	Gen
Russell, R.	Abstract No. 2	Gen
Rossi-Rocereto	Andantino, A♭	Vol
Sarlit, H. (comp.)	20 Etudes de Déchiffrage	ScF
Sarlit, H. (comp.)	20 Etudes de Déchiffrage	Sch
Saro, H.	Studies in Canon Form	CF
Saygun, A.	Sezisler (Intuitions)	SMP
Scarlatti, D.-Rosenthal	Duets from Piano Suites	TP
Scarlatti, D.-Skolnik	Neapolitan Suite	EdM
Scarlatti, D.-Wright	Pastorale	PrA
Schneider, W.	Heiteres Divertimento	SS
Schneider, W.	Partita	Bar
Schneider, W.	Sonata	MV
Schubert, F.	5 Little Duets, Version B	TP
Schuller, G.	Duo Sonata. *cl, bcl*	Bro
Schumann, R.	Fairy Tales, op. 132	CF
Schwadron, A. (arr)	Progressive Ensemble Studies, Vol. 1	Ken
Schwadron, A.	12 Tone Duos	SM
Schwartz, E.	4 Studies	Gen
Sestak, Z.	Sonata	Art
Siennicki, E.-Hite	Let Me Tell It	SM
Sirulnikoff, J.	Suite (1952)	Can
Skolnick, W.	10 Easy Pieces	B&H
Sobeck, J.	Duet, op. 8	CF
Souffriau, A.	Sonate	EMb
Soussmann, H.	12 Light Pieces	EdM
Spino, P.	First Duets	StM
Stadler, A.-Michaels	Duo, F	HSM
Stark, R.-Simon	4 Duets	Int
Stark, R.	Sonata No. 1, E♭	CF
Stern, R.	A Little Bit of Music	NVM
Stoker, R.	Little Suite	Pet
Stone (arr)	2 Mozart Pieces	B&H
Telemann, G.-Kell	6 Canonic Sonatas	Int
Thomas, R.	4 Duets for Young Musicians	GaM
Toll, R.	2 Duets in Canonic Treatment	CF

Two Clarinets

Troje-Miller, N.	Chinese Checkers	B-M
Tulou, J.	6 Duets	EdM
Twinn, S.	6 Old English Songs	Gal
Twinn, S. (arr)	12 Old Welsh Songs	Pet
Ulrich, J.	5 Duets (1966)	WH
Van Lyn Schooten, H.	4 Canons	HeE
Vierdanck, J.-Scheifes	7 Leichte Duetten	T-M
Vivaldi, A.	Sonata da Camera	EdM
Vogel, J.-Michaels	Duo IV, d	HSM
Von Kreisler, A.	2 Preludes	SM
Wahlich, M.	10 Easy Duets	Hug
Wardrop, L.	Two Part Inventions. *cl, acl*	UnP
Weber, C. von	Grand Duo Concertante, op. 48	CF
Wiedemann, L.	30 Easy Duets, 2 vols.	CF
Wiedemann, L.	30 Easy and Melodious Duets	Sim
Yost, M.-Michaels	Duo II, F	HSM
Yost, M.	6 Favorite Duets, op. 12	M&M

TWO CLARINETS - COLLECTIONS

	Tiroler Volksmusik aus	B&N
	dem Zillertal. *2cl, guit ad lib*	
	Vi can spela, Vol. 4	Nor
Ayres, T.	Intermediate Duos	Sha
Ayres, T.	30 Duets	Sha
Bach, J.S.-Simon	Bach for the Clarinet. Part II	Sch
Becker, H. (ed)	Clarinet Duets	BrH
Burgstahler, E. (arr)	Duets for Clarinets	PrA
Elkan, H.	Classical Album	HeE
Forbes & Frank, A.	2 Clarinets, 2 Vols.	OxU
Gabucci, A.	50 Duetti	Car
Gearhart, L.	Clarinet Sessions	Sha
Giampieri, A. (arr)	26 Pezzi di Celebri Autori	Ric
Glasenapp, F. (ed)	Duets	FrH
Joosen, B.	20 Eenvoudige Klassieke Duetten	MM
Kaplan, D. (arr)	Gotham Collection	Spr
Krtička, S.	Album der Kompositionen	ES
	für 2 Klarinetten	
Krtička (arr)	Duette aus Tschechischen Opern	Art
Lindeman (arr)	Concert Masters on Hit Parade	PrA
Merriman, L. (arr)	Duet Classics, Bk. 1	SM
Ostling-Weber	Duets, 2 vols.	B-M
Richter, C. (arr)	Duets for Clarinets, 2 vols.	CF
Richter, C. (ed)-Christoffersen	Klarinetten-Duos	FrH
Rosenthal, C. (arr)	Clarinet Duos	EBM
Rosenthal, C. (tr)	15 Easy Duets	KPM
Schaeffer, D. (arr)	Duets are Fun	PrA
Schaeffer, D. (arr)	21 Rhythmic Duets	PrA
Schneider, M. &	Duette für Klarinetten-	FrH
A. Hetschko (ed)	Anfänger	

Two Clarinets - Collections

Schneider, W.	Klassische Spielstücke	B&N
Stouffer, P.	Album of 10 Baroque Compositions	HeE
Voxman, H. (arr)	Duettist Folio	Rub
Voxman, H. (arr)	Selected Duets, 2 vols.	Rub
Weston, P. (ed)	Album of Duets: First Album	S&C
Weston, P. (ed)	Album of Duets: Second Album	S&C
Weston, P. (ed)	Album of Duets: Third Album	S&C

TWO BASSOONS

Almenraeder, W.	2 Duos, op. 8	Spr
Barrette-Mueller	6 Divertimenti, op. 1	Pet
Beckwith, J.	4 Pieces (1951)	Can
Blank, A.	2 Bagatelles (1962)	See
Boismortier, J.	9 petite Sonates, op. 66	B-M
Boismortier, J.	6 Sonates, op. 14	B-M
Boismortier, J.	6 Sonates, op. 40	CP
Boismortier, J.-Ruyssen	Sonata No. 1, G	Gal
Boismortier, J.-Ruyssen	Sonata No. 2, d	Gal
Boutry, R.	Prelude, Pastoral and Tarantella	ALe
Bozza, E.	Duettino	ALe
Bucquet, P.	Suite, g	EdM
Coste, G.	Fantaisie instrumentale	Heu
Couperin, F.-Bazelaire	Concert	ALe
Couperin, F.-Ruf	Duo, G	SS
Devienne, F.-Hess	Duos Concertants, op. 3	EK
Dieppo	Virtuoso Studies	EdM
Dubois, P.	Sonatina	ALe
Erbach-Noack	6 Duos	B&N
Farago, M.	4 Duets, op. 27	B&V
Ferling, W.-Thornton	3 Duo Concertantes, op. 13	SM
Gastyne, S. de	La Corbusiere (1968)	Fer
Gebauer-Thornton	3 Duo Concertantes	SM
Gebauer, F.-Wojciechowski	3 Ausgewählte Duos, op. 44	HSM
Goedicke, A.	6 Duets	MR
Houdy, P.	Canon	ALe
Jacobi, C.	Duets	MR
Jancourt, E.-Collins	Sonata No. 1	B-M
Jancourt, E.-Collins	Sonata No. 2	B-M
Kleinknecht, W.	3 Sonatas	M&M
Kont, P.	Duo	LDo
Kueffner, J.-Dherin	24 Duets	Int
Kunz, A.	Fun for Two (1964)	Can
Malige, F.	7 Duos	FrH
Mancinelli, D.-Ruf	2 Sonaten	Ric
Mozart, W.-Bazelaire	Sonata	ALe
Mozart, W.	Sonata	SM
Ozi, E.	6 grandes sonates, 2 vols.	EdH
Ozi, E.-Muccetti	6 Grandi Sonate	Ric

Two Bassoons

Ozi, E.	6 petites sonates, 2 vols.	EdH
Porret, J.	12 Easy Duos, op. 648	MM
Raphling, S.	Sonatina	EdM
Regner, H.	Spielheft 1	PG
Satzenhofer, J.-Kovar	24 Duets	Int
Schneider, G.-Pischkitl	Duette für tiefe Instrumente	FrH
Siennicki, E.	Duet No. 1	Spr
Siennicki, E.	Duet No. 2	Spr
Stahuljak, M.	Inventions	Kaw
Stoker, R.	4 Dialogues	Pet
Telemann, G.-Oromszegi	6 Kanonsonaten	EMB
Telemann, G.	Sonata No. 2	M&M
Telemann, G.	Sonata No. 4	M&M
Ticciati, N.-Solloway	"Voi, Che Sapete"	Pet
Tomasi, H.	Croquis	ALe
Ulrich, J.	5 Duets (1966)	WH

TWO BASSOONS - COLLECTIONS

	Duette für Fagotte	FrH
Blume, O.	12 Duets, 2 vols.	Int
Blume, O.	12 Melodious Duets	CF
Glasenapp-Karl (ed)	Duets	FrH
Siennicki, E. (arr)	Gotham Collection	Spr

TWO SAXOPHONES

Bach, J.S.	Canon No. 4. *asax, tsax*	EdM
Bach, J.S.-Teal	15 Two-Part Inventions	TP
Bach, W.F.	Duo Sonata	EdM
Beethoven, L. van	Allegro and Minuet	EdM
Berbiguier, T.	6 Easy Duets	EdM
Bernards, B.	10 Instruktive Duos	WZ
Bucquet, P.	First Suite	EdM
Bucquet, P.	Second Suite	EdM
Bumcke, G.	38 Duos (op. 43)	ABe
Butterworth	3 Dialogues	Pet
Chagrin, F.	6 Duets	Nov
Clergue, J.	Primavera - Volute	E-V
Cragun, J.	8 Concert Duets	Rub
Devienne, F.	6 Celebrated Sonatas	EdM
Ferling, W.-Gee	Duets, op. 31	SM
Gatti, D.-Iasilli	30 Progressive Duets	CF
Hansel, A.	Concertino, op. 80. *asax, tsax*	SM
Haydn, F.	The Witches Canon. *asax, tsax*	EdM
Klerk, J. de	Kleine Partita	MM
Klosé, H.	6 Duets	CF
Kuhlau, F.-Teal	3 Concert Duets, op. 10	TP

Two Saxophones

Lacour, G.	Suite en duo	Bil
Lancen, S.	The Twins	Pet
Lazarus, H.-Traxler	Grand Artistic Duets	B-M
Luft, J.	24 Etudes in Duet Form	CF
Maganini, Q.	Canonico Espressivo. *asax, tsax*	EdM
Maganini, Q.	In the Beginning	EdM
Maganini, Q.	Petite Suite Classique	EdM
Massias, G.	Dialogues	Bil
Mozart, L.	4 Short Pieces	HeE
Niehaus, L.	A Dozen and One	Wes
Paisner, B.	Swing Duets	KPM
Pelz, W.	Ballad	B-M
Porret, J.	12 Progressive Duets, op. 254	MM
Raphling, S.	Duograms	EdM
Rochow, E.	Duette	RBM
Ruggiero, G.	3 Pièces	ALe
Sellner, J.	12 Duos	Bil
Sellner, J.	12 Duos, 3 vols.	EdC
Sousmann, H.	12 Light Pieces	EdM
Twinn, S.	Old English Songs	Pet
Ulrich, J.	5 Duets (1966)	WH
Vallier, J.	Andantino - Scherzando	EPC
Vereecken, B.	16 Artistic Duets	Rub

TWO SAXOPHONES - COLLECTIONS

	3 Duets	FrH
Cori, C. (arr)	Melody Duets, Bk. 2	KPM
Gurewich, J.	17 Classic Duets	CF
Kaplan, D. (arr)	Gotham Collection	Spr
Letellier, L. (arr)	Recueil de duos et trios	EdR
Ostling-Weber	Duets, 2 vols.	B-M
Schaeffer, D. (arr)	Duets are Fun	PrA
Schaeffer, D. (arr)	21 Rhythmic Duets	PrA
Stouffer, P. (arr)	Album of 10 Baroque Compositions	HeE
Voxman, H. (arr)	Selected Duets, 2 vols.	Rub

TWO WOODWINDS

Alexander	A Brace of Duets. *cl, bsn*	Gen
Ames, W.	Pieces. *ob, cl*	CoF
Andriessen, J.	Aulos (1959). *fl, ob*	SD
Applebaum, S.	Descriptive Duets, 2 vols. *2 ww*	CCo
Applebaum, S.	Swinging Duets. *2 ww*	CCo
Arbatsky, Y.	From A to Z. *fl, cl*	M&M
Arma, P.	3 Transparencies. *fl, cl*	E-V
Bach, W.F.	Duo Sonata. *fl, ob(cl)*	EdM
Balbatre, L.	Air with Variations. *fl, cl(bsn)*	EdM

Two Woodwinds

Balbatre,L.	Noel with Four Variations.	
	fl, cl(bsn)	EdM
Balbo	3 Etchings. *fl(ob), cl*	SF
Bauer, M.	Improvisation, op. 25/2. *ob, cl*	Pet
Bavicchi, J.	6 Duets, op. 27. *fl, cl*	OxU
Beck, F.	Fanfare. *fl, cl*	AMC
Becker, J.	Soundpiece No. 6. *fl, cl*	CoF
Beethoven, L. van	First Duo. *cl, bsn*	EBM
Beethoven, L. van	Second Duo. *cl, bsn*	EBM
Beethoven, L. van	Third Duo. *cl, bsn*	EBM
Beethoven, L. van	3 Duets. *fl, cl*	SM
Beethoven, L. van-Mederacke	3 Duos. *cl, bsn*	FrH
Beethoven, L. van-Siber	3 Duos. *cl, bsn*	FrH
Beethoven, L. van-Wildgans	3 Duos. *cl, bsn*	LDo
Beethoven, L. van	3 Duos. *cl, bsn*	MR
Beethoven, L. van	3 Duos. *cl(ob,fl), bsn*	Spr
Bennett	Treatise for Two. *fl, cl*	SM
Berger	3 Duets. *2 ww*	B-M
Berger, A.	Duo. *ob, cl*	Pet
Berkowitz	10 Duets. *2 treble instr*	BM
Beyer, J.	4 Pieces. *ob, bsn*	AMC
Beyer, J.	Suite. *ob, cl*	AMC
Beyer, J.	Suite No. 3. *cl, bsn*	AMC
Binkerd, G.	Duo. *fl, ob*	B&H
Bishoff, R.	Duo, op. 3. *fl, cl*	LDo
Blank, A.	4 Bagatelles. *ob, cl*	See
Blezard, W.	3 Diversions. *cl, bsn*	CP
Bonvalet	Souvenir - Canzone. *fl, cl*	E-V
Borris, S.	Duo, op. 116/1 (1964). *fl, ob*	B&N
Bottenberg, W.	Sonata (1960). *fl, cl*	Can
Bozza, E.	Sonatina. *fl, bsn*	ALe
Brown, N.	4 Pieces. *fl, cl*	TP
Bückmann, R.	8 Zweistimmige Sätze. *2 like instr*	PG
Burkhard, W.	Serenade (1953). *fl, cl*	B&N
Cartan, J.	Sonatine. *fl, cl*	Heu
Chambers, S.	Duo. *fl, cl*	GaM
Childs, B.	Divertimento. *ob, cl*	CoF
Childs, B.	Duo. *fl, bsn*	CoF
Clarke, H.	A Game that Two Can Play. *fl, cl*	Wes
Clodomir, P.	12 Duos. *2 ww*	MM
Cranmer, P.	Variations on a French Tune. *fl, cl*	Nov
Crosse, G.	3 Inventions. *fl, cl*	OxU
Deak, C.	Duo Suite. *fl, cl*	Che
Defossez, R.	Duo. *cl, bsn*	EMb
d'Estrade-Guerra, O.	Sonatine Pastorale. *ob, cl*	Job
Dijk, J. van	Duo (1952). *cl, bsn*	SD
Dobrzynski, I.	Duo. *cl, asax*	Kaw
Donahue, R.	5 Canonic Duets. *fl, cl*	TP
Donatelli, V.	Duet No. 1. *ob(fl), cl*	Wes
Donatelli, V.	Duet No. 2. *ob(fl), cl*	Wes
Dubois, P.	Petite Suite. *fl, bsn*	ALe
Eklund, H.	Smaprat (1965). *fl, cl*	STI

Two Woodwinds

Elliot	3 Duets. *fl, bsn*	SM
Erb, D.	Conversation (1963). *fl, ob*	Can
Evans, R.	Duet Suite (1965). *fl(ob), cl*	Can
Farrand, N.	Duo. *ob, bsn*	CoF
Feld, J.	Duo. *fl, bsn*	ALe
Fernandez, O.	3 Inventions - Serenades. *cl, bsn*	SMP
Frank	3 Short Duos. *fl, cl*	Bou
Freund, D.	Pas de Deux. *cl, bsn*	See
Gabaye, P.	Sonatina. *fl, bsn*	ALe
Gallon, N.	Sonata. *fl, bsn*	ALe
Gates, E.	Odd Meter Duets. *2 treble instr*	SF
Gearhart, L.	Bass Clef Sessions. *2 b.c. instr*	Sha
Gearhart, L.	Duet Sessions. *2 treble clef instr*	Sha
Gebauer, F.-Wojciechowski	6 Duos Concertants, op. 8, 2 vol. *cl, bsn*	HSM
Genin, P.	Grand Duo Concertant, op. 51 *fl, ob(cl)*	Bil
Genzmer, H.	Sonata, f#. *fl, ob*	SS
Ghent, E.	2 Duos. *fl(ob), cl*	OxU
Ginastera, A.	Duo. *fl, ob*	TP
Glaser, W.	Liten duett (1967). *ob, cl*	STI
Grahn, U.	Chanson (1969). *fl, cl*	STI
Grahn, U.	Dialog (1969). *fl, cl*	STI
Grahn, U.	For Two English Horns (1968)	STI
Gramatges, H.	Prelude and Invention. *cl, bsn*	HeE
Grant, P.	Prelude and Canonic Piece. *fl, cl*	CoF
Grimm, H.	Duo. *cl, bsn*	SM
Grimm, H.	Scherzino. *fl, ob*	SM
Groot, C. de	Serenade (1949). *ob, bsn*	SD
Gyring, E.	10 Canons for Two and Three Woodwinds: Canon No. II *fl, ob*	CoF
Haan, S. de	Divertimento. *cl, bsn*	Pet
Haieff, A.	3 Bagatelles. *ob, bsn*	BB
Hall, R.	2 Diversions. *fl, bsn*	B&H
Hamilton, T.	Dialogue. *fl, asax*	CoA
Handel, G.	Allegro (Sonata No. 2). *fl, cl*	CF
Harris, A.	Original Duets. *2 ww*	CCo
Hart, W.	Interlude. *fl, bsn*	Spr
Hasquenoph, P.	Sonata Espressa. *cl, bsn*	EME
Haubiel, C.	Pastoral. *ob, bsn*	Wes
Haufrecht, H.	Dialogues. *fl, cl*	CoF
Haufrecht, H.	Overture for a New Year. *fl, cl*	CoF
Hawkins, J.	8 Movements (1966). *fl, cl*	Can
Haydn, F.-Skolnik	The Witches' Canon. *fl, cl*	EdM
Haydn, F.	3 Sonatas. *fl, cl*	EdM
Hedwall, L.	Duo (1952). *cl, bsn*	STI
Hedwall, L.	5 Epigrams (1959). *fl, cl*	Nor
Heinichen, J.-Steinbeck	Sonate, c. *ob, bsn*	BrH
Hekster, W.	Dialogues. *fl, cl*	SD
Henry, O.	3 Serial Duets. *fl, cl*	AMC
Heussenstamm, G.	Ambages, op. 29. *fl, cl*	See

Two Woodwinds

Homs, J.	Sonata (1942). *ob, bcl*	See
Hoskins, W.	Invention for Two Woodwinds.	
	fl, cl	CoF
Hovhaness, A.	Prelude and Fugue, op. 13.	
	ob(fl), bsn	Pet
Hovhaness, A.	Suite, op. 21 (1937). *ehn, bsn*	Pet
Hovhaness, A.	Suite, op. 23. *ob, bsn*	Pet
Hughes, K.	Second Chance. *fl, ob*	Wes
Jacob, G.	3 Inventions. *fl, ob*	GaM
Jacob, G.	3 Little Pieces. *ob, bsn*	MR
Johnson, H.	Serenade. *fl, cl*	NVM
Jolivet, A.	Sonatine (1961). *fl, cl*	B&H
Jolivet, A.	Sonatine (1963). *ob, bsn*	B&H
Kaplan, L.	Two-Part Invention. *cl, bsn*	PMP
Karkoff, M.	Duo, op. 3 (1951). *cl, bsn*	STI
Kay, U.	Suite. *fl, ob*	MCA
Kazacsay, T.	2 Duette, op. 113 (1956). *ob, ehn*	EMB
Keller, H.	5 Pieces. *cl, bsn*	AMP
Kelterborn, R.	Incontri brevi (1967). *fl, cl*	B&N
Kettering, E.	15 Carols. *2 ww*	Con
Keuler, J.	Piccola partita. *cl, bsn*	B&V
Klerk, A. de	Sarabande en Sicilienne. *fl, ob*	EdH
Klug, E.	Divertimento ticinese. *fl(ob), cl*	Hei
Knellwolf, J.	Duets, 4 vols. *2 instr*	Hug
Kocsar, M.	Ungaresca. *ob, cl*	B&V
Koechlin, C.	Sonatine Modale, op. 155. *fl, cl*	EME
Kolman, P.	Sonata canonica. *cl, bcl*	SHF
Kondorossy, L.	Serenade. *ob, bsn*	AMC
Konietzny, H.	Isometrisch — isorhythmisch. *2ww*	B&N
König, H.	Duo. *fl, cl*	PG
Kouguell, A.	3 Pieces. *ob, bsn*	AMC
Krenek, E.	Sonatina, op. 92/2b (1942). *fl, cl*	B&N
Kummer, G.	2 Duets, op. 46. *fl, cl*	CF
Kummer, G.	2 Duos Concertants. *fl, cl*	Bil
Kunert, K.-Adams	Sonata, G, op. 15. *fl, ob*	Vol
Kunert, K.	Sonate, op. 15a. *fl, ob*	PG
Kunert, K.	Sonata, op. 20. *cl, bsn*	FrH
Kunz, A.	Fun for Two (1964). *2 bcl*	Can
Kunz, A.	Fun for Two (1964). *bsn, bcl*	Can
Kupferman, M.	Available Forms (1966). *cl, bsn*	Gen
Kupferman, M.	Duo Divertimento. *cl, bsn*	Gen
Kupferman, M.	4 Charades. *fl, cl*	Gen
Kurz, W.	Variationensuite. *cl, bsn*	LDo
Lacome, P.	Passepied. *ob(fl), bsn(vc)*	Dur
Leichtling, A.	Nachtmusik, op. 36. *bcl, cbsn*	AMC
Levy, F.	Duo. *cl, bsn*	See
Lewin, G.	Caribbean Sketches. *fl, cl*	B&H
Lewin, G.	Nostalgia d'Espana. *fl, cl*	B&H
Lewin, G.	3 Latin American Impressions.	
	fl, cl	B&H
Lidholm, I.	Invention (1954). *cl, bcl*	STI
Maganini, Q.	Air and Double. *ob, cl*	CF

Two Woodwinds

Maganini, Q.	Boa Constrictor and the Bobolink	
	fl, bsn	CF
Maganini, Q.	Canonico Espressivo. *fl, cl(bsn)*	EdM
Maganini, Q.	Couperin Suite. *fl, ob(cl)*	EdM
Maganini, Q.	Petite Suite Classique. *fl, ob(cl)*	EdM
Mangs, R.	6 Bagatellen. *fl, cl*	STI
Margola, F.	Partita. *fl, ob*	Edi
Maschayeki, A.	9 Expressionen. *cl, bcl*	UE
Maves, D.	Duet. *fl, cl*	Can
McKusick, H.	Atonal Duets. *2 ww*	CCo
Melillo, P.	Duo. *fl, bsn*	AMC
Mellnäs, A.	Växlingar. *fl/pic, cl/bcl*	EMF
Miaskovsky, N.-Lester	Fugue in a Classic Style. *cl, bcl*	Wes
Michael, E.	Sonatine (1962). *fl, cl*	Ric
Migot, G.	Suite en Trois Mouvements. *fl, cl*	B&N
Moevs, R.	Duo. *ob, ehn*	EME
Mozart, W.-Dahm	3 Sonatas. *fl(ob), cl*	Vol
Mozart, W.-Bellison	12 Duets, K. 487. *fl(ob), bsn(ehn)*	FrC
Mozart, W.-Haskins	12 Duets. *ob, cl*	OxU
Mozart, W.	12 Duos. *2 ww*	BrH
Mozart, W.-Simon	12 Duos. *2 ww*	EBM
Mozart, W.-Smith	12 Easy Duets, K. 487. *2 ww*	Sch
Mueller, F.	Easy Duets. *2 treble clef instr*	Uni
Musgrave, T.	Impromptu. *fl, ob*	Che
Naumann, J.-Bormann	Duett, B♭. *ob, bsn*	HSM
Naumann, S.	Duo (1948). *cl, bsn*	STI
Nelhybel, V.	4 Duets. *2 wind instr*	Gen
Nixon, R.	4 Duos. *fl(ob), cl*	TP
Oller, J.	Duo (1936). *fl, cl*	EB
Organn, R.	Janina. *ob, bsn*	Reb
Ott, J.	5 Pieces (1968). *fl, cl*	CBP
Ott, J.	Suite (1965). *fl, cl*	CBP
Otten, L.	Duo (1965). *fl, bsn*	SD
Parik, I.	Hudba pre Troch. *fl(ob), cl*	SHF
Paulson, G.	Duo (1955). *ob, ehn*	STI
Peterson, W.	Phantasmagoria. *fl, cl*	See
Phillips, G.	Suite. *ob, cl*	SS
Pisk, P.	Duo, op. 106. *cl, bsn*	CoF
Plumby	Picture of a Hunt. *2 ww*	B-M
Poulenc, F.	Sonata. *cl, bsn*	Che
Presser, W.	5 Duets. *ob, bsn*	TP
Querat, M.	Lied - Canonica. *fl(ob), asax*	E-V
Raphling, S.	Prelude and Toccata. *fl, bsn*	EdM
Raphling, S.	Sonatina. *fl, cl*	EdM
Raphling, S.	Variations. *fl, cl*	EdM
Reizenstein, F.	Duo. *ob, cl*	Gal
Riegger, W.	Duos, op. 35. No. 1 - *fl, ob;* No. 2 -	
	fl, cl; No. 3 - *ob, cl*	TP
Riegger, W.	3 Canons, op. 9/2. *fl, cl*	TP
Rieti, V.	Canon. *cl, bsn*	Gen
Rivier, J.	Duo. *fl, cl*	Bil
Roy, K.	Duo. *fl, cl*	TP

Two Woodwinds

Rugolo, P.	Answering. *fl, bsn*	Wes
Russell, R.	Duo. *fl, cl*	Gen
Saeys, E.	Suite. *fl, bsn*	Mau
Sangiorgi	Duo-Sonata. *ob(cl), bsn*	FrC
Sangiorgi	Sonatina. *fl, cl*	FrC
Savnik, V.	Inventions. *cl, bsn*	Kaw
Scarlatti, D.-Skolnik	Neapolitan Suite. *fl, cl*	EdM
Scarmolin, A.	Duet Time. *2 ww*	Lud
Scheidt, S.-Schwadron	Bicinium (Cantio Sacra). *fl, cl*	PMP
Schönberg, S.	Dialogues (1960). *fl, cl*	Che
Schönberg, S.	Duo (1959). *cl, bsn*	STI
Schuller, G.	Duo Sonata. *cl, bcl*	BB
Schwadron, A.	Duo. *fl, ob*	PMO
Schwadron, A.	Duo. *fl, cl*	PMP
Schwadron, A.	Duo. *cl, ob*	PMP
Sehlbach, E.	Duo, op. 53/2. *fl, ob*	MV
Singer, S.	Cedar Lake. *fl, cl*	CF
Smith. L.	2 Duets. *cl, bsn*	CoF
Smith, R.	Duo. *fl(ob), bsn*	AMC
Smith, S.	One for J.C. *asax, bsn*	See
Smith, W.	5 Pieces. *fl, cl*	MJQ
Souffriau, A.	Sonate. *fl, cl*	Mau
Stahuljak, M.	Inventions. *cl, bsn*	Kaw
Stearns, P.	Nocturne. *fl, cl*	CoF
Stevens, H.	5 Duos. *fl, cl*	JB
Stevens, H.	6 Canons. *2 ww*	CoF
Strang, G.	5 Pieces. *fl, cl*	AMC
Stutschewsky, J.	Impressions. *cl, bsn*	See
Suter, R.	Duetti. *fl, ob*	Hei
Sweelinck-Schwadron	2 Contrapuntal Duos. *ob, bsn*	PMP
Sydeman, W.	Music. *ob, cl*	SMP
Szalowski, A.-Cray	Duo. *fl, cl*	SF
Tepper	Suite. *cl, bsn*	MCA
Thärichen, W.	Duo, op. 47. *fl, ob*	B&B
Tustin, W.	30 Duets. *2 ww*	SMP
Tuthill, B.	Sonatine in Canon. *fl, ob(cl)*	TP
Vellekoop, G.	Listen to Our Recorders. *2 ww*	Gal
Vellekoop, G. (arr.)	6 Suites. *2 ww*	Gal
Villa-Lobos, H.	Bachianas Brasilerias No. 6. *fl, bsn*	AMP
Villa-Lobos, H.	Choros No. 2 (1924). *fl, cl*	EME
Villa-Lobos, H.	Duo (1957). *ob, bsn*	EME
Von Kreisler, A.	Concertino. *fl, cl*	SM
Von Kreisler, A.	Little Suite. *fl, cl*	SM
Von Kreisler, A.	2 Dialogues. *fl, cl*	SM
Von Kreisler, A.	2 Pieces. *fl, cl*	SM
Walker, R.	3 Miniatures. *fl, cl*	Ken
Wardrop, L.	Two-Part Inventions. *ob, ehn*	Uni
Wardrop, L.	Two-Part Inventions. *cl, acl*	Uni
Weaver	7 Dialogues. *fl, cl*	Sha
Weber, A.	Sonatina. *fl, bsn*	ALe
Weegenhuise, J.	3 Pezzi (1954). *fl, cl*	SD
Weiner, I.	Duo. *fl, ob*	AMC

Two Woodwinds

Weinzweig, J.	Intermissions. *fl, ob*	SMP
Welander, S.	Sonatin (1966). *cl, bsn*	STI
Welin, K.	Sermo modulatus (1960). *fl, cl*	STI
Wigglesworth, F.	Duo. *ob, cl*	TP
Wildberger, J.	Rencontres. *fl/pic, cl/E♭ cl/* *basset hn*	HG
Williams, E.	Artistic Duets. *2 ww*	CCo
Williams, E.	Easy Duets. *2 ww*	CCo
Wolpe, S.	Suite im Hexachord. *ob, cl*	M&M
Zonn, P.	Dance Set. *cl, bsn*	CoF

TWO WOODWINDS - COLLECTIONS

	Duets. *cl, bsn*	MR
Andraud, A. (arr)	Duos Concertants, First Series. *fl(ob), cl*	SM
Andraud, A. (arr)	Duos Concertants, Second Series. *fl(ob), cl*	SM
Andraud, A.	Duos Concertants, Third Series. *fl(ob), cl*	SM
Elkan, H.	Duet Album. *fl(ob, cl), bsn*	HeE
Frank, M. (arr)	20 Duets. *ob(fl, cl), bsn(bcl)*	SF
Frank, M. (tr)	20 Easy Woodwind Duets. *fl(ob, cl), bsn(cl)*	KPM
Kaplan, D. (arr)	Gotham Collection. *fl, ob*	Spr
Lewis-Widmer	Beginning Duets. *2ww*	B-M
Nelson B. (arr)	Advanced Duets, 3 vols. *2ww*	CCo
Schaeffer, D. (arr)	Program Duets. *fl, cl*	PrA
Stouffer, P.	Duet Album. *fl, ob*	HeE
Voxman, H. (arr)	78 Duets, 2 vols. *fl, cl*	Rub
Waln, G. (arr)	Waln Duets. *fl, cl*	NK

WOODWIND AND BRASS

Barsam, Y.	3 Zugaben. *bsn, hn*	Pet
Beyer, J.	Duet. *ob, tu*	AMC
Blanc, J.	3 Sonatas. *bsn, hn*	Kaw
Childs, B.	Horn & Oboe Music. *ob, hn*	CoF
Devienne, F.-Mayhan	Duets. *fl(ob, cl), hn(bsn)*	Sch
Dobrzynski, I.-Kurkiewicz	Duet. *cl, hn*	PWM
Dobrzynski, I.-Leloir	Duo, E♭. *cl, hn*	Kaw
Duvernoy, F.-Leloir	3 Sonatas. *hn, bsn/vc*	Kaw
Hartley, W.	Duet. *fl, tu*	TP
Koechlin, C.	4 Little Pieces, op. 173. *cl, hn*	EME
Makovecky, J.-Weelink	Duo Concertant No. 1. *cl, hn*	Kaw
Makovecky, J.-Weelink	Duo Concertant No. 2. *cl, hn*	Kaw
Makovecky, J.-Weelink	Duo Concertant No. 3. *cl, hn*	Kaw
Makowecky, J.-Leloir	3 Sonatas. *cl(bsn), hn*	Kaw
Ott, J.	5 Duets. *ob, hn*	CBP

Woodwind and Brass

Schwadron, A.	Short Suite. *cl, trb*	Ken
Stich-Punto, J.-Leloir	Sonata. *hn, bsn*	Kaw
Sydeman, W.	Duo (1960). *bcl, hn*	See
Telemann, G.-Hartley	3 Dances, a. *fl, tu*	Ens
Vaughan, R.	Quattro Bicinie. *cl, tu*	JB
Wildgans, F.	3 Inventionen. *cl, hn*	Dob

WOODWIND & STRING

Abendroth, W.	Divertimento, op. 5. *fl, va*	WMS
Alexander, J.	3 Inventions. *ob, va*	Gen
Bach, C.P.E.	Duet. *fl, vn*	HU
Bach, C.P.E.	Duet, G. *fl, vn*	Int
Bach, C.P.E.	Duet. *fl, vn*	WIN
Bach, C.P.E.	2 Duets. *ob, vn*	TP
Bach, C.P.E.-Stephan	2 Duos. *fl, vn*	NV
Baeyens, A.	Piranesi. *fl, vc*	EMe
Balassa, S.	Dimensioni (1966). *fl, va*	EMB
Beck, C.	Sonatina. *fl, vn*	EME
Bentzon, J.	Intermezzo. *cl, vn*	Che
Berezowsky, N.	Duo. *cl, va*	AMC
Berg, G.	Pour Clarinette et Violon (1959). *cl, vn*	SPD
Bezanson, P.	5 Miniatures. *cl, vc*	ACA
Bischof, R.	Thema und 7 Variationen, op. 4. *ob, vc*	LDo
Bizet, G.	Little Duet, c. *bsn, vc*	MR
Blank, A.	Variations. *cl, va*	See
Borgulya, A.	4 duetti. *fl, va*	B&V
Bornefeld, H.	Choralsonate "Auf meinen lieben Gott." *fl, vn*	B&N
Bunge, S.	Duo. *fl, vc*	Pet
Busch, A.	Hausmusik, op. 26/1. *cl, vn*	BrH
Busch, A.	Hausmusik, op. 26/2. *cl, vn*	BrH
Calabro, L.	5 Duos. *cl, vc*	E-V
Campagnoli, B.	Duet, D. *fl, vn*	B&V
Cannabich, C.-Höckner-Twarz	6 Duets, 2 vols. *fl, va*	Sim
Chambers, S.	One Plus One. *fl, db*	AMC
Childs, B.	The Location of Music. *fl, db*	ACA
Cope, D.	Cycles. *fl, db*	CoA
Couperin, F.-Schmitz	Musik für Flote. *fl, vn*	B&N
Cunningham, M.	Romance. *va, bsn*	CoA
Danzi, F.-Sonntag	3 Duets, op. 64. *fl, vc*	HSM
David, J.	Sonate, op. 32/1. *fl, va*	BrH
David, J.	Sonate, op. 32/4. *cl, va*	BrH
David, T.	Sonatine (1958). *fl, va*	LDo
Degen, H.	Sonata. *fl, va*	Sim
Doran, M.	Sonatina. *fl, vc*	Wes
Dukelsky, V.	Etude. *vn, bsn*	MCA
Eckerberg, S.	Duo. *fl, vc*	STI

Woodwind & String

Eckhardt-Gramatté, S.	Duo Concertante (1956). *fl, vn*	Can
Eder, H.	Duo. *fl, vn*	LDo
Etler, A.	Duo. *ob(fl, vn), va(cl)*	NVM
Franco, J.	6 Variations on "The Flute that Lured the Listening Bird". *fl, va*	ACA
Franco, J.	Sonatina. *fl, va*	CoF
Gal, H.	Divertimento, op. 90/1. *bsn, vc*	ABe
Garlick, A.	Duo. *fl, va*	See
Genin, P.	Grand Duo Concertant. *fl, vn*	Bil
Genzmer, H.	Divertissement. *fl, vn*	Pet
Geraedts, J.	3 Inventies (1943). *fl, vn*	SD
Gilmore, B.	Duo (1969). *fl, va*	See
Gyring, E.	Duo. *cl, va*	CoF
Gyring, E.	Duo No. 2. *cl, va*	CoF
Haber, L.	6 Miniatures. *fl, vn*	Gen
Hallnäs, H.	Spel för två. *cl, va*	EMF
Hamilton, I.	Serenata. *cl, vn*	TP
Haydn, F.	3 Sonatas. *fl, va*	EdM
Hermanson, A.	A due voci. *afl, va*	EMF
Hindemith, P.	Stücke (1942). *bsn, vc*	SS
Hindemith, P.	2 Duets. *cl, vn*	SS
Honegger, A.	Prelude (Trois Contrepoints, No. 1.) *ob, vc*	Che
Huybrechts, A.	Sonatine (1934). *fl, va*	CBD
Hye-Knudsen, J.	2 Chamber Duets. *fl, vc*	Che
Jacob, G.	Miniature Suite. *cl, va*	MR
Jez, J.	Verses. *ob, va*	EdD
Johnston, B.	Duo. *fl, db*	M&M
Karlins, M.	Birthday Music No. II. *fl, db*	CoF
Kelterborn, R.	4 Miniaturen. *ob, vn*	B&N
Kenins, T.	Fantasy-Variations (1967). *fl, va*	Can
Klepper, W.	Sonata. *fl, va*	EMU
Kraus, J.-Winter	Sonata, D. *fl, va*	B&N
Kupferman, M.	3 for Two. *cl, vn*	Gen
Kuusisto, I.	Duo (1957). *fl, vc*	MT
Lacôme, P.	Passepied. *fl, vc*	Dur
Lacôme, P.	Passepied. *bsn, vn*	Dur
Lessard, J.	Music for the Occasion of the Wedding of Lydia Huntington and Edward Sparrow. *fl, vn*	CoF
Lewis, P.	Duet. *fl, vc*	CoF
Lipkin, M.	Suite (1961). *fl, vc*	Che
Lippolis, I.	Sonatina a due. *fl, va*	FrC
Lucke, G.	Kleiner Dialog (1966). *fl, vn*	B&N
Lucke, G.	Kleiner Dialog (1966). *cl, va*	B&N
Maes, J.	Sonatine (1934). *fl, va*	CBD
Maganini, Q.	Canonico Espressivo. *fl, vc*	EdM
Mamlok, U.	Sintra. *afl, vc*	ACA
Mann, L.	5 Bagatelles, op. 3 (1951) *cl (va), vc*	Can

Woodwind & String

Martino, D.	5 Frammenti. *ob, db*	M&M
Migot, G.	6 petits préludes, 2 vols. *fl, vn*	ALe
Moyse, L.	4 Dances. *fl, vn*	M&M
Mozart, W.	Sonate, B♭, K. 292. *bsn, vc*	BrH
Mozart, W.-Ade	Sonata, K. 292. *bsn, vc*	I-V
Mozart, W.-Korda	Sonata, B♭, K. 292. *bsn, vc*	LDo
Mozart, W.-Bellison	12 Duets, K. 487. *fl(ob), va(vc)*	FrC
Nielsen, C.	Faith and Hope Are Playing. *fl, va*	Che
Nordgren, E.	Sonatin. *cl, vn*	EMF
Orland, H.	Perpetuum Mobile and Inventionette. *fl, vc*	See
Parris, R.	Duo. *fl, vn*	CoF
Pedersen, P.	Ricercare (1958). *vn, cl*	Can
Praag, H. van	Kleine Suite (1936). *fl, vn*	SD
Praag, H. van	Voorspel, Intermezzo en Scherzo (1943). *cl, vc*	SD
Presser, W.	Serenade. *fl, va*	See
Raphael, G.	Divertimento, op. 74. *asax, vc*	BrH
Raphael, G.	Kammermusik, op. 47/6, Duo, E♭. *cl, vn*	B&N
Roos, R. de	Quattro per due. *ob, va*	Pet
Roussel, A.	Duo. *bsn, db*	Dur
Sacco, P.	Elegie. *fl, vc*	Wes
Scarmolin, A.	3 Pieces. *fl, va*	AMC
Schilling, H.	Suite en miniature (1964). *vn, bsn*	BrH
Schönberg, S.	5 Pieces. *cl, vc*	Che
Schröder, H.	Duo-Sonate. *fl, va*	FrH
Simons, N.	Design Groups No. 2. *fl, db*	CoF
Skold, Y.	Sonatin. *fl, va*	EMF
Smit, L.	Suite (1938). *ob, vc*	SD
Smith, W.	Suite. *cl, vn*	OxU
Spisak, M.	Duetto concertante. *bsn, va*	FrC
Stearns, P.	Duo. *afl, db*	CoF
Stearns, P.	Duo. *cl, vc*	AMC
Stout, A.	3 Canons, op. 61A. *fl, vc*	CoF
Suter, R.	Improvisation. *ob, va*	Hei
Swickard, R.	4 Duets. *fl, va*	See
Sydeman, W.	Duo (1959). *fl, db*	See
Sydeman, W.	Duo. *cl/bcl, db*	Pet
Sydeman, W.	Variations. *va, bsn*	AMC
Tate, Ph.	Sonata. *cl, vc*	OxU
Tatton, M.	Two by Two. *fl, va*	AMC
Tatton, M.	2 Duets, Eclogue, Dispute. *fl, va*	AMC
Telemann, G.-Ermeler	Duet, G. *fl, vn*	B&N
Telemann, G.-Loewer	6 Duets. *fl, vn*	B&V
Thomson, V.	Serenade. *fl, vn*	SMP
Valdambrini, F.	19 Movements. *fl, va*	UE
Valee, G.	Menuet et Rigodon. *fl(ob), vc*	GaM
Villa-Lobos, H.	Assobio a Jato (The Jet Whistle). *fl, vc*	SMP SMP
Wigglesworth, F.	Duo. *ob, va*	TP
Wiszniewski, Z.	Duo. *fl, va*	HMo

WOODWIND & HARP

Andriessen, H.	Intermezzo (1950). *fl, hp*	SD
Badings, H.	Ballade (1950). *fl, hp*	SD
Badings, H.	Cavatina (1952). *afl, hp*	SD
Bamert, M.	5 Aphorisms. *fl, hp*	See
Beecroft, H.	3 Pezzi brevi. *fl, hp*	UE
Bernier, R.	Sonate à deux (1939). *fl, hp*	CBD
Bon, W.	Riflessione. *fl, hp*	SD
Bozza, E.	2 Impressions. *fl, hp*	ALe
Broeckx, J.	Petite Suite. *fl, hp*	EMe
Chou, Wen-Chung	3 Folk Songs. *fl, hp*	Pet
Colaco Osorio-Swaab, R.	Fantasia (1950). *fl, hp*	SD
Damase, J.	Sonate. *fl, hp*	E-V
Delden, L. van	Catena di miniature. *fl, hp*	SD
Delden, L.	Duo, op. 27 (1950). *fl, hp*	SD
Donizetti, G.-Meylan	Sonate. *fl, hp*	Pet
Dresden, S.	Sonata. *fl, hp*	EdS
Eben, P.	Ordo modalis. *ob, hp*	CHF
Flosman, O.	Romanza e scherzo. *fl, hp*	Art
Flothuis, M.	Sonata da camera, op. 42 (1951). *fl, hp*	SD
Henkemans, H.	4 pezzi (1963). *fl, hp*	SD
Hilse, B.	Suite, op. 6. *fl, hp*	WZ
Hölliger, H.	Mobile (1962). *ob, hp*	SS
Ibert, J.	Entr'acte. *fl, hp*	ALe
Jolivet, A.	Alla Rustica. *fl, hp*	B&H
Jolivet, A.	Controversia. *ob, hp*	Bil
Jonák, Z.	MIM. *fl, hp*	ES
Jongen, J.	Danse Lente. *fl, hp*	Che
Kapr, J.	Dialoge. *fl, hp*	ES
Kelly, R.	Sonata. *ob, hp*	CoF
Krumpholtz, J.-Zingel	Sonata, F. *fl, hp(pf)*	B&N
Lasala, A.	Poema del pastor coya. *fl, hp*	FrC
Lauber, J.	4 Danses medievales, op. 45. *fl, hp*	WZ
Lehmann, H.	Spiele. *ob, hp*	SS
Maganini, Q.	La Romanesca. *fl, hp*	EdM
Melartin, E.	Sonata (1920). *fl, hp*	MT
Migot, G.	Le Premier Livre de Divertissements Francais. *cl, hp*	ALe
Mourant, W.	Elegy. *fl, hp*	CoF
Mozart, W.-Houdy	Cadenzas for the Concerto for flute and harp, K. 299. *fl, hp*	ALe
Mozart, W.-Flothuis	Cadenza to Concerto, K. 299. *fl, hp*	B&V
Mozart, W.-Reinecke	3 Cadenzas to Concerto, K. 299. *fl, hp*	BrH
Mozart, W.-Jongen	Cadenzas to Concerto, K. 299. *fl, hp*	HeE
Mozart, W.-Pillney	Cadenzas to Concerto, K. 299. *fl, hp*	WZ
Nielsen, C.	The Fog Is Lifting, *fl, hp*	Che
Obrovska, J.	Symbiozy. *fl, hp*	Art

Woodwind & Harp

Odstrcil, K.	Reflexy. *fl, hp*	Art
Otten, L.	Cassation (1959). *fl, hp*	SD
Pelemans, W.	Sonate. *fl, hp*	Mau
Persichetti, V.	Serenade No. 10. *fl, hp*	E-V
Polin, C.	Second Sonata. *fl, hp*	AMC
Praag, H. van	Impromptu (1964). *fl, hp*	SD
Praag, H. van	Sonatine (1934). *fl, hp*	SD
Praag, H. van	Sonatine (1955). *cl, hp*	SD
Ramovs, P.	Impulsions (1967). *ob, hp*	EdD
Ramovs, P.	3 Little Pastorals. *fl, hp*	EdD
Raphael, G.	Sonatine, op. 65/2. *ob, hp(pf)*	BrH
Ravel, M.	Pavane pour une Infante Defunte. *fl, hp*	EdM
Reiner, K.	2 composizioni. *ob, hp*	Art
Sauguet, H.	Barcarolle. *bsn, hp*	ChM
Slavicky, K.	Intermezzi mattutini. *fl, hp*	Art
Smit Sibinga, T.	3 images (1954). *fl, hp*	SD
Smutny, J.	3 Stücke (1969). *ob, hp*	B&N
Spelman, T.	Rondo. *fl, hp*	Che
Staempfli, E.	Duo (1965). *fl, hp*	B&B
Tausinger, J.	Le avventure. *fl, hp*	Art
Voss, F.	Notturno (1958). *ob, hp*	BrH
Vries-Robbé, W. de	Sonata. *fl, hp*	B&V
Williams, D.	Sonatina. *bsn, hp*	AMC
Wismer, P.	Sonatine — Croisière. *fl, hp*	Bil
Zamara, A.	Capriccietto. *fl, hp(pf)*	LDo
Zecchi, A.	Divertimento. *fl, hp*	EdB

WOODWIND & GUITAR

Antoniou, T.	Dialogue. *fl, guit*	EMo
Azpiazu, J.	Sonate basque. *fl, guit*	WZ
Bach, J.S.-Ragnossig	Sonata No. 4, C (S. 1033). *fl, guit*	EME
Ballou, E.	Dialogues. *ob, guit*	CoF
Barlow, F.	Pavane. *fl, guit*	E-V
Becker, G.	con buen ayre. *fl, guit*	WZ
Beecroft, H.	3 Pezzi brevi. *fl, guit*	UE
Beethoven, L. van-Scheit	Sonatine. *vn(fl), guit*	LDo
Behrend, S.	Legnaniana. *fl, guit*	WZ
Behrend, S.	Triptychon (1970). *fl(ob), guit*	B&N
Bozza, E.	Polydiaphonie. *fl, guit*	ALe
Braga, G.	Serenata. *fl, guit*	Dur
Braga, G.	Serenata. *ob, guit*	Dur
Braga, G.	Serenata. *ehn, guit*	Dur
Braga, G.	Serenata. *cl, guit*	Dur
Braga, G.	Serenata. *bsn, guit*	Dur
Braun, G.	Sonatine. *ob(fl), guit*	WZ
Burkhard, W.	Serenade, op. 71/3. *fl, guit*	B&N
Calatayud, B.	Divertimentos. *fl, guit*	UE
Campra, A.-Kovats	Menuet vif & gigue. *ob(fl), guit*	EME
Caroso, F.-Behrend	Balletto. *fl, guit*	WZ

Woodwind & Guitar

Carulli, F.	5 Serenades. *fl, guit*	CFV
Carulli, F.-Nagel	Serenade, op. 109/1. *fl, guit*	S&C
Castelnuovo-Tedesco, M.	Sonatina, op. 205 (1965). *fl, guit*	EME
Cilensek, J.	Sonate (1950). *fl, guit*	BrH
Couperin, F.-Kovats	Les Petits Moulins à vent *ob(fl), guit*	EME
David, J.	Variationen, op. 32/2. *fl, lute*	BrH
Diabelli, A.	Serenade, op. 99. *fl, guit*	Sim
Diabelli/Schubert-Götze	Tänze. *fl, gui,*	PrM
Duckworth, W.	An Imaginary Death Dance. *ob, guit*	CoA
Flagello, N.	Burlesca. *fl, guit*	Gen
Freundlich, R.	5 Little Melodies. *fl, guit*	FrC
Fuerstenau, K.-Nagel	Stücke, op. 37. *fl, guit*	Hei
Fürstenau, K.-Nagel	12 Stücke, op. 38. *fl, guit*	SS
Fuerstenau, K.-Homann	12 Originalkompositionen, op. 35. *fl, guit*	B&N
Fürstenau, K.-Behrend	Suite, op. 34. *fl, guit*	WZ
Fürstenau, K.-Behrend	Suite, op. 35. *fl, guit*	WZ
Giuliani, M.-Thomatos	Divertimento. *fl, guit*	WZ
Giuliani, M.	Grosse Sonate, op. 85. *fl, guit*	WZ
Goepfert, K.-Wojciechowski	Sonate, op. 13. *bsn, guit*	B&B
Handel, G.-Scheit	Sonata, a. *ob, guit*	LDo
Handel, G.-Scheit	Sonata, C. *ob, guit*	LDo
Handel, G.-Zanoskar	Sonata, D. *fl, guit*	HSM
Handel, G.-Schaller	Sonata, d. *ob, guit*	LDo
Handel, G.-Schaller	Sonata, F. *ob, guit*	LDo
Handel, G.-Scheit	Sonata, g. *ob, guit*	LDo
Handel, G.	Sonata No. II, g. *fl, guit*	WZ
Haug, H.	Capriccio (1963). *fl, guit*	EME
Henze, B. (arr)	Sterne über stillen Strassen. *fl, guit*	FrH
Ibert, J.	Entr'acte. *fl, guit*	ALe
Jelinek, H.	Ollapotrida, op. 30. *fl, guit*	EMo
Klebe, G.	Recitativo, Aria e Duetto, op. 44. *fl, guit*	B&B
Komter, J.	Divertimento, G (1943) *fl(vn), guit*	SD
Kont, P.	Ballade. *fl, guit*	LDo
Kovats, B.	Sonatina. *ob, guit*	EMo
Krejci, M.	Serenata. *fl, guit*	Art
Kretschmar, W.-Behrend	Music in C Major. *fl, guit*	WZ
Küffner, J.	Serenade. *fl, guit*	MV
Kummer, G.	Nocturne. *fl, guit*	FrH
Laruelle, J.	Esquisse and Toccata. *fl, guit*	S&C
Lauffensteiner, W.-Schaller	Duetto, A. *fl(ob), guit*	LDo
Locatelli, P.-Brojer	Sonata, D. *fl(ob), guit*	LDo
Locatelli, P.-Scheit	Sonata, D. *fl(ob), guit*	LDo
Locatelli, P.-Scheit	Sonata, G. *fl, guit*	LDo
Loeillet, J.-Brojer	Sonata, a, op. 1/1. *ob, guit*	LDo
Loeillet, J.-Brojer	Sonata, G, op. 1/3. *ob, guit*	LDo
Luck, H.	Kleine Vortragsstücke. *fl, guit*	FrH

Woodwind & Guitar

Maganini, Q.	La Romanesca. *fl, guit*	EdM
Maganini, Q.	La Romanesca. *cl, guit*	EdM
Margola, F.	4 Sonatine. *fl, guit*	GZ
Migot, G.	Sonate. *fl, guit*	EMT
Molino, G.-Henze	Nocturno, op. 37. *fl, guit*	WZ
Ochs, G. (arr)	Neues Spielbüchlein. *fl, guit*	FrH
Ochs, G. (arr)	Spielbuchlein. *fl, guit*	FrH
Pelemans, W.	Klein duo. *fl, guit*	Mau
Pepusch, J.-Schaller	Sonata, d. *ob, guit*	LDo
Pepusch, J.-Brojer	Sonata, F. *ob, guit*	LDo
Pepusch, J.-Brojer	Sonata, G. *ob, guit*	LDo
Pepusch, J.-Scheit	Sonata, G. *ob, guit*	LDo
Pergolesi, G.-Kovats	Siciliano. *ob(fl), guit*	EME
Praag, H. van	Complainte. *ob, guit*	B&V
Praag, H. van	Duettino. *ob, guit*	B&V
Schickele, P.	Windows (1966). *fl, guit*	AlB
Schickele, P.	Windows (1966). *cl, guit*	AlB
Shaughnessy, R.	Duo. *fl, guit*	See
Siegl, O.-Ragossnig	Sonata. *fl, guit*	WZ
Singer, L.	Musica a Due (1965). *ob, guit*	ESZ
Stingl, A.	5 Stücke, op. 34. *fl, guit*	WZ
Telemann, G.-Kämmerling	Partita, G. *ob, guit*	LDo
Telemann, G.-Scheit	Partita, G. *ob(fl), guit*	LDo
Truhlar, J.	Sonatina semplice, op. 18. *fl, guit*	WZ
Van den Broeck, L.	De Slangenbezweerder. *fl, guit*	Mau
Villa-Lobos, H.	Distribuicao de flores, Op. posth. (1932). *fl, guit*	EME
Vries, Robbé, W. de	Pavane-Sarabande-Gigue. *fl, guit*	SD
Wissmer, P.	Sonatina. *fl, guit*	EME
Worschech	12 Grands Classiques, Vol. 1. *fl, guit*	E-V

WOODWIND & PERCUSSION

Abramson, R.	Nightpiece. *fl, perc*	AMC
Amram, D.	Herakles. *fl, perc*	Pet
Back, S.	Favola (1962). *cl, perc*	WH
Back, S.	5 preludier (1966). *cl, perc*	WH
Beradinis, J. de	2 Sketches. *fl, vib*	See
Brehm, A.	Dialogues. *bsn, perc*	EBM
Cabus, P.	Sonate. *cl, perc*	Mau
Childs, B.	The Day Sequence: 2. *bcl, perc*	ACA
Childs, B.	The Golden Bubble. *sarrusophone, perc*	CoF
Childs, B.	Music for a Celebration. *pic, bdr*	CoF
Dahl, I.	Duettino Concertante (1966). *fl, perc*	AlB
Donovan, R.	Fantasia. *bsn, perc*	CoF
Dubois, P.	Circus Parade. *asax, perc*	ALe
Farberman, H.	Progressions. *fl, perc*	BB
Fink, S.	Impression No. 1. *fl, vib*	RS
Fink, S.	Trio Ostinato. *cl, perc*	Sim
Frock, G.	Variations. *fl, perc*	SM
Gesensway, L.	8 Miniatures. *fl, perc*	TP

31

Woodwind & Percussion

Gilbert	Percussinet. *cl, perc*	Ken
Harrison, L.	First Concerto. *fl, perc*	Pet
Hartzell, E.	Monologue 5. Variants (1965). *asax(tsax), perc*	LDo
Heussenstamm, G.	Double Solo. *cl, perc*	See
Hovhaness, A.	The Burning House Overture, op. 185a. *fl, perc*	Pet
Keetman, G.	Stücke. *fl, dr*	SS
Killmayer, W.	3 Dances. *ob, perc*	SS
Kopelent, M.	Canto intimo. *fl, vib*	EMo
Lacour, G.	Divertissement. *asax, perc*	Bil
Lazarof, H.	Asyptotes. *fl, vib*	AMP
Mamangakis, N.	Konstruktionen. *fl, perc*	EMo
Marttinen, T.	Alfa (1962). *fl, perc*	MT
Myers, R.	Fantasy Duos. *asax, perc*	ARM
Naumann, S.	Risposte I (1956). *fl, perc*	ESu
Pololanik, Z.	Musica spingenta III. *bcl, perc*	Art
Rosen, J.	Serenade. *cl, perc*	CoF
Sary, L.	Sonanti No. 2. *fl/afl/pic, perc*	EMB
Schropfer, W.	Mouvement perpetuel. *fl, dr*	EMo
Siennicki, E.	Journey. *cl, perc*	LMP
Siennicki, E.	Journey. *bsn, perc*	LMP
Simonis, J.	Suggestions, op. 20/2 (1970). *fl, perc*	CBD
Stein, L.	Introduction and Dance Chassidig. *fl, tambourine*	CoF
Stein, L.	Introduction and Rondo. *fl, perc*	CoF
Stout, A.	Suite, op. 73/1. *fl, perc*	CoF
Tomasi, H.	Le tombeau de Mireille. *fl, tambourine (dr, pf)*	ALe
Tomasi, H.	Le Tombeau de Mireille. *ob, tambourine (dr, pf)*	ALe
Tower, J.	Brimset. *fl, perc*	ACA
Walacinski, A.	Introspections (1964). *cl, perc*	AP

WOODWIND & TAPE

Booren, J.	Spiel No. 1. *ob, tape*	SD
Braun, P.	Essay (1960-69). *ob, tape*	HG
Davidovsky, M.	Synchronisms No. 1. *fl, tape*	M&M
Dobrowolski, A.	Music (1965). *ob, tape*	AP
Druckman, J.	Animus III. *cl, tape*	ACA
Grosskopf, E.	Proportion 1. *fl, tape*	B&B
Heussenstamm, G.	Saxoclone (1971). *sax, tape*	See
Maderna, B.	Musica su due dimensioni (1957). *fl, tape*	ESZ
Miller, E.	Piece for Clarinet and Tape. *cl, tape*	ACA
Persson, B.	Fyrhändig Invention (1966). *fl, tape*	STI
Sydeman, W.	Piece. *cl, tape*	See
Wahren, K.	Permutation (1967). *fl, tape*	B&B

THREE INSTRUMENTS

THREE FLUTES

Albisi, A.	Miniature Suite No. 1	CF
Albisi, A.	Miniature Suite No. 2	CF
Anderson, L.	Penny Whistle Song	B-M
André, J.	Original Trio, op. 27	B-M
André, J.	Trio, op. 29	EdH
Andriessen, J.	Petit Concert Champêtre	HU
Apothéloz, J.	Les pipeaux d'argent	EMP
Arensky, A.-Wood	The Cuckoo	HeE
Bach, J.S.-Taylor	Fughetta	B-M
Bach, J.S.-Berlinski	3 and 4 Part Canons and Rounds	TP
Badings, H.	Suite No. 2	HU
Barab, S.	Little Suite	B&H
Barab, S.	Sonatina	B&H
Barrère, G.	2 Short Pieces	CF
Beck, F.	Trio	AMC
Beck, F.	Second Trio	AMC
Beethoven, L. van	Allegro for a Flute Clock. *pic, 2 fl*	OxU
Beethoven, L. van	Grand Trio, op. 87	SM
Beethoven, L. van-McLin	Menuet, G	PrA
Beethoven, L. van-Fetherston	Rondo	B-M
Beethoven, L. van-Fetherston	Theme and Variations, op. 25	B-M
Benjamin, T.	4 Pieces	SM
Berbiguier, T.	3 Grands Trios, op. 40/1	EdH
Berbiguier, T.	3 Grands Trios, op. 40/2	EdH
Berbiguier, T.	3 Grands Trios, op. 40/3	EdH
Berbiguier, T.-Wienandt	Trio for Flutes, op. 51/1	SM
Berbiguier, T.-Wienandt	Trio for Flutes, op. 51/2	SM
Berbiguier, T.-Wienandt	Trio for Flutes, op. 51/3	SM
Boismortier, J.	Carillon	Heu
Boismortier, J.-Döflein	6 Sonatas, op. 7, 2 vols.	SS
Boismortier, J.	Sonata, op. 7/1	B&H
Boismortier, J.-Bergmann	Sonata, F, op. 7/1	S&C
Boismortier, J.	Sonata, op. 7/5	B&H
Boismortier, J.-Koch	Sonata, D	MV
Brooke, A.	Three Musketeers	CF
Buchtel, F.	Pipers Three	NK
Byrne, A.	Introduction, Blues and Finale	Pet
Cacavas, J.	Flutes 3	CF
Cacavas, J.	Shimmering Flutes	SM
Calmel	Clair Matin-Pastorale	E-V
Casterede, J.	Flûtes en vacances	ALe
Castle, A.	Flutocycle	Ken
Cavally, R.	Flute Family Sketch. *pic, fl, afl*	SM
Cherubini, L.-Godfrey	Fugue, G.	PrA
Classens, H.	Danza Scherzettino	E-V
Constantino, J.	Dance of the Dresden Doll	PrA
Costanzo-Wienandt	Trio No. 1	SM
Costanzo-Wienandt	Trio No. 2	SM
Costanzo-Wienandt	Trio No. 3	SM

Three Flutes

Costanzo-Wienandt	Trio No. 4	SM
Crist, B.	Old Spanish Melody	HeE
Crist, B.	Tap Dance	HeE
Croley, R.	Scherzetto	Ken
Demachi, G.-Steinbeck	Trio No. 1	LDo
Devienne, F.	Trio	Pet
Devienne, F.-Steinbeck	Trio, D	Eul
Devienne, F.	Trio No. 5	Sim
Dietter, C.-List	10 Stücke	FrH
Dillon, R.	Junanbe	B&H
Dussek, F.-Schultz-Hauser	Notturno	SS
Elias, de	9 berühmte mexikanische Melodien	Ric
Errante, B.	3 Trio Etudes	Sha
Filippi, A. de	Serenade	Gen
Finger, G.-Bergmann	Suite No. 1	S&C
Finger, G.-Bergmann	Suite No 2	S&C
Foster-Miller	Tioga Waltz	B-M
Frank, M.	3 Groovy Flutes	Bou
Gabrielsky, J.	Grand Trio, op. 31	SM
Garcia, M.	Canciones Populares de Espana	JB
Gibbs, C.	Harlequinade	Pet
Grabner, H.	Music (1956)	Kis
Graun, C.-Janetzky	Trio	FrH
Graupner, C.	Suite, F	Pet
Grundman, C.	Flutation	B&H
Guenther, R.	Folk Dance	B-M
Haager, M.	Music for 3 Instruments, op. 6a	AMP
Handel, G.-Schaeffer	Little Fugue	PrA
Haubiel, C.	In the Dorian Mode	See
Haubiel, C.	In the Lydian Mode	See
Haubiel, C.	In the Phrygian Mode	See
Haydn, F.-Eck	Allegro Deciso 2 fl, afl (cl)	Byr
Haydn, F.-Ostling	Allegro Giocoso	B-M
Haydn, F.-Spiegl	Flute Clock Sonatas	OxU
Haydn, F.-Taylor	Rondo Scherzando	B&H
Haydn, F.-Rampal	3 Trios	Int
Haydn, F.-Guenther	Trio	SM
Hermann	Flute Willow	CF
Hodgson	Fanfares	HE
Hoffmeister, F.	Terzetto	Pet
Hook, J.-Voxman	6 Trios, op. 83	Rub
Hook, J.	Sonata, G, op. 83/4	B&H
Hovhaness, A.	The Spirit of Ink	Pet
Jacobson, I.	3 Flights	B-M
Jemnitz, S.	Flötentrio Nr. 2	EMB
Keith, G.	Scherzo & Continuo	AMC
Küffner, J.	Trio, op. 34	EdH
Kuhlau, F.	3 Trios, op. 13	Bil
Kuhlau, F.	3 Grands Trios, op. 86	
	Published separately	Bil
Kuhlau, F.	Grand Trio, op. 90	Bil

Three Flutes

Kummer, G.	Trio, G, op. 24	CF
Kummer, G.	Trio, op. 24	EdH
Kummer, G.	Concert Trio, op. 24	EdM
Kummer, G.-Doeppler	Trio, op. 24	Int
Kummer, G.	Trio, C, op. 53	CF
Kummer, G.	Trio Brillant, D, op. 58	CF
Kummer, G.	Trio brillant, op. 58	EdH
Kummer, G.	Trio, A, op. 59	CF
Kummer, G.	6th Trio, Op. 59	WZ
Lancen, S.	12 Old French Songs	Pet
Langley, J.	Trio	Pet
Larson	Valse	Tem
Leeuwen, A. van	Sonatina in the Old Style	CF
Lester, L.	So Easy Trios	BM
Liadov, A.-Weston	Mosquito Dance	HeE
Liadov, A.-Wade	Musical Snuff Box	CF
Linke, N.	Coloratura	HG
Lorenzo, L. de	I tre virtuosi, op. 31	WZ
Maganini, Q.	3 Little Kittens	EdM
Maganini, Q.	Triple Play	EdM
Marie, G.-McLin	La Cinquantaine	PrA
Mattheson, J.-Hunt	Sonata, g, op. 1/3	S&C
Mattheson, J.-Hunt	Sonata, c, op. 1/4	S&C
Mattheson, J.-Hunt	Sonata, C, op. 1/5	S&C
Mattheson, J.-Hunt	Sonata, B♭, op. 1/6	S&C
Mattheson, J.-Hunt	Sonata, G, op. 1/7	S&C
Mattheson, J.-Hunt	Sonata, F, op. 1/8	S&C
Mattheson, J.-Hunt	Sonata, g, op. 1/9	S&C
Mattheson, J.-Hunt	Sonata, f, op. 1/10	S&C
McKay, F.	Lyric Poem	Bar
McKay, G.	4 Seasons	Bar
Mercadante, S.	3 Serenades	B-M
Mozart, W.-Guenther	Allegro (Divertimento No. 3, K.V. 229)	SM
Mozart, W.-Guenther	Menuetto (Divertimento No. 3, K.V. 229)	SM
Mozart, W.-Guenther	Minuet and Trio (Divertimento No. 3, K.V. 229)	SM
Mozart, W.-Guenther	Allegro and Concertante	B-M
Mozart, W.-Guenther	Allegro and Menuetto	B-M
Mozart, W.-Guenther	Larghetto and Menuetto	B-M
Mozart, W.-Guenther	Rondo	B-M
Neumann, H.	Grand Trio, op. 14	CF
Niehaus, L.	Memories to Share	Wes
Niehaus, L.	Salutes to Flutes	Wes
Organn, R.	The Marionettes Polka	Reb
Organn, R.	Parade of the Lilliputians	Reb
Ostling, A.	Yankee Doodle Dandies	B-M
Painter, P.	Trio (Semplicia)	AMC
Payne	Toccata	Sha
Pearson, W.	Pastorella	HE
Petz, J.-Schultz-Hauser	Symphonia	SS

Three Flutes

Porter, R.	Beaver Creek	HeE
Presser, W.	Suite (1961)	TP
Quantz, J.-Döflein	Sonate	B&N
Quantz, J.-Salkeld	Sonata à 3	S&C
Raymond, L.	Divertimento	Wes
Reicha, A.	Trio, op. 26	M&M
Reif, P.	Trio (1971)	See
Roxbury, R.	Maelcum Soul	CoA
Salieri, A.	Danse (Tarare)	EdM
Scarmolin, A.	Petite Suite	Bar
Schneider, W.	Suite capricieuse	MV
Skolnik, W.	3 Canonic Tunes	EdM
Steffes, G.	Holidays	Hal
Stoker, R.	Rounds and Canons	Pet
Tchaikovsky, P.-Ostling	Dance of the Reed Flutes	BM
Tchaikovsky, P.-Guenther	Dance of the Reed Flutes. *3 fl, pf opt*	SM
Tcherepnin, A.	Trio, op. 59	Be
Tomasi, H.	3 Pastorales	ALe
Tustin, W.	Happy Dirge	Ken
Walckiers, E.	Grand Trio, op. 93/1	EdM
Walckiers, E.	Grand Trio, op. 93/2	EdM
Walckiers, E.	Grand Trio, op. 93/3	EdM
Waln, G. (arr)	Classic Fantasy	NK
Wienandt, E.	3 Easy Canons	SM
Wigglesworth, F.	Trio	CoF
Ziller, D.	Divertimento, C. *2 fl, afl*	*BrH*

THREE FLUTES — COLLECTIONS

Elkan, H.	Ensemble Trio Album	HeE
Gearhart, L.	Flute Sessions	Sha
Guenther, R.	Trio Album for Flutes	B-M
Hudadoff, I. (arr)	24 Flute Trios	PrA
Schaeffer, D. (arr)	10 Woodwind Trios	PrA
Stuart, H. (arr)	BMCO Famous Flute Trios	BM
Voxman, H.	Chamber Music for Flutes	Rub

THREE OBOES

Bach, J.S.-Berlinski	Trio Album	TP
Berlinski, H.	Canons and Rounds	TP
Boismortier, J.-Döflein	6 Sonatas, op. 7, 2 vols.	SS
Byrne, A.	Introduction, Blues and Finale	Pet
Elkan, H.	Ensemble Trio Album	GaM
Gibbs, A.	Harlequinade	Pet
Hodgson	Fanfares	HE
Jacobson	3 Odes	B-M
Lancen, S.	Old French Songs	Pet

Three Oboes

Langley, J.	Trio	Pet
Raphling, S.	Suite in Modern Style	EdM
Sellner, J.	6 Easy Exercises	M&M
Stoker, R.	Rounds and Canons	Pet
Takahashi, Y.	Operation Euler	Pet

THREE CLARINETS

	Luigi's Polka	SLP
Agostini, L.	Trio Quebecois	B&H
Anonymous	Partita	FrH
Artot, J.	12 Trios	CF
Bach, J.S.-Simon	Bach for the Clarinet. Part III.	Sch
Bach, J.S.-Cochrane	15 Three-Part Inventions. 2 cl, bcl(cl)	CF
Bach, J.S.-Williams	Polonaise	SM
Bach, J.S.	Siciliano	EdM
Bach, J.S.-Dansby	Terzetto (Cantata No. 38)	Ken
Banco, G.	Sonatine	EHe
Beethoven, L. van	Minuet, G.	CF
Beethoven, L. van-Merriman	Prelude and Fugue. 2 cl, bcl	SM
Beethoven, L. van	Trio, E♭	MM
Beethoven, L. van-Merriman	Variations on "La Ci Darem." 2 cl, bcl	SM
Beethoven, L. van-Harris	Allegretto (Trio, op. 2)	CF
Beethoven, L. van-Waln	Adagio Cantabile (Op. 87)	NK
Beethoven, L. van-Hernried	Allegro (Op. 87)	War
Beethoven, L. van-Harris	Trio (Adagio Cantabile), op. 87	CF
Beethoven, L. van-Voxman	Menuetto and Finale (Op. 87)	Rub
Beethoven, L. van-Waln	Presto (Op. 87)	NK
Bergenfeld	Chroma-Trix	Tem
Bergenfeld	Two Moods	Tem
Berlinski, H.	Canons and Rounds	TP
Biggs, J.	3 Canzoni	Wes
Blatt, F.	Trio, C, op. 27	B&H
Blatt, F.-Bellison	Trio, E♭	FrC
Booren, J. van den	Sonata (1962)	SD
Bouffil, J.	3 Trios, op. 7 published separately	CF
Bouffil, J.	Grand Trio, op. 8	CF
Bouffil, J.-Janetzky	3 Trios, op. 8	FrH
Brandenburg	The Ash Grove	CF
Brenet	Melancolie	E-V
Buchtel, F.	Comrades	Bar
Bueche, G.	Fugue	CF
Busch, C.	Contentment	CF
Busch, C.	Frolic	CF
Busch, C.	Joyfulness	CF
Busch, C.	Solitude	CF
Butterworth, N.	Three Times Three	Cha
Butts, C.	Desert Dances	PrA
Byrne, A.	Introduction, Blues and Finale	Pet

Three Clarinets

Cacavas, J.	Clarinets 3	CF
Calmel	Petite Marche-Chanson d'Automne	E-V
Carulli, B.-Bellison	Trio, B♭	FrC
Chandler	Eudora	PrA
Cleber-Frank	Rickshaw Ride	SF
Clementi-Kuhlau-Tervoort	Trio	MM
Cohen, S.	Haunted House	B-M
Constantino, J.	Passacaglia	PrA
Constantino, J.	3 Fugues	PrA
Cooke, A.	Suite	OxU
Couperin, F.-Balent	Trio Sonata	PrA
Cox, C.	Divertissement	HeE
Cox, C.	Prelude	HeE
Cruft, A.	3 Bagatellen, op. 50	B&H
Dancla, C.-Waln	Petite Trio	NK
Dancla, C.-Waln	Tuneful Trio	NK
Dandrieu, J.-Seay	Les Tourbillons. 2 cl, bcl	Spr
Dansby, E. (arr)	Roman Bronze	Ken
Donato, A.	3 Pieces	TP
Endresen, R.	Woodwind Moods	Rub
Endresen, R.	Woodwind Revels	Rub
Errante, B.	Terzetto, g	PrA
Faber, J.	6 Melodies in Ancient Style	CF
Faber, J.-Hunt	Suite (Parties sur les fleunt dous)	B&V
Frangkiser, C.	Fugue a la Valse	B&H
Frangkiser, C.	Les Laviolettes	B&H
Furstenau, A.-Wienandt	3 Trios Published separately	SM
Fussell, C.	3 Inventions (1959). E♭ cl, cl, bcl	Can
Garlick, A.	2 Trios	See
Gay, E.	15 Miniatures, 2 vols.	Bil
Gay, E.	10 Petites Pieces Classiques, 2 vols.	Bil
Gee, H.	Fugue in Baroque Style	PrA
Gibbons, O.	Fantasia for Three	EdM
Gibbs, A.	Harlequinade	Pet
Glaser, W.	Fyra korta stycken	Nor
Gluck, C.	Gavotte	CF
Gordon, P.	Calling All Clarinets	NK
Gossec, F.-Phillips	Tambourin	Ken
Graupner, C.-Hunt	Suite No. 1	S&C
Graupner, C.-Hunt	Suite No. 2	S&C
Handel, G.	Bourree	CF
Handel, G.-Lawton	Overture, C	OxU
Handel, G.-Williams	Sonata	SM
Handel, G.	Sonata, D	TP
Hauptmann-Evertse	Trio	T-M
Haydn, F.-Merriman	Divertimento. 2 cl, bcl	SM
Haydn, F.-Voxman	Divertimento, E♭	Rub
Haydn, F.-Voxman	Menuet and Allegro	Rub
Haydn, F.	Minuetto (Divertimento No. 1)	PrA

Three Clarinets

Herbert, V.-Ostling	Melodies Modiste	B-M
Hodgson	Fanfares	HE
Holm, P.	To svenske viser	WH
Holm, P.	Videvidevit	WH
Holm, P.	Vildgaessene	WH
Hook, J.	Sonata	HeE
Hook, J.-Curwin	Sonatinas	Cha
Hook, J.-Curwin	Suite for Three	Cha
Hummel, J.	Trio, B♭	Sim
Jacobsen, I.	3 Caprices	B-M
Jenkins, J.-Merriman	Fantasy. *2 cl, bcl (bsn)*	SM
Katz, E.	3 Canonic Dances	SF
König, H.	5 kleine Sätze	PG
Kratochvil, J.	Suite	ES
Kummer, G.	Trio, op. 24	CF
Kummer, G.	Trio, op. 53	CF
Kummer, G.	Trio, op. 58	CF
Kummer, G.	Trio, op. 59	CF
Kurtz, S.	Suite	SF
Lamb, P.	Pastoral	B&H
Lancen, S.	Old French Songs	Pet
Langley, J.	Trio	Pet
Leonard	Sarabande and Waltz	B-M
Lester, L.	So Easy Trios	BM
Lester, L.	3 Pieces	Wes
Letellier, R.	Pièce récréative	EdR
Lotti, A.-Evertse	Vere Languorus	T-M
Lubin, E.	First Scherzo	SF
Maganini, Q.	3 Little Kittens	EdM
Maganini, Q.	Triple Play	EdM
Maganini, Q.	Troubadours	EdM
Marie, G.-McLin	La Cinquantaine	PrA
Mattheson, J.-Taylor	Air, Minuet and Sarabande	B-M
Mattheus le Maistre-Evertse	Dominus Noster Castellum	T-M
McKay, F.	At the Puppet Show	Bar
McKay, F.	Blue Tapestry	Bar
McKay, F.	Trail to Sunny Point	Bar
Melillo, P.	Clarinet Trio	AMC
Mendelssohn, F.	Lift Thine Eyes & Cast Thy Burden	NK
Meyer	Variations sur un theme classique. *3 cl (fl or ob, 2 cl)*	ALe
Michalsky	Divertimento. *cl, acl, bcl*	Wes
Mihalovici, M.	Sonata, op. 35. *E♭ cl, cl, bcl*	EdS
Miller, E.	3 Pieces	M&M
Mortiz, E.	Divertimento	TP
Mozart, W.-Hite	Allegro Vivace (K. 387)	SM
Mozart, W.-Whewell	Divertimenti	OxU
Mozart, W.-Dominik	Divertimento No. 5. *2 cl, bcl*	Reb
Mozart, W.-Ostling	Minuet & Trio	B-M
Mozart, W.-Neufeld	Serenade, B♭	Wes
Mozart, W.-de Kort	Sonatine	T-M

39

Three Clarinets

Mozart-Grieg-Tchaikovsky-Gee	3 Trios	PrA
Mozart, W.-Dahm	Trio. *2 cl, bcl (bsn)*	Vol
Mozart, W.	2 Adagios	OxU
Mozart, W.-Stone	2 Mozart Pieces	B&H
Mozart, W.-Finch	2 Themes and Variations, K. 547, K.547a	OxU
Mueller, I.-Bellison	Trio, g	FrC
Muller, J.	Comptines	Mau
Nelhybel, V.	9 Trios for Clarinet	FrC
Neumann, F.	5 Stücke	LDo
Norden, H.-McCathren	Miniature Suite	Bar
Ostling, A.	Alouette Clarinette	B-M
Ostrander	Suite for Three	EdM
Pala, J.	Prelude and Scherzo	HeE
Pelz, W.	Three of a Kind	B-M
Phillips, I.	6 Short Arrangements	OxU
Piket, F.	Legend and Jollity	SF
Pleyel, I.-Harris	6 Trios (Op. 8)	CF
Pleyel, I.-Paulson	Trio, C	PrA
Poot, M.	Terzetto	ALe
Purcell, H.	Chaconne	EdM
Rackley, L.	Trio	CoA
Rameau, J.-De Filippi	The Hen. *2 cl, bcl*	HeE
Regner, H.	Heiteres Idyll	PG
Regner, H.	Musikalische Bilder	PG
Reid, A.	Sketches of Youth	Ken
Rosenthal, C. (arr)	Clarinet Trios (18th Century)	EMB
Rosenthal, C. (arr)	Clarinet Trios from Corelli to Beethoven	EBM
Rosenthal, C. (arr)	Clarinet Trios — Russian	EMB
Ruelle, F.	Romance	EMb
Russell, A.	Trio. *E♭ cl, cl, bcl*	Roc
Russel-Smith, G.	Alice and the Mad Hatter	B&H
Ryan, P. (arr)	3 Couperin Movements	Cha
Saeys, E.	Lento et allegro	Mau
Savage	Momento Giojoso	CF
Scarlatti-Schwadron	Pastorale. *2 cl, bcl*	Ken
Scarlatti-DeJesu	Sonata Allegrissimo	Hal
Scarlatti-DeJesu	Sonata No. 1	Hal
Scarlatti-DeJesu	Sonata No. 2	Hal
Scarlatti-DeJesu	Sonata No. 3	Hal
Scarmolin, A.	Petite Suite	Bar
Schaeffer, D. (arr)	Ancient Fugue	PrA
Schalk, C.	Ricercare on an Old English Melody	Con
Scheiffes, H.	4 Short Pieces from Old Masters	HeE
Schneider	Altholländische Tanz-Suite	B&N
Schneider, W.	Erstes Klarinettenspiel	SS
Schramm, H.	Episodes	AMC
Schubert, F.	Trio Movement	Bal
Schwadron, A. (arr)	Progressive Ensemble Studies, Vol. 2	Ken

Three Clarinets

Seeger, P.	7 Spielstücke	PG
Semler-Collery, J.	Terzetto	EME
Shanks, E.	Sonata of Moods and Humors	War
Siennicki, E.-Hite	Let Me Tell It	SM
Siquiet, C.	Menuet	Mau
Skolnik, W.	3 Canonic Tunes	EdM
Snavely, J.	Woodwind Serenade	PrA
Starer, R.	Serenade	SMP
Stein, L.	Trio	TP
Stiebler, E.	Stadien. e^b cl, cl, bcl	EMo
Stoker, R.	Rounds and Canons	Pet
Stouffer, D.	Toccata	PrA
Tartini, G.	2 Trio Sonatas	EdM
Tcherepnin, A.	March for Three Trumpets	EBM
Tcherepnin, A.	Trio	EBM
Tervoort, L.	Clementi-Kuhlau	HeE
Tervoort, L.	Hofmanniana	HeE
Thompson (ed)	7 Pieces from a Music Book of 1826	AMP
Townsend, D.	Ballet Suite	Pet
Trowbridge, L.	Tranquillo	See
Tuthill, B.	Intermezzo. 2 cl, acl	CF
Tuthill, B.	Scherzo	CF
Tuthill, B.	Trio	Spr
Verrall, J.	Introduction and Rondino	CoF
Verrall, J.	Suite	CoF
Vivaldi, A.	Sonata da Camera	EdM
Vogt, G.-Voxman	Adagio Religioso	Rub
Walker, R.	Jeunesse	B-M
Walker, R.	Rondo Scherzando	PrA
Walker, R.	Trio in B♭	B-M
Walker, R.	Scherzino	Tem
Waterson, J.	First Grand Trio Concertante, g	CF
Waterson, J.	First Grand Trio Concertante, g	SM
Weelkes	A Gay Tune	EdM
Weijers, J.	Concertino	T-M
Wienandt, E.	3 Easy Canons	SM
Zeisl, E.	Greek Melody	B-M
Zenoni, B.-Smim	Sinfonia a Tre	EdM

THREE CLARINETS – COLLECTIONS

Bourne	Bourne Trio Album	Bou
Elkan, H.	Ensemble Trio Album	HeE
Gay, E.	10 petites pièces classiques	B&V
Gearhart, L.	Clarinet Sessions	Sha
Haughton, P. (arr)	12 Clarinet Trios	OuP

41

THREE CLARINETS - COLLECTIONS

Knight, V. (arr)	10 Trios	Sch
Kratochvil, J. (ed)	Trios Tscheschischer Klassiker	ES
Moore, J. (arr)	20 Trios for Clarinet Ensemble	BM
Müller-Medek, W.	Kleine Stücke alter	
	Meister, 2 vols.	PG
Schaeffer, D. (arr)	Clarinet Trio Album	PrA
Schaeffer, D. (arr)	Encore (12 Trios)	PrA
Schneider, W.	Allerlei alte Marschweisen,	
	2 vols.	PG
Voxman, H.	Chamber Music for Three	
	Clarinets, Vol. I	Rub
Voxman, H.	Chamber Music for Three	
	Clarinets, Vol. II	Rub

THREE BASSOONS

Alfvén, H.	Bourrée	CGM
Bach, J.S.-Berlinski	Trio Album	TP
Bergt, A.	Trio	FrH
Bozza, E.	Divertissements	ALe
Chagrin, F.	Fanfare for Adam	Nov
Chase, A.	4 Trios	Cor
Haan, S. de	March - Waltz - Quasi Adagio	HE
Jacobson	3 Bagatelles	B-M
Kummer, G.-Glasenapp-Karl	24 Trios, Op. 11 & 13	FrH
Mulder, E.	Trio in contrapuntische	
	stijl (1942)	SD
Snosko-Borovsky, A.	Scherzo, op. 13	Int
Vries Robbé, W. de	Variations	SD

THREE SAXOPHONES

Bach, J.S.-Schmidt	Fugue XXI. *sop sax, asax, bar sax*	Wes
Beethoven, L. van-Gee	Adagio and Finale, op. 87.	
	2 asax, tsax	SM
Beethoven, L. van	Fugue. *2 asax, tsax*	EdM
Bertouille, G.	Prelude et fugue (1955).	
	sop sax, asax, bar sax	CBD
Bourne-Leidzen	Bourne Trio Album. *2 asax, tsax*	Bou
Brenet, T.	Flanerie. *2 asax, asax (bar sax)*	E-V
Brown	Fugue. *asax, tsax, bar sax*	Wes
Butts, C.	Chameleon. *3 sax*	SHM
Butts, C.	Moderato and Allegro. *3 asax*	Sha
Butts, C.	Trio. *3 sax*	PrA
Cecconi, M.	Aubade - Danse. *3 asax*	E-V
Cherubini, L.	Canon. *sop sax, asax, tsax*	MM
Clark	Seicento. *2 asax, tsax*	EdM

Three Saxophones

Depelsenaire, J.	Divertissement. *3 asax*	EPC
Gibbons, O.-Clark	Fantasia for Three. *2 asax, tsax*	EdM
Gibbs, A.	Harlequinade. *3 sax*	Pet
Hook, J.-Gee	Adagio and Allegretto. *3 sax*	SM
Hook, J.-Voxman	6 Trios. *3 sax*	Rub
Lester, L.	So Easy Trios. *3 sax*	BM
Letellier, R.	Pièce récréative. *3 asax (3 tsax)*	EdR
Letellier, R. (arr)	Recueil de duos et trios	EdR
Lotti, A.-Evertse	Vere Languorus. *2 asax, tsax*	T-M
Maganini, Q.	3 Little Kittens. *3 sax*	EdM
Maganini, Q.	Triple Play. *3 sax*	EdM
Maganini, Q.	Troubadors. *2 asax, tsax*	EdM
Mattheus le Maistre-Evertse	Dominus Noster Castellum *2 asax, tsax*	T-M
Mozart, W.	Ave Verum Corpus. *2 asax, tsax*	EdM
Mozart, W.	Sonatine. *sop sax, asax, tsax*	MM
Mozart, W.-deKort	Sonatine. *3 sax*	T-M
Murphy	Notturno. *asax, tsax, bar sax*	Wes
Ostransky, L.	Peasant Dance. *2 asax, tsax*	Rub
Ostransky, L.	3 Miniatures. *2 asax, tsax*	Rub
Ostransky, L.	2 Portraits. *2 asax, tsax*	Rub
Purcell, H.-Rosenthal	Fantasia No. 3. *asax, tsax, bar sax*	Wes
Raphling, S.	Suite in Modern Style. *3 sax*	EdM
Skolnik, W.	3 Canonic Tunes. *2 asax, tsax*	EdM
Toebosch, L.	Thema met variaties, op. 42 (1952). *3 sax*	SD
Zenoni	Sinfonia a Tre. *asax, tsax, bar sax*	EdM

THREE SAXOPHONES - COLLECTIONS

Gee, H. (arr)	12 Trios. *2 asax, tsax (asax)*	PrA
Voxman, H. (arr)	Chamber Music for Three Saxophones. *2 asax, tsax*	Rub

THREE WOODWINDS

Albisi, A.	Miniature Suite No. 2. *fl, 2cl*	CF
Alden, J.	Variations on "Waltzing Matilda." *fl, 2cl*	OxU
Alexander, J.	Divertimento. *ob, cl, bsn*	Gen
Altmann, E.	Kleine Serenade. *2cl, bsn*	FrH
Andraud, A. (arr)	Classic Pieces. *fl, ob, cl*	SM
Andruad, A. (arr)	18 Trios. *fl, ob(fl), cl*	SM
Andriessen, J.	Trio (1957). *fl, ob, bsn*	SD
Andriessen, L.	Aanloop en sprongen (1961). *fl, ob, cl*	SD
Anonymous	Tuba Gallicallis. *ehn, 2bsn*	Heu
Apostel, H.	Bagatelles, op. 20. *fl, cl, bsn*	UE

Three Woodwinds

Composer	Title	Publisher
Archer, V.	Divertimento (1949). *ob, cl, bsn*	Can
Ardevol, J.	Fourth Sonata. *2ob, ehn*	SMP
Arma, P.	3 Mouvements (1949). *ob, cl, bsn*	EMT
Arnold, M.	Divertimento, op. 37. *fl, ob, cl*	Pat
Arnold, M.	Trio. *fl, cl, bsn*	Pat
Arrieu, C.	Trio, C. *ob, cl, bsn*	Amp
Artot, J.	12 Trios. *fl(cl), cl, acl(asax)*	CF
Auric, G.	Trio. *ob, cl, bsn*	EdL
Baaren, K. van	Trio (1936). *fl, cl, bsn*	SD
Bach, J.C.-Maganini	Allegretto Piacevole. *fl, cl, bsn*	CF
Bach, J.S./Mozart-Maros	Adagio e Fuga. *ob(fl), cl, bsn*	EMB
Bach, J.S.-Glasel	Canonic Fugue. *ob, cl, bsn*	SF
Bach, J.S.	15 Three-Part Inventions. *fl(ob, cl), ob(cl), bsn(bcl, cl)*	CF
Bach, J.S.-Cochrane	15 Three-Part Inventions. *fl, cl, acl(bcl)*	CF
Bach, J.S.-Johnson	Goldberg Variationen. *ob(fl), cl, bsn*	HE
Bach, J.S.-Hirsch	I Call Upon Thy Name O Jesus. *ob, cl, bsn*	CF
Bach, J.S.-Johnson	Inventionen. *ob(fl), cl, bsn*	HE
Bach, J.S.-Morsch	Little Bach Suite No. 1. *fl, cl, bsn*	TP
Bach J.S.-Morsch	Little Bach Suite No. 2. *fl, cl, bsn*	TP
Bach, J.S.-Williams	Polonaise. *fl(ob), cl, bsn*	SM
Bach, J.S.	Prelude et Fugue. *ob, cl, bsn*	EdL
Bach, J.S.-Atkins	Prelude, c. *ob, cl, bsn*	Wes
Bach, J.S.	Siciliano. *fl, cl, bsn*	EdM
Bach, J.S.	Sinfonia, a. *fl, ob, bsn*	B-M
Bach, J.S.-Seay	3 Three-Part Inventions. *2ob, ehn*	Spr
Bach, J.S.-Organn	2 Little Classics. *ob, cl, bsn*	Reb
Baden, C.	Trio. *fl, ob, cl*	Pet
Badings, H.	Trio No. 2 (1943). *ob, cl, bsn*	SD
Badings, H.	Trio No. 4. *2ob, ehn*	Pet
Badings, H.	Trio No. 4a (1946). *2ob, ehn*	SD
Baeyens, A.	Concertino. *ob, cl, bsn*	EMe
Baksa, R.	Running Tune, Lullaby and March. *fl, ob, cl*	Sha
Barraud, H.	Trio. *ob, cl, bsn*	EdL
Bartôs, F.	Trio. *ob, cl, bsn*	Art
Bartsch, C.	Suite. *ob, cl, bsn*	Mau
Bauernfeind, H.	Gay Play. *fl, cl, bsn*	LDo
Bauernfeind, H.	Heitere Musik. *ob, cl, bsn*	LDo
Baumann, H.	Divertimento. *ob, cl, bsn*	HSM
Baurle	6 leichte Stücke. *2fl, ob*	B&N
Beck	Trio. *fl, cl, bsn*	MV
Beethoven, L. van-Elkan	Bagatelle, op. 33/2. *fl, cl(ob), bsn*	HeE
Beethoven, L. van	Excerpts from Rondo (Sonata Pathetique). *2cl, bsn (asax, acl)*	CF
Beethoven, L. van	Fugue. *fl, cl, bsn*	EdM
Beethoven, L. van	Grand Trio, C, op. 87. *ob, fl, sax*	Bil
Beethoven, L. van	Grand Trio, C, op. 87. *2cl, asax*	Bil

Three Woodwinds

Beethoven, L. van-Tustin	Minuet, G. *fl, ob, cl*	B-M
Beethoven, L. van	Minuet in G, No. 2. 2cl, bsn	CF
Beethoven, L. van	Petit Trio. *ob, cl, bsn*	CF
Beethoven, L. van	Trio, C, op. 87. *2ob, ehn*	B&H
Beethoven, L. van	Trio, C, op. 87. *2ob, ehn*	BrH
Beethoven, L. van-Wildgans	Trio, op. 87. *2ob, ehn*	LDo
Beethoven, L. van	Trio, op. 87. *2oh, ehn*	Pet
Beethoven, L. van-Andraud	Trio, op. 87. *2ob, ehn*	SM
Beethoven, L. van-Langenus	Trio, op. 87. *fl, ob, cl*	CF
Beethoven, L. van-Stein	Variationen über "Reich mir die Hand mein Leben". *2ob, ehn*	BrH
Beethoven, L. van	Variations on "La ci darem." *ob, cl, bsn*	MR
Bennett, R.R.	Trio (1965). *fl, ob, cl*	UE
Bentley, A. (arr)	16th Century Trios. *fl(ob, cl), ob(cl), sax(bsn)*	Cha
Berger, J.	Divertimento. *3 treble instr*	BB
Berlinski, H.	Bach Trio Album. *2fl(2ob), bsn*	TP
Bertouille, G.	Prelude et fugue (1957). *ob, cl, bsn*	CBD
Betts, L.	Prelude, Pastoral and Dance (1949). *fl, ehn, bsn*	Can
Bialosky, M.	Suite. *fl, ob, cl*	Wes
Bielski, M.	6 Moods. *fl(ob, cl), bsn*	HeE
Bielski, m.	3 Sketches. *fl(ob, cl), bsn*	HeE
Biersack, A.	Divertimento. *fl, cl, bsn*	SS
Bland, E.	Trio. *fl, cl, bsn*	AMC
Blank, A.	Music for Three Players. *fl, ob, cl*	CoF
Blank, A.	3 Related Pieces. *fl, cl, bsn*	CoF
Blin, L.	Grupettino. *cl, asax, tsax*	GaM
Blomdahl, K.	Trio (1938). *ob, cl, bsn*	WH
Boccherini, L.-Waln	Terzetto. *fl, ob(cl), cl*	NK
Boder, G.	Trio. op. 1. *ob, cl, bsn*	ABe
Bois, Rob du	Trio (1961). *fl, ob, cl*	SD
Bonneau, P.	3 Noels anciens. *ob, ehn(cl), bsn*	ALe
Booren, J. van den	Trio, op. 2 (1960). *ob, cl, bsn*	SD
Borris, S.	Partita. *fl, 2cl*	MV
Borris, S.	Sonatina per tre, op. 45/1. *3ww*	S-V
Bottenberg, W.	Trio (1961-63). *fl, cl, bsn*	Can
Bourguignon, F.	Suite en trio, op. 80 (1944). *ob, cl, bsn*	CBD
Boutry, R.	Divertissement. *ob, cl, bsn*	ALe
Bove, J.	Andante and Allegro. *2cl, bcl(bsn)*	MCA
Bozza, E.	Serenade en Trio. *fl, cl, bsn*	ALe
Bozza, E.	Suite brève en trio. *ob, cl, bsn*	ALe
Brahms, J.-Dansby	Lilac Hillsides. *ob(cl), 2cl*	Ken
Brasher	Diadelphos. *fl, cl, bsn*	Wes
Brero, C.	Trio (1935). *fl, cl, bsn*	Ric
Briccetti, T.	Partita, op. 9 (1956). *ob, cl, bsn*	Can
Briegel, G.	Burlesque on "O Du Lieber Augustine." *fl, ob(cl), bsn*	GFB
Brogue, R.	Trio. *ob, cl, bsn*	AMC

Three Woodwinds

Brons, C.	Serenata II (1965). *ob, cl, bsn*	SD
Brown	Parmi les Prés. *fl, ob, cl*	E-V
Brown, C.	Trio. *ob, cl, bsn*	Bil
Brown, C.	Trio pour anches. *ob, cl, bsn*	B&V
Brown, H.	2 Experiments. *fl, cl, bsn*	CoF
Brugk, H.	Zum Vortrag. *3 B♭ or E♭ instr*	PG
Buchtel, F.	Enchanted Forest. *fl, ob, cl, bsn opt.*	NK
Buchtel, F.	Wood Nymphs, *fl, ob, cl*	NK
Bueche, G.	Fugue. *2cl, bsn*	CF
Bull, E.	3 Bucoliques. *ob, cl, bsn*	Amp
Butts, C.	Trio. *fl, 2cl*	PrA
Camara, J.	Suite. *fl, cl, bsn*	SMP
Cambini, J.	6 Trios, op. 45. *fl, ob, bsn*	WIN
Canteloube, J.	Rustiques. *ob, cl, bsn*	EdL
Carion, F.	Bagatelles, op. 19. *fl, ob, cl*	EMb
Carion, F.	Lied. *2ob, ehn*	EMb
Carman	Petit Rondo. *2cl, bsn*	CF
Carulli, B.-Stephan	Trio, C, op. 1. *2cl, bsn*	S&C
Cazden, N.	Trio No. 2, op. 40. *fl, ob, cl*	Spr
Chambers, S.	Reflections. *fl, ob, cl*	AMC
Chedeville, N.	Scherzo. *fl, ob, cl*	EdM
Chemin-Petit, H.	Trio im alten Stil. *ob, cl, bsn*	MRL
Childs, B.	Trio. *fl, ob, cl*	CoF
Clementi, A.	3 piccoli Pezzi (1955). *fl, ob, cl*	ESZ
Clementi, A.	Triplum (1960). *fl, ob, cl*	ESZ
Clementi, M.-Elkan	Sonatina, op. 36/3. *fl, cl(ob), bsn*	HeE
Cohen, S.	Madrigale. *2cl, bsn*	B-M
Constant, M.	Trio. *ob, cl, bsn*	Che
Corelli, A.	Air and Dance. *fl, ob, cl*	EdM
Corelli, A.-Auslender	Chamber Sonata, op. 2/2. *ob, cl, bsn*	Wes
Corroyez. G.	26 pieces concertantes en trios. *3 ww*	EdR
Couperin, F.	Kleine Suite. *fl, ob, bsn*	EMB
Couperin, F.-Elkan	Les Bacchanales. *fl, cl(ob), bsn*	HeE
Cruft, A.	3 Bagatelles. *fl, ob, cl*	B&H
Cunningham, M.	Serenade. *cl, asax, bsn*	CoA
Dandrieu, J.-Seay	Les Tourbillons. *ob(fl), cl, bsn(bcl)*	Spr
Daniels, M.	3 Observations, op. 41. *ob(fl), cl, bsn*	CF
Dansby, E.	Three for All. *fl, ob, cl*	Ken
Davidson, J.	Row No. 1. *ww trio*	PMP
Davis, D.	Preface & Fugue. *fl, ob, bsn*	AMC
Davis, D.	Trio. *fl, 2cl*	AMC
Decadt, J.	Trio. *ob, cl, bsn*	Mau
Defossez, R.	Trio (1946). *ob, cl, bsn*	CBD
Delmotte, C.	Trio. *ob, cl, bsn*	Mau
Delvaux, A.	Trio (1948). *ob, cl, bsn*	CBD
De Roye, E.	Trio. *ob, cl, bsn*	EMe
Desprez, F.	Prelude et Danse. *ob, cl, bsn*	EMb

46

Three Woodwinds

Devienne, F.-de Klerk	Sonatine No. 4. *2fl, bsn(vc)*	EdH
Devienne, F.-de Klerk	Sonatine No. 1. *2fl, bsn(vc)*	EdH
Devienne, F.-de Klerk	Sonatine No. 3. *2fl, bsn(vc)*	EdH
Devienne, F.-de Klerk	Sonatine No. 2. *2fl, bsn(vc)*	EdH
Devienne, F.	Trio. *2cl, tsax*	MM
d'Hoir, J.	Variaties op "Een kind	Mau
	is geboren." *ob, cl, bsn*	Mau
Dobrowolski, A.	Trio (1956). *ob, cl, bsn*	AP
Dodge, C.	Solos & Combinations. *ob, fl, cl*	CoF
Dondeyne, D.	Suite d'Airs populaires. *ob, cl, bsn*	EMT
Doppelbauer, J.	Trio No. 1 (1963). *fl, ob, cl*	LDo
Doppelbauer, J.	Trio. *ob, cl, bsn*	LDo
Doppelbauer, J.	Trio. *2cl, bsn*	LDo
Draeger, W.	Trio. *fl, ob, cl*	FrH
Dresden, S.	Klein trio (1912). *2ob, ehn*	DeW
Dubois, P.	Trio d'anches. *ob, cl, bsn*	ALe
Dufay, G.-Darvas	10 Chansons. *3 melody instr*	EMB
Durey, L.	Divertissement. *ob, cl, bsn*	ChM
Dussek-Elkan	Canzonetta. *fl, cl(ob), bsn*	HeE
Duyck, G.	Divertissement. *ob, cl, bsn*	Mau
Eckhardt-Gramatte, S.	Trio (1967). *fl, cl, bsn*	Can
Eder, H.	Waechter-Divertimento (1959).	OHN
	fl, cl, bsn	
Eisenmann, W.	Divertimento. *2cl, bsn*	HSM
Eisma, W.	Affairs No. 3. *ob, cl, bsn*	SD
Elkus, J.	5 Sketches. *2cl, bsn*	JB
Elliot	2 Creole Songs. *ob, cl, bsn*	SM
Escher, P.	Divertissement, Trio. *ob, cl, bsn*	EHe
Escher, R.	Trio d'Ances (1946), op. 4.	SD
	ob, cl, bsn	
Etler, A.	Suite (1960). *fl, ob, cl*	AMP
Etler, A.	3 Pieces. *3 treble instr*	Gal
Fasch, J.-Wojciechowski	Sonata, F. *2ob, bsn*	HSM
Favre, G.	Gouaches. *ob, cl, bsn*	Dur
Felderhof, J.	Rondo (1960). *ob, cl, bsn*	SD
Felderhof, J.	Thema met variaties (1944).	SD
	ob, cl, bsn	
Ferroud, P.	Trio, E. *fl, cl, bsn*	Dur
Filippi, A. de	Corydon Suite. *fl, cl, bsn*	Gen
Fine, A.	Dance Piece No. 2. *2fl, ob*	AMC
Flegier, A.-Voxman	Concert Suite. *ob, cl, bsn*	Rub
Fleming, R.	A Two Piece Suite (1959).	Can
	ob, cl, bsn	
Flothuis, M.	Nocturne, op. 11 (1941). *fl, ob, cl*	Che
Fontyn, Jacqueline	7 petites pieces (1956). *ob, cl, bsn*	CBD
Foret, F.	Suite en trio. *ob, cl, bsn*	Bil
Fortner, W.	Serenade (1945). *fl, ob, bsn*	SS
Francaix, J.	Divertissement. *ob, cl, bsn*	SS
Franck, M.	Deuxième Trio d'Anches.	EMT
	ob, cl, bsn	
Frangkiser, C.	Inventriole. *2cl, bsn*	B-M
Frangkiser, C.	Les Lavalettes. *2cl, bsn*	B&H

Three Woodwinds

Freistadt, M.	Woodwind Trio, op. 38. *3ww*	AMC
Fritter, J.	8 Rondels. *fl, cl, bsn*	UE
Gastyne, S. de	Trio, op. 65 (1970). *ob, cl, bsn*	Fer
Geraedts, J.	Divertimento No. 1 (1943). *ob, cl, bsn*	SD
Geraedts, J.	Divertimento No. 2 (1946). *ob, cl, bsn*	Sd
Gerschefski, E.	"America" Variations for Winds, op. 45/8. *ob, bsn, cbsn*	CoF
Gerschefski, E.	Interlude: Trio ("America" Variations, op. 44/4). *fl, cl, bsn*	CoF
Gessner, J.	Adagio and Allegro. *ww trio*	SHM
Gianella, L.-Wienandt	Nocturne, D, op. 28/3. *2fl, bsn*	SM
Gianella, L.-Wienandt	Nocturne, F, op. 28/2. *2fl, bsn*	SM
Gianella, L.-Wienandt	Nocturne, G, op. 28/1. *2fl, bsn*	SM
Gibbons, O.	Fantasia for Three. *fl, ob, cl*	EdM
Giltay, B.	Sonata a tre (1953). *ob, cl, bsn*	SD
Glass, P.	Divertimento (1958). *fl, cl, bsn*	Can
Goeb, R.	Suite. *fl, cl, ob*	SMP
Goleminov, M.	Trio. *ob, cl, bsn*	EMo
Golestan, S.	Petite suite bucolique. *fl, cl, bsn*	Dur
Goodenough, F.	Woodwind Trio. *fl, ob, bsn*	CoF
Goodman, A.	Kleine Suite. *fl, ob, cl*	MRL
Görner, H.	Trio, op. 24. *fl, ob, cl*	ABe
Gould, E.	Disciplines. *ob, cl, bsn*	E-V
Graap, L.	Divertimento (1964). *fl, ob, bsn*	Deu
Grabner, H.	Trio (1951). *ob, cl, bsn*	Kis
Grahn, U.	Trio (1967). *fl, ob, cl*	STI
Griend, K. van de	Trio (1929). *ob, cl, bsn*	SD
Grieg, E.-Elkan	Rigaudon. *fl, cl, bsn*	HeE
Groot, H. de	Souvenir Sud American. *ob, cl, bsn*	EMb
Groot, H. de	Variations on "Auprès de ma blonde." *ob, cl, bsn*	EMb
Haan, St. de	Trio. *fl, cl, bsn*	SS
Habash, J.	Adagio and Rondo. *fl, cl, bsn*	Bou
Häberling A.	Kleines Trio. *2cl, bsn*	MV
Häberling, A.	3 Tänze. *e Bb, Eb, or C instr*	PG
Hajdu, M.	Trio. *2fl, cl*	EMB
Handel, G.-Christensen	Bourée. *fl(ob), cl, bsn*	Ken
Handel, G.-Elkan	Fireworks Suite. *fl, cl(ob), bsn*	HeE
Handel, G.-Elkan	Fugue (Cello Sonata No. 2). *fl, cl(ob), bsn*	HeE
Handel, G.-Von Kreisler	Larghetto and Little Fugue. *3 equal instruments*	SM
Handel, G.-Morsch	Little Handel Suite. *fl, ob(cl), bsn*	TP-1964
Handel, G.-Busto	Minuet. *ob, cl, bsn*	CF
Handel, G.	Rigaudon, Bourree and March. *2ob, bsn, dr opt.*	MR
Handel, G.-Williams	Sonata. *ob(fl), cl, bsn*	SM
Handel, G.-Stone	3 Pieces.	Nov

Three Woodwinds

fl(ob, cl), ob(fl, cl), bsn(cl)

Handel, G.-Schwadron	Trio: Theme and Variations (Chaconne). *ob, cl, bsn*	PMP
Hanna, J.	Trio. *fl, cl, bsn*	Spr
Harris, A.	4 Pieces. *3 treble instr*	BB
Harris, R.	Concert Etudes. *cl, ehn, asax*	CoA
Hasselmann, V.	Menuett. *3ww*	EHe
Haydn, F.-Elkan	Theme and Variations. *fl(ob), ob, cl*	HeE
Hedwall, L.	Trio (1962). *fl, cl, bsn*	STI
Hemel, O. van	Pavane en Gigue (1958). *fl, ehn, bsn*	SD
Hemel, O. van	Trio (1959). *fl, ob, bsn*	SD
Hennessy, S.	Trio, op. 54. *2cl, bsn*	EME
Hermans, N.	Divertimento piccolo, op. 2 (1948). *ob, cl, bsn*	SD
Heussenstamm, G.	Canonograph No. 1. *3ww*	See
Heussenstamm, G.	7 Etudes, op. 17. *ob, cl, bsn*	Wes
Hilty	Fugue on B-A-C-H. *fl, ob, bsn*	Reb
Höffer, P.	Kleine Suite (1944). *ob, cl, bsn*	HSM
Höffer, P.	Thema mit Variationen (1944). *ob, cl, bsn*	HSM
Hollister, D.	Trio. *ob, cl, bsn*	CoF
Holyoke, S.-Carpenter & Luckenbill	The Instrumental Assistant *soprano, alto, and bass instr* (arr for 3 parts)	E-V
Homs, J.	Trio (1954). *fl, ob, bcl(bsn)*	See
Horvit, M.	Little Suite. *fl, cl, bsn*	Sha
Hoskins, W.	Prelude & Fugue. *ob, cl, bsn*	CoF
Hovey, H.	7 Pieces. *fl, cl, ob*	B&H
Husa, K.	2 Preludes. *fl, cl, bsn*	ALe
Ibert, J.	5 Pieces en Trio. *ob, cl, bsn*	EdL
Ida, C.	Scherzo. *fl, cl, bsn*	See
Ikonomow, B.	Trio, E. *ob, cl, bsn*	EdL
Im, K.	Suite. *fl, cl, bsn*	ES
Ippolitov-Ivanov, M.	2 Kirghiz Songs. *ob, cl, bsn*	TP
Jacob, G.	2 Pieces. *2ob, ehn*	Gal
Janacek, L.	Blaukehlchen-Marsch. *pic, fl, cl*	ES
Jelinek, H.	Aphorisms, op. 9/3. *2cl, bsn*	UE
Jelinek, H.	Sonatina a tre, op. 15/7 (1951). *ob, ehn, bsn*	UE
Jemnitz, S.	Woodwind Trio, op. 70 (1958). *fl, ob, cl*	EMB
Johannes, J.	Introduzione e fuga. *ob, cl, bsn*	EdH
Johanson, S.	Caccia (1968). *fl, cl, tsax*	STI
Johanson, S.	Lyrisk svit (1953). *ob, cl, bsn*	STI
Jong, M. de	Trio, op. 126 (1961)	CBD
Jongen, J.	Trio. *ob, cl, bsn*	B&H
Josten, W.	Trio. *fl, ob, bsn*	B&H
Juon, P.	Arabesken, op. 73 (1940). *ob, cl, bsn*	MRL
Jurdzinski, K.	Divertimento (1956). *2cl, bsn*	AP

Three Woodwinds

Kallstenius, E.	Piccolo trio seriale, op. 47 (1956). *fl, ehn, cl*	STI
Karg-Elert, S.	Trio, d, op. 49/1. *ob, cl, ehn*	FrH
Karkoff, M.	Trio piccolo, op. 55 (1961). *fl, cl, bsn*	STI
Kauffman, G.-Marx	Chorale Prelude. *ob, cl, bsn*	M&M
Keane, D.	Carpophagous Canon #4. *3 double reed instr*	LMP
Keldorfer, R.	Trio. *fl, cl, bsn*	LDo
Kelkel, M.	Divertimento, op. 3. *ob, cl, bsn*	Ric
Kendell, I.	Variations on a London Street Cry *3 melody instr*	Che
Kenins, T.	Prelude et Scherzo (1949). *fl, cl, bsn*	Can
Kersters, W.	Berceuse en Humoresque. *ob, cl, bsn*	Mau
Ketting, P.	Trio (1929). *fl, cl, bsn*	SD
Klein, R.	Serenade. *ob, cl, bsn*	Hei
Knight, M.	Selfish Giant Suite. *fl, cl, bsn (trb)*	TP
Kochan, G.	Divertimento, op. 12. *fl, cl, bsn*	Pet
Kocsár, M.	Divertimento (1956). *ob, cl, bsn*	EMB
Koechlin, C.	Trio. *fl, cl, bsn*	EdS
Koepke, P.	Badinage. *fl, ob(fl), cl*	Rub
Koetsier, J.	6 Bagatellen, op. 16/2 (1937). *ob, cl, bsn*	SD
Kogoj, M.	Episodes. *fl, cl, bsn*	EdD
Korinek, M.	Trio, A. (1962). *2ob, ehn*	SHF
Koskey, G.	Fugue. *3ww*	AMC
Kötschau, J.	Divertimento. *fl, cl, bsn*	Pet
Kötschau, J.-Voxman	Divertimento, B♭. fl, cl, bsn	Rub
Koumans, R.	Trio, op. 30. *ob, cl, bsn*	SD
Kowalski, J.	Divertimento. *fl, ob, bsn*	SHF
Kraft, L.	Short Suite. *fl, cl, bsn*	Gen
Kratochvil, J. (ed)	Trios tschechischer Klassiker. *2ob(2cl), bsn*	ES
Kreisler, A. von	Little Trio. *2ob, ehn*	SM
Kreisler, A. von	3 Pastels. *fl, ob, cl*	SM
Kreutzer, R.-Wienandt	Trio. *ob(fl), cl, bsn*	PrA
Kriens, C.	Rondo des Lutins. *fl, ob, cl*	CF
Kroeger, K.	*ob, cl, bsn*	CoF
Kubik, G.	Little Suite. *fl, 2cl*	Har
Kubizek, A.	4 Pieces. *fl(ob), cl, bsn(bcl)*	BrH
Kubizek, A.	Kleine Tanz-Suite. *3 melody instr*	LDo
Kuhlau, F.-Tustin	Allegro (op. 20/2). *fl, cl, bsn(bcl)*	Spr
Kuhlau, F.-Tustin	Sonatina (op. 20/1). *fl, ob, cl*	Spr
Kummer, K.-Voxman	Trio, F. *fl, cl, bsn*	Rob
Kunert, K.-Adams	Trio, c, op. 7. *fl, cl, bsn*	Vol
Kunz, A.	Fun for Three (1964). *fl, cl, bcl(bsn)*	Can
Kurzbach, P.	Trio. *ob, cl, bsn*	Pet
Kurtz, J.	2 Studies. *fl, cl, bsn*	Can
Lachowska, S.	Triptych (1964). *fl, cl, bsn*	AP

Three Woodwinds

Legley, V.	Trio, op. 11 (1942). *ob, cl, bsn*	CBD
Lesur, D.	Suite. *ob, cl, bsn*	EdL
Lewin, G.	Scherzola. *ob, cl, bsn*	B&H
Limmert, E.	Serenade (1962). *fl, ob, bsn*	BrH
Lorenzo, L. De	Trio Eccentrico, op. 76. *fl, cl, bsn*	Pet
Lorenzo, L. De	Trio Romantico, op. 78. *fl, ob, cl*	Pet
Loucheur, R.	Portraits. *ob, cl, bsn*	Bil
Luening, O.	Suite for Diverse High and Low Instruments. *2 treble, 1 bass*	GaM
Lully, J.-Muller	Airs de table. *ob, cl, bsn*	Mau
Lutoslawski, W.	Trio (1944-45). *ob, cl, bsn*	AP
Lutyens, E.	Trio, op. 52. *fl, cl, bsn*	S&C
Maasz, G.	Divertimento. *fl, cl, bsn*	HSM
Machaut, G.	Double Hoquet. *3ww*	EdL
Maegaard, J.	Trio (1950). *ob, cl, bsn*	SPD
Maes, J.	Miniature Trio. *ob, cl, bsn*	HeE
Maessen, A.	Cassation (1958). *ob, cl, bsn*	SD
Maessen, A.	Trio (1956). *fl, cl, bsn*	SD
Maganini, Q.	Ars Contrapunctus. *fl, cl, bsn*	EdM
Maganini, Q.	Havana. *fl, cl, bsn*	CF
Maganini, Q.	Istanboul. *fl(ob), cl, bsn*	CF
Maganini, Q.	La Rubia. *ob, cl, bsn*	CF
Maganini, Q.	3 Little Kittens. *fl, ob, cl*	EdM
Maganini, Q.	Vienna Waltz. *fl, cl, bsn*	CF
Maniet, R.	Concert d'anches. *ob, cl, bsn*	Mau
Maniet, R.	Trio d'anches I. *ob, cl, bsn*	Mau
Maniet, R.	2me trio d'anches. *ob, cl, bsn*	Mau
Marcello-Rocereto	Toccata, c. *2cl, bsn*	Vol
Maros, R.	Serenata (1951). *ob, cl, bsn*	EMB
Martelli, H.	Trio, op. 45. *ob, cl, bsn*	Bil
Martini, J.-Hirsch	Gavotte. *ob, cl, bsn*	CF
Martinon, J.	Sonatine No. 4. *ob, cl, bsn*	Bil
Martinu, B.	4 Madrigale. *ob, cl, bsn*	EME
Mason, J.	Canonic Device. *2cl, bsn*	See
Mayr, A.	Little Suite. *fl, ob, bsn*	AMP
Mayr, G.	12 Bagatelles. *fl, cl, bsn*	AlB
Mayr, S.	Bagatelle a tre. *fl, cl, bsn*	EK
Maxwell	Trio. *fl, cl, bsn*	Wes
McBride, R.	Fugue. *ob, 2cl*	CoF
McBride, R.	Variations on Various Popularisms. *cl, ehn, bsn*	CoF
McCall, H. (arr)	Instrumental Hymn Favorites. *3ww*	CF
McKay, F.	At the Puppet Show. *ob, cl, cl(bcl, bsn)*	Bar
McKay, F.	Blue Tapestry. *ob, cl, cl(bcl, bsn)*	Bar
McKay, F.	Trail to Sunny Point. *fl, ob, cl*	Bar
Mecham, K.	Trio. *ob, cl, bsn*	ECS
Mellnäs, A.	Divertimento. *fl, cl, bsn*	STI
Mendelssohn, F.	Lift Thine Eyes & Cast Thy Burden. *fl, ob, cl*	NK
Mengelberg, K.	Trio (1940. *fl, ob, bsn*	SD

Three Woodwinds

Metral, P.	Petite Suite. *ob, cl, bsn*	CF
Meulemans, A.	Trio. *ob, cl, bsn*	EMb
Meulemans, A.	Trio No. 2 (1960). *ob, cl, bsn*	CBD
Michel (Yost)-Voxman	Trio No. 1. *2cl, bsn(bcl)*	Rub
Migot, G.	Thrène. *ob, cl, bsn*	ALe
Migot, G.	Trio. *ob, cl, bsn*	ALe
Mihalovici, M.	Trio, op. 71. *ob, cl, bsn*	A&S
Milhaud, D.	Pastorale. *ob, cl, bsn*	ChM
Milhaud, D.	Suite d'après Corrette. *ob, cl, bsn*	EdL
Moeschinger, A.	5 Capricci (1960). *fl, cl, bsn*	Hei
Moortel, L. Van de	Divertimento I. *ob, cl, bsn*	Mau
Moortel, L. Van de	Divertimento III. *ob, cl, bsn*	Mau
Moortel, A. Van de	Trio No. 1. *ob, cl, bsn*	Mau
Moritz, E.	Divertimento, op. 150. *fl, cl, bsn*	WZ
Moser, F.	Trio, op. 38. *2ob, ehn*	Bos
Mozart, W.-Elkan	Adagio (Sonatina No. 5). *fl, cl(ob), bsn*	HeE
Mozart, W.-Caputo	Allegro. *2cl, bsn*	Vol
Mozart, W.-Elkan	Alleluia. *fl, cl(ob), bsn*	HeE
Mozart, W.-Marx	Canon. *2cl, bsn*	M&M
Mozart, W.-Marx	Canon. *2ob(ob, cl), bsn*	M&M
Mozart, W.-Morsch	Contredanse and Minuet. *fl, cl, bsn*	TP
Mozart, W.	Divertimenti Nos. 4, 5, B$\flat$, K. 439b. *2cl, bsn*	MR
Mozart, W.	Divertimento, K.V. 229/1. *2cl, bsn*	HU
Mozart, W.-Thurston	Divertimento No. 1. *2cl, bsn*	B&H
Mozart, W.-Wienandt	Divertimento No. 1. *2cl, bsn*	PrA
Mozart, W.	Divertimento No. 6, B$\flat$, K. 439b. *2cl, bsn*	MR
Mozart, W.-Wienandt	Divertimento No. 3, K. 439b. *ob(cl), cl, bsn*	PrA
Mozart, W.	Divertimento No. 3, B$\flat$, K. 439b. *2cl, bsn*	MR
Mozart, W.-Wienandt	Divertimento No. 2, K. 439b. *ob(cl), cl, bsn*	PrA
Mozart, W.-Thurston	Divertimento No. 2. *2cl, bsn*	B&H
Mozart, W.	5 Divertimenti, K. 229. *2cl, bsn* Published separately	BrH
Mozart, W.	5 Divertissements, K. 439. *ob, cl, bsn* Sold separately	EdL
Mozart, W.-Wojciechowski	Kanonisches Adagio, K.V. 410. *2basset hn, bsn*	HSM
Mozart, W.-Muller	Pieces. *3 wind instr*	Mau
Mozart, W.-Trinkaus	Rondo (8th Violin Sonata). *fl, cl, bsn*	CF
Mozart, W.-Irmer/Marguerre	Serenade No. 1, K.V. 439b. *2ob, bsn*	B&N
Mozart, W.-Irmer/Marguerre	Serenade No. 2, K.V. 439b. *2ob, bsn*	B&N
Mozart, W.-Irmer/Marguerre	Serenade No. 3, K.V. 439b.	B&N

Three Woodwinds

	2 ob, bsn	
Mozart, W.-Irmer/Marguerre	Serenades Nos. 4, 5, K.V. 439b.	B&N
	2ob, bsn	
Mozart, W.-Scheifes	Sonatine. *2cl, bar sax*	MM
Mozart, W.-Dahm	Trio. *fl(ob), cl, bsn(bcl)*	Vol
Muczynski, R.	Fragments. *fl, cl, bsn*	Sha
Mulder, E.	Fuga No. 7 (1940). *fl, cl, bsn*	SD
Mulder, H.	Trio, op. 17 (1960). *fl, ehn, bsn*	SD
Nabert	Métabole No. 1 & No. 2.	E-V
	fl, ob, bsn	
Nemiroff, I.	Perspectives. *fl, ob, bsn*	M&M
Nemiroff, I.	Variations to a Theme. *fl, ob, bsn*	M&M
Newman-Taylor	Rondo Brillante. *fl, ob, bsn*	B-N
Nilsson, B.	20 Gruppen. *pic, ob, cl*	UE
Nordgren, E.	Serenata à tre, op. 77 (1966-68).	STI
	fl, cl, bsn	
Olivadoti, J.	Divertimento. *fl, ob, cl*	Rub
Olivadoti, J.	Scherzetto. *fl, ob, cl*	War
Olsen, L.	Trio. *ob, cl, bsn*	CoA
Olsen, S.	Suite, op. 10. *fl, ob, cl*	Pet
Organn, R.	Dance of the Saracens. *ob, cl, bsn*	Reb
Organn, R.	Dance of the Teddy Bears.	Reb
	2ob, bsn	
Organn, R.	Dance of the Teddy Bears.	Reb
	ob, cl, bsn	
Organn, R.	Impromptu. *2ob, bsn*	Reb
Orland, H.	Fughetta. *fl, cl, bsn*	See
Orrego-Salas, J.	Divertimento. *fl, ob, bsn*	SMP
Ostransky, L.	Trio, g. *fl, ob, cl*	Rub
Paciokiewicz, T.	Reed Trio (1963). *ob, cl, bsn*	AP
Paciokiewicz, T.	Trio Stroikowe. *ob, cl, bsn*	EBM
Pahor, K.	Divertimento. *fl, ob, bsn*	EdD
Parik, I.	Music for three. *fl, ob, cl*	SHF
Parris, R.	5 Easy Canons & a Fugue.	CoF
	wind trio	
Pasquini, B.-Rocereto	Sonata. *2cl, bsn*	Vol
Payne, F.	Woodwind Trio. *fl, cl, ob*	CoA
Pedersen, P.	Woodwind Trio No. 1 (1956).	Can
	fl, cl, bsn	
Pedersen, P.	Woodwind Trio No. 2 (1957).	Can
	fl, cl, bsn	
Peeters, F.	Trio, op. 80. *fl, cl, bsn*	Pet
Pelemans, W.	Trio, No. 3. *ob, cl, bsn*	Mau
Pelemans, W.	Trio No. 2. *ob, cl, bsn*	Mau
Perceval, J.	Serenata. *fl, cl, bsn*	SMP
Pescetti, G.-Elkan	Presto. *fl, cl(ob), bsn*	HeE
Petrassi, G.	3 per 7 (1966). *fl/pic, ob/ehn, cl*	ESZ
Pfeiffer, G.-Cailliet	Musette. *ob, cl, bsn*	SM
Pfeiffer, G.	Musette, op. 47/1. *ob, cl, bsn*	EdS
Phillips, G.	Pastorale. *fl, ob, cl*	Pet
Phillips, I.	6 Short Arrangements. *cl, ob, bsn*	OxU
Pierne, P.	Bucolique Variee. *ob, cl, bsn*	Bil

Three Woodwinds

Pijper, W.	Trio (1927). *fl, cl, bsn*	SD
Piket, F.	Trio. *fl, cl, bsn*	SF
Pisk, P.	Trio, op. 100. *ob, cl, bsn*	CoF
Piston, W.	3 Pieces (1926). *fl, cl, bsn*	AMP
Pleyel, I.	Trio, E♭. *2cl, bsn*	MR
Ponse, L.	Trio (1941). *fl, cl, bsn*	SD
Poot, M.	Ballade. *ob, cl, bsn*	EME
Poot, M.	Divertimento. *ob, cl, bsn*	EME
Pospisil, J.	Tri Invencie. *fl, cl, bsn*	SHF
Praag, H. van	Fantasia a tre (1956). *fl, ob, bsn*	SD
Quinet, M.	Trio (1967). *ob, cl, bsn*	CBD
Rameau, J.-De Filippi	The Hen. *fl, ob, bsn*	HeE
Rathaus, K.	Gavotte classique. *fl, ob, bsn*	B&H
Razzi, F.	Invenzione a Tre (1964).	ESZ
	ob, E♭ cl, bcl	ESZ
Reger, M.-Schwadron	Canon, d. *fl, cl, bsn(bcl)*	Ken
Regner, H.	Spiel. *2cl, bsn*	SS
Regner, H.	Spielheft II. 3 *B♭ instr*	PG
Regner, H.	Divertimento. *fl, 2cl*	OHN
Reizenstein, F.	Trio. *fl, cl, bsn*	Gal
Ribari, A.	5 Miniaturen. *fl, cl, bsn*	EMB
Rieti, V.	Prelude. *fl, cl, bsn*	Gen
Riisager, K.	Conversazione, op. 26a. *ob, cl, bsn*	Pet
Rimsky-Korsakov, N.-Ruggiero	Scherzo (Tsar Sultan). *fl, cl, bsn*	GZ
Röntgen, J.	Trio, op. 86. *fl, ob, bsn*	Als
Ropartz, J.	Entrata a scherzetto. *ob, cl, bsn*	EdS
Rosenberg, H.	Trio (1927). *ob, cl, bsn*	STI
Rosseau, N.	3 jouets, op. 53 (1955). *ob, cl, bsn*	CBD
Rossi, S.	3 Sinfonias. *fl, ob, cl*	SM
Rueff, J.	3 Pieces. *ob, cl, bsn*	ALe
Ruelle, F.	Autour du château. *ob, cl, bsn*	Mau
Ruelle, F.	Romance. *sop sax, 2cl*	EMb
Rugolo, P.	Offbeat. *fl, cl, bsn*	Wes
Salieri, A.	Danse (Tarare). *fl, ob, cl*	EdM
Salomon, K.	Elegie und Tanz. *ob, 2fl*	Pet
Sauguet, H.	Trio. *ob, cl, bsn*	EdL
Savnik, V.	Fughetta. *fl, ob, bsn*	Kaw
Scarmolin, A.	Barcarolle & Petite Humoresque.	Lud
	2cl, bsn(bcl)	
Scarmolin, A.	A Ghostly Tale. *ob, cl, bsn*	Bar
Schaeffer, D. (arr)	Grant Us Peace. *fl, ob(fl), cl*	PrA
Schaeffer, D. (arr)	10 Woodwind Trios. *fl, ob(fl), cl*	PrA
Schalk, C.	Ricercare on an Old	Con
	English Melody. *2fl, cl*	
Schiff, H.	Divertimento. *ob, cl, bsn*	LDo
Schiske, K.	Trio Sonata, op. 41 (1954).	LDo
	2ob, bsn	
Schlemm, G.	Trio. *ob, cl, bsn*	PG
Schmidt, W.	Prelude and Fugue. *fl, cl, bsn*	Wes
Schmit, C.	Trio (1945). *ob, cl, bsn*	CBD
Schoemaker, M.	Suite Champêtre (1940).	CBD
	ob, cl, bsn	

Three Woodwinds

Schröder, H.	Divertimento. *fl, ehn, bsn*	Pet
Schubert, F.-Greene	Trio Movement. *2cl, bsn*	Gal
Schumann, R.-Seay	Suite. *ob(fl), cl, bsn*	Spr
Schumann, R.-Seay	Suite. *2cl, bsn(cl)*	Spr
Schwadron, A.	Trio. *ob, cl, bsn*	PMP
Seeger, P.	Kleines Konzert zu dritt. *3 B♭ instr*	PG
Serebrier, J.	Suite Canina. *ob, cl, bsn*	SMP
Shapero, H.	3 Pieces. *ww trio*	SMP
Shostakovitch, D.	Preludes. *fl, cl, bsn*	EdM
Siennicki, E.-Hite	Vicarswood. *fl, cl, bsn*	SM
Sister Ida	Scherzo. *fl, cl, bsn*	SM
Skolnik, W.	3 Canonic Tunes. *fl, ob, cl*	EdM
Slavicky, K.	Trio (1937). *ob, cl, bsn*	Art
Smit, A.	Trio. *ob, cl, bsn*	Mau
Smit, S.	Plain music (1950). *fl, ob, cl*	SD
Smith, L.	Trio for Woodwinds. *ob, cl, bsn*	CoF
Sörenson, T.	Trio No. 1, op. 19. *fl, cl, ehn*	STI
Sörenson, T.	Trio No. 2, op. 33 (1959). *fl, cl, bsn*	STI
		STI
Souffriau, A.	Trio, op. 49. *ob, cl, bsn*	Mau
Spisak, M.	Sonatina (1946). *ob, cl, bsn*	AP
Spratt, J.	3 Miniatures. *ob(fl), cl, bsn*	Spr
Srebotnjak, A.	Serenata. *fl, cl, bsn*	EdD
Stamitz	Andantino. *fl, cl, bsn*	EdM
Stearns, P.	5 Short Pieces. *ob, cl, bsn*	CoF
Steiner, G.	Suite (1958). *fl, cl, bsn*	See
Stevens, H.	Trio. *fl, cl, bsn*	CoF
Stieber, H.	Spielmusik Nr. 1. *2ob, bsn*	FrH
Stieber, H.	Spielmusik Nr. 2. *2fl, cl*	FrH
Stravinsky, I.	Pastorale. *fl, cl, bsn*	EdM
Strietman, W.	Divertissement d'anches. *ob, cl, bsn*	SD
Stringfield, L.	Chipmunks. *fl, cl, bsn*	EdM
Stutschewsky, J.	Terzetto. *ob, cl, bsn*	See
Suter, R.	Divertimento. *ob, cl, bsn*	EMo
Sydeman, W.	Trio. *3 treble instr*	See
Szalowsky, A.	Trio. *ob, cl, bsn*	Che
Szekely, E.	Divertimento (1958). *ob, cl, bsn*	EMB
Szoñyi, E.	5 alte Tänze. *ob, cl, bsn*	EMB
Tansman, A.	Suite. *cl, ob, bsn*	EME
Tapkoff, D.	La Grenouille Presomptueuse, 3 contes musicaux. *pic, ob(ehn), cl(bcl), nar ad lib*	ALe
Tapkoff, D.	Der dünkelhafte Frosch. *fl, cl, ehn, V ad lib*	B&N
Tchaikovsky, P.-Tustin	Humoresque, op. 10/2. *fl, ob, cl*	B-M
Tcherepnin, N.	Divertimento. *fl, ob, bsn*	Be
Telemann, G.-Polnauer	6 Minuets (Sept Fois Sept et Un). *fl, ob, cl*	CF
Telemann, G.-Polnauer	6 Minuets (Sept Fois Sept et Un). *2ob, cl*	CF

55

Three Woodwinds

Telemann, G.-Polnauer	6 Minuets (Sept Fois Sept et Un). *fl(ob), cl, bsn*	CF
Telemann, G.	Trio, c. *ob, cl, bsn*	SM
Toch, E.	Sonatinetta, op. 84. *fl, cl, bsn*	B-M
Tomasi, H.	Concert Champêtre. *ob, cl, bsn*	HLe
Tustin, W.	Pastorale Moderne. *fl, ob, cl*	Bar
Tustin, W.	Tarantella. *fl, ob, cl*	Bar
Tustin, W.	Waltzing Woodwinds. *fl, ob, cl*	Bar
Urbanner, E.	8 Aphorismen. *fl, cl, bsn*	LDo
Vachey, H.	4 Instantanes. *ob, cl, bsn*	ALe
Velden, R. van der	Divertimento (1957). *ob, cl, bsn*	CBD
Vellère, L.	Bagatelles. *ob, cl, bsn*	Mau
Veremans, M.	Trio No. 1 (1953). *ob, cl, bsn*	EMe
Veress, S.	Sonatina (1931). *ob, cl, bsn*	ESZ
Verhaar, A.	Trio, op. 38 (1949). *fl, ob, cl*	SD
Villa Lobos, H.	Trio. *ob, cl, bsn*	EdK
Villa-Lobos, H.	Trio. *ob, cl, bsn*	EME
Villa-Lobos, H.	Trio. *ob, cl, bsn*	Int
Vitali-Wienandt	3 Dances. *ob(fl), cl, bsn*	PrA
Vivaldi, A.	Concerto, g, P. 402. *fl, ob, bsn*	MR
Vivaldi, A.-Oubradous	Concerto No. 25, g. *fl, ob, bsn*	EMT
Vogler, E.	Die kleine Stadt (1962). *fl, cl, bsn*	BrH
Vogt, G.	Adagio Religioso. *2ob, ehn*	Bil
Vogt, G.	Adagio Religioso. *2cl, asax*	Bil
Von Kreisler, A.	3 Pastels. *fl, ob, cl*	SM
Von Kreisler, A.	3 Pastels. *2fl, cl*	SM
Von Kreisler, A.	Trio. *ob, cl, bsn*	SM
Voxman, H. (arr)	Chamber Music for Three Woodwinds, Vol I. *fl, ob(fl), cl*	Rub
Voxman, H. (arr)	Chamber Music for Three Woodwinds, Vol. II. *fl, cl, bsn(bcl)*	Rub
Wailly, P.-Voxman	Aubade. *fl, ob, cl*	Rub
Wailly, P.	Aubade. *fl, ob, cl*	EdS
Walker, R.	Air and Dance. *ob, cl, bsn*	Bar
Walker, R.	Bagatelle. *fl, ob, cl*	AMP
Walker, R.	Ballet Dance. *fl, ob, cl*	Bar
Walker, R.	Caravan. *fl, ob, cl*	Tem
Walker, R.	Spring Dance. *fl, ob(cl), cl*	Ken
Walker, R.	Rococo. *ob, cl, bsn*	Ken
Walthew, R.	Triolet, E♭. *ob, cl, bsn*	B&H
Warfield, G.	2 for Three. *fl, ob(cl), cl*	FrC
Washburn, R.	3 Pieces. *fl, cl, bsn (bcl)*	OxU
Waters, C.	Serenade. *ob, cl, bsn*	Pet
Waxman, D.	Trio. *ob, cl, bsn*	GaM
Weber, A.	Trio d'anches. *ob, cl, bsn*	ALe
Weis, F.	Music (1928). *fl, cl, bsn*	SPD
Weiss, A.	Petite Suite. *fl, cl, bsn*	CoF
Welander, S.	Preludier (1966). *fl, cl, bsn*	STI
Welander, W.	Divertimento. *ob, cl, bsn*	STI
Wennig, H. (arr)	Volksliedsätze. *ob, cl, bsn*	FrH
Wenth	Petite Serenade concertee. *2ob, ehn*	EK

Three Woodwinds

Werner, J.	Trio. *ob, cl, bsn*	Bil
Wiener, K.	3 Pièces, op. 20. *fl, ehn, cl*	UE
Wijdeveld, W.	Trio, op. 64 (1958). *fl, ob, bsn*	SD
Wildberger, J.	Trio. *ob, cl, bsn*	EMo
Wildgans, F.	Kleines Kammertrio. ob, ehn, bsn	LDo
Wildgans, F.	Kleines Trio. *fl, cl, bsn*	LDo
Wilhelmer, A.	2 kleine Sätze. *3 B♭ instr*	PG
Willis	Minuet and Trio. *2cl, bsn*	Reb
Wissmer, P.	Serenade. *ob, cl, bsn*	EdC
Woestijne, D. van de	Divertimento (1941). *ob, cl, bsn*	CBD
Worth-Tustin	Music Box. *fl, ob, cl*	Bar
Yost, M.-Schultz/Hauser	Trio, F. *2cl, bsn*	SS
Zagwijn, H.	Trio (1944). *fl, ob, cl*	SD
Zagwijn, H.	Trio No. 2 (1949). *fl, ob, cl*	SD
Zanaboni, G.	Piccola Suite. *ob, cl, bsn*	GZ
Zbinden, J.	Trio, op. 12. *ob, cl, bsn*	HLe

TWO FLUTES, KEYBOARD

	Blue Tail Fly	NK
	Collection	MR
	Czech Dance Song	NK
	Easy Flute Solos or Duets. *2fl, pf*	MS
	Merry Hearts	NK
	More Easy Flute Solos	MS
	O Sole Mio	NK
	Tiritomba	NK
	Two Imps	NK
	Two Tooters	NK
	Waltz "Sibyl"	NK
	Woodland Whispers	NK
Abaco, E.	Trio Sonata, op. 3/2, F. *2 fl, bc*	Pet
Able, C.-Sonntag	Sonata, op. 16/1, G. *2 fl, bc*	Pet
Able, C.-Sonntag	Sonata, op. 16/4, C. *2 fl, bc*	Pet
Adam, A.	O Holy Night	Rub
Adams, S.-DeLamater	The Holy City	Rub
Arma, P.	3 Resonances	Bil
Bach, C.P.E.-Walther	Trio, E♭	WZ
Bach, C.P.E.	12 Little Pieces, W. 81	Pet
Bach, C.P.E.-Johnen	12 kleine Stücke, Wq. 82	Pet
Bach, J.C.-Moyse	Divertissement	SM
Bach, J.S.	Sonate, G, BWV 1039	BrH
Bach, J.S.	Sonata, G	Har
Bach, J.S.-Seiffert	Trio, G. *2fl, pf, vc ad lib*	BrH
Bach, J.S.-Landshoff	Trio Sonata No. 2, G. *2fl, bc*	Pet
Bach, J.S.	Trios	Dur
Bach, J.S.-Schmitz/Schneider	Triosonate, G, BWV 1039. *2fl, bc*	B&N
Bach, W.F.-Van Leeuwen	Sonate, D.	WZ
Bach, W.F.-Seiffert	Trio (Allegro), a. *2fl, bc*	BrH

Two Flutes, Keyboard

Bach, W.F.-Seiffert	Trio, D. [No 1]. *2fl, bc*	BrH
Bach, W.F.-Seiffert	Trio, D. [No. 2]. *2fl, bc*	BrH
Bach, W.F.	Trio No. 1, D. *2fl, pf, vc ad lib*	Int
Bach, W.F.	Trio No. 2, D. *2fl, pf, vc ad lib*	Int
Bach, W.F.	Trio No. 3, a. *2fl, pf, vc ad lib*	Int
Barnard, G.	Gloriana. *2 Db pic, pf*	CF
Barnard, G.	Gloriana	CF
Beaumont	Con Amore	Cen
Beckerath, A.	Sonatina	S&C
Beethoven, L. van-Spiegl	Adagio for a Flute Clock	OxU
Beethoven, L. van	Moonlight Sonata (Adagio)	Cen
Bellini, V.	Duet (Norma)	CF
Benda, F.-Rampal	Trio, G	Int
Bent, R.	Swiss Boy. *2pic, pf*	CF
Bent, R.	Swiss Boy	CF
Berlioz, H.-Butterworth	Trio (The Childhood of Christ)	Cha
Berlioz, H.	Trio of the Young Ishmaelites (L'Enfance du Christ)	EdM
Bizet, G.	Adagietto	EdM
Bizet, G.	Aragonaise	EdM
Bizet, G.	Carillon (L'Arlesienne)	EdM
Bizet, G.	Entr'acte	EdM
Bizet, G.	Minuet	EdM
Bizet, G.	Second Minuet	EdM
Bizet, G.	Serenade Espagnole	EdM
Bizet, G.	3 Pieces	SM
Boismortier, J.-Ruf	Concerto, a	Ric
Boismortier, J.-Ruf	Concerto, C	Ric
Boismortier, J.-Ruf	Trio-Sonate, F. *2fl, bc*	SS
Boismortier, J.-Ruf	Trio-Sonate, G. *2fl, bc*	SS
Bonner	Over the Hills	EdM
Bononcini, G.-Giesbert	7 Suites, 2 vols.	SS
Borodin, A.	Solicitude	EdM
Bousquet, N.	Golden Robin Polka. *2 Db pic, pf*	CF
Britten, B.	Gemini Variations	Sch
Buchtel, F.	Bonita	B-M
Burghardt, H.	Partita brevis II	B&N
Burkhard, W.	Canzona, op. 76a	B&N
Chedeville, N.	Scherzo	EdM
Christensen, J.	Holiday on Ice	Ken
Cimarosa, D.	Concertante	EMT
Cimarosa, D.	Concerto, G. *2fl, pf*	B&B
Cimarosa, D.-Moyse	Concerto, G	SM
Cimarosa, D.-Piccioli	Concerto, G	Int
Cimarosa, D.-Rampal	Concerto, G	JB
Cimarosa, D.-Wollheim	Konzert, G	B&B
Conley, L.	Dialogue	Ken
Conley, L.	Reflections	Ken
Coppola	The Piccolo Polka	BVC
Corbett, W.-Dawes	Sonata, g	S&C
Corbett, W.	3 Sonatas. *2fl, bc*	Pet
Corelli, A.	Air and Dance	EdM

Two Flutes, Keyboard

Corelli, A.	Gavotte and Gigue	EdM
Corelli, A.	Gigue	EdM
Corelli, A.	Sonata da camera, op. 2/1, 5, 7. *2fl, bc*	Pet
Corelli, A.-Moeck	Sonata No. 2. *2fl, pf, vc ad lib*	S&C
Corrette, M.-Ruf	Concerto, A, op. 3/3. *2fl, bc*	SS
Dansby	Dandy Duo	Ken
Donizetti, G.	Sextette (Lucia di Lammermoor)	CF
Doppler, F.	Andante and Rondo, op. 25	MR
Doppler, F.-Rampal	Andante and Rondo [op. 25]	Int
Doppler, F.	Hungarian Phantasy, op. 35	MR
Dornel, L.-Ruf	Suite, d	SS
Endresen, R.	Prairie Warblers	Rub
Endresen, R.	Promenade	Rub
Endresen, R.	The Two Fliers	Rub
Erbach, F.-Schultz	3 Divertissements melodieux. *2fl, bc*	SS
Exaudet	La Cour de la Marquise	EdM
Fabre, C.-Harris	Reverie	CF
Fabre, C.	Second Reverie	CR
Fasch, J.	Sonata à 3, e. *2fl(ob), bc*	MV
Felderhof, J.	Short Story	HU
Fesch, W. de-Ruf	Concerto, G, op. 10/8	SS
Fesch, W. de-Noske	Sonate, op. 12/1-3	EdH
Fesch, W. de	3 Sonatas, op. 12/1-3. *2fl, bc*	Pet
Fesch, W. de-Schroeder	3 Sonaten, op. 7/2, 4, 8. *2fl, bc*	Hei
Fesch, W. de-Schouwman	Triosonaten, op. 21/1-3. *2fl, bc*	B&N
Filtz, A.-Sonntag	Sonata, op. 2/3, G. *2fl, pf, vc ad lib*	Hei
Filtz, A.-Sonntag	Sonata, op. 2/4, D. *2fl, pf, vc ad lib*	Hei
Flotow, F.	Ah! So Fair (Martha)	NK
Foster, S.-tr. Maganini	A Village Festival	EdM
Fote, R.	Tutti Fluti	Ken
Frescobaldi, G.-David	5 Canzoni per Sonar. *2fl, bc*	SS
Frid, G.	12 Metamorphosen, op. 54 (1957)	SD
Fuerstenau, A.	Rondo brillant, op. 102	EdH
Fuerstenau, A.	Introduction and Rondo Brilliant, op. 115	MR
Fuerstenau, A.	L'Union	MR
Fürstenau, A.	Rondo Brilliant	EdM
Galuppi, B.-Schroeder	Concerto, e	Pet
Gaubert, P.	Divertissement Grec. *2fl, pf(hp)*	ALe
Genzmer, H.	Sonata	S&C
Gossec, F.-Maganini	Gavotte	CF
Gounod, C.-Laube	Ave Maria	CF
Graf zu Erbach, F.-Erbecht	Divertissement melodieux. *2fl, bc*	Kis
Graun, C.-Kölbel	Sonate, E♭. *2fl, bc*	B&N
Graun, C.-Gerlach	Triosonate, F. *2fl, bc*	HMo
Graupner, C.	Canon, F. *2fl(2ob), bc*	MV
Grieg, E.	To Spring	Cen
Groneman, A.	Sonata, op. 2/2	HeE

Two Flutes, Keyboard

Grooms (arr)	Dark Eyes (Russian Song). *2fl, pf*	Cen
Handel, G.-Glaser	Allegro (Sonata No. 2)	CF
Handel, G.-Seiffert	Chamber Trio No. 8, g. *2fl(2ob)(fl, ob), bc*	BrH
Handel, G.-Seiffert	Chamber Trio No. 14, g. *2fl(2ob), bc*	BrH
Handel, G.-Seiffert	Chamber Trio No. 19, G. *2fl, bc*	BrH
Handel, G.-Seiffert	Chamber Trio No. 13, g. *2fl(2ob), bc*	BrH
Handel, G.-Parkinson	Trio Sonata, g. *2fl, bc*	OxU
Handel, G.	Triosonate. *2fl, bc*	B&V
Handel, G.-Nagel	Triosonate, e	SS
Handel, G.-Schneider	Triosonaten, op. 5. *2fl, bc*	Bar
Harris, F.	Petite Mazurka	Lud
Harris, F.	2 Buckaroos	Lud
Harris, F.	2 Larks	Lud
Harris, F.	2 Marionettes	Lud
Hasse, J.-Schenk	Sonata a 3, D, op. 3/6. *2fl, bc*	LDo
Hasse, J.	Trio Sonata, D. *2fl, bc*	NV
Hasse, J.-Ruf	Trio-Sonate, e	SS
Hasse, J.-Ruf	Trio-Sonate, G	SS
Havlicek, L.	2 Canaries	PrA
Haydn, F.	Oxen Minuet	CF
Hotteterre, J.-Ruf	Trio-Sonate, g, op. 3/1	SS
Jacchini, G.	Trio Sonata, op. 5/3, G. *2fl, bc*	Pet
Jomelli, N.	Triosonate	FrH
Kennedy-Harris	Star of the East	Lud
Kesnar, M.	Un Petit Rien	EdM
Kling, H.-Catlin	Two Little Bulfinches Polka. *2pic, pf*	CF
Krebs, J.-Erbrecht	Triosonate, b. *2fl, bc*	Kis
Krebs, J.-Ruf	Trio-Sonate, b. *2fl, bc*	SS
Kuhlau, F.	Trio, op. 119	Bil
Labitzky, A.	The Herd Girl's Dream	CF
Leclair, J.	Deuxième Recréation de Musique, op. 8. *2fl, bc*	B&N
Leclair, J.	Sonate à trois	HU
LeMare, E.-Maganini	Andantino	CF
Lester, L.	Crimson Blushes	Cen
Linde, H.	Trio. *fl, afl, pf*	SS
Linicke, J.	Overture, C. *2fl, pf, vc ad lib*	Pet
Linicke, J.-Rucker	2 Suiten	Mit
Linicke, J.	2 Suites	Pet
Locatelli, P.	Aria	EdM
Locatelli, P.	Trio, G, op. 3/1. *2fl, pf, vc ad lib*	Int
Locatelli, P.-Riemann	Trio, G, op. 3/1. *2fl, bc*	BrH
Locatelli, P.-Albrecht	Trio Sonata, d, op. 5/5. *2fl, bc*	Kis
Locatelli, P.-Albrecht	Trio Sonata, G, op. 5/1. *2fl, bc*	Kis
Locatelli, P.-Albrecht	Trio-Sonate, C, op. 5/4. *2fl, bc*	Kis
Locatelli, P.-Ruf	Trio-Sonate, E, op. 5/3. *2fl, bc*	SS
Locatelli, P.-Kolbel	Triosonate, op. 5/1, G. *2fl, bc*	Hei
Loeillet, J.B.	Sonata a Trois, No. 17	CF

60

Two Flutes, Keyboard

Loeillet, J.-Beon	Sonata, e	Int
Loeillet, J.-Beon	Sonata, g	Int
Loeillet, J.B.-Ruf	Trio Sonata, D, op. 1/4. *2fl, bc*	SS
Loeillet, J.B.-Ruf	Trio Sonata, e, op. 1/6. *2fl, bc*	SS
Loeillet, J.B.-Ruf	Trio Sonata, G, op. 1/2. *2fl, bc*	SS
Loeillet, J.B.-Ruf	Triosonate, G, op. 2/12. *2fl, bc*	B&N
Lully, J.-Rikko	French Dances	M&M
Maganini, Q. (arr)	Concert Album	EdM
Maganini, Q. (arr)	Paris Soir	EdM
Maganini, Q.	Twins	CF
Martini, J.	Plaisir d'Amour	EdM
McCaughey, W.	Enchanted Isle	CF
Mondonville, J.	Sonata, G	EdS
Monti, V.	Csardas	CF
Nardini, P.	Shepherd's Pipes	EdM
Nardini, P.-Gümbel	Trio, C. *2fl, bc*	B&N
Offenbach, J.	Barcarolle (Tales of Hoffman)	NK
Packer, W.	Sea Breeze	Ken
Paisible, J.-Friedrich	Sonatas No. 1, 4, 5. *2fl, pf*	S&C
	Published separately	
Paisible, J.-Friedrich	Sonatas 2 and 3	S&C
Paulson	Impromptu	GFB
Pepusch, J.-Ruf	Trio Sonata, B¹. *2fl, bc*	SS
Pez, J.	Trio Sonata, C. *2fl, bc*	Pet
Ponce, M.-Maganini	Estrellita	CF
Prowo, P.-Friedrich	Sonata a 3 No. 5	S&C
Prowo, P.-Friedrich	Sonata à 3, No. 6	S&C
Puccini, G.-Stebbing	Musetta's Waltz Song	Ric
Puccini, G.-Stebbing	Vissi d'Arte, Vissi d'Amore	Ric
Purcell, D.-Ruf	Trio-Sonate, d. *2fl, bc*	SS
Purcell, H.-Bergmann	Chaconne	S&C
Purcell, H.-Bergmann	3 Symphonies	S&C
Purcell, H.-Just	Triostücke. *2fl, bc*	SS
Quantz, J.	Sonata Andante	CF
Quantz, J.-Sonntag	Sonata, D. *2fl, bc*	Hei
Quantz, J.-Sonntag	Sonata, G. *2fl, bc*	Hei
Quantz, J.-Koch	Trio, a. *2fl(2ob), bc*	MV
Quantz, J.-Ruf	Trio Sonata, D	Ric
Quantz, J.-Erbrecht	Triosonate, a. *2fl, bc*	Kis
Quantz, J.-Ruf	Triosonate, G. *2fl, bc*	B&N
Rachmaninoff, S.	Polka Italienne	EdM
Rameau, J.	Rigodon de Dardanus	EdM
Rebikov, V.	A Little Girl Rocking her Doll	EdM
Renosto	Mixage	Ric
Ricker	Oriental Dance	PrA
Röntgen, J.	Lamento (1956)	SD
Rosas	Over the Waves	Cen
Rose, D.	Holiday for Flutes	BVC
Rossini, G.	Power Eternal (Stabat Mater)	NK
Saint-Saens, C.	My Hear at Thy Sweet Voice	Cen
Salieri, A.	Danse (Tarare)	EdM
Sammartini, G. (Rampal)	6 Sonatas, op. 6, 2 vols.	Int

Two Flutes, Keyboard

Sammartini, G.-Giesbert	12 Sonatas, 3 vols. *2fl, bc*	SS
Sargent-Barrington	Nip and Tuc. *2pic, pf*	CF
Schaeffer, D. (arr)	Christmas Duets	PrA
Schickhardt, J.	Sonata No. 6	HMP
Schmitt, J.-Gottron	Concerto, G, op. 15	B&N
Schubert, F.-Frank	Moment Musical	SHM
Schubert, F.	Serenade	Cen
Schultze, J.-Friedrich	Ouverture I in F	S&C
Schultze, J.-Moeck	Ouverture II in B	S&C
Schultze, J.-Moeck	Ouverture III in a	S&C
Schultze, J.-Friedrich	Suite	S&C
Segerhammar, R.	Little Cascade Waltz	PrA
Serradell	La Golondrina	Cen
Simeone, H.	Flute Cocktail	Sha
Stamitz	Andantino	EdM
Stamitz, A.-Lebermann	Concerto, G	SS
Stölzel, G.-Frotscher	Triosonate, G. *2fl, bc*	HSM
Sydeman, W.	Study (1956)	See
Tchaikovsky, P.	Suite (Album for Children)	EdM
Telemann, G.-Kölbel	Concerto, A	Pet
Telemann, G.-Oubradous	Concerto. *2fl, bc*	EMT
Telemann, G.-Draths	Kleine Trio-Sätze	SS
Telemann, G.-Schreiter	Sonata	Int
Telemann, G.-Schreiter	Sonata, A. *2fl, bc*	BrH
Telemann, G.-Fussan	Sonata, F. *2fl, bc*	SS
Telemann, G.-Monkemeyer	Sonata, g. *2fl, bc*	SS
Valentine, R.	3 Trio Sonatas. *2fl, bc*	MRL
Valentine, R.-Pearson	Trio Sonata, a. *2fl, pf, vc ad lib*	S&C
Valentine, R.-Pearson	Trio Sonata, C. *2fl, pf, vc ad lib*	S&C
Valentine, R.-Pearson	Trio Sonata, d. *2fl, pf, vc ad lib*	S&C
Viotti, G.-Rampal	Symphonie Concertante	Int
Vivaldi, A.-Ghedini	Concerto, C	Int
Vivaldi, A.-Rampal	Concerto, C	JB
Vivaldi, A.	Giga	EdM
Wagner, R.-Roberts	Song to the Evening Star (Tannhauser)	CF
Williams, W.-Dart	Sonata in Imitation of Birds. *2fl, bc*	OxU
Wood	Let 'Er Go	Cen
Zagwijn, H.	Pastorale and Scherzo	Pet
Zimmerman	Play a Song of America	TP
Zimmerman	Play a Song of Christmas	TP

TWO OBOES, KEYBOARD

Aydlette-Organn	Even Song	Reb
Bach, J.S.-Hindermann	Trio Sonata, b. *2 ob d'Amore, bc*	Pet

Two Oboes, Keyboard

Barre, M. de la-Viollier	Sonate V, G. *2 ob, bc*	Hei
Bodinus, S.-Koch	Triosonate No. 1. *2 ob, bc*	MV
Boismortier, J.-Ruf	Concerto, a	Ric
Boismortier, J.-Ruf	Concerto C	Ric
Boismortier, J.-Ruf	Trio Sonata, F. *2 ob, bc*	SS
Corelli, A.	Sonate, a, op. 4/5. *2 ob, bc*	HU
Corelli, A.	Sonate, F, op. 4/7. *2 ob, bc*	HU
Fasch, J.	Sonata à 3, e. *2ob (2fl), bc*	MV
Handel, G.	Sonata, D	Int
Handel, G.	Sonata, d	Int
Handel, G.	Sonata, g, op. 2/2. *2 ob, pf, vc ad lib*	Int
Handel, G.	Sonata, E♭	Int
Handel, G.	Trio No. 5. *2 ob, bc*	MR
Heinichen, J.	Sonata à 3, c. *2 ob, bc*	B&N
Heinichen, J.-Ruf	Triosonate, c. *2 ob, bc*	SS
Hovhaness, A.	Sonata. *2 ob, org*	Pet
Lully, J.	French Dances	M&M
Pala, J.	3 Miniaturen	MM
Pepusch, J.-Ruf	Trio-Sonate, B♭. *2 ob, bc*	SS
Pepusch, J.-Erbrecht	Triosonate, D. *2 ob, bc*	Kis
Pepusch, J.-Erbrecht	Triosonate, F. *2 ob (2 fl), bc*	Kis
Pepusch, J.-Ruf	Triosonate, F. *2ob, bc*	SS
Pepusch, J.-Erbrecht	Triosonate, G. *2 ob (2 fl), bc*	Kis
Quantz, J.-Ruf	Trio Sonata, D	Ric
Quantz, J.-Ruf	Triosonate, e. *2 ob, bc*	SS
Quantz, J.-Ruf	Triosonate, G. *2 ob, bc*	B&N
Roman, J.	Sonata à tre	Che
Schaeffer, D. (arr)	Christmas Duets	PrA
Stölzel, G.-Osthoff	Triosonate, f. *2 ob, bc*	B&N
Stradella, A.-Kolneder	Sinfonia à 3. *2 ob, bc*	SS
Telemann, G.-Draths	Kleine Trio-Sätze	SS
Vivaldi, A.-Nagy	Concerto, C, F. VII. No. 3	B&H
Zagwijn, H.	Pastorale and Scherzo	Pet
Zimmerman (arr)	Play a Song of Christmas	TP

TWO CLARINETS, KEYBOARD

Blue Tail Fly	NK
Czech Dance Song	NK
Easy Clarinet Solos	MS
Easy Clarinet Solos or Duets	MS
Marianina	NK

63

Two Clarinets, Keyboard

	Merry Hearts	NK
	Mexican Clapping Song	NK
	More Easy Clarinet Solos	MS
	Nip and Tuck	NK
	O Sole Mio	NK
	Pierrot and Pierrette	NK
	Tiritomba	NK
	Two Imps	NK
	Two Pals	NK
	Waltz "Aphens"	NK
	Waltz "Sibyl"	NK
Adam, A.-Holmes	Cantique de Noel	Rub
Adam, A.	O Holy Night	Rub
Adam, S.	The Holy City	HeE
Adams, S.-DeLamater	The Holy City	Rub
Aletter, W.	Rendezvous	Bos
Andre, P.	Concertino	Bil
Arditi, L.	Il Bacio (The Kiss)	Cen
Bach, C.P.E.-Ambrosio	Spring's Awakening	CF
Balbatre	Noel	EdM
Barnard, G.	Gloriana	CF
Barnard, G.	Merriment Polka	CF
Barnard, G.	Merriment Polka	Wat
Barnard, G.	Punch and Judy	Bar
Beaumont	Con Amore	Cen
Beethoven, L. van	Trio, op. 11. *cl, bcl, pf*	CF
Beethoven, L. van-Trinkaus	Minuet	CF
Beethoven, L. van-Harris	Minuet, G	CF
Beethoven, L. van	Theme (Symphony No. 2)	Cen
Bellini, V.-Sambin	Duet (La sonnambula)	EdS
Bellini, V.-Lewis	Hear Me Norma (Norma)	CF
Bellini, V.-Lewis	Hear Me Norma (Norma). *E♭ cl (cl), E♭ cl, pf*	CF
Benda	Introduction and Dance	EdM
Bennett, D.	Clarinet Carousel	SM
Bent	Swiss Boy	CF
Bent	Swiss Boy. *E♭ cl (cl), E♭ cl, pf*	CF
Bizet, G.	Carillon	EdM
Bizet, G.	Entr'acte (Carmen)	EdM
Bizet, G.	Prelude (Scène Bohèmiennes)	MM
Bizet, G.	Serenade Espagnole	EdM
Borodin, A.	Introduction en Allegro Vivo	MM
Bousquet, N.-Bettoney	Golden Robin Polka	CF
Braga, G.	Angels Serenade	CF
Brahms, J.-Harris	Famous Waltz, op. 39/15	CF
Brahms, J.	Hungarian Dance No. 5	CF
Brahmstedt	Frivolities (Concert Polka)	Rub
Brahmstedt	Souvenir of Venice	Rub
Briegel, G.	Staccato-Legato	GFB
Bruniau, A.	Toi et Moi	Bil
Buchtel, F.	Nina Mia (Spanish Serenade)	Rub
Buot-Pillevestre	La Chanson des Nids	ALe

64

Two Clarinets, Keyboard

Chaminade, C.	Scarf Dance	Cen
Chedeville, N.	Scherzo	EdM
Cherubini, L.	Ave Maria	CF
Chopin, F.	Minute Waltz, op. 64/1	GFB
Chopin, F.	Preludes, Op. 28/7,20	Cen
Christophe	Grand Duo	T-M
Cirri, G	Arioso	EdM
Corelli, A.	Air and Dance	EdM
Corelli, A.	Gavotte and Gigue	EdM
Corelli, A.	Gigue	EdM
Dahm, P. (arr)	Concert Album	EdM
Dahm, P.	Paris Soir	EdM
Dame, E.	Contes de Grand-Mère	Mau
Dansby, E.	Dandy Duo	Ken
D'Auvergne, B.	Plains of Peace	Bos
Debussy, C.	Mandoline	EdM
DeLamater, E. (arr)	Adeste Fidelis	Rub
Delbecq	Dans les Montagnes	MM
Delbecq	Fantasie Duo	MM
Depelsenaire, J.	Incantations	E-V
DeVille, P.	The Swiss Boy	CF
Di Capua, E.	O Sole Mio (My Sunshine)	Cen
Donizetti, G.-DeVille	Sextette (Lucia Di Lammermoor)	CF
Dorado-Wheeler	2 Friends	Vol
Dvorak, A.	Humoresque	Cen
Elgar, E.-Trinkaus	Salut d'Amour	CF
Endresen, R.	Pepperino	Rub
Endresen, R.	Prairie Warblers	Rub
Endresen, R.	Promenade	Rub
Endresen, R.	The Two Flyers	Rub
Fabré, C.-Harris	Reverie	CF
Fabré, C.	Second Reverie	Bil
Fabré, C.-Harris	Second Reverie	CF
Filas, T.	Clarinet Echoes	CF
Filas, T.	Double or Nothing	CF
Flotow, F.	Ah! So Fair (Martha)	NK
Franck-Cluwen	Aux petits Enfants	T-M
Ghys, J.-Harris	Amaryllis & Country Gardens	Lud
Giordani, T.	An 18th Century Air	EdM
Gluck, C.-Davis	Spirit Dance	Rub
Godard, B.-Trinkaus	Berceuse (Jocelyn)	CF
Gossec, F.-Ruyssen	Andantino	Gal
Andantino	Andantino	Gal
Gossec, F.-Rochon	Overture	MM
Gounod, C.-DeVille	Flower Song (Faust)	CF
Grieg, E.	Watchman's Song, Op. 12/3	Cen
Grooms, C.	Dark Eyes (Russian Song)	Cen
Grooms, C.	Two Guitars (Russian Song)	Cen
Handel, G.	Adagio and Allegro	Int
Handel, G.-Glaser	Allegro (Sonata No. 2)	CF
Handel, G.	Sonata No. 3. 2 cl, bc	MR
Harris, F.	Andante & Gavotte	Lud

65

Two Clarinets, Keyboard

Harris, F.	Gay Minuet	Lud
Harris, F.	2 Marionettes	Lud
Hasse, J.	Canzone	EdM
Hawthorne, A.	Whispering Hope	GFB
Haydn, F.	Oxen Minuet	CF
Heuberger, R.	Midnight Bells	CFo
Holmes, G. (arr)	Auld Lang Syne. $E\flat$ cl (cl), $E\flat$ cl, pf	CF
Holmes, G.	Auld Lang Syne	CF
Howell	Rustic Dance	Cen
Hook, J.-Curwin	Guida di Musica	Cha
Hummel, H. (arr)	Clarinet Polka	Rub
Iljinsky, A.	Berceuse	Cen
Kammell, A.-Thompson-Eades	Notturno No. 2	Cha
Kendall, R.	6 Clarinet Duets	Vol
Kennedy	Star of Hope (Reverie)	Cen
Ketèlbey, A.	Sanctuary of the Heart	Bos
Kiefer, W.	Elena Polka. $E\flat$ cl, cl, pf	Bar
King, K.	A Night in June	Bar
King, K.	A Night in June	Wat
Kling, H.-Catlin	Two Little Bulfinches Polka. $E\flat$ cl (cl), $E\flat$ cl, pf	CF
Kling, H.-Catlin	Two Little Bulfinches Polka	CF
Kreisler, F.-Leidzen	Liebesfreud	CFo
Kreisler, F.-Leidzen	Rondino on a theme of Beethoven	CFo
Kreisler, F.-Leidzen	Schön Rosmarin	CFo
Krommer, F.	Concerto, op. 35	MR
Labitzky, T.	Dream of the Shepherdess	Cen
Labitzky, T.	The Herd Girl's Dream	CF
Lake, M.	Annie Laurie	CF
Lawton, S.	A Book of Clarinet Duets	OxU
Lemare, E.-Trinkaus	Andantino	CF
Lemare, E.	Cathedral Meditation	Cen
Lester	Crimson Blushes. 2 cl, pf	Cen
Lincke, P.-Walters	The Glowworm	Rub
Liszt, F.	Love Dreams (Liebestraum)	Cen
Locatelli, P.	Aria	EdM
Lotti, A.	Arietta	EdM
Loumey	Shadows on the Water	Cen
Nurie-Neufeld (arr)	Classics for Clarinets	CF
Marsal, E.	Nanine	CF
Martini, J.	Plaisir d'Amour	EdM
Massenet, J.-Trinkaus	Elegy	CF
McBride, R.	Hot-Shot Divertimento	CoF
Meacham-Hummel	American Patrol	Rub
Mendelssohn, F.-Gee	Concert Piece No. 2, op. 114	SM
Mendelssohn, F.-Hunt	Concert Piece, op. 113, f	S&C
Mendelssohn, F.-Simon	Concertpiece No. 1, f, op. 113	Int
Mendelssohn, F.-Simon	Concertpiece No. 2, D, op. 114	Int
Mendelssohn, F.-Kreiselman	Conzertstück No. 2, op. 114. cl, bcl, pf	M&M

Two Clarinets, Keyboard

Mendelssohn, F.-Kreiselman	Konzertstück No. 1, op. 113.	
	cl, bcl, pf	M&M
Mendelssohn, F.	Konzertstück, op. 114.	
	cl, basset hn, pf	M&M
Mendelssohn, F.	Konzertstück, op. 113.	
	cl, basset hn, pf	M&M
Mendelssohn, F.-Michaels	2 Konzertstücke, op. 113-114	HSM
Mendelssohn, F.	Duet	MR
Mendelssohn, F.	Evening Song	HeE
Mendelssohn, F.	Ich wollt'meine lieb ergosse sich	HeE
Mendelssohn, F.	Maiglockchen und die Blumelein	HeE
Mendelssohn, F.-Davis	Nocturne	Rub
Mendelssohn, F.-Trinkaus	Nocturno (Mid-Summer	
	Nights Dream)	CF
Mendelssohn, F.-Trinkaus	On Wings of Song	CF
Mendelssohn, F.	Song Without Words No. 48	Cen
Mercier	Duo curieux	EdR
Meyerbeer, G.-Trinkaus	Coronation March (The Prophet)	CF
Meyerbeer, G.-Lazarus	Robert le Diable	CF
Monti, V.	Csardas	CF
Moser, C.	Variazioni diatoniche	FrC
Mozart, W.-Toll	Excerpt from Piano Sonata No. 2	CF
Mozart, W.	Minuet and Trio	
	(Symphony in E♭)	Cen
Mozart, W.-Frank	Presto (Sinfonia Concertante)	OxU
Mozart, W.-Phillips	Rondo (Serenade, B♭)	OxU
Mozart, W.- de Smet	Trio, K. 498	Pet
Nardini, P.	Shepherd's Pipes	EdM
Nevin, E.-Hummel	Narcissus	Rub
Offenbach, J.-Davis	Barcarolle	Rub
Offenbach, J.	Barcarolle (Tales of Hoffman)	NK
Packer, W.	Sea Breeze	Ken
Paderewski, I.-Trinkaus	Minuet a l'Antique	CF
Paganini, N.-Falcone	Perpetual Motion, op. 11	SM
Pala, J.	Bonjour	M&M
Pala, J.	3 Miniaturen	M&M
Paque, J.	Duo de la Norma, No. 2	ScF
Perfect, A.	Two Little Chums	CF
Perfect, A.	Two Little Chums.	
	E♭ cl (cl), E♭ cl, pf	CF
Pillevestre, J.	Idylle Bretonne	ALe
Pillevestre, J.	Le Mouvement Perpetuel	ALe
Pillevestre, J.	Les Anches Rebelles	ALe
Porret, J.	8th duo de concours	EdR
Porret, J.	7th duo de concours	EdR
Puccini, G.-Stebbing	Musetta's Waltz Song	Ric
Puccini, G.-Stebbing	Vissi d'Arte, Vissi d'Amore	Ric
Rachmaninoff, S.	Vocalise	EdM
Raphling, S.	Square Dance	EdM
Rameau, J.	Rigondon de Dardanus	EdM
Ranger, A. (arr)	Country Gardens	CF
Ranger, A. (arr)	A Wreath of Holly	CF

Two Clarinets, Keyboard

Ravel, M.-Walters	Pavane	Rub
Rebikov, W.	A Little Girl Rocking Her Doll	EdM
Rimsky-Korsakoff, N.	Song of India	Cen
Rosas	Over the Waves	Cen
Saint-Saens, C.-Trinkaus	The Swan	CF
Sargent	Nip and Tuc	CF
Sargent	Nip and Tuc. $E\flat$ cl (cl), $E\flat$ cl, pf	CF
Saupe	Air varie	ScF
Schaeffer, D. (arr)	Christmas Duets	PrA
Scholtes	Swiss Boy	Wat
Schonherr, M.	Im Duett	LK
Schubert, F.	Ave Maria	HeE
Schumann, R.-Conley	Knight Rupert. 2 bcl, pf	Ken
Schumann, R.-Davis	Melody, Op. 68/1	Rub
Schumann, R.	Soldier's March, Op. 68/2	Cen
Sibelius, J.-Trinkaus	Valse Triste (Kuoleman)	CF
Slechta, T.	Father of Waters	CF
Smetana, B.-Harris	Polka (Bartered Bride)	Lud
Smith, C.	From Day to Day	CF
Smith, C.	Helen	CF
Smith, C.	Life's Lighter Hours	Bar
Smith, C.	On Pleasure Bent	CF
Smith, C.	The Spirit of Joy	CF
Smith, C.	The Spirit of Joy. $E\flat$ cl (cl), $E\flat$ cl, pf	CF
Smith-Holmes	Drink To Me Only With Thine Eyes	CF
Smith-Holmes	Drink to Me Only with Thine Eyes. $E\flat$ cl (cl), $E\flat$ cl, pf	CF
Smith-Holmes	Old Black Joe	CF
Smith-Holmes	Old Black Joe. $E\flat$ cl (cl), $E\flat$ cl, pf	CF
Smith & Holmes	Through Shadowed Vales	Bar
Sousa, J.-Walters	The Stars and Stripes Forever	Rub
Spencer, J.	Silvatones	CF
Spencer, J.	Silvatones. $E\flat$ cl (cl), $E\flat$ cl, pf	CF
Staigers, D.	Hazel	CF
Stamitz, C.-Lebermann	Concerto, $B\flat$	Pet
Steen	Nocturne, $E\flat$	Wat
Strauss, J.-Bettoney	Tales from the Vienna Woods, op. 325	CF
Strauss, J.-Jolliff	Tritsch-Tratsch Polka	Rub
Strauss, O.-Harris	A Waltz Dream	Lud
Stravinsky, I.	Berceuse	EdM
Stravinsky, I.	Dance of the Ballerina	EdM
Stravinsky, I.	Dance of the Princesses	EdM
Stravinsky, I.	Pastorale	EdM
Tartini, G.	Sonata. 2 cl, bc	MR
Taylor, L.	The Minor and the Major Polka	Hal
Tchaikovsky, P.-Trinkaus	Chant Sans Paroles	CF

Two Clarinets, Keyboard

Tchaikovsky, P.-Hummel	Concerto in B♭ Minor	Rub
Thome, F.	Simple Aveu	CF
Titl, A.	Serenade	CF
Vivaldi, A.-Schwadron	Corrente	Ken
Vivaldi, A.	Giga	EdM
Wagner, R.-Trinkaus	Song to the Evening Star (Tannhauser)	CF
Wagner, R.-Trinkaus	Walther's Prize Song (Die Meistersinger)	CF
Wallace, W.-Gruenwald	Cavatina (Maritana)	CF
Waln, G.	Concert Trios	NK
Walters, H.	Shindig (Folk Song Fantasy)	Rub
Walters, H. (arr)	When The Saints Go Marching In	Rub
Warren, D.	Grenadilla Caprice	Lud
Weber, C. von-Davis	Hunter's Chorus	Rub
Werkmeister	Souvenir de Sfax	EdR
Wheeler	Meditation	Vol
White, C.	Petite Suite. E♭ cl, acl, pf	SF
White, C.	Petite Suite. cl, bcl, pf	SF
Wood	Let 'Er Go	Cen
Zimmerman (arr)	Play a Song of Christmas	TP

TWO SAXOPHONES, KEYBOARD

	Black Eyes. 2 asax, pf	GFB
	Blue Tail Fly. 2 asax, pf	NK
	Czech Dance Song. 2 asax, pf	NK
	Deep River. 2 asax, pf	GFB
	Easy Saxophone Solos. 2 sax, pf	MS
	Easy Saxophone Solos or Duets. 2 sax, pf	MS
	More Easy Saxophone Solos. 2 sax, pf	MS
	Fair Are the Meadows. 2 asax, pf	NK
	Londonderry Air. 2 asax, pf	GFB
	Marianina. 2 asax, pf	NK
	Merry Hearts. 2 asax, pf	NK
	Mexican Clapping Song. 2 asax, pf	NK
	Song of the Bolga Boatmen. 2 asax, pf	GFB
	Tiritomba. 2 asax, pf	NK
	Two Pals. 2 asax, pf	NK
	Wlatz "Sibyl." 2 asax, pf	NK
	Woodland Whispers. 2 asax, pf	NK
Adam, A.	O Holy Night. 2 asax, pf	Rub
Adams, S.-DeLamter	The Holy City. 2 asax, pf	Rub
Aldrich	Love and Flowers. asax, tsax, pf	Ecn
André, P.	Romance d'automne. 2 asax, pf	EdR

Two Saxophones, Keyboard

Arditi, L.	Il Bacio (The Kiss).	
	asax, tsax (asax), pf	Cen
Bach, J.S.-Gounod	Ave Maria. *asax, tsax, pf*	Cen
Barnhouse, C.	Milennial. *asax, tsax, pf*	Bar
Barnhouse, C.	Silver Lining. *asax, tsax, pf*	Bar
Beaumont	Con Amore. *asax, tsax, (asax), pf*	Cen
Beethoven, L. van-Trinkaus	Minuet. *asax, asax (tsax), pf*	CF
Beethoven, L. van-Harris	Minuet, G. *2 tsax, pf*	CF
Beethoven, L. van	Minuet in G. *asax, tsax (asax), pf*	Cen
Beethoven, L. van	Moonlight Sonata (Adagio).	
	asax, tsax (asax), pf	Cen
Bellini, V.	Duet (Norma). *2 sax, pf*	CF
Bent	Swiss Boy. *2 asax, pf*	CF
Bléger, A.	Souvenir de Valence. *2 tsax, pf*	MM
Borodin, A.	Solicitude. *asax, tsax, pf*	EdM
Braga, G.	Angel's Serenade. *asax, tsax, pf*	Cen
Braga, G.	Angel's Serenade. *asax, tsax, pf*	CF
Brahms, J.-Harris	Famous Waltz, op. 39/15.	CF
	2 sax, pf	
Briegel, G.	Cathedral Echoes. *2 asax, pf*	GFB
Briegel, G.	Soloette. *asax, tsax, pf*	GFB
Briegel-Tucker	Triplets. *asax, tsax, pf*	GFB
Buchtel, F.	Enchantment. *asax, tsax, pf*	NK
Buchtel, F.	Roving Minstrels. *asax, tsax, pf*	NK
Buchtel, F.	Skylarks. *asax, tsax, pf*	NK
Butterfield, N.	When you and I Were Young.	
	asax, tsax, pf	Cen
Chedeville, N.	Scherzo. *asax, tsax, pf*	EdM
Chopin, F.	Minuet Waltz, op. 64/1.	
	asax, tsax, pf	GFB
Clodomir, P.	12 Duos. *2 tsax, pf*	HeE
Conklin	Handy Andy. *2 sax, pf*	CF
Danks, H.	Silver Threads Among the Gold.	
	asax, tsax, pf	Cen
DeLamater, E. (arr)	Adeste Fidelis. *2 asax, pf*	Rub
Deschamps, J.	Sonatine. *2 sax, pf*	Bil
Di Capua, E.	O Sole Mio. *asax, tsax, pf*	Cen
Di Capua, E.	O Sole Mio (My Sunshine).	
	asax, tsax (asax), pf	Cen
Donizetti, G.	Lucia di Lammermoor.	
	asax, tsax, pf	Cen
Dorado-Wheeler	2 Friends. *asax, tsax, pf*	Vol
Dorado-Wheeler	2 Friends. *2 asax, pf*	Vol
Drigo, R.	Harlequin Serenade.	Cen
	asax, tsax, pf	
Drigo, R.	Serenade. *asax, tsax, pf*	Cen
Drigo, R.-Saenger	Valse Bluette. *2 asax, pf*	CF
Dvorak, A.	Humoreske. *asax, tsax (asax), pf*	Cen
Dvorak, A.	Songs My Mother Taught Me.	
	2 asax, pf	GFB
Elgar, E.	Salut d'Amour. *asax, tsax, pf*	Cen
Emmett, D.	Dixie's Land. *2 sax, pf*	McK

Two Saxophones, Keyboard

Fabré, C.-Harris	Reverie. *2 asax, pf*	CF
Fabré, C.	Second Reverie. *2 asax, pf*	CF
Fauré, J.	Les Rameaux (The Palms). *asax, tsax, pf*	Cen
Foster, S.-Brooke	Come Where My Love Lies Dreaming. *2 tsax, pf*	CF
Fote, R.	Amigos. *2 asax, pf*	Ken
Giordani, G.	An 18th Century Air. *asax, tsax, pf*	EdM
Godard, B-Trinkaus	Berceuse (Jocelyn). *asax, asax (tsax), pf*	CF
Godard, B.	Lullaby (Jocelyn). *asax, tsax, pf*	Cen
Gorner, H.	Concertino, op. 31. *asax, tsax, pf*	FrH
Grieg, E.	I Love You. *asax, tsax, pf*	Cen
Grieg, E.	To Spring. *asax, tsax (asax), pf*	Cen
Grooms (arr)	Famous Scotch Airs, Var. *asax, tsax, pf*	Cen
Grooms (arr)	Home Favorites, Var. *asax, tsax, pf*	Cen
Grooms (arr)	Neapolitan Favorites, Var. *asax, tsax, pf*	Cen
Grooms (arr)	Ocean Echoes, Var. *asax, tsax, pf*	Cen
Grooms (arr)	Plantation Echoes, Var. *asax, tsax, pf*	Cen
Grooms (arr)	Two Guitars (Russian Song). *asax, tsax (asax), pf*	Cen
Harris, F.	The Old Refrain & Dark Eyes. *2 asax, pf*	Lud
Harris, F.	2 Buckarros. *2 asax, pf*	Lud
Harris, F.	2 Buckaroos. *2 tsax, pf*	Lud
Harris, F.	2 Marionettes. *2 tsax, pf*	Lud
Hawthorne, A.	Whispering Hope. *2 asax, pf*	GFB
Haydn, F.	Oxen Minuet. *2 asax, pf*	CF
Herbert, V.-Harris	Gypsy Love Song. *2 asax, pf*	Lud
Heuberger, R.-Kreisler-Leidzen	Midnight Bells. *2 asax, pf*	CFo
Holmes, G. (arr)	Auld Lang Syne. *asax (tsax), asax (tsax), pf*	CF
Iasilli, G.	Goldie. *2 sax, pf*	CF
Jahrl	Frolic of the Keys. *asax, tsax, pf*	GFB
Kennedy	Star of Hope (Reverie). *asax, tsax (asax), pf*	Cen
Kiefer, W.	Elena Polka. *tsax (asax), tsax, pf*	Bar
King, K.	Night in June. *2 asax, pf*	Bar
King, K.	Night in June. *tsax, (asax), tsax, pf*	Bar
Klickmann, F.	Sweet Hawaiian Moonlight. *2 sax, pf*	McK
Klickmann, F.	Trail to Long Ago. *2 sax, pf*	McK
Koch, E. von	Concerto piccolo. *ssax, asax, pf*	EMF
Lack, T.	Idilio. *asax, tsax, pf*	Cen
Lake, M. (arr0	Annie Laurie. *asax (tsax) asax (tsax), pf*	CF

71

Two Saxophones, Keyboard

Lange, G.	Blumenlied (Flower Song).	
	asax, tsax, pf	Cen
Lemare, E.	Andantino. *asax, asax (tsax), pf*	CF
Lemare, E.	Cathedral Meditation.	
	asax, tsax (asax), pf	Cen
Leoncavallo, R.	Arioso (Pagliacci). *asax, tsax, pf*	Cen
Leybach, I.	Fifth Nocturne, G.	
	asax, tsax (asax), pf	Cen
Liszt, F.-Smith	Liebestraum. *2 asax, pf*	Bar
Liszt, F.-Smith	Liebestraum.	
	tsax (asax), tsax, pf	Bar
Liszt, F.	Love Dreams (Liebestraum).	
	asax, tsax (asax), pf	Cen
Massenet, J.-Trinkaus	Elegy. *asax, asax (tsax), pf*	CF
Mendelssohn, F.	Evening Song. *2 tsax, pf*	T-M
Mendelssohn, F.	Ich wollt' meine liebe	
	ergosse sich. *2 tsax, pf*	T-M
Mendelssohn, F.	Maiglockchen und die Blumelein.	
	2 tsax, pf	HeE
Mendelssohn, F.-Trinkaus	Nocturno (Mid-Summer Nights	
	Dream). *asax, asax*	CF
	(tsax), pf	
Mendelssohn, F.-Trinkaus	On Wings of Song.	
	asax, asax (tsax), pf	CF
Mendelssohn, F.	Spring Song. *asax, tsax, pf*	Cen
Meyerbeer, G.-Trinkaus	Coronation March (The Prophet).	
	asax, asax (tsax), pf	CF
Molloy, J.	Love's Old Sweet Song.	
	2 sax, pf	McK
Morel	Norwegian Cradle Song.	
	asax, tsax, pf	Cen
Mozart, W.	Ave Verum Corpus. *asax, tsax, pf*	EdM
Offenbach, J.	Barcarolle (Tales of Hoffman).	
	asax, tsax, pf	Cen
Offenbach, J.	Barcarolle (Tales of Hoffmann).	
	2 asax, pf	CF
Offenbach, J.	Barcarolle (Tales of Hoffmann).	
	2 sax, pf	McK
Offenbach, J.	Barcarolle (Tales of Hoffman).	
	2 asax, pf	NK
Packer	Sea Breeze. *2 asax, pf*	Ken
Paderewski, I.-Trinkaus	Minuet a L'Antique.	
	asax, asax (tsax), pf	CF
Pala, J.	3 Miniatures. *2 tsax, pf*	HeE
Panella, F.	Jack and Jill. *2 asax, pf*	Vol
Panella, F.	Jolly Two. *2 asax, pf*	Vol
Panella, F.	Tom and Jerry. *2 asax, pf*	Vol
Panella, F.	2 Bachelors. *2 asax, pf*	Vol
Panella, F.	2 Gnomes. *2 asax, pf*	Vol
Panella, F.	2 Lovers. *2 asax, pf*	Vol
Paque, J.	Duo de la Norma, No. 7.	
	2 tsax, pf	S&C

Two Saxophones, Keyboard

Perfect, A.	Two Little Chums. *2 asax, pf*	CF
Pergolesi, G.	Sicilian Air. *asax, tsax, pf*	EdM
Pitts	Church in the Wildwood.	
	asax, tsax, pf	GFB
Ponce, M.	Estrellita. *2 asax, pf*	CF
Porret, J.	Ingres. *asax, tsax, pf*	MM
Porret, J.	Jenner. *asax, tsax, pf*	MM
Rameau, J.	Rigadon de Dardanus.	
	asax, tsax, pf	EdM
Ranger, A.	A Wreath of Holly. *asax (tsax),*	
	asax (tsax), pf	CF
Rimsky-Korsakoff, N.	Song of India.	
	asax, tsax (asax), pf	Cen
Saint-Saens, C.	Le Cygne (The Swan).	
	asax, tsax, pf	Cen
Saint-Saens, C.	My Heart At Thy Sweet Voice.	
	asax, tsax, (asax), pf	Cen
Saint-Saens, C.-Trinkaus	The Swan. *asax, asax (tsax), pf*	CF
Schaeffer, D. (arr)	Christmas Duets. *2 asax, pf*	PrA
Schubert, F.	Ave Maria. *2 tsax, pf*	HeE
Schubert, F.	Serenade. *asax, tsax, pf*	Cen
Schubert, F.	Wandering Brooklet.	
	asax, tsax, pf	NK
Sibelius, J.-Trinkaus	Valse Triste (Kuolema).	
	asax, asax (tsax), pf	CF
Sibelius, J.	Valse Triste. *asax, tsax, pf*	Cen
Slechta, T.	Father of Waters. *2 sax, pf*	CF
Smetana, B.-Harris	Polka (Bartered Bride).	
	2 tsax, pf	Lud
Smim, P. (arr)	Duet Album. *2 asax, pf*	EdM
Smim, P. (arr)	Duet Album. *asax, tsax, pf*	EdM
Smim, P. (arr)	Paris Soir. *asax, tsax, pf*	EdM
Smith, C.	Among the Sycamores.	
	tsax (asax), tsax (asax), pf	Bar
Smith, C.-Holmes, G.	Believe Me If All Those Endearing	
	Young Charms. *asax (tsax),*	
	asax (tsax), pf	CF
Smith, C.	Call of the Sea.	
	tsax (asax), tsax, pf	Bar
Smith, C.-Holmes, G.	The Caribbean. *asax (tsax),*	
	asax (tsax), pf	CF
Smith, C.-Holmes, G.	Drink To Me Only With Thine	
	Eyes. *asax (tsax), asax*	
	(tsax), pf	
Smith, C.	From Day to Day. *asax (tsax),*	
	asax (tsax), pf	CF
Smith, C.	Helen. *asax (tsax),*	
	asax (tsax), pf	CF
Smith, C.	Imogene. *2 tsax, pf*	Bar
Smith, C.	Italiana. *tsax (asax), tsax, pf*	Bar
Smith, C. & Holmes, G.	Italiana. *2 asax, pf*	Bar
Smith, C.	Life's Lighter Hours. *tsax (asax),*	

Two Saxophones, Keyboard

	tsax (asax), pf	Bar
Smith, C. & Holmes, G.	Massa's in the Cold, Cold, Ground.	
	tsax (asax), tsax (asax), pf	Bar
Smith, C.	Milady's Pleasure. *tsax (asax),*	
	tsax (asax), pf	Bar
Smith, C.	My Song of Songs. *asax (tsax),*	
	asax (tsax), pf	CF
Smith, C.-Holmes, G.	Old Black Joe. *asax (tsax),*	
	asax (tsax), pf	CF
Smith, C.	On Pleasure Bent. *asax (tsax),*	
	asax (tsax), pf	CF
Smith, C.	Rainbow Hues. *tsax (asax),*	
	tsax (asax), pf	Bar
Smith, C. & Holmes, G.	Silver Threads Among the Gold.	
	tsax (asax), tsax (asax), pf	Bar
Smith, C.	Smithsonian. *tsax (asax),*	
	tsax (asax), pf	Bar
Smith, C.	The Spirit of Joy. *asax (tsax),*	
	asax (tsax), pf	CF
Smith, C. & Holmes, G.	Through Shadowed Vales.	
	tsax (asax), tsax, pf	Bar
Smith, C.	The Trumpeter. *2 tsax, pf*	Bar
Smith, C. & Holmes, G.	The Wayfarer. *tsax (asax),*	
	tsax (asax), pf	Bar
Spencer, F.	Silvatones. *2 asax, pf*	CF
Staigers, D.	Hazel. *asax, asax (tsax), pf*	CF
Strauss, O.-Harris	A Waltz Dream. *2 tsax, pf*	Lud
Sullivan, A.	The Lost Chord. *asax, tsax, pf*	Cen
Tchaikovsky, P.-Trinkaus	Chant Sans Paroles.	
	asax, asax (tsax), pf	CF
Thomas	Romance. *asax, tsax, pf*	Cen
Thome, F.	Simple Aveu (Confession).	
	asax, tsax, pf	Cen
Thompson	Bubble and Squeak. *2 asax, pf*	Vol
Thompson	Song of Spring. *2 asax, pf*	Vol
Thompson	Song of Spring. *2 tsax, pf*	Vol
Thompson	Valse Minah. *2 asax (2 tsax), pf*	Vol
Titl, A.	Serenade. *asax, tsax, pf*	CF
Tosti, F.	Good-Bye. *asax, tsax, pf*	Cen
Trinkaus, G.	Lament. *asax, asax (tsax), pf*	CF
Verdi, G.	Celeste Aida (Aida).	
	asax, tsax, pf	Cen
Verdi, G.	La Donna e Mobile.	
	asax, tsax, pf	Cen
Verdi, G.	Miserere, Il Trovatore.	
	asax, tsax, pf	Cen
Vogt	Boat Song. *asax, tsax, pf*	Cen
Vogt	Dream Waltz. *asax, tsax, pf*	Cen
Vogt	Remembrance. *asax, tsax, pf*	Cen
Vogt	Sax-o-moan.*asax, tsax, pf*	Cen
Vogt	Saxonade. *asax, tsax, pf*	Cen
Vogt	Saxonola. *asax, tsax, pf*	Cen

Two Saxophones, Keyboard

Wagner, R.	Bridal Chorus (Lohengrin). *2 sax, pf*	McK
Wagner, R.	Romance (Tannhauser). *asax, tsax, pf*	Cen
Wagner, R.-Trinkaus	Song to the Evening Star Tannhauser. *asax, asax (tsax), pf*	CF
Wagner, R.	Walther's Prize Song (Die Meistersinger). *asax, asax (tsax), pf*	CF
Wendland	Twin Stars. *2 asax, pf*	Vol
Westendorf	I'll Take You Home Again Kathleen. *2 asax, pf*	GFB
Wilson	Moonlight on the Hudson, Op. 60. *asax, tsax, pf*	Cen
Wilson	The Wayside Chapel. *asax, tsax, pf*	Cen
Wood	Let 'Er Go. *asax, tsax (asax), pf*	Cen
Yradier, S.	La Paloma. *asax, tsax, pf*	CF
Yradier, S.	The Dove (La Paloma). *asax, tsax, pf*	Cen
Zindars, E.	Quiddity. *2 asax, pf*	AMC

TWO BASSOONS - KEYBOARD

Carolo	Sonata No. 1, B♭	MR
Giggy, F.	Little Sonata	CoA
Jancourt, E.	3 Grandes Sonates	Bil
Schumann, R.-Conley	Knight Rupert	Ken
Selma y Salaverde, B. de-Kastner	Canzon a 2 Bassi. *2bsn, bc*	SS
Selma y Salaverde, B. de	XXIII Canzon. *2bsn, bc*	B&V

TWO WOODWINDS - KEYBOARD

Adams, S.-de Rooy	The Holy City. *2B♭ instr, pf*	MM
Addison, J.	Trio. *fl, ob, pf*	GaM
Adolphys, M.	Tribrach. *fl, cl, pf*	CoF
Allegra, S.	Sonata in un tempo. *fl(cl), bsn, pf*	Car
Altena, L. van	Divertimento. *fl, ob, pf*	SD
Andriessen, J.	Trio No. 1 (1955). *fl, ob, pf*	SD
Andriessen, H.	Thema met variaties (1953). *fl, ob, pf*	SD
Arvin, A.	3 Seasons. *fl, cl, pf*	Cha
Aubin, T.	Le calme de la mer. *fl, cl, pf*	ALe
Auclert, P.	Trio No. 2. *fl, cl, pf*	FrC
Bach, C.P.E.	6 Sonates. *cl, bsn, pf*	B&V
Bach, C.P.E.-Balassa	6 Sonatas. *cl, bsn, bc*	EMB

Two Woodwinds, Keyboard

Bach, C.P.E.	6 Sonatas. *cl, bsn, pf*	Int
Bach, C.P.E.	Trio No. 1, D. *fl, cl, pf*	Int
Bach, C.P.E.	Trio No. 2, a. *fl, cl, pf*	Int
Bach, C.P.E.	Trio No. 3, G. *fl, cl, pf*	Int
Bach, J.C.	Divertissement. *fl, ob, pf*	SM
Bach, J.S.	Andante from Trio Sonata. *fl, ob, pf*	OxU
Bach, J.S.-Marx	Canonic Trio. *fl, ob, pf*	M&M
Bach, J.S.-Langenus	Concerto No. 3, d. *fl, cl, pf*	CF
Bach, W.F.	Siciliano. *ob, bsn, pf*	M&M
Bamert, M.	Trio. *fl, cl, pf*	See
Barnard, G.	Gloriana. *fl, cl, pf*	CF
Beethoven, L. van	Duo No. 1. *cl(fl, ob), bsn, pf*	CF
Beethoven, L. van	Duo No. II. *cl(fl, ob), bsn, pf*	CF
Beethoven, L. van	Duo No. III. *cl(fl, ob), bsn, pf*	CF
Beethoven, L. van-Trinkaus	Menuet. *2ww, pf*	CF
Beethoven, L. van-Badura-Skoda	Trio. *fl, bsn, pf*	BrH
Beethoven, L. van	Trio, G. *fl, bsn, pf*	Int
Beethoven, L. van-Odé	Trio, G. *fl, bsn, pf*	Kaw
Beethoven, L. van	Trio, op. 38. *cl, bsn(vc), pf*	MR
Benguerel, X.	Trio (1960). *fl, cl, pf*	See
Bent, R.	Swiss Boy. *fl, cl, pf*	CF
Berlioz, H.	Trio of the Young Ishmaelites. *fl, ob, pf*	EdM
Berlioz, H.	Trio of the Young Ishmaelites. *fl, cl, pf*	EdM
Bishop, H.-Lax	Lo! Here the Gentle Lark. *fl, cl, pf*	CF
Bizet, G.	Adagietto. *fl, cl, pf*	EdM
Bizet, G.	Aragonaise. *fl, ob, pf*	EdM
Bizet, G.	Aragonaise. *fl, cl, pf*	EdM
Bizet, G.	Carillon. *fl, cl, pf*	EdM
Bizet, G.	Entr'acte. *fl, cl, pf*	EdM
Bizet, G.	Minuet. *fl, ob, pf*	EdM
Bizet, G.	Minuet. *fl, cl, pf*	EdM
Bizet, G.	Second Minuet. *fl, cl, pf*	EdM
Bizet, G.	Serenade Espagnole. *fl, cl, pf*	EdM
Bizet, G.	3 Pieces. *fl, cl, pf*	SM
Blake, H.	Fantasy Allegro. *fl(ob, cl), bsn, pf*	Cha
Blake, H.	Trio. *fl, cl, pf*	Cha
Bloch, E.	Concertino. *fl, cl, pf*	Sch
Boedijn, G.	Folklorische suite, op. 87 (1937). *fl, ob, pf*	SD
Boismortier, J.-Ruf	Concerto, a. *fl, ob, bc*	Ric
Boismortier, J.-Ruf	Concerto, C. *fl, ob, bc*	Ric
Boismortier, J.-Ruf	Sonate, e, op. 37/2. *ob, bsn(vc), bc*	B&N
Boismortier, J.	Trio Sonata, a, op. 37/5. *fl(ob, vn), bsn(vc), bc*	MR
Boismortier, J.-Ruf	Trio Sonata, a. *ob, bsn(vc), bc*	SS
Borgulya, A.	Trio. *fl, bsn, pf*	Gen
Borodin, A.	Solicitude. *fl, ob, pf*	EdM
Borodin, A.	Solicitude. *fl, cl, pf*	EdM
Borris, S.	Rhapsodie, op. 103. *ob, bsn, hpcd*	S-V

76

Two Woodwinds, Keyboard

Borris, S.	Trio, op. 90. *ob, bsn, pf*	S-V
Borris, S.	Trio, op. 116/1b (1965). *fl, ob, pf*	B&N
Bortolotti, M.	Parentesis (1968). *cl, bsn, pf*	ESZ
Bottenberg, W.	Trio (1963-64). *fl, cl, pf*	Can
Bousquet, N.-Brooke	Golden Robin Polka. *fl, cl, pf*	CF
Braga, G.	Angel's Serenade. *fl, asax(tsax), pf*	CF
Braga, G.	Angel's Serenade. *fl, cl, pf*	CF
Brahms, J.-Harris	Famous Waltz, op. 39/15. *fl, cl, pf*	CF
Brahms, J.	Hungarian Dance No. 5. *cl, asax, pf*	CF
Brahms, J.	Hungarian Dance No. 5. *fl, cl, pf*	CF
Breck, E. (arr)	Christmas Joys. *2ww, pf*	CF
Breval, J.	Symphonie Concertante, F, op. 31. *fl, bsn, pf*	MR
Brogue, R.	Sonatina. *fl, cl, hpcd*	AMC
Bruniau, A.	Toi et Moi (Fantaisie-Duo). *ob, cl, pf*	Bil
Buchtel, F.	Enchantment. *fl, cl, pf*	NK
Buchtel, F.	Roving Minstrels. *fl, cl, pf*	NK
Buchtel, F.	Skylarks. *fl, cl, pf*	NK
Bush, G.	Trio. *ob, bsn, pf*	Nov
Canino, B.	Impromptu No. 1 (1969). *fl, ob, pf*	ESZ
Castello	Quarta Sonata a Due. *2 C or B♭ treble or bass instr, bc*	Sha
Chedeville, N.	Scherzo. *fl, ob, pf*	EdM
Chedeville, N.	Scherzo. *fl, cl, pf*	EdM
Cherubini, L.	Ave Maria. *fl, cl, pf*	CF
Chopin, F.	Minute Waltz, op. 64/1. *fl, cl, pf*	GFB
Christiansen, F.	Caprice. *fl, cl, pf*	NK
Cima, G.-Weast	Sonata a Tre. *2ww, pf*	PrA
Cimarosa, D.	Concerto, G. *fl, ob, pf*	SM
Cirri, M.	Arioso. *fl, cl, pf*	EdM
Cliquet-Pleyel	Chant d'Esperance. *cl, bsn, pf*	E-V
Cole, H.	Trio. *fl, cl, pf*	Nov
Corelli, A.	Air and Dance. *fl, ob, pf*	EdM
Corelli, A.	Air and Dance. *fl, cl, pf*	EdM
Corelli, A.	Gavotte and Gigue. *fl, ob, pf*	EdM
Corelli, A.	Gavotte and Gigue. *fl, cl, pf*	EdM
Corelli, A.	Gigue. *fl, cl, pf*	EdM
Damase, J.	Trio. *fl, ob, pf*	E-V
Dansby	Dandy Duo. *fl, ob, pf*	Ken
David, F.	Thou Brilliant Bird. *fl, cl(ob), pf*	CF
Debussy, C.	Il Pleure dans mon Coeur. *fl, cl, pf*	EdM
Debussy, C.	Mandoline. *fl, cl, pf*	EdM
Depelsenaire, J.	Sur l'Albaicin. *ob, fl(cl), pf*	E-V
Dessau, P.	Variations on "Hab mein Wagen vollgeladen." *cl, bsn, pf*	Pet
Destenay, E.	Trio, op. 27. *ob, cl, pf*	Ham
Diamond, D.	Partita. *ob, bsn, pf*	SMP
Dijk, J. van	Canzon all capriccio (1958). *ob, bsn, pf*	SD
Donizetti, G.	Mad Scene (Lucia di	CF

Two Woodwinds, Keyboard

Donizetti, G.	Lammermoor). *fl, cl, pf*	
	Sextet (Lucia di Lammermoor).	CF
	fl, cl, pf	
Donizetti, G.	Trio. *cl, bsn, pf*	MR
Dring	Trio. *fl, ob, pf*	Bou
Dubois, P.	Double Concertino. *ob, bsn, pf*	ALe
Dubois, P.	Les Treteaux. *fl, asax, pf*	ECh
Dvorkin, J.	Suite. *ob, bsn, pf*	AMC
Ebseyeb, S.	Trio. *cl, bsn, pf*	MR
Elgar, E.-Trinkaus	Love's Greeting. *2ww, pf*	CF
Emmanuel, M.	Sonata. *fl, cl, pf*	E-V
Exaudet, J.	La Cour de la Marquise. *fl, cl, pf*	EdM
Fabre, C.-Harris	Reverie. *fl, cl, pf*	CF
Fabre, C.-Harris	Reverie. *cl, sax, pf*	CF
Fabre, C.-Harris	Second Reverie. *cl, sax, pf*	CF
Fabre, C.-Harris	Second Reverie. *fl, cl, pf*	CF
Fauré, G.	En Prière. *fl, cl, pf*	EdM
Finger, B.-Kratochvil	Adagio (Sonata, F). *fl, bcl, pf*	ES
Foster	A Village Festival. *fl, cl, pf*	EdM
Foster, S.-Brooke	Come Where My Love	CF
	Lies Dreaming. *fl, cl, pf*	
Freedman, H.	Variations (1965). *ob, fl, hpcd*	Can
Fricker, P.	Trio, op. 35 (Serenade No. 2).	SS
	fl, ob, pf	
Fux, J.	Nürnberger Partita. *fl, ob, bc*	MV
Fux, J.-Kunter	Sinfonia. *fl, ob, bc*	B&N
Galuppi, B.-Ruf	Triosonate, G. *fl, ob, bc*	B&N
Gaubert, P.	Tarentelle. *fl, ob, pf*	E&C
Genin, P.	Grand Duo Concertant, op. 51.	Bil
	fl, ob(cl), pf	
Giordani, G.	An 18th Century Air. *fl, cl, pf*	EdM
Giordani, G.	An 18th Century Air. *fl, bsn, pf*	EdM
Glinka, M.-Oubradous	Trio Páthetique. *cl, bsn, pf*	EMT
Glinka, M.	Trio Pathetique. *cl, bsn, pf*	Int
Glinka, M.	Trio Pathetique. *cl, bsn(vc), pf*	MR
Godard, B.-Trinkaus	Berceuse (Jocelyn). *2ww, pf*	CF
Goossens, E.	Pastoral and Harlequinad.	ALe
	fl, ob, pf	
Gordon, H.	Stotiniana (1960). *ob, bsn, pf*	SD
Görner, H.	Duo, op. 37. *cl, bsn, bc*	Pet
Gounod, C.-Laube	Ave Maria. *fl, cl, pf*	CF
Gruber, H.	Bossa nova. *fl, bsn, pf*	LDo
Grundman, C.	Waltz and Interlude. *fl, cl, pf*	B&H
Gyring, E.	Trio. *ob, cl, pf*	CoF
Gyring, E.	Trio. *cl, bsn, pf*	CoF
Haieff, A.	3 Bagatelles. *ob, bsn, hpcd (pf)*	BB
Haletzki, P.	Father and Son. *pic, bsn(asax), pf*	S&C
Handel, G.-Glaser	Allegro (Sonata No. 2). *fl, cl, pf*	CF
Handel, G.-Seiffert	Kammertrio No. 24, F. *ob, bsn, bc*	BrH
Hartzell, E.	Trio (1969). *fl, bcl(bsn), pf*	LDo
Hasse, J.	Canzone. *fl, cl, pf*	EdM
Haydn, F.-Robbins/Landon	5 Lyre Concerti. *fl, ob, pf*	LDo

78

Two Woodwinds, Keyboard

Published separately

Haydn, F.	Oxen Minuet. *fl, cl, pf*	CF
Haydn, F.	Oxen Minuet. *fl, asax, pf*	CF
Haydn, F.	Oxen Minuet. *cl, sax, pf*	CF
Haydn, F.	Trio No. 29, F. *fl(cl), bsn(vc), pf*	CF
Haydn, F.	Trio No. 31, G. *fl, bsn(vc, bcl), pf*	CF
Heinichen, J.-Hausswald	Sonata, G. *fl, ob, bc*	BrH
Heinichen, J.-Janetzky	Trio-Sonate, F. *fl(ob), ob, bc*	WMS
Hétu, J.	Trio (1960). *fl, ob, hpcd*	Can
Holst, G.	A Fugal Concerto. *fl, ob, pf*	Nov
Honegger, A.	Concerto da camera (1948). *fl, ehn, pf*	EdS
Honegger, A.	Petite Suite. *2 instr in C, pf*	ChM
Ibert, J.-Hoeree	Aria. *fl(ob), cl(vn), pf*	ALe
Isaac, M. (arr)	Sacred Music. *2ww, pf*	CF
Jacob, G.	Trio. *fl, ob, pf*	OxU
Jancourt, E.	Concertino. *ob, bsn, pf*	Bil
Johnson, J.	Trio. *fl, ob, pf*	GaM
Jones, K.	Sonata da camera (1957). *fl, ob, hpcd*	Can
Jones, K.	Sonata da Chiesa (1967). *fl, ob, hpcd*	Can
Kahmann, C.	Dances. *fl, ob, pf*	AMC
Kalinnikov, V.	Chanson Triste. *fl, cl, pf*	EdM
Kalinnikov, V.	Chanson Triste. *fl, bsn, pf*	EdM
Karlins, M.	Celebration. *fl, ob, hpcd*	ACA
Karlins, M.	Music. *ob, bcl, pf*	CoF
Kauffmann, G.-Gore	6 Chorales. *ob, cl(tpt), org*	Con
Kennaway, L.	Downstream. *ob, cl, pf*	HE
Kennedy-Harris	Star of the East. *fl, cl, pf*	Lud
Ketting, O.	Thema en Variaties (1958). *cl, bsn, pf*	SD
Ketting, P.	Sonata (1936). *fl, ob, pf*	SD
King, K.	Night in June. *fl, cl, pf*	Bar
Koechlin, C.	Epitaphe de Jean Harlow, op. 164. *fl, asax, pf*	EME
Klauss, N.	Fugue, C. *fl, cl, pf*	Leb
Kleinknecht, J.-Weiss	Sonata, c. *fl, ob(vn), bc*	Deu
Koetsier, J.	Trio, op. 13/1 (1936). *fl, ob, pf*	SD
Kopsch, J.	Trio. *ob, cl, pf*	UE
Krauss	Allegro. *fl, cl, pf*	MM
Krebs, J.-Ruf	Triosonate, G. *fl, ob, bc*	Hei
Kreutzer, K.-Schütz	Trio, op. 43. *cl, bsn, pf*	FrH
Kummer, K.	2 Duets, op. 46. *fl, cl, pf*	CF
Kuri-Aldana, M.	Cantares. *fl, cl, pf*	MR
Labitzky, T.	The Herd Girl's Dream. *fl, cl, pf*	CF
Lacombe, P.	Serenade, op. 47. *fl, ob, pf*	Int
Lalliet, T.	Terzetto. *ob, bsn, pf*	Ham
Langley, J.	Invocation and Dance. *fl, ob, pf*	HE
Lavallée, C.-Bourdon	The Butterfly. *fl, cl, pf*	CF
Leeuw, T. de	Trio (1952). *fl, cl, pf*	SD
Leigh, W.	Trio. *fl, ob, pf*	OxU

79

Two Woodwinds, Keyboard

Lemare, E.-Trinkaus	Andantino. *2ww, pf*	CF
Levitin, H.	Concerto. *cl, bsn, pf*	MR
Lilien, I.	Music for the smiling tomorrow (1955). *fl, ob, pf*	SD
Locatelli, P.	Aria. *fl, cl, pf*	EdM
Loeillet, J.B.	Courante. *fl, cl, pf*	EdM
Loeillet, J.B.	Sonata, c. *fl, ob, pf*	E-V
Loeillet, J.B.	Sonata, c. *fl, ob, pf*	Int
Loeillet, J.B.	Sonata, d. *fl, ob, pf*	E-V
Loeillet, J.B.	Sonata, d. *fl, ob, pf*	Int
Loeillet, J.B.-Bergmann	Trio Sonata, F, op. 1/1. *fl, ob, pf*	S&C
Loeillet, J.U.-Ruf	Triosonate, op. 2/2, F. *fl, ob, bc*	B&N
Loeillet, J.-Ermeler/Kluge	Triosonate, F, op. 2/2. *fl, ob(fl), bc*	Hei
Loeillet, J.B.-Ruf	Triosonate, op. 2/4, d. *fl, ob, bc*	B&N
Loeillet, J.B.-Ruf	Triosonate, op. 2/6, c. *fl, ob, bc*	B&N
London, E.	Trio. *fl, cl, pf*	MJQ
Lovreglio, D.-Bellison	Duo Concertante. *fl, cl, pf*	Ric
Lucas, L.	Aubade. *bsn, hn, pf*	Che
Maganini, Q.	The Boa Constrictor and the Bobolink. *fl, bsn, pf*	CF
Maganini, Q.	Concert Album. *fl, cl, pf*	EdM
Maganini, Q.	Moonlight on the Painted Desert. *fl, cl, pf*	EdM
Maganini, Q.	Paris Soir. *fl, cl, pf*	EdM
Marsal, E.-Laube	Nanine. *fl, cl, pf*	CF
Martelli, H.	Concerto. *cl, bsn, pf*	HMo
Martin, D.	5 Sketches (1961). *ob, bsn, pf*	Can
Martini, J.	Plaisir d'Amour. *fl, ob, pf*	EdM
Martini, J.	Plaisir d'Amour. *fl, cl, pf*	EdM
Massenet, J.-Trinkaus	Elegy. *2ww, pf*	CF
Massenet, J.	Under the Linden Trees. *fl, cl, pf*	EdM
Massenet, J.	Under the Linden Trees. *fl, bsn, pf*	EdM
Massenet, J.-Leonard	Under the Lindens. *ob(cl), cl(asax, tsax, bsn), pf*	TP
Masséus, J.	Introductie en Allegro, op. 19 (1952). *ob, cl, pf*	SD
Mathé, O.	Die Saufersonne. *fl, bsn, accordeon*	EMo
Mathias, W.	Divertimento. *fl, ob, pf*	OxU
Matsudaira, Y.	Orbits 1, 2, 3 (1960). *fl, cl, pf*	ESZ
Mayer, W.	Celebration. *fl, cl, pf*	AMC
McBride, R.	Hot-Shot Divertimento. *ob, cl, pf*	CoF
McCaughey, W.	Enchanted Isle. *fl, cl, pf*	CF
McKay	Instrumental Duo Suite. *2ww, pf*	Wes
Mendelssohn, F.	Concertpiece No. 1, f, op. 113. *cl, bsn, pf*	Int
Mendelssohn, F.	Concertpiece No. 2, d, op. 114. *cl, bsn, pf*	Int
Mendelssohn, F.-van der Veken	Ich wollt' meine Lieb' ergösse sich. *2 wind instr, pf*	T-M
Mendelssohn, F.-Trinkaus	Nocturno. *2ww, pf*	CF

Two Woodwinds, Keyboard

Mendelssohn-Trinkaus	On Wings of Song. *2ww, pf*	CF
Mendelssohn, F.	Spring Song. *fl, cl, pf*	CF
Mersson, B.	Kleine Suite, op. 10. *fl, ob, pf*	HG
Merten	Duo Valse. *fl, cl, pf*	EdM
Mestres-Quadreny, J.	Invencions Movlis I (1960). *fl, cl, pf*	See
Meyerbeer, G.-Trinkaus	Coronation March (The Prophet). *2ww, pf*	CF
Milne, J.	Scherzetto. *ob(cl), bsn, pf*	Che
Moore, T.	Poem. *fl, sax, pf*	AMC
Morawetz, O.	Trio (1960). *fl, ob, hpcd(pf)*	Can
Moszowski, M.	Serenade, op. 15/1. *fl, cl, pf*	CF
Mozart, W.-Collins	A Spring Rondo (K. 320). *fl, ob, pf*	Bos
Mozart, W.-Rothwell	Divertimento (K.V. 240 & K.V. 252). *ob(cl, fl), bsn, pf*	Che
Mozart, W.-Schwedler	Phantasie f. eine Orgelwalze. *fl, ob(fl), pf*	WZ
Mozalt, W.	Rondo (Serenade, B♭). *fl, cl, bsn ad lib, pf*	OxU
Mozart, W.-Naumann	2 Divertimenti, E♭, K. 252, B♭, K. 240. *ob, bsn, pf*	BrH
Musgrave, T.	Trio. *fl, ob, pf*	Che
Myers, T.	Introduction and Allegro. *fl, cl, pf*	CoA
Nancarrow, C.	Sarabande & Scherzo. *ob, bsn, pf*	AMC
Nardini, P.	Shepherd's Pipes. *fl, ob, pf*	EdM
Nardini, P.	Shepherd's Pipes. *fl, cl, pf*	EdM
Otten, L.	Musette et Pastourelle (1955). *fl, ob, pf*	SD
Paderewski, I.-Trinkaus	Minuet. *fl, bsn, pf*	CF
Paderewski, I.-Trinkaus	Minuet a l'Antique. *2ww, pf*	CF
Paque, J.	Duo de la Norma, No. 1. *cl, bsn, pf*	ScF
Paulson, G.	Divertimento, op. 113 (1961). *ob, ehn, pf*	STI
Pelemans, W.	Sonate I. *fl, ob, pf*	Mau
Pelemans, W.	Sonate II. *fl, ob, pf*	Mau
Pentland, B.	Canzona (1961). *fl, ob, hpcd*	Can
Pepusch, J.	Trio Sonata, g. *fl, ob, bc*	Pet
Pergolesi, G.	Sicilian Air. *fl, cl, pf*	EdM
Pfister, H.	Mobili a tre. *fl, cl, pf*	Pet
Pinos, A.	Karrikaturen. *fl, bcl(bsn), pf*	ES
Pisk, P.	Suite, op. 85. *ob, cl, pf*	CoF
Pitfield, T.	Trio. *fl, ob, pf*	Gal
Pitfield, T.	Trio. *ob, bsn, pf*	Gal
Pitfield, T.	Variegations. *fl, ob, pf*	Cha
Porret, J.	Kleber. *cl, asax, pf*	MM
Porret, J.	Lavoisier. *cl, asax, pf*	MM
Porret, J.	Marivaux. *cl, tsax, pf*	MM
Porret, J.	Nelson. *cl, tsax, pf*	MM
Poulenc, F.	Trio. *ob, bsn, pf*	Che
Prévost, A.	Triptyque (1962). *fl, ob, pf*	Can
Quantz, J.-Bergmann	Trio Sonata, C. *fl, ob, bc*	SS
Quantz, J.-Blumenthal	Trio-Sonate, c. *fl, ob(fl), pf*	WZ

Two Woodwinds, Keyboard

Quantz, J.-Ruf	Trio Sonata, D. *fl, ob, bc*	Ric
Quantz, J.-Ruf	Triosonate, G. *fl, ob d'amore, bc*	Hei
Quensel, A.	Entr'acte, op. 12. *fl, cl, pf*	CF
Rachmaninoff, S.	Polka Italienne. *fl, cl, pf*	EdM
Rachmaninoff, S.	Vocalise. *fl, cl, pf*	EdM
Rachmaninoff, S.	Vocalise. *fl, bsn, pf*	EdM
Rameau, J.	Rigodon de Dardanus	EdM
Raphling, S.	Square Dance. *fl, cl, pf*	EdM
Ravel, M.	Pavane pour une Infante Defunte. *fl, cl, pf*	EdM
Rawsthorne, A.	Sonatina. *fl, ob, pf*	OxU
Rebikov, V.	A Little Girl Rocking Her Doll. *fl, cl, pf*	EdM
Regteren Altena, L. van	Divertimento. *fl, ob, pf*	SD
Richter, F.	Triosonata, G. *fl, ob, bc*	MR
Robbins, G.	Bagatelle. *fl, ob, pf*	E-V
Robbins, G.	Pastorale. *fl, ob, pf*	E-V
Roetscher, K.	"Risser"-Trio, op. 29. *cl, bsn, pf*	B&B
Rosseau, N.	Rapsodie, op. 81 (1958). *fl, bsn, pf*	CBD
Rovics, H.	Cybernetic Study No. 2. *cl, bsn, pf*	See
Rudzinski, W.	Canzonetta (1940). *fl, ob, pf*	AP
Ruyneman, D.	Amaterasu (1953). *fl, ob, hpcd*	SD
Saint-Saens, C.-Brooke	Serenade. *fl, cl, pf*	CF
Saint-Saens, C.	Tarentelle, op. 6. *fl, cl, pf*	Dur
Saint-Saens, C.	Tarantella, op. 6. *fl, cl, pf*	Int
Saint-Saens, C.-Trinkaus	The Swan. *2ww, pf*	CF
Salieri, A.	Danse (Tarare). *fl, ob, pf*	EdM
Salieri, A.-Wojciechowski	Konzert, C Major. *fl, ob, pf*	Pet
Sambin, V.	Duo de la Somnambule. *ob, cl, pf*	EdS
Sandré, G.	Sous la feuillée. *fl, cl, pf*	E&C
Schafer, R.	Divisions for Baroque Trio (1963). *fl, ob, hpcd*	Can
Schlemm, G.	Burleske. *E♭ cl, bsn, pf*	PG
Schmitt, F.	Sonatine en Trio, op. 85. *fl, cl, pf*	Dur
Schollum, R.	Trio, op. 45. *fl, bsn, pf*	LDo
Schollum, R.	Trio, op. 71. *ob, cl, pf*	LDo
Schouwman, H.	Trio, op. 36 (1944). *cl, bsn, pf*	SD
Schumann, R.-Parrott	Etude. *ob(fl), cl, pf*	Cha
Schuyt, N.	Sonata a tre (1954). *ob, bsn, pf*	SD
Schwartz, E.	Trio. *fl, cl, pf*	BM
Sgrizzi, L.	Elegia e scherzo. *fl, bsn, pf*	EdB
Shostakovitch, D.-Atoumyan	4 Waltzes. *fl, cl, pf*	MR
Sibelius, J.-Trinkaus	Valse Triste (Kuolema). *2ww, pf*	CF
Slechta, T.	Father of Waters. *fl, cl, pf*	CF
Sontag, H.	An Evening Serenade. *fl, asax(tsax), pf*	CF
Sontag, H.	An Evening Serenade. *fl, cl, pf*	CF
Spencer, J.	Silvatones. *cl, sax, pf*	CF
Spencer, J.	Silvatones. *fl, asax, pf*	CF
Spencer, J.	Silvatones. *fl, cl, pf*	CF
Stamitz	Andantino. *fl, cl, pf*	EdM
Stamitz, K.-Wojciechowski	Double Concerto, B♭. *cl, bsn, pf*	HSM

82

Two Woodwinds, Keyboard

Stanley, J.-Finch	Trio Movement. *fl, ob, pf*	S&C
Steiner, G.	Suite. *fl, cl, pf*	See
Still, W.	Miniatures based on American	OxU
Folk Songs. *fl, ob, pf*		
Stoker, R.	4 Miniatires. *fl, cl, pf*	Cha
Strauss, J.-Bettoney	Tales from the Vienna Woods,	CF
	op. 325. *fl, cl, pf*	
Strauss, R.	Duet Concertino. *cl, bsn, pf*	B&H
Strauss, R.	Zueignung. *fl, bsn, pf*	EdM
Strauss, R.	Zueignung. *fl, cl, pf*	EdM
Stravinsky, I.	Berceuse. *fl, cl, pf*	EdM
Stravinsky, I.	Dance of the Ballerina	EdM
	(Petrouchka). *fl, cl, pf*	EdM
Stravinsky, I.	Dance of the Princesses. *fl, cl, pf*	EdM
Stravinsky, I.	Pastorale. *fl, cl, pf*	EdM
Stringfield, L.	Morning. *fl, cl, pf*	EdM
Stringfield, L.	To a Star. *fl, cl, pf*	EdM
Stuhec, I.	Sonata à tre. *cl, bsn, pf*	EdD
Sydeman, W.	Trio (1968). *bcl, bsn, pf*	See
Tchaikovsky,P.-Trinkaus	Chant sans paroles. *2ww, pf*	CF
Tchaikovsky, P.	Suite (Album for Children).	EdM
	fl, cl, pf	
Tcherepnin, I.	Cadenzas in Transition. *fl, cl, pf*	B&H
Telemann, G.	Concerto, G. *fl, ob d'amore, pf*	Pet
Telemann, G.	Concerto No. 2. *fl, ob, pf*	GaM
Telemann, G.	Sonata, a. *fl, ob, pf, vc ad lib*	Int
Telemann, G.	Sonata, c. *fl, ob, pf, vc ad lib*	Int
Telemann, G.-Ruf	Sonate, d. *fl, ob, bc*	B&N
Telemann, G.-Hinnenthal	Trio, e. *fl, ob, bc*	B&N
Telemann, G.-Scheurich/Braun	Trio Sonata, a. *fl, hpcd, bc*	HSM
Telemann, G.-Ruf	Trio-Sonate, A (Essercizii Musici).	SS
	fl, hpcd obl, bc	
Telemann, G.-Woehl	Trio Sonata, c (Essercizii Musici).	Pet
	fl, ob, pf, bsn ad lib	
Telemann, G.-Toettscher/Scholz	Trio Sonata, E♭. *ob, hpcd, bc*	HSM
Telemann, G.-Ruf	Trio Sonata, F. *ob, bsn(vc), bc*	SS
Telemann, G.-Seiffert	Trio (Tafelmusik II, No. 4).	BrH
	fl, ob, bc	
Templeton, A.	Trio, d. *fl, ob, pf*	Sha
Tenaglia	Aria Antica. *fl, cl, pf*	EdM
Thilman, J.	4 Gespräche. *fl, bcl, pf*	Pet
Thome, F.	Simple Aveu. *fl, cl, pf*	CF
Titl, A.	Serenade. *cl, sax, pf*	CF
Titl, A.	Serenade. *fl, cl(ob), pf*	CF
Titl/Buchtel	Serenade. *fl, cl, pf*	NK
Toll, R.	Pals. *fl, asax, pf*	CF
Trinkaus, G.	Lament. *fl, bsn, pf*	CF
Trinkaus, G.	Lament. *2ww, pf*	CF
Verhaar, A.	Trio, op. 18 (1940). *fl, ob, pf*	SD
Villa-Lobos, H.	Fantaisie Concertante. *cl, bsn, pf*	EME
Vivaldi, A.	Concerto, g, P. 402. *fl(cl), ob, bc*	JB
Vivaldi, A.	Giga. *fl, cl, pf*	EdM

Two Woodwinds, Keyboard

Vivaldi, A.	Giga. *fl, ob, pf*	EdM
Vivaldi, A.-Schroeder	Sonata a due, a. *fl, bsn, bc*	Hei
Vivaldi, A.	Trio, a. *fl, bsn, bc*	MR
Von Kreisler, A.	Trio Sonata. *fl, ob(fl), pf*	SM
Wagner, R.-Trinkaus	Song to the Evening Star	CF
	(Tannhauser). *2ww, pf*	CF
Wagner, R.-Trinkaus	Walther's Prize Song	CF
	(Meistersinger). *2ww, pf*	
Wallace, W.-Gruenwald	Cavatina (Maritana). *fl, cl, pf*	CF
Weckerlin, J.	Pastorale. *fl, ob, pf*	Heu
Weisgarber, E.	Sonatine. *fl, cl, pf*	Cor
Wernick, R.	Quadrignomes. *fl(vn), bsn(vc), pf*	B-M
Williams, D.	Suite. *ob, cl, pf*	Roc
Wuensch, G.	Trio, op. 1. *cl, bsn, pf*	Can
Zachow, F.-Seiffert	Kammertrio, F. *fl(ob), bsn, bc*	Kis
Zagwijn, H.	Pastorale (1937). *fl, ob, pf*	SD
Zagwijn, H.	Pastorale e Scherzo (1951).	SD
	fl, ob, hpcd	
Zagwijn, H.	Sonata (1950). *fl, cl, hpcd*	SD
Zagwijn, H.	Trio (1952). *ob, cl, pf*	SD
Zilcher, H.	3 Stücke. *fl, pf, accordeon*	Hoh

TWO WOODWINDS, KEYBOARD - COLLECTIONS

	Collection. *2 ob, pf*	MR
	Comrades' Repertory	CF
	Intermediate Pieces. *2 fl, pa*	Ash
	Easy to Play Pieces. *2 fl, pf*	Ash
	Easy to Play Pieces. *2 cl, pf*	Ash
	Easy to Play Pieces. *2 asax, pf*	Ash
	Intermediate Pieces. *2 cl, pf*	Ash
	Intermediate Pieces. *2 asax, pf*	Ash
	Masters of the Baroque.	
	2 fl, pf, vc ad lib	Pet
	Niedersächsisch Dorftänze.	
	2 ob (2 cl), bc	MV
Dearnley, C. (arr)	More Easy Pieces.	
	2 fl (ob, cl, basn), pf	Che
Ostrander, A.	Duet Album. *fl, cl, pf*	EdM
Ostrander, A.	Duet Album. *fl, bsn, pf*	EdM
Ostrander, A.	Duet Album. *2 cl, pf*	EdM
Trinkaus, G. (arr)	World's Best Known Pieces,	
	2 ww, pf	CF

WOODWIND, BRASS

Amram, D.	Trio. *bsn, tsax, hn*	Pet
Böck, I. & A.-Janetsky	10 Pieces. *bsn, 2hn*	FrH
Bottje, W.	Trio Sonate. *fl, hn, bsn*	CoF
Brings, A.	Burlette. *fl, cl, trb*	AMC
Chailley, J.	Suite du XV siècle. *ob(ehn), hn, bsn(va), tabor ad lib*	ALe
Childs, B.	3 Players I. *cl, bsn, hn*	CoF
Cowell, J.	Trio. *cl, bsn, hn*	Cor
Delmotte, C.	Trio. *ob, cl, hn*	Mau
Devienne, F.	3 Trios. *cl, hn, bsn*	Int
Devienne, F.-Leloir	Trio No. 1, C. *cl, bsn, hn*	Kaw
Devienne, F.-Leloir	Trio No. 3, d. *cl, bsn, hn*	Kaw
Devienne, F.-Leloir	Trio No. 2, F. *cl, bsn, hn*	Kaw
Dressel, E.	Trio miniature. *cl, bsn, hn*	R&E
Duvernoy, F.-Leloir	Trio No. 1, F. *cl, bsn, hn*	Kaw
Duvernoy, F.-Leloir	Trio No. 3, F. *cl, bsn, hn*	Kaw
Duvernoy, F.-Leloir	Trio No. 2, E♭. *cl, bsn, hn*	Kaw
Emmert, A.-Höckner	Trio, E. *bsn, 2hn*	Sim
Ferritto, J.	4 Madrigali. *fl, cl, bar*	ACA
Fuchs, G.	Trio. *2cl, hn*	MR
Glass, P.	Diversions (1960). *2fl, trb*	Can
Graun, K.	Trio No. 1, D. *ob, bsn, hn*	M&M
Graun, K.	Trio No. 1, G. *cl, bsn, hn*	M&M
Graun, K.	Trio No. 2, e. *ob, bsn, hn*	M&M
Graun, K.	Trio No. 2, e. *cl, bsn, hn*	M&M
Grossi, P.	Composition No. 3 (1958). *cl, bsn, hn*	AMP
Handel, G.-Haas	Ouverture (Suite). *2cl, hn*	SS
Handel, G.-Coopersmith/LaRue	Sonata, D. *2cl, hn(cl)*	TP
Haubiel, C.	Atheneum Suite. *cl, bsn, hn*	See
Haydn, F.-Werner	Divertimento Trio. *cl, hn, bsn(vc)*	Cha
Helmschrott, R.	Invention (1967). *cl, bsn, trb*	B&N
Horrod, N.	Trio. *hn, trb, bsn*	Kaw
Jacobsohn, G.	Adagio and Allegro. *ob, cl, hn*	Isr
Klein, R.	3 Chorales for Advent, Christmas and New Years. *2fl(2ob), bsn*	Hei
Klein, R.	3 Chorales for Passion, Ostern and Pfingsten. *2fl(2ob), bsn*	Hei
Levy, F.	Trio. *cl, bsn, hn*	Cor
Lickl, J.	3 Trios. *cl, bsn, hn*	Pet
Lickl, J.	Trio, E♭. *cl, hn, bsn*	B&V
Lickl, J.-Steinbeck	Trio, E♭. *cl, hn, bsn*	Eul
Lybbert, D.	Trio for Winds. *cl, hn, bsn*	Pet
Maxwell, C.	Trio. *fl, bsn, hn*	See
Michalsky, D.	Trio Concertino. *fl, ob, hn*	Wes
Mozart, W.	Adagio, K. 580a. *ehn, 2hn(2cl)*	EK
Mozart, W.	Trio. *2cl, hn*	PWM
Otten, L.	Divertimento No. 2 (1963). *fl, bsn, hn*	SD
Parris, R.	4 Pieces. *cl, bsn, hn*	CoF
Platti, G.	Sonata. *cl, bsn, hn*	Cor
Prunty, W.	Trio Allegria. *cl, tpt, trb*	Acc

Woodwind, Brass

Reicha, A.-Leloir	Trios, op. 92, 2 vols. *2hn, bsn*	Kaw
Roberts, W.	A Walk in the Country.	Cor
	cl, bsn, hn(cl)	
Sabatini, G.	Puppet Waltz. *cl(ob), bsn, hn*	Cor
Schumann, G.	Miniatur-Trio. *ob, hn, bsn*	S-V
Thurner, E.	Trio, op. 56. *cl, bsn, hn*	PG
Verrall, J.	Divertissement. *cl, bsn, hn*	CoF
Viecenz, H.	Terzett. *2ob, hn*	FrH
Weber, C.M. von	Der Freischutz. *cl, bsn, hn*	SM

WOODWIND, STRINGS

Aeschbacher, W.	Trio, op. 72. *fl, va, db (vc)*	Hei
Agersnap, H.	Interludium (1936). *fl, vn, vc*	SPD
Ahlgrimm, H.	Divertimento. *fl, vn, va*	MRL
Ahnell, E.	5 Sketches. *fl, vn, vc*	CoA
Ambrosius, H.	3 Preludes and Fugues. *fl, 2 vn*	Pet
Ames, W.	Trio. *ob, vn, vc*	CoF
Andersen, K.	Trio, op. 5. *fl, cl, vc*	Nor
Andriessen, H.	Serenade. *fl, vn (ob), vc (bsn)*	HU
Antoniou, T.	Trio, op. 14. *fl, va, vc*	EMo
Archer, V.	Divertimento No. 2 (1957).	
	ob, vn, vc	Can
Ardevol, J.	2 Sonatas. No. 1 - *ob, cl, vc;*	
	No. 2 - *2 fl, va*	SMP
Arnold, M.	Trio. *fl, bsn, va*	CF
Ascough, R.	Trio. *fl, cl, vn*	ExM
Bach, J.C.-Marguerre	Sonata, F. *fl, vn, vc*	HMo
Bach, J.S.-Cochrane	15 Three-Part Inventions. *2 cl, vc*	CF
Bach, J.S.	21 Selected Pieces.	
	2 fl (2 ob), vc (bsn)	SS
Bach, W.F.-Ermeler	Trio, G. *2 fl, va*	B&N
Badings, H.	Trio No. 5 (1947).	
	fl, vn, va	SD
Ballif, C.	Trio, op. 35/2. *fl, ob, vc*	B&B
Balorre, C.	Trio. *ob, va, vc*	Ham
Bartsch, C.	Suite en trio. *fl, va, db*	Mau
Beale, J.	3 Miniatures, op. 3. *ob, cl, vc*	CoF
Beethoven, L. van	Fugue. *fl, vn, vc*	EdM
Beethoven, L. van	Serenade, D, op. 25. *fl, vn, va*	BrH
Beethoven, L. van	Serenade, op. 25. *fl, vn, va*	EdK
Beethoven, L. van	Serenade, op. 25. *fl, vn, va*	Int
Beethoven, L. van	Serenade, op. 25. *fl, vn, va*	Pet
Beethoven, L. van	Trio, C, op. 87. *2 ob, va*	BrH
Benker, H.	Serenade. *fl, vn, va*	MV
Beyer, J.-Höckner	Partita No. 1. *fl, vn, vc*	ABe
Beyer, J.-Höckner	Partita No. 2. *fl, vn, vc*	ABe
Bialas, G.	Trio (1946). *fl, va, vc*	B&N
Binkerd, G.	Trio. *cl, va, vc*	B&H

Woodwind, Strings

Bjerre, J.	Mosaique musicale (1936). *fl, vn, vc*	SPD
Bjerre, J.	Serenade. *fl, ob, va*	SPD
Bois, R. du	2 Pieces. *fl, ob, vc*	SD
Borris, S.	Villanellen, op. 97. *fl, vn, vc*	S-V
Breuer, P.	Serenade. *2 fl, db*	Ger
Brown, R.	Trio. *fl, cl, va*	Wes
Buczynski, W.	Trio/67. *cl, db, mandolin*	Can
Busch, A.	Hausmusik, op. 26/3. *cl, vn, vc*	BrH
Cambini, G.-Schultz-Hauser	Trio No. 5, F; Trio No. 6, G. *2 fl, va*	SS
Chambers, S.	Abstractions for Three. *fl, ob, vc*	AMC
Chevreuille, R.	Trio, op. 90 (1968). *fl, va, vc*	CBD
Childs, B.	Interbalances. I. *ob/ehn, bcl/a sax, db*	CoF
Cope, D.	5 Pieces. *fl, bsn, vn*	CoA
Custer, A.	Permutations. *cl, vn, vc*	Gen
Danzi, F.-Sonntag	Trio, D, op. 71/3. *fl, vn, vc*	B&N
Danzi, F.-Sonntag	Trio, e, op. 71/2. *fl, vn, vc*	B&N
Danzi, F.-Wojciechowski	Trio, F, op. 24. *vn, hn, bsn*	Sim
Danzi, F.-Rampal	Trio No. 1, op. 71. *fl, vn, vc*	Int
Danzi, F.-Rampal	Trio No. 2, op. 71. *fl, vn, vc*	Int
Danzi, F.-Peters	Trio, op. 71/1. *fl, vn, vc*	Hei
Danzi, F.	Trio, op. 71/2, e. *fl, vn, vc*	Pet
Danzi, F.	Trio, op. 71/3, D. *fl, vn, vc*	Pet
Danzi, F.-Janetzky	2 Trios, op. 71. *fl, vn, vc*	FrH
David, T.	Trio, op. 8. *fl, vn, va*	BrH
David, T.	Trio, op. 1/1. *fl, vn, va*	BrH
David, J.	Trio, op. 30. *fl, vn, va*	BrH
Davidovsky, M.	Junctures. *fl, cl, vn*	EBM
Dijk, J. van	Divertimento (1941). *cl, va, vc*	SD
Doppelbauer, J.	Trio. *ob, va, vc*	LDo
Dure, R.	Trio. *fl, cl, vc*	AMC
Eklund, H.	Small Serenade. *cl, vn, db*	Che
Etler, A.	Sonata. *ob, cl, va*	NVM
Farkas, F.	Serenade (1965). *fl, 2 vn*	EMB
Feld, J.	Trio. *fl, vn, vc*	Art
Fiorillo, F.	Op. 29/1. *fl, vn, va*	ABe
Gal, H.	Huyton-Suite, op. 92. *fl, 2 vn*	B&N
Gal, H.	Serenade, op. 93. *cl, vn, vc*	RS
Gal, H.	Trio, op. 94. *ob, vn, va*	B&N
Gal, H.	Trio, op. 94. *ob, vn, vc*	RS
Gal, H.	Trio Serenade, op. 88. *fl, vn, vc*	Sim
Gassmann, F.-Albrecht	Trio Sonata, A. *fl, vn, va*	Kis
Gassmann, F.-Albrecht	Trio Sonata, B♭. *fl, vn, va*	Kis
Gassmann, F.-Albreoht	Trio Sonata, C. *fl, vn, va*	Kis
Gassmann, F.-Albrecht	Trio Sonata, D. *fl, vn, va*	Kis
Gassmann, F.-Albrecht	Trio Sonata, E♭, *fl, vn va*	Kis
Gassmann, F.-Albrecht	Trio Sonata, G. *fl, vn, va*	Kis
Gebauer, F.	Trio, op. 33/3. *bsn, vn, vc*	MR
Gentilucci, A.	Epitaffio per Cesare Pavese.	

Woodwind, Strings

	cl, vn, vc	FrC
Gilse, J. van	Trio. fl, vn, va	Als
Giordani, T.-Schultz-Hauser	6 Trios, op. 12, 2 vols.	
	fl, va, vc	SS
Giordani, T.-Janetzky	Trio, G. fl, va, vc	PrM
Graf, F.-Ermeler	Trio, D. fl, vn, vc	Hei
Grofe, F.	Table d'Hote. fl, vn, va	NK
Haydn, F.-Janetzky	Divertimento, D. fl, va, vc	PrM
Haydn, F.	4 London Trios. 2 fl, vc	EdK
Haydn, F.	4 London Trios. 2 fl, vc	Int
Haydn, F.	4 London Trios. 2 fl, vc	SM
Haydn, F.	4 London Trios. fl, cl, vc (va, bsn)	SM
Haydn, F.-Balet	4 London Trios, Hob. IV, 1-4.	
	2 fl, vc	B&N
Haydn, F.	London Trio. 2 fl, vc	HU
Haydn, F.	Trios, op. 11/4-6. fl, vn, vc	B&V
Haydn, F.	6 Trios, op. 100, 2 vols.	
	fl, vn, vc	WZ
Haydn, F.	3 Trios. fl, vn, vc	Sch
Haydn, F.	3 Trios, op. 11/4,5,6. fl, vn, vc	MR
Haydn, F.	3 Trios, op. 11/4-6. fl, vn, vc	Pet
Haydn, F.	Trio, D. fl, vn, vc	Pet
Haydn, F.-Kölbel	Trio, D. fl, vn, vc	Hei
Haydn, M.-Rainer	Divertimento, C. ob, va, vn	LDo
Hedwall, L.	Trio (1945). fl, va, vc	EMF
Heussenstamm, G.	Trio, op. 26. cl, vn, vc	See
Holst, G.	Terzetto. fl, ob, va	Che
Homs, J.	Trio (1953). fl, bcl, vn	See
Honegger, A.	Choral à 3 Voix (Trois Contre-	
	points No. 2). ehn, vn, vc	Che
Horst, A. van der	Theme, Variations et Fugue,	
	op. 76 (1957). fl, vn, va	SD
Huber, K.	6 Miniaturen. cl, vn, vc	Hei
Huggler, J.	Trio, op. 40. cl, vn, vc	CoF
Humel, G.	Trio (1964). fl, va, vc	B&B
Husa, K.	Evocations de Slovaquie.	
	cl, va, vc	SS
Jemnitz, A.	Trio, op. 19. fl, vn, va	WZ
Jettl, R.	Trio, c. cl, vn, va	LDo
Josephs, W.	Trio, op. 50. fl, vn, vc	Cha
Juon, P.	Divertimento, op. 34. cl, 2 va	MRL
Kallstenius, E.	Trio divertente, op. 38. fl, vn, va	EMF
Kallstenius, E.	Lyrisk svit, op. 55.	
	fl, sax (cl), vc	EMF
Kallstenius, E.	Piccolo trio seriale, op. 47.	
	cl, vn, va	EMF
Kanitz, E.	Notturno. fl, vn, va	NVM
Karkoff, M.	Miniatyrsvit No. 1, op. 34A.	
	fl, cl, va	EMF
Karkoff, M.	Miniatyrsvit No. 2, op. 34B.	
	ob, bsn, vn	EMF
Karkoff, M.	Serenata, op. 61a. fl, vn, va	EMF

Woodwind, Strings

Karlins, M.	Birthday Music (1962).	
	fl, cl/bcl, db	CoF
Karlins, M.	Trio (1960). *fl, vn, vc*	CoF
Katz, E.	Trio. *2 fl, va (vn)*	SF
Kechley, D.	Trio. *cl/bcl, va, vc*	CoA
Kelterborn, R.	Lyrische Kammermusik (1959).	
	cl, vn, va	B&N
Kempe, H.	Trio senza pretese. *cl, va, vc*	EMF
Kerkhof, F.	Trio. *fl, vn, va*	B&V
Kont, P.	Serenata a tre, op. 61/1.	
	fl, vn, va	LDo
Koppel, H.	Divertimento pastorale, op. 61	
	(1955). *ob, va, vc*	SPD
Korn, P.	Aloysia Serenade, Op. 19.	
	fl, va, vc	ABe
Koutzen, B.	Music. *asax, bsn, vc*	AMP
Kreutzer, C.	Trio. *2 cl, va*	Pet
Krommer, F.	13 Pieces, op. 47. *2 cl, va*	Pet
Kunert, K.	Trio, op. 5. *fl, vn, vc*	PG
Legley, V.	Sérénade, op. 44/3 (1957).	
	fl, vn, vc	CBD
Lerich, R.	Trio, C. *fl, 2 vn*	MRL
Linde, B.	Vinjettsvit (1959). *ob, va, vc*	EMF
Luening, O.	Trio. *ob, bsn, vc*	CoF
Mann, L.	Trio, op. 6 (1952). *fl, cl, vc*	Can
Mann, L.	Taccata alla Barocco, op. 15	
	(1956). *fl, cl, vc*	Can
Mannino, F.	A Little Music For Three Friends.	
	fl, vn, va	Edi
Markevitch, I.	Serenade. *cl, vn, bsn*	SS
Marteau, J.	Terzetto, op. 32. *fl, vn, va*	Sim
McCabe, J.	Movements, op. 29. *cl, vn, vc*	Nov
Mellnäs, A.	Sonata a tre. *fl, vn, va*	EMF
Mestres-Quadreny, J.	Divertimento "La Ricarda"	
	(1962). *fl, cl, db*	See
Miller, E.	Trio. *fl, cl, db*	ACA
Moss, L.	Windows. *fl, cl, db*	See
Moyse, L.	Suite, C. *2 fl, va*	SM
Mozart, W.	Adagio (K. 356). *fl, ob, va*	Pet
Mozart, W.	Adagio for Glasharmonika.	
	fl, ob (fl), va	WZ
Mozart, W.-Schwedler	Andante f. eine Walze einer	
	kleinen Orgel. *fl, ob (fl), va*	WZ
Myers, R.	Trio. *asax, bsn, vc*	ArM
Myslivecek, J.-Riemann	Trio, op. 1/4. *fl, vn,*	
	vc, pf ad lib	Int
Nedbal, M.	Kleines Trio. *cl, bsn, vc*	LDo
Nemiroff, I.	Variations to a Theme.	
	fl, ob, vc	M&M
Neubauer, F.-Bormann	Trio, C, op. 3/3.	
	fl, vn, va	HSM
Nowak, L.	Trio. *cl, vn, vc*	CoF

Woodwind, Strings

Peterson, W.	Phantasmagoria. *fl, cl, db*	See
Philipp, F.	Serenade, op. 23. *fl, vn, va*	ABS
Pichl, V.-Klement	2 Divertimenti. *fl, vn, vc*	ES
Poot, M.	Concertino (1963). *fl, vn, vc*	CBD
Porter, Q.	Little Trio. *fl, vn, va*	NVM
Racek, F.	Eine kleine Hausmusik.	
	fl (ob), vn, va	LDo
Raphael, G.	Trio (1940), B, op. 48.	
	fl, vn, va	B&N
Reger, M.-Schnirlin	Serenade No. 1, op. 77a.	
	fl, vn, va	B&B
Reger, M.	Serenade No. 2, op. 141a.	
	fl, vn, va	Pet
Reger, M.	Serenade, op. 77a. *fl, vn, va*	Int
Reimann, A.	Canzoni e Ricercari. *fl, va, vc*	SS
Richter, N.	Serenade (1945). *fl, vn, va*	SD
Rigel, A.-Koch	Trio No. 4, F. *fl, vn, vc*	Hug
Riisager, K.	Serenade. *fl, vn, vc*	Che
Rohwer, J.	Trio. *ob, vn, va*	MV
Rosenberg, H.	Serenad, op. 82. *fl, vn, va*	EMF
Rosenberg, H.	Trio. *fl, vn, va*	Che
Roussel, A.	Trio, op. 40. *fl, va, vc*	Dur
Salomon, K.	Elegie und Tanz. *ob, 2 vn*	Hei
Saunders, M.	Trio. *fl, bsn, va*	FrC
Schadewitz, C.	Serenade, op. 49. *fl, vn, vc*	PG
Schmidt, W.	Sonata Breve. *fl, cl, va*	Wes
Schmitt, J.	Trio, G. *fl, vn, vc*	Che
Schulhoff, E.	Concertino. *fl, va, db*	UE
Schwantner, J.	Entropy. *sop sax, bcl, vc*	ACA
Schwartz, E.	Trio. *fl, cl, vc*	Gen
Schweizer, K.	2 Sätze über bewegliche	
	Zeitmasse. *fl, vn, va*	EMo
Senstius, K.	Serenade, op. 36 (1952).	
	ob, va, bsn	SPD
Shostakovitch, D.	Preludes. *fl, vn, vc*	EdM
Siegl, O.	Trifolium, op. 145. *fl, ob, va*	FrH
Sigtenhorst Meyer, B. van	Trio, op. 49 (1952). *fl, vn, va*	Als
Simons, N.	Facets-2. *fl/pic, cl, db*	CoF
Sirulnikoff, J.	Trio (1959). *cl, vn, vc*	Can
Sköld, Y.	Serenad, op. 25. *fl, vn, va*	EMF
Somers, H.	Trio (1950). *fl, vn, vc*	Can
Sorenson, T.	Serenata per Tre (1966).	
	fl, va, vc	STI
Stamitz	Andantino. *fl, vn, vc*	EdM
Stamitz, C.-Upmeyer	Trio, op. 14/1. *fl, vn,*	
	vc, pf ad lib	B&N
Stamitz, C.-Schnapp	Trio, G. *2 fl, vc*	B&N
Stearns, P.	May 27th, 1956. *fl, cl, vc*	AMC
Stearns, P.	Summer Nocturne. *cl, vn, vc*	AMC
Stearns, P.	Trio. *fl, bcl, db*	CoF
Stewart, R.	Trio No. 4. *fl, vn, vc*	CoF
Stringfield, L.	Chipmunks. *fl, vn, vc*	EdM

Woodwind, Strings

Suck, C.-Rothwell	Trio. *ob, vn, vc*	Che
Sulyok, I.	Trio. *fl, vn, vc*	B&H
Sylyok, I.	Trio (1958). *fl, ob, vc*	EMB
Suter, R.	Inventions 1956. *fl, vn, vc*	Hei
Sydeman, W.	Trio. *fl, vn, db*	M&M
Sydeman, W.	Trio (1957). *cl, vn, db*	See
Sydeman, W.	2 Short Pieces & Finale. *cl, vn, db*	AMC
Szczeniowski, B.	Trio No. 2 (1960). *2 fl, vc*	Can
Szervánszky, E.	Trio (1951). *fl, vn, va*	EMB
Tanenbaum, E.	Trio. *fl, vc, db*	CoF
Tartini, G.	2 Trio Sonatas. *fl, vn, va*	EdM
Tartini, G.	2 Trio Sonatas. *fl, vn, vc*	EdM
Telemann, G.-Polnauer	6 Minuets (Sept Fois Sept et Un). *fl, vn (ob), cl (va)*	CF
Telemann, G.-Polnauer	6 Minuets (Sept Fois Sept et Un). *fl, va (cl), bsn (vc)*	CF
Telemann, G.-Polnauer	6 Minuets (Sept Fois Sept et Un). *ob, vn, vl (va)*	CF
Telemann, G.-Polnauer	6 Minuets (Sept Fois Sept et Un). *ob, cl, vc*	CF
Thiele, S.	Serenade. *fl, vn, vc*	Deu
Thilman, J.	Trio Piccolo, op. 90. *afl, bcl, va*	Pet
Tomasi, H.	Inca Pastoral. *fl, 2 vn*	ALe
Trinkaus, G.	16 Original and Transcribed Compositions. *fl (ob, vn), vn(cl), bsn(vc)*	CF
Turchi, G.	Trio (1945). *fl, cl, va*	ESZ
Vivaldi, A.	Concerto, D. *fl, vn, bsn*	M&M
Wagner, Joseph	Serenade. *ob (fl, cl), vn, vc*	SMP
Weber, B.	Concertino, op. 11b. *cl, vn, vc*	CoF
Weis, F.	Sonatina. *fl, vn, vc*	Pet
Weber E. von-Höckner	Trio. *ob, bsn, va*	ABe
Weisgarber, E.	Divertimento. *cl, vn, va*	Cor
Weiss, A.	Trio. *fl, va, vc*	AMC
Weiss, A.	Trio. *cl, va, vc*	CoF
Welander, S.	Sonatin i gammal stil. *cl, vn, vc*	EMF
Wiesner, H.	Sonata. *vn, va, bsn*	CoA
Wildgans, F.	Kleine Haus - und Spielmusik. *fl, vn, va*	LDo
Wuorinen, C.	Turetzky Pieces. *fl, cl, db*	CoF
Zechlin	Trio. *ob, va, vc*	Pet
Zender H.	Serenade (1956). *fl, vn, vc*	BrH
Zonn, P.	Periphrasis. *ob, cl, vc*	CoF

WOODWIND, BRASS, STRING

Adaskin, M.	Divertimento No. 3 (1965). *vn, hn, bsn*	Can
Ballif, C.	Trio, op. 35/3. *cl, hn, vn*	B&B
Bortolotti, M.	Studi (1960). *cl, va, hn*	ESZ

Woodwind, Brass, String

Danzi, F.	Trio, op. 24. *vn, hn, bsn*	ABe
Ghent, E.	Triality I and II. *vn, tpt, bsn*	OxU
Jez, J.	Nomos II. *cl, vc, trb*	EdD
Kallstenius, E.	Trio svagante, op. 51. *cl, hn, vc*	EMF
Pennisi, F.	Trio (1968). *fl, hn, db*	ESZ
Raphael, G.	Sonatine, op. 65/4. *vn, hn, bsn*	BrH
Rosenboom, D.	Trio. *cl, tpt, db*	CoA
Schiske, K.	Music, op. 27. *cl, tpt, va*	UE
Schwartz, E.	Music. *ob, tpt, vc*	Gen
Smith, L.	Suite for Trio. *cl, tpt, vn*	CoF
Stearns, P.	Trio Variations. *bcl, tpt, va*	CoF
Stewart, R.	Trio No. 5. *cl, trb, va*	CoF
Wolff, C.	Trio I. *fl, tpt, vc*	Pet

WOODWIND, BRASS, KEYBOARD

	My Song of Songs. *asax (tsax),*	
	tpt (trb), pf	CF
Barboteu, G.	Esquisse. *fl, hn, pf*	Ech
Beethoven, L. van-Trinkaus	Menuet. *cl, tpt, pf*	CF
Beethoven, L. van-Trinkaus	Menuet. *fl, trb (tpt), pf*	CF
Beethoven, L. van-Trinkaus	Menuet. *sax, tpt (trb), pf*	CF
Bellini, V.-Lewis	Hear Me Norma.	
	asax, tpt (trb), pf	CF
Bellini, V.-Lewis	Hear Me Norma.	
	cl (sax), tpt, pf	CF
Bezanson, P.	Trio. *cl, hn, pf*	CoF
Bizet, G.	Serenade Espagnole. *fl, tpt, pf*	EdM
Bohm, C.-Hamilton	Calm As the Night. *cl, hn, pf*	CF
Bohm, C.-Hamilton	Calm As the Night. *fl, hn, pf*	CF
Copland, A.	Quiet City (1940).	
	ob (ehn), tpt, pf	B&H
Cowell, J.	Trio. *cl, hn, pf*	Cor
DeVille, P.	The Swiss Boy. *cl (sax), tpt, pf*	CF
Dohl, F.	Toccata (1962-63). *fl, tpt, pf*	HG
Donizetti, G.-DeVille	Sextet (Lucia). *cl, tpt, pf*	CF
Doppler, F.-Hosmer	Souvenir du Rigi, Idylle, op. 34.	
	cl, tpt (hn), pf	CF
Doppler, F.-Hosmer	Souvenir du Rigi, Idylle, op. 34.	
	fl, tpt (hn), pf	CF
Duvernoy, F.-Leloir	Trio No. 1, C. *fl (cl), hn, pf*	Kaw
Duvernoy, F.-Leloir	Trio No. 2, F. *fl (cl), hn, pf*	Kaw
Elgar, E.-Trinkaus	Love's Greeting. *bsn, trb, pf*	CF
Elgar, E.-Trinkaus	Love's Greeting. *cl, tpt, pf*	CF
Elgar, E.-Trinkaus	Love's Greeting. *fl, trb (tpt), pf*	CF
Elgar, E.-Trinkaus	Love's Greeting. *sax tpt (trb), pf*	CF
Fisher, S.	Involution. *pic, tpt, hpcd*	AMC
Godard, B.-Trinkaus	Berceuse (Jocelyn). *bsn, trb, pf*	CF

Woodwind, Brass, Keyboard

Godard, B.-Trinkaus	Berceuse (Jocelyn). *cl, tpt, pf*	CF
Godard, B.-Trinkaus	Berceuse (Jocelyn). *fl, trb (tpt), pf*	CF
Godard, B.-Trinkaus	Berceuse (Jocelyn). *sax, tpt (trb), pf*	CF
Gounod, C.-Deville	Flower Song (Faust). *cl, tpt, pf*	CF
Hartley, W.	Double Concerto. *asax, tu, pf*	JB
Hessen, A. von	Trio, op. 3. *cl, hn, pf*	Sim
Hindemith, P.	Concerto (1949). *bsn, tpt, pf*	SS
Holmes, G. (arr)	Auld Lang Syne. *asax (tsax), tpt (trb), pf*	CF
Holmes, G. (arr)	Auld Lang Syne. *cl (sax), tpt, pf*	CF
Johnson, R.	Trio. *cl, hn, hpcd*	CoA
Kling	Olifant en Mug. *pic, trb, pf*	MM
Kowalski, J.	Miniatury. *cl, hn, pf*	SHF
Lake, M. (arr)	Annie Laurie. *asax (tsax), tpt (trb), pf*	CF
Lake, M. (arr)	Annie Laurie. *cl (sax), tpt, pf*	CF
Lemare, E.-Trinkaus	Andantino. *bsn, trb, pf*	CF
Lemare, E.-Trinkaus	Andantino. *cl, tpt, pf*	CF
Lemare, E.-Trinkaus	Andantino. *fl, trb (tpt), pf*	CF
Lemare, E.-Trinkaus	Andantino. *sax, tpt (trb), pf*	CF
Massenet, J.-Trinkaus	Elegy. *bsn, trb, pf*	CF
Massenet, J.-Trinkaus	Elegy. *cl, tpt, pf*	CF
Massenet, J.-Trinkaus	Elegy. *fl, trb (tpt), pf*	CF
Massenet, J.-Trinkaus	Elegy. *sax, tpt (trb), pf*	CF
Mendelssohn, F.-Trinkaus	Nocturno. *bsn, trb, pf*	CF
Mendelssohn, F.-Trinkaus	Nocturno. *cl, tpt, pf*	CF
Mendelssohn, F.-Trinkaus	Nocturno. *fl, trb (tpt), pf*	CF
Mendelssohn, F.-Trinkaus	Nocturno. *sax, tpt (trb), pf*	CF
Mendelssohn, F.-Trinkaus	On Wings of Song. *bsn, trb, pf*	CF
Mendelssohn, F-Trinkaus	On Wings of Song. *cl, tpt, pf*	CF
Mendelssohn, F.-Trinkaus	On Wings of Song. *fl, trb (tpt), pf*	CF
Mendelssohn, F.-Trinkaus	On Wings of Song. *sax, tpt (trb), pf*	CF
Merten	Duo Valse. *fl, tpt, pf*	EdM
Meyerbeer, G.-Trinkaus	Coronation March (The Prophet). *bsn, trb, pf*	CF
Meyerbeer, G.-Trinkaus	Coronation March (The Prophet). *cl, tpt, pf*	CF
Meyerbeer, G.-Trinkaus	Coronation March (The Prophet). *fl, trb (tpt), pf*	CF
Meyerbeer, G.-Trinkaus	Coronation March (The Prophet). *sax, tpt (trb), pf*	CF
Mills, C.	Serenade. *fl, hn, pf*	CoF
Ostrander, A.	Duet Album. *fl, hn, pf*	EdM
Paderewski, I.-Trinkaus	Minuet a l'Antique. *bsn, trb, pf*	CF
Paderewski, I.-Trinkaus	Minuet a l'Antique. *cl, tpt, pf*	CF
Paderewski, I.-Trinkaus	Minuet a l'Antique. *fl, trb (tpt), pf*	CF
Paderewski, I.-Trinkaus	Minuet a l'Antique.	

Woodwind, Brass, Keyboard

	sax, tpt (trb), pf	CF
Ranger, A. (arr)	A Wreath of Holly. asax (tsax), tpt (trb), pf	CF
Ranger, A. (arr)	A Wreath of Holly. cl (sax), tpt, pf	CF
Reinecke, C.	Trio, a, op. 188. ob, hn, pf	BrH
Reinecke, C.	Trio, a, op. 188. ob, hn, pf	Int
Reinecke, C.	Trio, B♭, op. 274. cl, hn (va), pf	MR
Reinecke, C.	Trio, op. 274. cl, hn, pf	Wes
Rivier, J.	Concerto. asax, tpt, pf	Bil
Saint-Saens, C.-Trinkaus	The Swan. bsn, trb, pf	CF
Saint-Saens, C.-Trinkaus	The Swan. cl, tpt, pf	CF
Saint-Saens, C.-Trinkaus	The Swan. fl, trb (tpt), pf	CF
Saint-Saens, C.-Trinkaus	The Swan. sax, tpt (trb), pf	CF
Saint-Saens, C.-Brooke	Serenade. fl, hn, pf	CF
Schumann, R.-Buchtel	Voice of Love. fl, hn, pf	NK
Schwartz, E.	Divertimento. cl, hn, pf	Gen
Sibelius, J.-Trinkaus	Valse Triste (Kuolema). bsn, trb, pf	CF
Sibelius, J.-Trinkaus	Valse Triste (Kuolema). cl, tpt, pf	CF
Sibelius, J.-Trinkaus	Valse Triste (Kuolema). fl, trb (tpt), pf	CF
Sibelius, J.-Trinkaus	Valse Triste (Kuolema). sax, tpt (trb), pf	CF
Smith, C.-Holmes, G.	Believe Me If All Those Endearing Young Charms. asax (tsax), tpt (trb), pf	CF
Smith, C.-Holmes, G.	The Caribbean. asax (tsax), tpt (trb), pf	CF
Smith, C.	De Die in Diem. asax (tsax), tpt (trb), pf	CF
Smith, C.	De Die in Diem. cl (sax), tpt, pf	CF
Smith, C.-Holmes, G.	Drink To Me Only With Thine Eyes. cl (sax), tpt, pf	CF
Smith, C.-Holmes, G.	Drink To Me Only With Thine Eyes. asax (tsax), tpt (trb), pf	CF
Smith, C.	Helen. asax (tsax), tpt (trb), pf	CF
Smith, C.	Helen. cl (sax), tpt, pf	CF
Smith, C.-Holmes, G.	Old Black Joe. cl (sax), tpt, pf	CF
Smith, C.-Holmes, G.	Old Black Joe. asax (tsax), tpt (trb), pf	CF
Smith, C.	One Pleasure Bent. asax (tsax), tpt (trb), pf	CF
Smith, C.	On Pleasure Bent. cl (sax), tpt, pf	CF
Smith, C.	The Spirit of Joy. asax (tsax), tpt (trb), pf	CF

Woodwind, Brass, Keyboard

Smith, C.	The Spirit of Joy.	
	cl (sax), tpt, pf	CF
Sontag	An Evening Serenade. *fl, hn, pf*	CF
Sontag	An Evening Serenade. *cl, hn, pf*	CF
Staigers, D.	Hazel. *cl (sax), tpt, pf*	CF
Staigers, D.	Hazel. *asax (tsax), tpt (trb), pf*	CF
Stouffer, P.	Concertino for Two. *cl, tpt, pf*	HeE
Stravinsky, I.	Dance of the Princesses.	
	fl, hn, pf	EdM
Stravinsky, I.	Dance of the Ballerina. *fl, tpt, pf*	EdM
Tchaikovsky, P.-Trinkaus	Chant sans Paroles. *bsn, trb, pf*	CF
Tchaikovsky, P.-Trinkaus	Chant sans Paroles. *cl, tpt, pf*	CF
Tchaikovsky, P.-Trinkaus	Chant sans Paroles.	
	fl, trb (tpt), pf	CF
Tchaikovsky, P.-Trinkaus	Chant sans Paroles.	
	sax, tpt (trb), pf	CF
Telemann, G.-André	Concert, C. *ob, tpt, pf*	B&V
Titl, A.-DeVille	Serenade. *cl, hn, pf*	CF
Titl, A.	Serenade. *fl, hn, pf*	MM
Titl, A.-Buchtel, F.	Serenade. *fl, hn, pf*	NK
Trinkaus, G.	Lament. *bsn, trb, pf*	CF
Trinkaus, G.	Lament. *cl, tpt, pf*	CF
Trinkaus, G.	Lament. *fl, trb (tpt), pf*	CF
Trinkaus G.	Lament. *sax, tpt (trb), pf*	CF
Vazzana, A.	Trio. *cl, hn, pf*	AMC
Wagner, R.-Trinkaus	Song to the Evening Star	
	(Tannhauser). *cl, tpt, pf*	CF
Wagner, R-Trinkaus	Song to the Evening Star	
	(Tannhauser). *fl, trb (tpt), pf*	CF
Wagner, R-Trinkaus	Song to the Evening Star (Tann-	
	hauser). *fl, trb (tpt), pf*	CF
Wagner, R.-Trinkaus	Song to the Evening Star (Tann-	
	hauser). *sax, tpt (trb), pf*	CF
Wagner, R.-Trinkaus	Walther's Prize Song (Meister-	
	singer). *bsn, trb, pf*	CF
Wagner, R.-Trinkaus	Walther's Prize Song (Meister-	
	singer). *cl, tpt, pf*	CF
Wagner, R.-Trinkaus	Walther's Prize Song (Meister-	
	singer). *fl, trb (tpt), pf*	CF
Wagner, R.-Trinkaus	Walther's Prize Song (Meister-	
	singer). *sax, tpt (trb), pf*	CF
Weigl, V.	The Cherry Tree - Version II.	
	ob (fl), hn, pf	ACA

WOODWIND, STRING, KEYBOARD

Able, K.-Möbius	Triosonate, C. *fl, vn, bc*	HMo
Abendroth, W.	Sonatina, op. 39. *fl, vn, hpcd*	Sim
Adaskin, M.	Trio (1970). *fl, vc, pf*	Can

Woodwind, String, Keyboard

Albicastro, H.	Sonata, op. 1/3, b. *fl, vn, bc*	Pet
Altmann, E.	Suite im alten Stil, op. 14. *fl, vn, pf*	FrH
Andriessen, H.	Pastorale (1942). *fl, vn, pf*	SD
Andriessen, J.	Trio No. 2 (1955). *fl, va, pf*	SD
Angerer, P.	Chanson gaillarde. *ob, vc(bsn), hpcd (pf)*	LDo
Applebaum, E.	Montages. *cl, vc, pf*	Che
Archduke Rudolph	Trio. *cl, vc, pf*	MR
Auclert, P.	Trio. *fl, va, pf*	Ric
Bach, C.P.E.-Ermeler	Trio, b. *fl, vn, bc*	WZ
Bach, C.P.E.	Trio, B♭. *fl, vn, pf, vc ad lib*	Int
Bach, C.P.E.	Trio, F. *bsn, va, pf*	Int
Bach, C.P.E.	Trio No. 1, D. *fl, va, pf*	Int
Bach, C.P.E.	Trio No. 3, G. *fl, va, pf*	Int
Bach, C.P.E.	Trio No. 2, a. *fl, va, pf*	Int
Bach, C.P.E.-Lorenz/Tschierpe	Trio Sonate II. *fl, vn, pf*	WZ
Bach, C.P.E.-Dürr	Triosonate, A. *fl, vn, bc*	HMo
Bach, C.P.E.-Ruf	Triosonate, C, Wq 147. *fl, vn, bc*	B&N
Bach, C.P.E.-Dürr	Triosonate, d. *fl, vn, bc*	HMo
Bach, C.P.E.	Triosonata, G. *fl, vn(fl, ob), pf*	B&V
Bach, C.P.E.-Walther	12 kleine Stücke. *fl, vn, pf*	WZ
Bach, J.C.-Smith	6 Sonatas, op. 2/1-6. *fl, vc, pf* Published separately	LDo
Bach, J.C.-Frotscher	Sonata, A. *fl, vn, bc*	HSM
Bach, J.C.-Nagel	Sonata, C. *fl, vn, pf*	SS
Bach, J.C.-Nagel	Trio, B♭. *fl, vn, bc*	WMS
Bach, J.C.-Schünemann	Trio No. 2, C. *fl, vn, pf*	Kis
Bach, J.C.-Koelbel	Trio Sonata, B♭. *fl, vn, pf*	Pet
Bach, J.C.F.	Sonata. *fl, vn, bc*	WIN
Bach, J.C.F.-Ruf	Sonate, D. *fl, vc, pf*	B&N
Bach, J.S.-Boeringer	Adagio and Affetuoso. *fl, vn, pf*	Aug
Bach, J.S.	Concerto, c. *ob, vn, pf*	Pet
Bach, J.S.-Berner	Concerto, c, S. 1060. *ob, vn, pf*	SS
Bach, J.S.-Schneider	Concerto, d. *vn, ob, pf*	BrH
Bach, J.S.-Gounod	Meditation (Ave Maria). *fl(ob, cl), vc, pf*	Pet
Bach, J.S.-Frotscher	6 Trio Sonatas (Orgeltrios), 2 vols. *fl(ob), vn, bc*	Pet
Bach, J.S.-Hindermann	Sonate a tre, g. *ob, va, bc*	B&N
Bach, J.S.-Moyse	3 Trio Sonatas. *fl, vn, pf vc ad lib*	Sch
Bach, J.S.-David	2 Sonaten, C, D. *fl, vn, pf*	BrH
Bach, J.S.	Trios. *fl, vn, pf*	Dur
Bach, J.S.-Seiffert	Trio (the Musical Offering). *fl, vn, vc ad lib, pf*	BrH
Bach, J.S.-Landshoff	Trio Sonatas Nos. 3, 4, G, c. *fl, vn, bc*	Pet
Bach, J.S.-Walther	Triosonate, g. *fl, vn, bc*	WZ
Bach, W. F.-Seiffert	Sonata, B♭. *fl, vn, pf, vc ad lib*	Int
Bach, W.F.	Sonata, F. *fl, vn(fl, ob), pf*	B&V
Bach, W.F.	Sonata, F. *fl, vn, bc*	Pet
Bach, W.F.	Trio, B♭. *fl(vn), vn, vc ad lib, pf*	BrH

Woodwind, String, Keyboard

Bancquart, A.	Possibles. *cl, vn, pf*	Job
Barlow, F.	Sonatine. *fl, vn, pf*	E-V
Bartok, B.	Contrasts. *cl, vn, pf*	B&H
Bassett, L.	Trio. *cl, va, pf*	CoF
Bauer, M.	Trio Sonata No. 1. *fl, vc, pf*	CoF
Becerra-Schmidt, G.	Trio. *fl, vn, pf*	SMP
Beethoven, L. van-Trinkaus	Menuet. *fl(ob, cl, bsn), vn(vc), pf*	CF
Beethoven, L. van	Trio, B♭, op. 11.	CF
	cl(fl), va(bsn, bcl, vc), pf	
Beethoven, L. van	Trio, B♭, op. 11. *cl(vn), vc(va), pf*	BrH
Beethoven, L. van	Trio, B♭, op. 11. *cl(vn), vc, pf*	Int
Beethoven, L. van	Trio, E♭, op. 38. *cl(vn), vc, pf*	Int
Beethoven, L. van	Trio No. 4, op. 11. *cl, vc, pf*	Gal
Beethoven, L. van	Trio, op. 11. *cl, vc, pf*	Pet
Beethoven, L. van	Trio No. 4, op. 11. *cl, vc, pf*	Sch
Benda, F.	Sonata. *fl, vc, bc*	Art
Berg, A.	Adagio (Chamber Concerto).	UE
	cl, vn, pf	
Berger, W.	Trio. *cl, vc, pf*	Pet
Beyer, J.-Gronefeld	Partita, C. *fl, vn, bc*	Leu
Bizet, G.	Adagietto. *fl, vn(va, vc), pf*	EdM
Bizet, G.	Aragonaise. *fl, vn(va), pf*	EdM
Bizet, G.	Minuet. *fl, vn(va), pf*	EdM
Bizet, G.	Serenade Espagnole. *fl, vn(va), pf*	EdM
Bloch, E.	Concertino. *fl, va, pf*	Sch
Blomdahl, K.	Trio. *cl, vc, pf*	S&C
Blume, J.	Musik. *cl, vc, pf*	MV
Boeddecker, P.-Seiffert	Sonata sopra "La Monica."	Kis
	vn, bsn, bc	
Boismortier, J.-Ruf	Concerto, a. *fl(ob), vn, bc*	Ric
Borodin, A.	Solicitude. *fl, va(vc), pf*	Edm
Braal, A. de	Pastorale en Scherzo 1946).	SD
	fl, vn, pf	
Braga, G.	La Serenata. *fl, vc, pf*	Dur
Braga, G.	La Serenata. *fl, vn, pf*	Dur
Brahms, J.	Berceuse. *fl, vn, pf*	Ham
Brahms, J.	Trio, a, op. 114. *cl, vc, pf*	BrH
Brahms, J.	Trio, op. 114. *cl, vc, pf*	Pet
Brahms, J.	Trio, a, op. 114. *cl(vn, va), vc, pf*	Int
Britten, B.	Gemini Variations, op. 73.	Fab
	fl, vn, pf	
Brogue, R.	Quodlibet. *fl, vc, hpcd*	AMC
Brogue, R.	Trio. *cl, vn, pf*	AMC
Bruch, M.	8 Pieces, op. 83. *cl, va, pf*	Sim
	Published separately	
Bruch, M.	8 Stücke, op. 83. *cl, va, pf*	B&N
Bruno, C.	Danze americane No. 2. *fl, vc, pf*	Cur
Buxtehude, D.-Peyrot & Rebuffat	Sonata, F. *fl, vc, bc*	EdS
Buxtehude, D.-Peyrot & Rebuffat	Sonata, G. *fl, vc, bc*	EdS
Califano, A.-Brinckmann/Mohr	Sonata à tre, G. *fl, vn, bc*	B&N
Cammarota	Arioso and Fugue. *fl, vn, pf*	EdB
Champagne, C.	Suite Miniature (1958).	Can

Woodwind, String, Keyboard

	fl, vc, hpcd(pf)	
Christiansen, L.	Trio. *cl, vc, pf*	CoA
Cima-Grebe	Sonata No. 3, A. *ob, vn, bc*	HSM
Cima-Grebe	3 Sonatas (1610). *ob, vn, bc*	HSM
Corelli, A.	Gavotte and Gigue. *fl, vn(va), pf*	EdM
Corelli, A.	Gigue. *fl, vn(va), pf*	EdM
Corghi	Musica 3. *cl, vn, pf*	FrC
Corrette, M.-Boulay	Sonatille. *fl, vc, pf*	EMT
Couperin, F.-Boulay	L'Astrée. *ob, vn, bc*	EMT
Couperin, F.	L'Astrée, Sonata. *fl, vc, pf*	EMT
Couperin, F.	Les Gouts-Reunis, 6th Concert.	EMT
	fl, vc, pf	
Couperin, L.-Bouvet	2 Symphonies. *fl, vc, bc*	EME
Crawford, J.	Trio. *cl, vc, pf*	CoF
Creston, P.	Suite. *fl, va, pf*	Sha
Cui, C.	5 Pieces, op. 56. *fl, vn, pf*	Int
Custer, A.	Pastorale & Hornpipe. *cl, vn, pf*	
Custer, A.	Permutations. *cl, vn, pf*	Gen
Damase, J.	Sonate for Concert. *fl, vc, pf*	E-V
Davison, J.	Suite (1954). *fl, vn, pf*	Can
Debussy, C.	Il Pleure dans mon Coeur.	EdM
	fl, va(vc), pf	
Debussy, C.	Mandoline. *fl, vn(va), pf*	EdM
Dela, M.	Suite (1954). *fl, vc, pf*	Can
D'Indy, V.	Trio, op. 29. *cl, vc, pf*	E-V
Donizetti, G.-DeVille	Sextet (Lucia). *fl, vn, pf*	CF
Doppler, F.-Hosmer	Souvenir du Rigi, Idylle, op. 34.	CF
	fl, vc, pf	
Doran, M.	Andante & Allegro. *fl, vc, pf*	Wes
Doran, M.	Trio. *fl, vc, pf*	Wes
Driessler, J.	Serenata a tre, op. 34/2.	B&N
	fl, va da gamba, pf	
Duruflé, M.	Prélude récitatif et variations,	Dur
	op. 3. *fl, va, pf*	
Eckerberg, S.	Trio Concertante (1966). *fl, vc, pf*	STI
El-Dabh, H.	Thulathiya. *ob, va, pf*	Pet
Elgar, E.-Trinkaus	Love's Greeting.	CF
	fl(ob, cl, bsn), vn(vc), pf	
Exaudet, J.	La Cour de la Marquise.	EdM
	fl, vn(va), pf	
Eychenne, M.	Cantilene et Danse. *asax, vn, pf*	Bil
Fasch, J.-Winschermann & Buck	Double Concerto, d. *ob, vn, pf*	HSM
Fasch, J.-Grebe	Trio Sonata, G. *fl, vn, bc*	HSM
Fauré, G.	En Prière. *fl, vn(va, vc), pf*	EdM
Ferritto, J.	Quattro Diversioni. *cl, va, pf*	CoF
Fesch, W. de	Sonate a tré. *fl, vn(fl, ob), pf*	B&V
Foster	A Village Festival. *fl, vn(va), pf*	EdM
Francaix, J.	Musique de Cour. *fl, vn, pf*	SS
Frankel, B.	Pezzi Pianissimi, op. 41. *cl, vc, pf*	Nov
Frankel, B.	Trio, op. 10. *cl, vc, pf*	Gal
Franken, W.	Serenade (1958). *fl, db, pf*	SD
Frühling, C.	Trio, a, op. 40. *cl, vc, pf*	Leu

Woodwind, String, Keyboard

Fux, J.-Hillemann	Sonata a tre, d. *fl(ob), vn, pf*	Hei
Gagnebin, H.	Trio, D. *fl, vn, pf*	Cur
Gal, H.	Trio, op. 97. *cl, vn, pf*	ABe
Ghedini, G.	Musiche per tre strumenti. *fl, vc, pf*	FrC
Giordani, G.	An Eighteenth Century Air. *fl, vn(va, vc), pf*	EdM
Glaser, W.	Bröllopsmusik (1966). *fl, vc, hpcd*	STI
Glaser, W.	Kammarmusik (1952). *cl, vc, pf*	STI
Glick, S.	Trio (1958-59). *cl, vc, pf*	Can
Gluck, C.-Bouvet	Sonata, g. *vn, fl, pf*	EME
Godard, B.-Trinkaus	Berceuse (Jocelyn). *fl(ob, cl, bsn), vn(vc), pf*	CF
Godron, H.	Serenade occidentale (1942). *cl, vc, pf*	SD
Goeyvaerts, K.	Pièce pour trois (1960). *fl, vn, pf*	CBD
Goodman, J.	Trio. *fl, vn, pf*	AMP
Goossens, E.	5 Impressions of a Holiday. *fl, vc, pf*	Che
Goossens, E.	4 Sketches, 2 vol. *fl, vn, pf*	Che
Gounod, C.-DeVille	Flower Song (Faust). *fl, vn, pf*	CF
Graun, J.-Riemann	Trio, F. *ob, vn, bc*	BrH
Graun, J.-Fischer	Trio Sonata, F. *fl, vn, bc*	WZ
Graupner, C.-Flattschacher/ Frotscher	Sonata, C. *fl, va d'amore, bc*	B&N
Graupner, C.-Goebels-Kammerling	Triosonate, B♭. *fl, va, bc*	Leu
Griffis, E.	Suite for Trio. *cl, vc, pf*	AMC
Gyring, E.	Trio. *cl, va, pf*	CoF
Gyrowetz, A.-Albrecht	Divertissement, A. *fl, vc, pf*	Kis
Haber, L.	Parade, Blues & Allegro. *fl, vn, pf*	Gen
Haber, L.	Trio. *fl, vn, pf*	Gen
Hacquart, C.	3 Sonaten (Harmonia Parnassia). *fl, vn(fl, ob), pf*	B&V
Hahn, R.	Romanesque. *fl, va, pf*	Heu
Handel, G.-Moyse	4 Trio Sonatas. *fl(ob), vn, pf*	Sch
Handel, G.-Seiffert	Kammertrio No. 7, c. *fl, vn(vc), pf*	BrH
Handel, G.-Kolneder	Trio. *ob, vn, bc*	SS
Handel, G.-Krause	Trio Sonata, F, op. 2/5. *fl, vn, bc*	SS
Handel, G.-Hinnenthal	Trio Sonate, B♭. *ob, vn, bc*	B&N
Hasse, J.-Winschermann	Trio Sonata, F. *ob, vn, bc*	HSM
Haubile, C.	In the French Manner. *fl, vc, pf*	See
Haubiel, C.	Pastoral Trio. *fl, vc, pf*	See
Haufrecht, H.	Caprice. *cl, va, pf*	Bou
Haydn, F.-Nagel	Cassation. *fl, vn, bc*	Pet
Haydn, F.-David	Klaviertrio Nr. 30, D. *fl, vc, pf*	BrH
Haydn, F.-David	Klaviertrio No. 31, G. *fl, vc, pf*	BrH
Haydn, F.-Rampal	3 Trios, F, D, G. *fl, vc, pf*	Int
Haydn, F.	Trio No. 28, D, Hob. XV: 16. *fl, vc, pf*	LDo
Haydn, F.	Trio No. 29, G, Hob. XV: 15. *fl, vc, pf*	LDo
Haydn, F.	Trio No. 30, F, Hob. XV: 17.	LDo

	fl, vc, pf	
Haydn, F.-Bergmann	Trio, op. 2/4. *fl, vn, pf, vc ad lib*	SS
Haydn, M.-Beyer	Sonata, G. *fl, pf, db*	JB
Heinichen, J.-Winschermann	Trio Sonata, c. *ob(fl), vn, bc*	HSM
Heinichen, J.	Trio Sonata, c. *ob, va, bc*	Pet
Hier, E.	Scherzo. *fl, vc, pf*	CoF
Hindemith, P.	Trio, op. 47.	SS
	heckelphone(tsax), va, pf	
Hodge, T.	3 Sketches. *fl, vn, pf*	Che
Höffer, P.	Triosonate. *fl, va, pf*	Pet
Holmes, M.	Street Scenes. *cl, vn, pf*	CoA
Homilius, G.-Blejer	Kleines Trio, G. *fl, vn, bc*	HG
Hubicki (arr)	4 Scottish and Irish Airs.	S&C
	ob, vc, pf	
Hummel, J.N.	Trio, op. 78. *fl, vc, pf*	MR
Huybrechts, A.	Trio (1926). *fl, va, pf*	CBD
Ibert, J.	2 Interludes. *fl, vn, hpcd(hp)*	ALe
Imbrie, A.	Serenade. *fl, va, pf*	Sha
Indy, V. d'	Trio, op. 29. *cl, vc, pf*	Int
Ives, C.	Largo. *cl, vn, pf*	SMP
Jachino, C.	Trio. *fl, vc, pf*	Edi
Jacob, G.	Trio. *cl, va, pf*	MR
Jacobson, J.	Tre stycken. *cl, va, pf*	EMF
Jacobson, M.	Suite for Four Pieces. *fl, vc, pf*	Gal
Jeppesen, K.	Little Summer Trio. *fl, vc, pf*	Che
Johanson, S.	Marina Skisser (1965). *fl, vc, pf*	STI
Johanson, S.	Trio. *cl, vc, pf*	EMF
Juon, P.	Trio-Miniaturen (op. 18, op. 24).	MRL
	cl, vc, pf	
Kahn, E.	Divertimento. *fl, vn, hpcd*	CoF
Kalinnikov, V.	Chanson Triste. *fl, va(vc), pf*	EdM
Keiser, R.-Schenk	Triosonate No. 3, D. *fl, vn, bc*	B&N
Keiser, R.-Schenk	Triosonate No. 2, G. *fl, vn, bc*	B&N
Kelterborn, R.	5 Fantasien. *fl, vc, pf*	B&N
Kelterborn, R.	Kammermusik. *fl, vn, pf*	EMo
Kerr, H.	Trio. *cl, vc, pf*	TP
Khachaturyan, A.	Trio. *cl, vn, pf*	B&H
Khachaturyan, A.	Trio. *cl, vn, pf*	ChM
Khachaturyan, A.	Trio. *cl, vn, pf*	HSM
Khachaturyan, A.	Trio. *cl(va), vn, pf*	Int
Khachaturyan, A.	Trio. *cl, vn, pf*	MCA
Khachaturyan, A.	Trio. *cl, vn, pf*	MR
Khachaturyan, A.	Trio (1932). *cl, vn, pf*	Pet
Kleinknecht, J.-Weiss	Sonata, c. *fl, ob, bc*	B&N
Klughardt, A.	"Schilflieder," op. 28. *ob, va, pf*	M&M
Knab, A.	Lindegger Ländler. *cl, vc, pf*	SS
Koetsier, J.	Trio. *afl, va da gamba, hpcd*	SD
Köhler, E.	Au vol d'Oiseau, op. 98.	WZ
	fl, vn, pf, vc ad lib	
Komma, K.	Estampie. *fl, va, hpcd*	Pet
Kouguell, A.	Melodie & Danse Hebraique.	AMC
	fl, vc, pf	

Woodwind, String, Keyboard

Kounadis, A.	4 Pezzi. *fl, vc, pf*	EdT
Krebs, J.-Ruf	Suite, D. *fl, vn, bc*	SS
Krebs, J.-Riemann	Trio, D. *fl, vn, bc*	BrH
Krejci, I.	Trio. *vn, cl, pf*	Art
Krenek, E.	Trio. *vn, cl, pf*	AMP
Krützfeld, W.	Relationen, op. 34. *fl, va, pf*	EMo
Kubizek, A.	Trio, op. 26a. *cl, vc, pf*	LDo
Kuhlau, F.	Trio, op. 119. *fl, vn(vc), pf*	Bil
Lannoy, E.	Grand Trio, op. 15. *cl, vc, pf*	MR
LeClair, J.-Eitner	Sonate No. 8, D. *fl, va(vc), pf*	BrH
Leclair, J.-Polnauer	Sonata, op. 9/2. *fl, vc, hpcd*	Che
Leclair, J.-Bouvet	Trio Sonata, D, op. 2/8. *fl, vc, bc*	EME
Leclair, J.-Döbereiner	Trio Sonata, D, op. 2/8. *fl, va, bc*	SS
Lefèvre, C.	Ballade. *fl, vc, pf*	EdS
Lege, G.	Trio. *fl, vn, pf*	MV
Lemare, E.-Trinkaus	Andantino.	CF
	fl(ob, cl, bsn), vn(vc), pf	CF
Lessard, J.	Trio. *fl, vn, pf*	Gen
Levy, E.	Trio (1968). *cl, va, pf*	See
Lewis, R.	Trio. *cl, vn, pf*	LDo
Linde, B.	Divertimento, op. 25. *fl, vc, pf*	EMF
Locatelli, P.	Aria. *fl, vn(va, vc), pf*	EdM
Loeffler, C.	2 Rhapsodies. *ob, va, pf*	M&M
Loeillet, J.B.	Courante. *fl, vn(va), pf*	EdM
Loeillet, J.B.-Ruf	Trio Sonata, G, op. 1/2. *ob, vn, bc*	SS
Loeillet, J.B.-Ruf	Trio Sonata, D, op. 1/4. *ob, vn, bc*	SS
Loeillet, J.B.-Ruf	Trio Sonata, e, op. 1/6. *ob, vn, bc*	SS
Longue, A.	Melodie. *cl, vn, pf*	Mau
Lotti, A.	Sonata, G. *fl, vc, bc*	WZ
Lotti, A.	Sonata, G. *fl, vc(va), pf, vc ad lib*	Int
Lotti, A.-Ruf	Trio, A. *fl, vn, bc*	Ric
Luening, O.	Trio. *fl, vn, vc(bsn) ad lib, pf*	CoF
Luening, O.	Trio No. 2. *fl, vc, pf*	CoF
Maganini, Q.	Concert Album. *fl, vn(va), pf*	EdM
Maganini, Q.	Moonlight on the Painted Desert.	EdM
	fl, vc, pf	
Mainardi, E.	Trio (1967). *fl, vc, pf*	SS
Manziarly, M. de	Trio. *fl, vc, pf*	Dur
Martelli, H.	Trio, op. 77. *fl, vc, pf*	ECh
Martinu, B.	Madrigal-Sonate (1936). *fl, vn, pf*	SS
Martinu, B.	Promenades (1940). *fl, vn, pf*	B&N
Martinu, B.	Trio. *fl, vc, pf*	SS
Mascitti, M.	Sonata, g. *fl, vc, bc*	EdS
Mascitti, M.-Ruf	Trio Sonata, g, op. 6/15. *fl, vc, bc*	SS
Massenet, J.-Trinkaus	Elegy. *fl(ob, cl, bsn), vn(vc), pf*	CF
Massenet, J.	Under the Linden Trees.	EdM
	fl, va(vc), pf	
Masseus, J.	Trio, op. 8 (1948). *fl, vn, pf*	SD
Mason, D.	Pastorale. *cl, vn, pf*	EdS
Matteis, N.-Tilmouth	Suite, g. *fl, vn, pf, vc ad lib*	S&C
Mayuzumi, T.	Metamusica. *sax, vn, pf*	Pet
McCabe, J.	Sonata (1969). *cl, vc, pf*	JB

Woodwind, String, Keyboard

Mellers, W.	Trio. *fl, vc, pf*	Nov
Mendelssohn, F.	Concertpiece No. 1, f, op. 113. *cl, vc, pf*	Int
Mendelssohn, F.	Concertpiece No. 2, d, op. 114. *cl, vc, pf*	Int
Mendelssohn, F.-Trinkaus	Nocturno. *fl(ob, cl, bsn), vn(vc), pf*	CF
Mendelssohn, F.-Trinkaus	On Wings of Song. *fl(ob, cl, bsn), vn(vc), pf*	CF
Meyerbeer, G.-Trinkaus	Coronation March (The Prophet). *fl(ob, cl, bsn), vn(vc), pf*	CF
Michaelis, A.-Schäfer	3 Sonaten. *fl, vc, pf*	HG
Mihelcic, S.	3 Pieces. *cl, vn, pf*	EdD
Milhaud, D.	Concerto. *fl, vn, pf*	EdS
Milhaud, D.	Suite. *cl, vn, pf*	EdS
Miller, M.	Trio Fantasy. *fl, va, pf*	AMC
Morrison, J.	Julia Street. *asax, db, pf*	AMC
Mozart, W.	Trio No. 7, K. 498. *cl, va, pf*	CF
Mozart, W.	Trio, E♭, K. 498. *cl, va, pf*	Dur
Mozart, W.	Trio, E♭, K. 498. *cl(vn), va, pf*	Int
Mozart, W.	Trio, K. 498. *cl, va, pf*	Gal
Mozart, W.-Adamowski	Trio, K. 498. *cl, va, pf*	Sch
Mozart, W.-Wachernagel	Trio No. 4, K.V. 498. *cl, va, pf*	MRL
Muczynski, R.	Fantasy Trio, op. 26. *cl, vc, pf*	Sch
Münzing, A.	Trio (1966). *cl, vn, pf*	STI
Nagel, R.	Trio Concerto. *fl, vc, pf*	CoF
Norgard, P.	Trio. *cl, vc, pf*	Che
Nowak, L.	Suite. *cl, vc, pf*	CoF
Olsen, P.	Prolana, op. 33. *cl, vn, pf*	Pet
Ostrander, A.	Duet Album. *fl, vc, pf*	EdM
Paderewski, I.-Trinkaus	Minuet a l'Antique. *fl(ob, cl, bsn), vn(vc), pf*	CF
Parris, R.	Trio. *cl, pf, vc*	CoF
Penn, W.	Trio. *cl, vn, pf*	CoA
Pepusch, J.-Hoffman	6 Triosonaten, 2 vol. *ob, vn, bc*	BrH
Pepusch, J.-Hausswald	Sonata, C. *fl, vn, pf, vc ad lib*	SS
Pepusch, J.-Erbrecht	Sonata da camera, g. *fl(ob), vn, bc*	Kis
Pepusch, J.-Ruf	Trio-Sonate, d. *fl, va, bc*	B&N
Pepusch, J.-Ruf	Trio Sonata, e. *fl, va, bc*	SS
Pepusch, J.-Ruf	Triosonate, F. *fl, vn, bc*	Hei
Pergolesi, G.	Sicilian Air. *fl, vn(va, vc), pf*	EdM
Philidor, P.	Suite. *fl, vc, pf*	EMT
Pierné, G.	Sonata da Camera, op. 48. *fl, vc, pf*	Dur
Pisk, P.	Moresca Figures. *cl, fn, pf*	CoF
Pleskow, R.	Bagatelles No. 2 (1966). *fl, va, pf*	See
Pleskow, R.	Movement (1962). *fl, vc, pf*	See
Pleskow, R.	Movement (1966). *ob, vn, pf*	See
Pleyel, I.	Grand Trio, op. 29. *fl, vc, pf*	MR
Pleyel, I.-Albrecht	Sonata, C, op. 16/2. *fl, vc, pf*	Kis
Pleyel, I.-Albrecht	Sonata, e, op. 16/5. *fl, vc, pf*	Kis
Pleyel, I.-Albrecht	Sonata, G, op. 16/1. *fl, vc, pf*	Kis

Woodwind, String, Keyboard

Ponce, M.	Estrellita. *fl, vn(vc), pf*	CF
Quantz, J.	Trio, F. *fl, vn, bc*	Pet
Quantz, J.-Schultz-Hauser	Trio Sonata, c. *fl, vn, bc*	SS
Quantz, J.-Seiffert	Triosonate, D. *fl(ob), vn, bc*	Kis
Quantz, J.-Ruf	Trio Sonata, D. *fl(ob), vn, bc*	Ric
Quantz, J.-Schroeder	Triosonate, D.	BrH
	fl, vn(fl, ob), vc(bsn), pf	
Quantz, J.-Ruf	Triosonate, G. *fl, vn, bc*	Hei
Quentin, J.-Ruf	Sonata, e. *fl, vn(va), pf*	SS
Rabaud, H.	Andante et Scherzo. *fl, vn, pf*	Heu
Rachmaninoff, S.	Vocalise. *fl, va(vc), pf*	EdM
Rameau, J.-Peyrot & Rebuffat	5 Concerti. *fl, vc, hpcd*	EdS
	Published separately	
Rameau, J.-Horusitzky	Pièces de clavecin, Konzert 1 & 2.	EMB
	fl, va(vn), hpcd	
Rameau, J.-Horusitzky	Pièces de clavecin, Konzert	EMB
	3, 4 & 5. fl, va(vn), hpcd	
Raphael, G.	Trio, op. 70. *cl, vc, pf*	BrH
Raphael, G.	Trio-Suite, op. 44. *fl, vc, pf*	B&N
Ravel, M.	Pavane pour une Infante Defunte.	EdM
	fl, vn(va, vc), pf	
Rebikov, V.	A Little Girl Rocking her Doll.	EdM
	fl, vn(va), pf	
Reif, P.	Trio. *fl, vc, pf*	See
Reinecke, C.	Trio, A, op. 264. *cl, va, pf*	B&N
Reinecke, C.	Trio, A, op. 264. *cl, va, pf*	B&V
Reinecke, C.	Trio, B♭, op. 274. *cl, va(hn), pf*	MR
Reinecke, C.	Trio, op. 264. *cl, va, pf*	Int
Reinecke, C.	Trio, op. 264. *cl, va, pf*	RS
Reinhold, O.	Konzertante Music. *fl, va, pf*	BrH
Reynolds, R.	Acquaintances. *fl, db, pf*	Pet
Richter, F.	Sonata da camera. *fl, vc, pf*	BrH
Richter, F.-Weigart	Sonata, G. *fl, vc, pf*	SS
Ries, F.	Trio, op. 28. *cl, vc, pf*	MR
Riethmueller, H.	Trio, op. 46. *cl, vn, pf*	HSM
Rieti, V.	Pastorale e Fughetta. *fl, va, pf*	Gen
Rogers, B.	Ballade. *va, bsn, pf*	SMP
Rorem, N.	Trio. *fl, vc, pf*	Pet
Rosseau, N.	Trio, op. 60 (1956). *fl, vc, pf*	CBD
Roussakis, N.	Concert Trio. *ob, db, pf*	CoF
Rovsing Olsen, P.	Prolana, op. 33 (1955). *cl, vn, pf*	SPD
Rudhyar, D.	3 Melodies. *fl, vc, pf*	CoF
Rubinstein, A.	Mélodie. *fl, vn, pf*	Ham
Rüdinger, G.	Divertimento, g, op. 75.	ABS
	va(cl), tsax(bcl, vc), pf	
Saint-Saens, C.	Reverie du Soir. *fl, vn(va), pf*	EdM
Saint-Saens, C.-Brooke	Serenade. *fl, vc, pf*	CF
Saint-Saens, C.-Trinkaus	The Swan.	CF
	fl(ob, cl, bsn), vn(vc), pf	
Salieri, A.	Danse (Tarare). *fl, vn(va), pf*	EdM
Schaper, H.-Hohner	Divertimento I. *fl, vc, accordeon*	Hoh
Schmelzer, J.-Janetzky	Sonata. *vn, bsn, bc*	FrH

Woodwind, String, Keyboard

Schmelzer, J.-Janetzky	Sonata. *vn, bsn, pf*	FrH
Schollum, R.	Trio, op. 45. *fl, vc, pf*	LDo
Schroeder, H.	Concertino. *ob, vn, org*	SS
Schroeder, H.	Piano Trio No. 3, op. 43. *cl, vc, pf*	SS
Schumann, R.	Märchenerzählungen, op. 132. *cl(vn), va, pf*	BrH
Schumann, R.	Fairy Tales, op. 132. *cl, va, pf*	CF
Schumann, R.	Fairy Tales, op. 132. *cl(vn), va, pf*	Int
Schwartz, E.	Trio. *fl, vc, pf*	Gen
Sherman, R.	Trio Sonate. *asax, vn, pf*	CoF
Sibelius, J.-Trinkaus	Valse Triste (Kuolema). *fl(ob, cl, bsn), vn(vc), pf*	CF
Slavicky, K.	Trialog (1966). *cl, vn, pf*	Art
Smit, J.	Trio. *fl, vc, pf*	CoA
Smit, L.	Trio (1938). *cl, va, pf*	SD
Smith, L.	Trio. *vl(vn), vc, pf*	CoF
Smith, W.	4 Pieces. *cl, vn, pf*	MJQ
Sollberger, H.	Divertimento. *fl, vc, pf*	ACA
Stamitz, C.	Andantino. *fl, va, pf*	EdM
Stamitz, C.	Concerto. *cl, vn, pf*	EMB
Stamitz, C.-Upmeyer	Trio, G, op. 14/1. *fl, vn, bc*	B&N
Stamitz, C.	Trio No. 1, op. 14. *fl, vn, pf, vc ad lib*	Int
Stamitz, C.-Hillemann	Triosonate, F, op. 14/5. *fl, vn, bc*	BrH
Stein, L.	Trio Concertante. *asax, vn, pf*	CoF
Still, R.	Clarinet Trio. *cl, vn, pf*	AIL
Stölzel, G.-Hausswald	Sonata. *fl, vn, bc*	BrH
Stölzel, G.-Hausswald	Sonate, G. *fl, vn, pf*	B&N
Stölzel, G.	Sonata, G. *fl, vn, pf*	Pet
Stölzel, G.-Frotscher	Trio Sonata, D. *fl, vn, bc*	HSM
Stölzel, G.-Frotscher	Trio Sonata, e. *fl(ob), vn, bc*	BrH
Strauch (arr)	Weihnachtliche Kammermusik. *fl, vn, bc*	B&N
Strauss, R.	Zueignung. *fl, va(vc), pf*	EdM
Stravinsky, I.	Berceuse. *fl, va(vc), pf*	EdM
Stravinsky, I.	Dance of the Princesses. *fl, va(vc), pf*	EdM
Stravinsky, I.	Suite (L'Histoire du Soldat). *cl, vn, pf*	Che
Stravinsky, I.	Suite (L'Histoire du Soldat). *cl, vn, pf*	Int
Stringfield, L.	Morning. *fl, vn(va, vc), pf*	EdM
Stutschewsky, J.	Hassidic Fantasy. *cl, vc, pf*	See
Suk, J.	Bagatelle. *fl, vn, pf*	B&N
Suk, J.	Mit dem Blaumenstrauss in der Hand. *fl, vn, pf*	ES
Sydeman, W.	Fantasy and 2 Epilogues (1964). *fl, vc, pf*	See
Sydeman, W.	Trio (1961). *ob, va, pf*	See
Szalonek, W.	Proporzioni II. *fl, vc, pf*	See
Tamano, Y.	Reaction Relativiste (1959). *cl, vn, pf*	ESZ

Woodwind, String, Keyboard

Tanenbaum, E.	Trio. *cl, vc, pf*	CoF
Tate, P.	Air and Variations. *cl, vn, pf*	OxU
Taylor, C.	Trio. *cl, vc, pf*	AMC
Tchaikovsky, P.-Trinkaus	Chant Sans Paroles. *fl(ob, cl, bsn), vn(vc), pf*	CF
Tchaikovsky, P.	Suite (Album for Children). *fl, vn(va), pf*	EdM
Tcherepnin, A.	Kammerkonzert, D, op. 33. *fl, vn, pf*	SS
Telemann, G.	Concerto No. 2. *fl, vc, pf*	GaM
Telemann, G.-Hinnenthal	Concerto, a. *fl, vn, bc*	B&N
Telemann, G.-Hinnenthal	Concerto, A. *fl, vn, bc*	B&N
Telemann, G.-Hinnenthal	Concerto, b. *fl, vn, bc*	B&N
Telemann, G.-Hinnenthal	Concerto, D. *fl, vn, bc*	B&N
Telemann, G.-Hinnenthal	Concerto, e. *fl, vn, bc*	B&N
Telemann, G.-Hechler	Concerto, F. *ob, vn, bc*	Hei
Telemann, G.-Hinnenthal	Concerto, g. *fl, vn, bc*	B&N
Telemann, G.-Hinnenthal	Sonate, G. *fl, vn, bc*	B&N
Telemann, G.-Hinnenthal	Suite, a. *fl, vn, bc*	B&N
Telemann, G.-Hinnenthal	Suite, b. *fl, vn, bc*	B&N
Telemann, G.-Hinnenthal	Suite, B♭. *fl, vn, bc*	B&N
Telemann, G.-Hinnenthal	Suite, d. *fl, vn, bc*	B&N
Telemann, G.-Hinnenthal	Suite, E. *fl, vn, bc*	B&N
Telemann, G.-Töttcher & Grebe	Trio Sonata, g. *ob, vn, bc*	HSM
Telemann, G.-Hinnenthal	Suite, G. *fl, vn, bc*	B&N
Telemann, G.-Upmeyer	Trio, F. *fl, va(vc), bc*	B&N
Telemann, G.-Upmeyer	Trio, F. *fl, vc(va), bc*	NV
Telemann, G.-Schultz-Hauser	Trio No. 1, B♭. *ob, vn, bc*	CFV
Telemann, G.-Schultz/Hauser	Trio No. 3, G. *fl, vn, bc*	CFV
Telemann, G.	Trio No. 2, a. *fl, vn, bc*	CFV
Telemann, G.	Trio Sonata, a (Essercizii Musici). *fl, vn, bc*	Pet
Telemann, G.-Lauschmann	Trio Sonata, A. *ob d'amore (ob), vn, bc*	HSM SS
Telemann, G.-Ruf	Trio Sonata, b (Essercizii Musici).	
Telemann, G.-Ruf	Triosonate, B♭. *ob(fl), vn, bc*	B&N
Telemann, G.-Veyron-Lacroix	Trio Sonata, B♭. *ob(fl), vn, pf*	Int
Telemann, G.-Winschermann	Trio Sonata, c. *ob, va, bc*	HSM
Telemann, G.-Kölbel	Triosonate, e. *fl, vn, bc*	Hei
Telemann, G.-Ermeler/Päsler	Triosonate, E. *fl, vn, bc*	B&N
Telemann, G.-Hunt	Trio Sonata, F. *fl, vn, pf, vc ad lib*	S&C
Telemann, G.-Ruf	Trio Sonata, g. *ob, vn, bc*	SS
Telemann, G.-Grebe	Trio Sonata, G. *fl, vn, bc*	HSM
Tenaglia	Aira Antica. *fl, vc, pf*	EdM
Trinkaus, G.	Lament. *fl(ob, cl, bsn), vn(vc), pf*	CF
Turner, R.	Diversities (1967). *vn, bsn, pf*	Can
Uhl, A.	Kleines Konzert. *cl, va, pf*	LDo
VanBoer	Pastorale. *fl, vc, pf*	Wat
Vanhall, J.-Weston/Bergmann	Trio, E♭, op. 20/5. *cl, vn, pf*	SS
Vanhal, J.	Trio, E♭. *cl, vc, pf*	MR
Veracini, A.-Polnauer	Sonata da Camera, op. 3/2. *fl, vc, hpcd*	Che

Woodwind, String, Keyboard

Verhaar, A.	Trio-sonate, op. 7 (1934). *fl, vc, pf*	SD
Vivaldi, A.-Rampal	Concerto, d. *fl, vn, pf*	Int
Vivaldi, A.	Concerto, D, FXII, 43. *fl, vn, bc*	MR
Vivaldi, A.-Barbé	Concerto, g. *fl, vn, pf, bsn(vc) ad lib*	B&N
Vivaldi, A.	Pastorale, A, op. 13/4. *fl(ob), vc, pf*	NV
Vivaldi, A.-Upmeyer	Pastorale (op 13/4). *fl, vc, bc*	B&N
Vivaldi, A.-Upmeyer	Pastorale, op. 13/4. *fl(vn), vc, pf*	Int
Von Winter, P.-Michaels/Guedel	Concertino. *cl, vc, pf*	HSM
Wagner, R.-Trinkaus	Song of the Evening Star (Tannhauser). *fl(ob, cl, bsn), vn(vc), pf*	CF
Wagner, R.-Trinkaus	Walther's Prize Song (Meistersinger). *fl(ob, cl, bsn), vn(vc), pf*	CF
Warland	Adagio. *cl, vc, pf*	Wes
Weber, C.M. von	Trio, g, op. 63. *fl, vc, pf*	Int
Weber, C.M. von	Trio, op. 63. *fl, vc, pf*	MR
Weber, C.M. von-Wackernagel	Trio, g, op. 63. *fl, vc, pf*	MRL
Weber, C.M. von	Trio, op. 63. *fl, vc, pf*	Pet
Weigl, V.	New England Suite. *cl(fl), vc, pf*	CoF
Weismann, J.	Kammermusik, op. 86. *fl, va, pf*	B&N
Weiss, A.	Trio. *fl, vn, pf*	CoF
Werner, F.	Concertino. *fl, vc, pf*	Dur
Werner, G.-Moder	Concerto a tre, G. *fl, vn, bc*	LDo
Westrup, J.	Divertimento. *bsn(tsax), vc, pf*	GaM
Widor, C.	Sérénade. *fl, vn, pf*	Ham
Wigy, F.	2 Esquisses. *fl, vn, pf*	Mau
Wolpe, S.	Trio. *fl, vc, pf*	M&M
Wood, H.	Trio. *fl, va, pf*	UE
Wuorinen, C.	Piece for Stefan Wolpe. *fl, vc, pf*	M&M
Wuorinen, C.	Trio Concertante. *ob, vn, pf*	CoF
Wuorinen, C.	Trio (1961). *fl, vc, pf*	ACA
Zaninelli, L.	Arioso. *fl, vc, pf*	Sha
Zender, H.	Trifolium (1966). *fl, vc, pf*	B&B
Zilcher, H.	Trio, a, op. 90. *cl, vc, pf*	B&N

THREE INSTRUMENTS INCLUDING HARP

Arma, P.	Divertimento No. 2. *fl, v c, hp*	EMT
Backes, L.	Ballade. *fl, hp, pf*	S-V
Ballif, C.	Trio, op. 35/1. *fl, bsn, hp*	B&B
Bax, A.	Elegiac Trio. *fl, va, hp*	Che
Berlioz, H.	Trio of the Young Ishmaelites. *fl, ob, hp*	EdM
Bernier, R.	Trio (1942). *fl, vc, hp*	CBD

Three Instruments including Harp

Bondon, J.	Le soleil multicolore. *fl, va, hp*	B&V
Bozic, D.	Sonata in cool no. 3. *fl, bcl, hp*	EdD
Brott, A.	Three on a Spree (1963). *fl, ob, hp*	Can
Canning, T.	Mudras. *fl, hp, perc*	CoF
Charpentier, J.	Mouvement. *fl, vc, hp*	ALe
Colaco Osorio-Swaab, R.	Trio No. 4 (1956). *cl, vc, hp*	SD
Cowell, H.	Trio. *fl, vn, hp*	Pet
Damase, J.	Trio. *fl, vc, hp*	HLe
Debussy, C.	Sonate. *fl, va, hp*	Dur
Edler, R.	Vaarianten (1962). *fl, hn, hp*	EdT
Franco, J.	Trio. *fl, vc, hp*	CoF
Gelbrun, A.	Concerto Fantasia (1963). *fl, hp, pf*	Isr
Glanville-Hicks, P.	Musica Antiqua No. 1. *fl, hp, perc*	CoF
Gubitosi, E.	Colloqui. *fl, vc, hp*	Edi
Guillou, J.	Colloques No. 3. *hp, ob, perc*	ALe
Holliger, H.	Trio. *ob, va, hp*	SS
Holoubek, L.	Trio, op. 21. *fl, vn, hp*	SHF
Hovhaness, A.	Koke No Niwa (Moss Garden), op. 181. *ehn(cl), perc, hp*	Pet
Howard, R.	Trilogue. *asax, va, hp*	ArM
Huber, K.	Sabeth (1966/67). *afl, ehn, hp*	SS
Jez, J.	Assonances. *ob, hp, pf*	EdD
Jolivet, A.	Pastorales de Noel. *fl, bsn(va, vc), hp*	Heu
Jongen, J.	2 Pieces en trio, op. 80 (1925). *fl, vc, hp*	CBD
Kilpatrick, J.	4 Choreographs. *fl, cl, hp*	CoF
Koechlin, C.	Epitaphe de Jean Harlow, op. 164. *fl, asax, hp*	EME
Lajtha, L.	Trio, op. 22. *fl, vc, hp*	ALe
Lajtha, L.	Trio No. 2, op. 47. *fl, vc, hp*	ALe
Ma'Ayani, A.	Improvisation variée. *fl, vn, hp*	Hei
Meulemans, A.	Sonate (1948). *fl, va, hp*	CBD
Migot, G.	Concert. *fl, vc, hp*	ALe
Migot, G.	Le livre des danceries. *fl, vc, hp(pf)*	ALe
Migot, G.	Le premier livre de divertissements Francais. *fl, cl, hp*	ALe
Miroglio, F.	Fluctuances (1961). *fl, hp, perc*	ESZ
Mourant, W.	Remembrance of Things Past, Rhapsody. *ob, hp, pf*	ACA
Mozart, W.-Salzedo	Concerto, C, K. 299. *fl, pf, hp* Cadenzas by Reinecke	SM
Mozart, W.	Concerto, K. 299. *fl, hp, pf*	CF
Mozart, W.-Burchard	Konzert, C, K. 299. *fl, hp, pf*	BrH
Nordoff, P.	Trio. *fl, va, hp*	AMC
Poston, E.	Trio. *fl, cl, hp(pf)*	Che
Raphael, G.	Sonatine, op. 65/1. *fl, va, hp*	BrH
Rohozinsky, L.	Suite Brève. *fl, va, hp*	EdS
Smit, L.	Trio. *fl, va, hp*	EdS
Steel, C.	Trio (1965). *fl, vc, hp*	Nov

Three Instruments including Harp

Stravinsky, I.	Epitaphium (1959). *fl, cl, hp*	B&H
Surinach, C.	Tientos. *ehn, hp(pf), timp*	AMP
Tocchi, G.	Arie e danze tedesche. *fl, va, hp*	FrC
Vellones, P.	Trio, op. 94. *fl, ob(va), hp*	Dur
Voss, F.	Serenade (1959). *fl, vn, hp*	BrH
Weber, B.	Aubade. *fl, vc, hp*	CoF
Wiszniewski, Z.	Trio (1963). *ob, va, hp*	AP
Wüsthoff, K.	Nocturno. *fl, va, hp*	WZ
Wyttenbach, J.	3 Sätze (1963). *ob, hp, pf*	SS
Zagwijn, H.	Introduzione en Scherzetto (1940). *fl, va, hp*	SD

THREE INSTRUMENTS INCLUDING GUITAR

Andriessen, J.	Sonata da camera (1959). *fl, va, guit*	SD
Apostel, H.	Kleines Kammerkonzert, op. 38. *fl, va, guit*	LDo
Badings, H.	Trio No. 9 (1962). *fl, va, guit*	SD
Baumann, H.-Behrend	Sonatine über finnische Volkslieder. *ob, bsn, guit*	WZ
Buck, O.	Summer Trio (1968). *fl, vc, guit*	Che
Call, L. de [von]	Notturno, op. 85. *fl, va, guit*	CFV
Call, L. de [von]	Notturno, op. 89. *fl, va, guit*	CFV
Call, L. de [von]	Notturno, op. 93. *fl, va, guit*	CFV
Call, L. de [von]	Serenade, op. 75. *fl, va, guit*	CFV
Call, L. de [von]	Trio, Op. 134. *fl, va, guit*	WZ
Carulli, F.	Notturno, a. *fl, vn, guit*	CFV
Carulli, F.	Notturno, C. *fl, vn, guit*	CFV
Daube, J.	Trio, d. *fl, lute, pf*	CFV
David, J.	Sonate, op. 26a. *fl, va, guit*	BrH
Delas, J. de	Trio (1971). *fl, guit, perc*	HG
Geszler, G.	Trio (1963). *fl, vc, guit*	EMB
Hasse, J.-Brojer	Triosonate, C. *fl, vn, guit*	LDo
Hibbard, W.	Trio. *cl, vn, guit*	AMC
Kalmar, L.	Trio (1968). *fl, guit, mar*	EMB
Kont, P.	Trio. *fl, va, guit*	LDo
Kotonski, W.	Trio (1960). *fl, guit, perc*	AP
Kreutzer, J.-Scheit	Trio, D, op. 9/3. *fl, vn, guit*	LDo
Kreutzer, J.	Trio, op. 16. *fl, cl, guit*	WZ
Küffner, J.	Notturno, op. 110. *fl, va, guit*	CFV
Küffner, J.	Serenade, op. 21. *cl, va, guit*	CFV
Lechthaler, J.	Freundliche Abendmusik, op. 53. *fl (vn), cl (vn), guit (pf)*	B&B
Leeuw, T. de	Schelp (1964). *fl, va, guit*	SD
Legley, V.	Trio, op. 55 (1959). *fl, va, guit*	CBD
Lotti, A.-Behrend	Sonate. *fl, vc, guit*	B&B
Lundén, L.	Aftonstund. *fl, ob, guit*	EMF
Maasz, G.	Suite. *fl, vc, guit*	Hei
Mar-Chaim, J.	Trio. *fl, va, guit*	Hei

Three Instruments including Guitar

Matiegka, W.-Huber	Notturno, op. 21. *fl, va, guit*	WZ
Matiegka, W.	Serenade, op. 26. *fl, va, guit*	WZ
Miyake, H.	Musik. *pic, fl, guit*	WZ
Molino, F.	Trio, op. 45. *fl, va, guit*	WZ
Mozart, W.-Schmidt	Flötenuhrstück, Andante (K.V. 616). *fl, vn, guit*	WZ
Pfister, H.	Preambolo, Aria e Ballo. *cl, db, guit*	Hei
Praag, H. van	Sonata (1963). *ob, guit, pf*	SD
Richter, N.	Trio (1935). *fl, va, guit*	SD
Ruyneman, D.	Reflexions No. 2. *fl, va, guit*	SD
Skorzeny, F.	Trio (1957). *fl, va, guit*	LDo
Tcherepnin, I.	Sombres lumières. *fl, vc, guit*	Be
Ultan, L.	Explorations. *fl, guit, db*	ACA
Weber, C.M. von-Scheit	Menuet and Trio. *fl, va, guit*	LDo
Weber, C.M. von-Behrend	Menuett (Donna Diana). *fl, va, guit*	B&B
Weber, C.M. von-Berger	Menuett und Trio. *fl, vn (va), guit*	Hei

THREE INSTRUMENTS INCLUDING PERCUSSION

Arma, P.	Celui qui dort et dort. *bsn, xyl, perc*	Bil
Back, S.	Favola. *cl, pf, cel*	WH
Bentzon, N.	Concerto, op. 176. *cl, vn, perc*	WH
Blomdahl, K.	Dans-svit nr 2. *cl, vc, perc*	EMF
Brant, H.	Ice Age (1954). *cl, glockenspiel, pf*	TP
Brown, E.	Hodograph I. *fl, pf, cel*	AMP
Burghauser, J.	Possibilita (Moznosti). *cl, 2 perc*	Art
Canning, T.	Mudras. *fl, hp, perc*	CoF
Chihara	Branches. *2 bsn, perc*	Pet
Chihara	Willow, Willow. *fl, tu, perc*	Pet
Cunningham, M.	Incantation. *fl, cel, pf*	CoA
Delas, J. de	Trio (1971). *fl, guit, perc*	HG
Diemente, E.	Trio (1969). *fl, tpt, perc*	See
Donovan, R.	Soundings. *bsn, tpt, perc*	CoF
Duckworth, W.	An Unseen Action. *fl, pf, perc*	CoA
Epstein, A.	Canons & Postlude. *fl, bsn, perc*	See
Epstein, A.	4 Dialogues. *fl, db, perc*	See
Finney, R.	2 Acts for 3 Players. *cl, pf, perc*	Pet
Fox, F.	BEC-4. *fl, db, perc*	See
Gaber, H.	Ludus Primus: Foreplay. *2 fl, perc*	ACA
Gastyne, S. de	Abacus in Trio, op. 60 (1969). *bsn, hn, perc*	Fer
Glanville-Hicks, P.	A Scary Time. *cl, vn, perc*	CoF
Grosskopf, E.	Nexus (1968). *fl, tape, perc*	B&B

109

Three Instruments including Percussion

Guinjoan, J.	3 Mouvements (1964). *cl, pf, perc*	See
Hartwell, H.	3 X 3: An Epigram (1968).	
	cl, va, vib	Can
Heider, W.	Musik im Diskant. *pic, pf, perc*	Pet
Heussenstamm, G.	Music for Three, op. 33.	
	bfl, perc, vib	See
Heussenstamm, G.	Poikilos, op. 32. *afl, perc, vib*	See
Hibbard, W.	Gestures. *fl, db, perc*	AMC
Hoskins, W.	Prelude & Dance for PVC.	
	pic, cbsn, vib	ACA
Hummel, B.	Ludi à tre. *ob, pf, perc*	RS
Jager, R.	Concerto. *asax, brass, perc*	Vol
Kalmár, L.	Trio (1968). *fl, guit, mar*	EMB
Kohs, E.	Night Watch (1944). *fl, hn, timp*	TP
Lachenmann, H.	Trio fluido (1966).	
	cl, va, marimba	HG
Mamlok, U.	Movements. *fl, db, perc*	CoF
Merkelt (ed)	11 Celebrated Marches. *2 fl, dr*	Sim
Michael, E.	3 rituels. *2 ob, perc*	Ech
Moszumanska, K.	Rendition. *fl, perc, tape*	EBM
Pablo, L. de	Reciproco, op. 16. *fl, pf, perc*	EMo
Papp, L.	Impressioni. *fl, pf, gong*	EMB
Porena, B.	Neumi (1963). *fl, mar, vib*	ESZ
Pyle, F.	Sonata for Three. *cl, pf, perc*	Leb
Reiner, K.	Trio (1964). *fl, bcl, perc*	ES
Schmidt, W.	Septigrams (1956). *fl, pf, perc*	Wes
Schollum, R.	Mosaik, op. 75. *ob, pf, perc*	LDo
Schwartz, E.	Serenade. *fl, db, perc*	Gen
Sivic, P.	Interpunkcije. *cl, pf, xyl*	EdD
Stock, D.	Triple Play. *pic, db, perc*	ACA
Stout, A.	Capriccio (1967). *ob, hp, perc*	JB
Surinach, C.	Ritmo Jondo - Flamenco.	
	cl, tpt, perc	AMP
Surinach, C.	Tientos. *ehn, hp (pf), timp*	AMP
Sydeman, W.	Trio (1963). *fl, db, perc*	See
Touma, H.	Oriental Rhapsodie. *2fl, dr*	Isr
Weber, B.	Nocturno, op. 55. *fl, vc, cel*	UE
Whittenberg, C.	A Due, op. 49.	
	fl/afl, pic, perc	ACA
Wyner, Y.	The Old Glory Music.	
	fl, perc, clavichord	CoF

THREE INSTRUMENTS INCLUDING RECORDER

Doppelbauer, J.	Trio I. *rec, ob, cl*	LDo
Fux, J.-Kuntner	Sinfonia. *rec(fl), ob, bc*	B&N
Graun, C.-Gerlach	Triosonate, F. *rec, ob, bc*	HMo
Kukuck, F.	Kammermusik. *rec, ob, gamba*	MV

Three Instruments including Recorder

Linde, H.	Trio (1960). *rec, fl, pf*	SS
Loeillet, J.-Ruf	Triosonate, op. 1/1, F. *rec, ob, bc*	HMo
Loeillet, J.-Ruf	Triosonate, op. 1/3, g. *rec, ob, bc*	HMo
Loeillet, J.-Ruf	Triosonate, op. 1/5, c. *rec, ob, bc*	HMo
Loeillet, J.-Ermeler/Kluge	Trio-Sonate, F, op. 2/2. *rec, ob, bc*	Hei
Loeillet, J.-Ruf	Triosonaten, op. 2/2, F. *rec(fl), ob, bc*	B&N
Loeillet, J.-Ruf	Triosonaten, op. 2/4, d. *rec(fl), ob, bc*	B&N
Loeillet, J.-Ruf	Triosonaten, op. 2/6, c. *rec(fl), ob, bc*	B&N
Mills, C.	Music. *rec, sax, db*	CoF
Quantz, J.-Birke	Triosonate, C. *rec, fl, bc*	B&N
Reuter-Hense	9 Pieces for 3 Wind Instruments. *rec, fl, vn*	RS
Schroeder-Hofmann	Sonate, c. *rec, ob, bc*	B&N
Schroeder-Hofmann	Sonate, F. *rec, ob, bc*	B&N
Telemann, G.	Sonata, a. *rec, ob, bc*	Pet
Telemann, G.-Hofmann	Sonata, c. *rec, ob, bc*	B&N
Telemann, G.-Hofmann	Sonata, F. *rec, ob, bc*	B&N
Telemann, G.-Rodemann	Sonata, F. *rec, ob, bc*	HMo
Telemann, G.-Ruf	Trio Sonata, a. *rec, ob, bc*	SS
Telemann, G.-Ruetz	Triosonate, e. *rec(fl), ob, bc*	B&N
Vivaldi, A.	Trio, a. *rec(fl), bsn, bc*	MR

THREE INSTRUMENTS INCLUDING TAPE

Bergeijk, G. van	Sonate. *ehn, pf, tape*	SD
Grosskopf, E.	Nexus (1968). *fl, tape, perc*	B&B
Hughes, K.	Second Chance. *fl, ob, tape*	Wes
Moszumanska, K.	Rendition. *fl, perc, tape*	EBM
Schwartz, E.	Ninas. *fl, ob, tape*	CF

111

FOUR INSTRUMENTS

FOUR FLUTES

	4 Miniatures	SM
Arnold, J. (ed)	Flute Quartets	MS
Bach, J.S.-Troxell	Menuetto and Polacca (Brandenburg No. 1)	PrA
Bach, J.S.-Eck	Minuet	B-M
Bach, J.S.-Taylor	Minuet	B-M
Bartolozzi, B.	Sinaulodia (1970)	ESZ
Bennett, R.R.	Rondo Capriccioso	Cha
Berthomieu, M.	Chats	Bil
Bizet, G.-Brooke	Andante and Minuet (L'Arlesienne). *3fl, afl*	CF / CF
Bizet, G.-Freedman	Suite from "Carmen"	MCA
Bornschein, F.-Cellars	The French Clock	TP
Bottenberg, W.	Divertimento (1968). *2fl/2pic, fl, afl*	Can
Bozza, E.	Jour d'été a la montagne (1953)	ALe
Bozza, E.	2 Esquisses	ALe
Braun, G.	Porträt I (1969)	B&N
Butts, C.	Quartet	Sha
Cavally, R. (arr)	Under the Double Eagle. *3fl, afl(cl)*	BM
Chevreuille, R.	Musique lilliputienne, op. 22 (1942)	CBD
Cheyette & Roberts	Four-Tone Folio, 3 vols.	CF
Clementi, M.-Yates	Sonatina, op. 36/1	SM
Cohen, S.	Colonial Sketches	B&H
Cohen, S.	Divertimento	Wes
Cohen, S.	Song of Summer	B&H
Corelli, A.	Allemanda	EdM
Corelli, A.-Johnson	Sarabanda and Gavotta	Rub
Dahl, I.	Serenade (1960)	B&H
Davison, J.	Canzona and Chorale (1965)	Can
De Elias	4 überlieferte mexikanische Melodien	Ric
Desportes, Y.	Italian Suite	SM
Dittersdorf, C.-Steinbeck	Cassation, D.	LDo
Dittersdorf, K.-Schultz/Hauser	Notturno	SS
Dubois, P.	Quartet	ALe
Eck, E.	Quartet Album	B-M
Eck, E.	Valsette	B-M
Elgar, E.	Salut D'Amour, op. 12. *3fl, afl*	CF
Farrenc, J.-Brook	Andante	CF
Fetherston, E.	Valse Staccato [Rubinstein]	B-M
Frescobaldi, G.-Johnson	Gailliard and Courante	Rub
Gabrielski, W.	Grand Quartet	EdM
Galuppi, B.	Toccata	EdM
Gearhart, L.	Flute Sessions	Sha
Gluck, C.-Johnson	Andante and Caprice	Rub
Gluck, C.-Ephross	Lovely Fields So Gentle	TP

Four Flutes

Gossec, F.-Eck	Gavotte	B-M
Guillemain, G.-Taylor	Tambourin	B-M
Haydn, F.-Spiegl	Flute Clock Sonatas	OxU
Hermann, R.	Flute Willow	CF
Hervig, R.	3 Pieces	Rub
Holmes-Long	Symphony Ensemble Series	Rub
Jessel, L.-Cavally	Parade of the Wooden Soldiers	SM
Jongen, J.	Elegy	SM
Jongen, J.	2 Paraphrases on Walloon Christmas Carols	SM
Koepke, P.	Autumn Idyll	Rub
Koepke, P.	Danse Capriole	Rub
Koepke, P.	Fox Fire	Rub
Köhler, E.-Cochrane	Grand Quartette, op. 92	CF
Köhler, E.	Grand Quartet, op. 92	SM
Köhler, E.-Voxman	Scherzo (Quartet, op. 92)	Rub
Kuhlau, F.-Andraud	Grand Quartet, op. 103	SM
Kuhlau, F.	Quartet, E, op. 103	Lit
Kuhlau, F.-Nagel	Quartet, op. 103	Pet
Kuhlau, F.	Quatuor, E, op. 103	Bil
La Violette, W.	Filigree	B&H
Leeuwen, A. van	4 Miniatures	SM
Leeuwen, A. van (arr)	Turkey in the Straw	SM
Legley, V.	Quatuor, op. 14 (1943)	CBD
Liadov, A.-Ephress	Musical Snuff Box	TP
Lorenzo, L. de	Capriccio, op. 82/3	Pet
Lorenzo, L. de	I Seguaci de Pan, op. 32	WZ
Maganini, Q.	Beginners' Luck	EdM
Maganini, Q.	Patrol of the Wooden Indians (Realm of Dolls)	CF
Maganini, Q.	Shepherds in Arcadia	EdM
Maurice, P.	Suite	Bil
McKay, G.	Chorale, Aubade and Noel	SF
McKay, G.	Christmas Morning Suite	SM
McKay, G.	Lyric Poem	SM
McKay, G.	Sonatina Giocosa	Bar
McKay, G.	Suite Matinale	Bar
McKay, G.	Suite Pastorale	Bar
Mendelssohn, F.-Johnson	Andante Con Moto	Rub
Meulemans, A.	Andante et scherzo (1945)	CBD
Ott, J.	Suite	CBP
Paschedag/Buchtel	First Ensemble	NK
Paubon, P.	Quatuor	Bil
Reicha, A.-Leopold	Minuet (Quartet, op. 12)	WZ
Reicha, A.	Sinfonico, op. 12	Bil
Reicha, A.	Sinfonico Quartette	CF
Reynolds, R.	4 Etudes. *pic, 2fl, afl*	Pet
Rimsky-Korsakov, N.-Koepke	Song of India	Rub
Scarlatti-Johnson	Aria and Minuet	Rub
Scarmolin, A.	4 of a Kind	Bar
Schmitt, F.	Quatuor, op. 106	Dur
Schubert, F.-Johnson	Menuet and Trio	Rub

Four Flutes

	(Sonata, op. 78)	
Schumann, R.-Williams	A-Maying	SM
Schumann, R.	Traumerei. *3fl, afl*	CF
Schwarz, I.	Parthenia	Rub
Severn, A.	Scherzo Brilliante	B-M
Sollberger, H.	Grand Quartet. In Memoriam: Friedrich Kuhlau	M&M
Spies	Canon	EMB
Tchaikovsky, P.-Johnson	Chanson Triste	Rub
Tcherepnin, A.	Quartet, op. 60	Be
Vivaldi, A.	Giga	EdM
Voxman, H. (arr)	Quartet Repertoire	Rub
Wagner, J.-Cavally	Under the Double Eagle. *3fl, afl*	SM
Walker	Amusement	Ken
Walker, R.	Bergomask	PrA
Walker, R.	2 Lyrical Pieces	Hal
Woodforde-Finden, A.-Johnson	Kashmiri Song	Rub
Wouters, A.-Voxman	Adagio and Scherzo	Rub

FOUR CLARINETS (4 B♭ Clarinets unless otherwise indicated)

	John's Tune	SLP
Amani-Donatelli	Orientale. *2 cl, acl(cl), bcl*	Wes
Arensky, A.	Cuckoo	GFB
Arne, T.-Barr	2 Dances (Corrus). *2 cl, acl (cl), bcl (cl)*	B-M
Arnold, J.	Clarinet Quartets	MS
Arrieu, C.	5 Mouvements	Bil
Artot, J.	12 Quartettes. *2 cl, acl (cl), bcl (cl)*	CF
Avni, T.	2 Pieces	Isr
Bach, J.S.-Ayres	Andante and Fughetta. *2 cl, acl (cl), bcl (cl)*	Bar
Bach, J.S.-Johnson	Bach Chorales	Rub
Bach, J.S.-Simon	Bach for the Clarinet. Part III	Sch
Bach, J.S.-Brandenburg	Bourree	CF
Bach, J.S.-Rosenthal	Fuga IX. *2cl, acl, bcl*	Wes
Bach, J.S.-McKay	Fugue No. 4. *2 cl, acl (cl), bcl (cl)*	Bar
Bach, J.S.-Pentz	Fugue XVI, g. *2 cl, acl (cl), bcl (cl)*	B-M
Bach, J.S.-Stouffer	Gavotte. *2 cl, acl (cl), bcl (cl)*	Ken
Bach, J.S.-Grisez	Loure	CF
Bach, J.S.-Maganini	Prelude No. 12. *2 cl, acl, bcl*	EdM
Bach, J.S.-Von Kreisler	3rd Prelude and Fugue. *2 cl, acl, bcl*	SM
Bach, J.S.-Barr	2 Gavottes (Suite in D). *2 cl, acl (cl), bcl (cl)*	B-M
Bagatini	Ode to Hiawatha	B-M

Four Clarinets

Bagley-Harris	Thistledown.	
	2 cl, acl (cl), bcl (cl)	CF
Baines, A.	9 Easy Pieces	OxU
Balay, G.-Waln	Sarabande and Menuet.	
	2 cl, acl (cl), bcl	NK
Barab, S.	Quartet	B&H
Bartok, B.-Gordon	3 Folk Dances. *2 cl, acl (cl), bcl*	SM
Beethoven, L. van-Renard	Adagio	B&H
Beethoven, L. van-Wilson	Allegro Con Brio (Op. 18/1).	
	2 cl, acl, bcl	CF
Beethoven, L. van-Geiger	Andante Cantabile (Symphony	
	No. 1). *2 cl, acl, bcl*	War
Beethoven, L. van-Ayres	Minuet and March.	
	2 cl, acl (cl), bcl (cl)	Bar
Beethoven, L. van-Toll	Rondo Excerpt (Sonata Pathetique)	
	2cl, acl (cl), bcl (cl)	CF
Beethoven, L. van-Ostling	Scherzo and Trio.	
	2 cl, acl (cl), bcl (cl)	B-M
Beethoven, L. van-Hite	Scherzo, op. 18/1. *3 cl, bcl*	SM
Beethoven, L. van-Rex	Scherzo (Quartet No. 1).	
	2 cl, acl (cl), bcl (cl)	B-M
Beethoven, L. van-Lemarc	Zweiter Satz (Sonata, G)	T-M
Bennett, D.	Argentine. *2 cl, acl, bcl*	CF
Bennett, D.	Candid Clarinets	CF
Bennett, D.	Clarinet Polka	War
Bennett, D.	Clarinet Rhapsody. *2 cl, acl, bcl*	CF
Bennett, D.	Clarinets in Residence	SM
Bennett, D.	Loch Lomond	War
Bennett, D.	Prelude and Scherzo	CF
Bennett, D.	Way of the Wasp. *2 cl, acl, bcl*	CF
Berlinski, H.	Canons and Rounds	TP
Bizet, G.	Adagietto (L'Arlesienne)	MM
Bizet, G.-Erickson	Agnus Dei	SHM
Bizet, G.	Carillon. *2 cl, acl (cl), bcl*	EdM
Boccherini, L.-Lemarc	Menuet	T-M
Bochsa-Schmidt-Voxman	Andante and Minuetto	Rub
Böhm, C.-Voxman	Quartet, F. *3 cl, bcl (cl)*	Rub
Böhne, R.-Voxman	Andante (Quartet, D).	
	2 cl, acl, bcl	Rub
Bozza, E.	Sonatine. *E♭ cl, 2 cl, bcl*	ALe
Bradac, J.-Voxman	Bohemian Suite	Rub
Brahms, J.-Wood	Allegretto Grazioso	HeE
Brahms, J.-Brandenburg	Waltz	CF
Braun, R.	Divertimento	YM
Braun, R. (arr)	Songs from Ye Olde England	YM
Briegel, G.	Staccato-Legato.	
	2 cl, acl (cl), bcl	GFB
Buchtel, F.	First Ensembel Book	NK
Burgstahler, E. (arr)	Let's Play Quartets	PrA
Busch, C.	Evening Promenade	CF
Busch, C.	In Playful Mood	CF
Busch, C.	Quietude	CF

Four Clarinets

Butterworth, N. (arr)	3 Mozart Movements	Cha
Byrd, W.-Skolnik	Pavana	SM
Cabus, P.	Clarinet Quartet	Mau
Cacavas, J.	Impressions	SM
Cacavas, J.	Romantica	Spr
Cailliet, L.	Fantaisie. E^b *cl/cl, 3 cl*	Leb
Cailliet, L.	Youthful Adventure	Leb
Carion, F.	Petite Pièce	EMb
Carles, M.	Prelude and Dance	ALe
Carter, E.	Canonic Suite	AMP
Caurroy	Double Canon	EdM
Cazden, N.	Round Dance No. 6, op. 40.	
	2 cl, acl, bcl	Spr
Chaminade, C.-De Bueris	Dance Creole.	
	2 cl, acl (cl), bcl (cl)	B-M
Chance, J.	Allegro Festoso	B&H
Chopin, F.-Sarber	Minute Waltz	Rub
Chopin, F.-Liegl	Prelude	CF
Chopin, F.-David	Prelude, B^b. *2 cl, acl, bcl*	Wes
Clementi, M.-Yates	Sonatina	SM
Cohen, S.	Alabama Sketches	War
Cohen, S.	Twilight in the Forest	BM
Cohen, S.	Will o' the Wisp	BM
Conley, L.	A Christmas Carol	Ken
Corelli, A.	Allemanda. *2 cl, acl (cl), bcl (cl)*	EdM
Corelli, A.	Gavotte and Gigue.	
	2 cl, acl (cl), bcl (cl)	EdM
Corelli, A.-Harris	Gigue. *2 cl, acl (cl), bcl (cl)*	CF
Corelli, A.	Gigue. *2 cl, acl (cl), bcl (cl)*	EdM
Corelli, A.-Skornicka	Praludium	B-M
Corelli, A.-Johnson	Sarabanda and Gavotta.	
	2 cl, acl (cl), bcl (cl)	Rub
Cox, H.	Concertino	Mau
Crosse, W.	Petite Quartet	B&H
Crosse, W.	3 Clarinet Quartets	B&H
Cui, C.-Harris	Orientale. *2cl, acl (cl), bcl (cl)*	CF
Dallin, L.	Autumn Vignette. *2 cl, acl*	
	(cl), bcl (cl)	B-M
Dallin, L.-Westphal	Concert/Rondo	B-M
Dallin, L.	Fountains at Dawn	B-M
Davison, J.	Canzona and Chorale (1965)	Can
De Bueris, J.	Gavotte Caprice. *2 cl, acl (cl), bcl*	CF
Debussy, C.-Donatelli	Clair de Lune.	
	2 cl, acl (cl), bcl	Wes
Debussy, C.-Howland	Nocturne. *2 cl, acl, bcl*	SHM
Deemer, C.	Ten Little Indians.	
	2 cl, acl (cl), bcl (cl)	B-M
Deemer, C.	Tepee	B-M
DeJesu, J.	Ave Verum Corpus. *2 cl, acl, bcl*	Hal
DeJesu, J.	Menuetto	Hal
Del Baroni	Novelette No. 1	NK
Denza, L.-Harris	Funiculi-Funicula.	

Four Clarinets

	2 cl, acl (cl), bcl (acl)	CF
Desportes, Y.	French Suite	SM
Desportes, Y.	Normandie Suite	SM
Dewit, A.-Harris	Harvest Dance. *2 cl, acl (cl), bcl (cl)*	CF
Dewit, A.-Harris	Hungarian Fantasie. *2 cl, acl (cl), bcl (acl)*	CF
Dewit, A.-Harris	On the Lake. *2 cl, acl (cl), bcl (cl)*	CF
Dewit, A.-Harris	Polonaise No. 1. *2 cl, acl (cl), bcl (cl)*	CF
Dewit, A.	Spanish Waltz. *2 cl, acl (cl), bcl (cl)*	CF
Dewit, A.	Summertime. *2 cl, acl (cl), bcl (acl)*	CF
d'Harcourt & Bennett	Peruvian Inca Melodies. *2 cl, acl, bcl*	FrC
Dillon, R.	Allegretto Festoso	B&H
Dillon, R.	4 Quartets	SHM
Dillon, R.	March	B&H
Dillon, R.	Rhythmic Dance	B&H
Dillon, R.	Song	B&H
Dillon, R.	3 Clarinet Ensembles	B&H
Dittersdorf, K. von-Barr	Andante (Quartet, B♭). *2 cl, acl (cl), bcl (cl)*	Lud
Donato, A.	Pastorale and Dance	Sch
Dont, J.-Waln	Larghetto and Scherzo	NK
Dubois, P.	Quartet	ALe
Dvorak, A.-DeBueris	Humoresque. *2 cl, acl (cl), bcl (cl)*	B-M
Eklund, H.	4 Temperamenti (1965)	STI
Endresen, R.	Clarinet Quartet No. 1. *2 cl, acl (cl), bcl (cl)*	B-M
Erickson, M.-Waln	Petite Suite	CF
Farrenc, J.-Brooke	Andante. *2 cl, acl (cl), bcl (cl)*	CF
Feldsher, H.	2 Fugues. *2 cl, acl, bcl*	Ken
Ferneyhough	Sonatina. *3 cl, bcl*	Pet
Frangkiser, C.	Amber Nocturne. *2 cl, acl (cl), bcl (cl)*	B-M
Frangkiser, C.	Autumn Skies. *2 cl, acl (cl), bcl (cl)*	B-M
Frangkiser, C.	Dancing Nymphs. *2 cl, acl (cl), bcl (cl)*	B-M
Frangkiser, C.	En Escapades. *2 cl, acl (cl), bcl (cl)*	B-M
Frangkiser, C.	Fuguerest. *2 cl, acl (cl), bcl (cl)*	B-M
Frangkiser, C.	Melodie Petite. *2 cl, acl (cl), bcl (cl)*	PrA
Frangkiser, C.	Snowflakes. *2 cl, acl (cl), bcl (cl)*	B-M
Frangkiser, C.	Stars at Dawn	B&H

Four Clarinets

Frangkiser, C.	Three Blind Mice.	
	2 cl, acl (cl), bcl (cl)	B-M
Frescobaldi, G.-Johnson	Galliard and Courante.	
	3 cl, bcl (cl)	Rub
Gabrielsky, W.-Andraud	Grand Quartet, op. 53/1	SM
Gabrielsky, W.-Andraud	Grand Quartet, op. 53/2	SM
Gabrielsky, W.	Grand Quartet, op. 53/3	SM
Galuppi, B.-Maganini	Toccata. *2 cl, acl, bcl*	EdM
Gariglio, R.	Fantasie and Fugue. *3 cl, bcl*	PrA
Gay, E.	10 Petites Pieces Classiques,	
	2 vols.	Bil
Gearhart, L.	Clarinet Sessions.	
	2 cl, acl (cl), bcl (cl)	Sha
Gee, H.	Prelude-Scherzo	Reb
Gershwin, G.-Sears	Liza. *3 cl, bcl*	War
Glaser, W.	Fyra korta stycken (1968)	STI
Glazounov, A.-Bettoney	In Modo Religioso.	
	2 cl, acl, bcl	CF
Gluck, C.-Johnson	Andante and Caprice.	
	3 cl, bcl (cl)	Rub
Gluck, C.-Liegl	Dance of the Happy Spirits	CF
Godard, B.-Donatelli	Andante, op. 16. *2 cl, acl, bcl*	Wes
Goeb, R.	Second Clarinet Quartet	CoF
Goeb, R.	Suite in Folk Style	AMP
Green, B.	Idyl	B&H
Green, D.	4 Conversations (1959)	AMP
Grieg, E.-Donatelli	An der Wiege. *2 cl, acl, bcl*	Wes
Grieg, E.-Williams	Anitra's Tanz, op. 46/3.	
	2 cl, acl, bcl	SM
Grieg, E.-Liegl	Ase's Death (Peer Gynt	
	Suite No. 1)	CF
Grieg, E.-Carini	Elf Dance	Sch
Grieg, E.-Donatelli	Last Spring. *3 cl, bcl*	Wes
Grieg, E.-Donatelli	Sarabande, op. 40/2.	
	2 cl, acl, bcl	Wes
Grundman, C.	Bagatelle	B&H
Grundman, C.	Caprice. *2 cl, acl, bcl*	B&H
Guenther, R.	Rustic Scherzo	B-M
Gyring, E.	Capriccio	CoF
Gyring, E.	Chorale	HeE
Haberling, A.	New Chamber Music	HeE
Handel, G.-Barr	Air (Water Music).	
	2 cl acl (cl), bcl (cl)	Lud
Handel, G.	Bourree (Water Music).	
	2 cl, acl (cl), bcl (cl)	B-M
Handel, G.-Schaeffer	Hallelujah Chorus	PrA
Handel, G.-Stang	How Beautiful Are The Feet	
	(Messiah). *2 cl, acl (cl),*	
	bcl (cl)	CF
Handel, G.-Stang	Largo (Xerxes). *2 cl, acl, bcl*	CF
Handel, G.-Moore	Pastorale. *2 cl, acl, bcl*	Wes
Handel, G.-Liegl	Sarabande	CF

Four Clarinets

Handel, G.-Gordon	Sarabande. *2 cl, acl (cl), bcl*	SM
Handel, G.-Stang	Sinfonia (Messiah).	
	2 cl, acl (cl), bcl (acl)	CF
Harris, A. (arr)	Farewell to Cucullain.	
	2 cl, acl (cl), bcl (acl)	CF
Harris, A. (arr)	4 Heart Songs.	
	2 cl, acl (cl), bcl (acl)	CF
Harris, A. (arr)	Sacred Melodies.	
	2 cl, acl (cl), bcl (acl)	CF
Harris, A. (arr)	Scottish Airs.	
	2 cl, acl (cl), bcl (acl)	CF
Harris, A. (arr)	Songs of America.	
	2 cl, acl (cl), bcl (acl)	CF
Haubiel, C.	Nostalgia	See
Haubiel, C.	Will O' Wisp	See
Hausdörfer	Suite	MM
Haydn, F.-Geiger	Adagio	CF
Haydn, F.-Hite	Allegro, a (Op. 74/3)	Lud
Haydn, F.-Stouffer	Allegro. *2 cl, acl, bcl*	PrA
Haydn, F.-Williams	Emperor Variations, op. 76/3.	
	2 cl, acl, bcl	SM
Haydn, F.-Hite	Finale (String Quartet, op. 77/1)	SM
Haydn, F.-Lang	Gipsy Rondo	Lan
Haydn, F.-Hite	Menuetto. & Presto (Op. 1/1)	Lud
Haydn, F.-Brandenburg	Menuetto al Rovescio	
	(Sonata No. 4)	CF
Haydn, F.-Feldsher	Menuetto and Trio (Symphony	
	No. 88). *2 cl, acl, bcl*	Ken
Haydn, F.-Painter	Minuet de Boeuf	War
Haydn, F.-Troxell	Rondo (Divertimento No. 1).	
	2 cl, acl, bcl	PrA
Haydn, F.-Hite	Rondo (String Quartet, C)	SM
Haydn, F.-DeBueris	Serenade. *2 cl, acl (cl), bcl (cl)*	B-M
Henderson, K.	Nocturne Exotik	Ken
Herbert, V.-Briegel	Ocean Breezes	GFB
Herbert, V.-Briegel	2 Impressions. *2 cl, acl, bcl*	GFB
Herold, T.-Skornicka	Zampa "Prayer"	B-M
Heyer, F.	Quartet, F	Hal
Holmes, G.-Long	Symphony Ensemble Series	Rub
Houdy, P.	Quatre a quatre	ALe
Hovhaness, A.	Divertimento, op. 61/5. *3 cl, bcl*	Pet
Hudadoff, I. (arr)	24 Clarinet Quartets.	
	3 cl, bcl (cl)	PrA
Huffnagle	Black Velvet	SF
Huffnagle	Chopin Ballade	SF
Hunt, R.	Moto Perpetuo	B&H
Hurrell, C.	Galway Pipers	Rub
Hurrell, C.	2 Impressions. *3 cl, bcl*	GFB
Ippolitov, I.-DeBueris	Procession of the Sardar	B-M
Johnson, C.	Red Sunset	Rub
Johnson, C.	Snow Birds	Rub
Johnson, C.	White Forests	Rub

119

Four Clarinets

Jones, C.	3 Allegros	AMC
Jones, S.	Suite Moderne	Vol
Kabalevsky, D.-Green	Allegro (Sonatina No. 1).	
	2 cl, cl, bcl	YM
Kaplan, D.	A Country Story	B-M
Kaplan, D.	Frolic	SF
Karkoff, M.	5 Aforismer. *3 cl, bcl*	STI
Karkoff, M.	Liten musik, op. 74 (1965)	STI
Keith, G.	Interlude	B&H
Kersters, W.	Kleine suite	Mau
Kersters, W.	Variations op thema	
	van Farnaby, op. 41	CBD
Klauss, N.	The Clowns	Tem
Knighton, M.	Little Minuet	B&H
Knighton, M.	March Miniature	B&H
Knighton, M.	Quartet No. 1	B&H
Kraehenbuehl, D.	Variations. *3 cl, bcl*	AMP
Krenek, E.	Country Dance	B-M
Kuhlau, F.-Andraud	Grand Quartet, op. 103	SM
Lang, R.	Humoreske	Lan
Lang, R.	Nocturne and Tarantelle	Lan
Lecuona, E.-Gordon	La Comparsa	EBM
Leduc, J.	3 stukjes, op. 9bis	Mau
Lefebvre, C.-Waln	Intermezzo (2nd Suite)	NK
Lefebvre, C.-Waln	Prelude. *2 cl, acl (cl), bcl*	NK
Legron, L.	Petite Suite	Bil
Leonard, B.	Drink To Me Only With Thine	
	Eyes. *2 cl, acl (cl), bcl (cl)*	B-M
Leoni, C.	Conclave and Fugue Patrol	PrA
Leoni, C.	Southern Waltz. *2 cl, acl (cl), bcl*	B-M
Liadow, A.-Haydn, F.-Voxman	Sarabande and Finale.	
	2 cl, acl, bcl	Rub
Liedbeck, S.	Svit	EMF
Liegl, L. (arr)	Collection of Clarinet Quartets.	
	2 cl, acl (cl), bcl (cl)	War
Linde, B.	Quatuor en miniature,	
	op. 31 (1965)	STI
Long, N.	In the Aquarium	CF
Lowman, K.	Los Angeles Sketches.	
	2 cl, acl, bcl	Wes
Macbeth, A.-Harris	Intermezzo "Forget Me Not".	
	2 cl, acl (cl), bcl (acl)	CF
MacDowell, E.-Henderson	A Deserted Farm.	
	2 cl, acl (cl), bcl	Ken
MacDowell, E.-Williams	In Autumn. *2 cl, acl, bcl*	SM
MacDowell, E.-Wood	Intermezzo. *2 cl, acl (cl), bcl*	HeE
MacDowell, E.-Isaac	To A Wild Rose	CF
MacDowell, E.-Estes	To A Wild Rose. *2 cl, acl, bcl*	Ken
MacDowell, E.-McKay	2 Tone Poems. *2 cl, acl*	
	(cl), bcl (cl)	Bar
MacDowell, E.-Harris	Woodland Sketches.	
	2 cl, acl (cl), bcl (cl)	Lud

Four Clarinets

Maes, J.	4 Contrastes (1965)	CBD
Maganini, Q.	Beginners' Luck	EdM
Mahler, G.-Leonard	In Praise of Lofty Intellect.	
	2 cl, acl, bcl	TP
Maniet, R.-Ruelle	Cuba, Suite-quartett	EMb
Maniet, R.-Rulst	Habanera. *2 cl, acl (cl), bcl (cl)*	EMb
Martini, P.	Plaisir d'Amour	EdM
Massenet, J.-Henderson	Elegy. *2 cl, acl (cl), bcl (cl)*	Ken
Massenet, J.-Harris	Last Slumber of the Virgin.	
	2 cl, acl (cl), bcl (acl)	CF
Mayeur, L.-Voxman	First Quartet. *2 cl, acl, bcl*	Rub
McBride, R.	2 Mexican Folk Songs	CoF
McCathren, D.-Norden	Introduction, Round and Fugue	Ken
McKay (arr)	2 Schumann Selections.	
	2 cl, acl, bcl	Fit
McKay, F.	American Sketch.	
	2 cl, acl (cl), bcl (cl)	Bar
McKay, F.	Chromatic Caprice.	
	2 cl, acl (cl), bcl (cl)	Bar
McKay, F.	Clarinet Quartets.	
	2 cl, acl (cl), bcl (cl)	Bar
McKay, F.	Musette. *2 cl, acl (cl), bcl (cl)*	Bar
McKay, F.	On the Boulevard.	
	2 cl, acl (cl), bcl (cl)	Bar
McKay, F.	Pastoral. *2 cl, acl (cl), bcl (cl)*	Bar
McKay, F.	Song and Dance.	
	2 cl, acl (cl), bcl (cl)	Bar
McKay, F.	Summer Etching.	
	2 cl, acl (cl), bcl (cl)	Bar
McKay, F.	2 Promenades.	
	2 cl, acl (cl), bcl (cl)	Bar
McKay, F.	With Gay Spirit.	
	2 cl, acl (cl), bcl (cl)	Bar
McKay, F.	Woods in April.	
	2 cl, acl (cl), bcl (cl)	Bar
McKay, G.	American Panorama	CF
McKay, G.	Episodes. *2 cl, acl (cl), bcl (cl)*	Bar
McKay, G.	Fiesta Mejicana	CF
McKay, G.	5 Pieces. *2 cl, acl bcl*	Wes
McKay, G.	On a Pastorale Theme	TP
McLin, E. (arr)	For Four B♭ Clarinets	PrA
Mendelssohn, F.-DeBueris	Canzonetta. *2 cl, acl (cl), bcl (cl)*	B-M
Mendelssohn, F.-Lang	Capriccio No. 2	Lan
Mendelssohn, F.-Langenus	Folk Song. *3 cl, bcl*	CF
Mendelssohn, F.	Folk Song. *2 cl, acl, bcl*	CF
Mendelssohn, F.-Whitney	A Joyous Song	Sch
Mendelssohn, F.	Menuet en trio	MM
Mendelssohn, F.-Langenus	Morning Song. *3 cl, bcl*	CF
Mendelssohn, F.	Morning Song. *2 cl, acl, bcl*	CF
Mendelssohn, F.-Langenus	Retrospection. *3 cl, bcl*	CF
Mendelssohn, F.	Retrospection. *2 cl, acl, bcl*	CF
Mendelssohn, F.-Howland	Rondo Capriccioso. *2 cl, acl, bcl*	SHM

Four Clarinets

Composer	Title	Publisher
Mendelssohn, F.-Donatelli	The Shepherd's Complaint, op. 67/5	Spr
Mendelssohn, F.-Henderson	Song of the Heather. 2 cl, acl (cl), bcl	Ken
Mendelssohn, F.-Donatelli	Spinning Song. 2 cl, acl, bcl	Wes
Merriman, L. (arr)	Clarinet Quartet Album. 2 cl, acl (cl), bcl (cl)	S-B
Meulemans, A.	Serenata (1961)	CBD
Meyer, L.	Reflections	Leb
Meyerbeer, G.-Harris	Coronation March (The Prophet). 2 cl, acl (cl), bcl (acl)	CF
Miller, R.	Prelude and Scherzo, op. 20. 2 cl, acl (cl), bcl (cl)	B-M
Miller, R.	Prelude to Autumn. 2 cl, acl (cl), bcl (cl)	B-M
Molloy, A.-Harris	Kerry Dance. 2 cl, acl (cl), bcl (acl)	CF
Morsch, J. (arr)	12 Clarinet Quartets. 2 cl, acl, bcl	TP
Moszkowski, M.-Vognar	March of the Dwarfs, op. 53/4. 2 cl, acl, bcl	War
Mozart, W.-Laube	Adagio (Clarinet Concerto). 2 cl, acl, bcl	CF
Mozart, W.-Waln	Allegro (K. 464). 2 cl, acl (cl), bcl	NK
Mozart, W.-Voxman	Allegro (Quartet, K. 157). 2 cl, acl, bcl	Rub
Mozart, W.-Hite	Allegro Vivace, K. 387. 2 cl, acl, bcl	SM
Mozart, W.	Alleluia. 2 cl, acl (cl), bcl (cl)	EdM
Mozart, W.-Rosenthal	Divertimenti	EBM
Mozart, W.-Lemarc	Dritter Satz (Sonata, C)	T-M
Mozart, W.-Toll	Excerpt from Piano Sonata No. 10. 2 cl, acl, bcl	CF
Mozart, W.-Smith	Lullaby	PrA
Mozart, W.-Liegl	Menuet (Don Juan)	CF
Mozart, W.-Gee	Menuetto	PrA
Mozart, W.-Hite	Menuetto (String Quartet, C)	SM
Mozart, W.-Stephens	Minuet (Symphony, E♭). 2 cl, acl (cl), bcl (cl)	CF
Mozart, W.-Seay	Minuetto (K. 282)	Spr
Mozart, W.-Gee	Rondo. 2 cl, acl, bcl	SM
Mozart, W.-Gee	Rondo Alla Turca. 2 cl, acl, bcl	SM
Mozart, W.-Toll	Rondo (Piano Sonata No. 1)	CF
Mozart, W.-Neufeld	Serenade, B♭	Wes
Mozart, W.-Bellison	Suite No. 2, G. 2 cl, acl, bcl	FrC
Murray, L.	Canon a Go Go. 2 cl, acl, bcl	Wes
Mussorgsky, M.-Skolnik	Mushrooms	EdM
Norden, H.	Delicate Sounds of the King	CF
Norden, H.-McCathren	Rondo, F	CF
Nyquist	3 Bagatelles	B-M

Four Clarinets

Organn, R.	Autumn	Reb
Organn, R.	Chief Big Horn Goes To Town	Reb
Organn, R.	Divertimeto	Reb
Ostling, A.	Pop Goes the Woodwinds.	
	2 cl, acl (cl), bcl (cl)	B-M
Ostrander, A.	Baroque Suite	EdM
Owen, H.	Chamber Music	Wes
Owings, J.	Auditorium Quartets	CF
Owings, J.	Lamentoso. 2 cl, acl (cl), bcl (cl)	B-M
Owings, J.	Quartet Album	B-M
Pala	Quartet, c	MM
Palestrina, G-Mendelssohn, F.-Skornicka	Alleluia and Choral	B-M
Palestrina, G.-Schaeffer	A Quite Theme	PrA
Paulson, J.	Clarinette Moderne.	
	2 cl, acl (cl), bcl (cl)	GFB
Pelemans, W.	Kwartet	Mau
Pestalozza, H.-Bennett	Ciribiribin	War
Pierné, G.-Grisez	March of the Little Tin Soldiers	CF
Piersol, F.	Scherzo	Hal
Piket, F.	Reflection and Caprice	SF
Pisk, P.	Suite	CF
Pleyel, I.	Andante and Rondo, op. 48/1.	
	2 cl, 2 acl (2 cl)	CF
Poot, M.	Legend	JB
Porter, C.-Sears	Begin the Beguine. 3 cl, bcl	War
Porter, R.	Beaver Creek	HeE
Powell, L.	Quartet. 2 cl, acl, bcl	CF
Presser, W.	Song and Workout	Leb
Puccini, G.-Leidzen	Musetta's Waltz (La bohème).	
	2 cl, acl (cl), bcl (cl)	FrC
Puccini, G.-Leidzen	One Fine Day (Madama Butterfly).	
	2 cl, acl (cl), bcl (cl)	FrC
Puccini, G.-Leidzen	They Call Me Mimi (La bohème).	
	2 cl, acl (cl), bcl (cl)	FrC
Puccini, G.-Leidzen	Vissi d'arte. 2 cl, acl	
	(cl), bcl (cl)	FrC
Quinet, M.	Petite Suite (1959)	CBD
Rachmaninoff, S.-Donatelli	Prelude, op. 3/2.	
	2 cl, acl, bcl	Wes
Rameau, J.-Donatelli	Le Tambourin. 2 cl, acl, bcl	Wes
Rameau, J.-De Filippi	The Hen. 2 cl, acl (cl), bcl (cl)	HeE
Rathaus, K.	Country Serenade	B&H
Ready, E.	Petite Classique	CF
Ready, E.	Romance. 2 cl, acl, bcl	War
Rimsky-Korsakov, N.-Donatelli	Flight of the Bumble Bee.	
	2 cl, acl, bcl	Wes
Roden, R.	The Brook	CF
Roden, R.	Cerise	CF
Roden, R.	Sounds of the Sea	Bar
Rodgers, R.-Sears	The Blue Room. 3 cl, bcl	War
Rohinsky, A.	Clarinet Chorales	CF

Four Clarinets

Rosen, J.	Petite Suite	Leb
Rosenthal, C.	Clarinet Quartettes	EBM
Rowley, A.	Nocturne	GaM
Ruger, M.-Yates	Allegro (String Quartet No. 1).	
	2 cl, acl, bcl	Ken
Sanders, R.	The Imp. 2 cl, acl, bcl	CF
Scarlatti, A.-Johnson	Aria and Minuet. 3 cl, bcl (cl)	Rub
Scarmolin, L.	Four of a Kind	Bar
Scarmolin, L.	Merrymakers. 2 cl, acl	
	(cl), bcl (cl)	Bar
Schaeffer, D.	Conversations	PrA
Schaeffer, D.	15th Century Madrigal	PrA
Scharwenka, X.-Liegl	Andante	CF
Schlabach, K.	Caprice	War
Schmutz, A.	Allegro Capriccioso	CF
Schmutz, A.	Preludial Fantasia.	
	2 cl, acl, bcl	Fit
Schmutz, A.	Scherzoso	Fit
Schoemaker, M.	Volière (1961)	CBD
Schubert, F.	Cantilena-Presto	EdM
Schubert, F.-Willaman	Finale (Quartet No. 6)	Sch
Schubert, F.-Tustin	4 Schubert Waltzes.	
	2 cl, acl (cl), bcl (cl)	Bar
Schubert, F.-DeBueris	Menuet (Fantasia, op. 78)	B-M
Schubert, F.-del Busto	Theme from D Minor Quartet	CF
Schuman, W.-Tustin	Quartettino	SMP
Schumann, G.	Audiogramme	S-V
Schumann, R.	Allegretto (Sonata No. 1, op. 105).	
	2 cl, acl, bcl	CF
Schumann, R.-Simon	7 Miniatures	B&H
Schwadron, A. (arr)	Progressive Ensemble Studies,	
	Vol. 3	Ken
Schwadron, A.	Waltz. 2 cl, acl, bcl	Ken
Sears, J.	Buckjumper Suite	Cha
Sears, G.	Licorice-Stick Suite	CF
Sears, G.	Serenade, F.	PrA
Semler-Collery, J.	Quartetto	EME
Sibelius, J.-Beeler-Rode	Andante Festivo	SMP
Silcher, F.-Harris	Loreley-Paraphrase.	
	2 cl, acl (cl), bcl (acl)	CF
Simon, E. (arr)	3 Minuets	EBM
Skinner, I.	Capricietta	B-M
Skornicka, J.-Rush	Quartet Album	B-M
Smith, T.	Suite. 3 cl, acl (cl)	Bar
Stamitz-Kesnar	Andante. 2 cl, acl (cl), bcl (cl)	CF
Stevens, H.	2 Pieces (1961)	CoF
Stolz, R.	Twilight in Blue.	
	2 cl, acl, (cl), bcl (cl)	B&H
Stone, G.	Joyful Four	DGo
Stouffer	Tick-Tack-Toe.	
	2 cl, acl (cl), bcl (cl)	PrA
Stravinsky, I.-De Filippi	Berceuse (Firebird).	

Four Clarinets

Summers, S.
Suppiger, R.

Taylor, C.
Tchaikovsky, P.-De Bueris

Tchaikovsky, P.-Johnson
Tchaikovsky, P.-Erickson

Tchaikovsky, P.-Skornicka
Tchaikovsky, P.
Tchaikovsky, P.
Tchaikovsky, P.-Gee
Tcherepnine, N.
Telemann, G.
Telemann, G.-Simon
Thomé, F.-Harris
Thompson, T. (ed)

Thompson, T. (arr)
Thompson, T. (arr)
Thornton, R.
Toll, R. (arr)
Tomasi, H.
Trowbridge, L.
Tufilli, W.
Turini, G.-Wienandt
Tustin, W.

Uhl, A.
Vaughan Williams, R.

Vecchi, O.
Velden, R. van der
Vellère, L.
Verdi, G.-Harris

Vivaldi, A.
Vivaldi, A.

Von Kreisler, A.
Voxman, H.

Voxman, H.

Voxman, H.

Walckiers, E.-Harris
Walker, R.
Walker, R.

2 cl, acl (cl), bcl (cl)	HeE
Allegro Breve. *2 cl, acl, bcl*	Wes
Impressions. *2 cl, acl*	
(cl), bcl (cl)	War
3 Novelties	CF
Andante Cantabile.	
2 cl, acl (cl), bcl (cl)	B-M
Chanson Triste	Rub
Light and Lively.	
2 cl, acl (cl), bcl (cl)	B-M
Overture "1812"	B-M
Scherzo. *2 cl, acl, bcl*	Fit
Traumerei. *2 cl, acl (cl), bcl (cl)*	GFB
Waltz (Symphony No. 5)	PrA
6 Pieces. *2 cl, acl (cl), bcl (cl)*	EdM
Concerto	SM
Concerto for Four Clarinets	EBM
Pizzicato. *2 cl, acl (cl), bcl (acl)*	CF
Captain Morgan's March &	
6 Other Pieces	S&C
6 Traditional Tunes, Bk. 1	Cha
6 Traditional Tunes, Bk. 2	Cha
Diversion Project	Byr
6 Little Gems from the Masters	CF
3 Divertissements	ALe
Chorale	See
Charm	B-M
Fanfare and Processional	SM
Cheerful Elegy.	
2 cl, acl (cl), bcl (cl)	Bar
Divertimento. *3 cl, bcl*	SS
3 Preludes (Household Music).	
3 cl, bcl (cl)	OxU
The Cricket. *2 cl, acl (cl), bcl (cl)*	EdM
Fantaisie (1967)	CBD
Quatuor	Mau
Quartet (Rigoletto).	
2 cl, acl (cl), bcl (acl)	CF
Giga. *2 cl, acl (cl), bcl (cl)*	EdM
Sonata da Camera.	
2 cl, acl (cl), bcl (cl)	EdM
Scherzo. *2 cl, acl, bcl*	SM
Ensemble Classics, Vol. I.	
2 cl, acl (cl), bcl (cl)	Rub
Ensemble Classics, Vol. II.	
2 cl, acl, bcl	Rub
Quartet Repertoire.	
2 c, acl (cl), bcl (cl)	Rub
Rondo. *2 cl, acl (cl), bcl (acl)*	CF
Appalachian Dance	PrA
Aubade. *2 cl, acl (cl), bcl*	Ken

Four Clarinets

Walker, R.	Chase of the Centaurs.	
	2 cl, acl (cl), bcl (cl)	Bar
Walker, R.	Masquerade.	
	2 cl, acl (cl), bcl (cl)	Bar
Walker, R.	Quiet Brook	Ken
Walker, R.	Serbian Dance	Spr
Walker, R.	Valse-Scherzo.	
	2 cl, acl (cl), bcl (cl)	Bar
Waterson, J.-Langenus	Andantino and Scherzo	CF
Waterson, J.-Andraud	Grand Quartet	SM
Weigl-Dancla-Harris	Air Varie. *2 cl, acl (cl), acl (cl)*	CF
Weinzweig, J.	Clarinet Quartet (1964-65).	
	3 cl, bcl	Can
White, C.	Suite Spiritual	HeE
Whitney, M.	Roulade	CF
Wilkinson, P.	Suite	Nov
Willaman, R. (arr)	6 Easy Excerpts	Sch
Willbye, J.	English Madrigal	PrA
Wilson, K.	Variations on a Theme	
	of Paganini	B&H
Wood, C.	Ensemble Album of	
	Famous Melodies	HeE
Yoder, P.	Clarumba. *3 cl, bcl, perc ad lib*	NK
Yoder, P. (arr)	Dark Eyes. *3 cl, bcl*	NK
Yoder, P. (arr)	Dry Bones. *2 cl, acl*	
	(cl), bcl, perc opt	NK
Yoder, P.	Relax! *2 cl, acl*	
	(cl), bcl, perc opt	NK
Zingarelli-Wienandt	Adagio and Allegro.	
	2 cl, acl, bcl	SM
Zonn, P.	Movement	CoF
Zonn, P.	2 Movements	CoF

FOUR SAXOPHONES

	Believe Me If All Those	GFB
	Endearing Young Charms.	
	2asax, tsax, bar sax, opt pf	
	Black Eyes.	GFB
	2asax, tsax, bar sax, opt pf	
	Deep River.	GFB
	2asax, tsax, bar sax, opt pf	
	Londonderry Air	GFB
	2asax, tsax, bar sax, opt pf	
Thompson (arr)	The Old Refrain.	Alf
	2asax, tsax, bar sax	

Four Saxophones

	Song of the Volga Boatmen.	GFB
	2asax, tsax, bar sax, opt pf	
Thompson (arr)	Swing Low, Sweet Chariot.	Alf
	2asax, tsax, bar sax	
	The Last Rose of Summer.	GFB
	2asax, tsax, bar sax, opt pf	
Able, C.-Brink	Andante (Symphony No. 3)	
Absil, J.	ler Quartet, op. 31	HLe
Absil, J.	Pieces in Quartet, op. 35	HLe
Absil, J.	Suite sur des thèmes populaires roumains, op. 90 (1956)	CBD
Albeniz, I.-Mule	3 Pieces	ALe
Applebaum	Quartet	SM
Arend, J.	Boismortier Suite	MM
Arend, J.	Suite Antique	MM
Arensky, A.	The Cuckoo.	GFB
	2asax, tsax, bar sax, opt pf	
Arnold, H.	Dithyramb (1969)	ArM
Artot, J.-Harris	12 Quartets.	CF
	2asax, tsax, bar sax	
Ashford	American Folksong Suite	SM
Bach, J.C.	Sinfonia, B♭	MM
Bach, J.S.-Hekker	Air (Suite No. 3)	T-M
Bach, J.S.-Gilet	Celèbre aria	EdR
Bach, J.S.-Kasprzyk	Fugue, e	ArM
Bacp, J.S.-Rosenthal	Fuga IX	Wes
Bach, J.S.-Schmidt	Fugue VII	Wes
Bach, J.S.-Evertse	Jesu, Joy of Man's Desiring	HeE
Bach, J.S.-Evertse	Jesu, Joy of Man's Desiring	HeE
Bach, J.S.-Evertse	Koraalbewerking (Cantata 147)	T-M
Bach, J.S.-Eymann	Prelude and Fugue, d.	CF
	2asax, tsax, bar sax	
Bach, J.S.-Eymann	Prelude and Fugue, e.	B-M
	2asax, tsax, bar sax	
Bach, J.S.-Eymann	Prelude and Fugue, g.	B-M
	2asax, tsax, bar sax	
Bach, J.S.	Prelude No. 4.	EdM
	2asax, tsax, bar sax(tsax)	
Bach, J.S.-Hemke	Sarabande. *sop sax(asax),*	SM
	asax, tsax, bar sax	
Bach, J.S.-Johnson	Sarabande and Badinerie.	Rub
	2asax, tsax, bar sax	
Bach, J.S.	7th Fugue.	GFB
	2asax, tsax, bar sax, opt pf	GFB
Bach, J.S.-Avignon	3 inventions à deux voix	EdR
Balfe, W.-Holmes	Bohemian Girl.	Bar
	2asax, tsax, bar sax	
Barbier, R.	Quatuor, op. 99 (1961)	CBD
Barnby, J.-Thompson	Sweet and Low	Alf
	2asax, tsax, bar sax	
Bartok, B.	3 Folk Dances.	SM
	2asax, tsax, bar sax	

Four Saxophones

Baudrier	Mes Amis	MM
Beethoven, L. van-Tilliard	Larghetto (Symphony No. 2)	EdR
Beethoven, L. van-Cailliet	Minuet, G. *2asax, tsax, bar sax*	B-M
Bennett, D.	Saxophone Symphonette. *2asax, tsax, bar sax*	CF
Berthomieu, M.	Rondo	E-V
Bertouille, G.	Prélude et fugue (1955)	CBD
Bizet, G.-Cailliet	Adagietto. *2asax, tsax, bar sax*	B-M
Bizet, G.-Martin	Adagietto de l'Arlesienne	EdR
Bizet, G.	Agnus Dei. *2asax, tsax, bar sax, opt pf*	GFB
Bizet, G.-Cailliet	Intermezzo (Suite l'Arlesienne). *2asax, tsax, bar sax*	B-M
Bizet, G.-Johnson	Quartet de l'Arlesienne. *2asax, tsax, bar sax*	Rub
Boccherini, L.	Menuet	MM
Boccherini, L.-Cailliet	Menuet	SM
Bockemuehl, E.	Cortège	YM
Boedijn, G.	Badinage in een knollenland, op. 163 (1961)	MM
Boucard, M.	Quartett-Sinfonia	EdR
Boyce, W.	Overture for His Majesty's Birthday (1770)	MM
Bozza, E.	Andante and Scherzo	ALe
Bozza, E.	Nuages	ALe
Brahms, J.-Martin	Célèbre valse	EdR
Briegel, G.	Cathedral Echoes. *2asax, tsax, bar sax, opt pf*	GFB
Briegel, G. (arr)	Home on the Range. *2asax, tsax, bar sax, opt pf*	GFB
Brott, A.	Three Acts for Four Sinners (1961)	Can
Burgstahler, E. (arr)	13 Saxophone Quartets. *2asax, tsax, bar sax*	PrA
Cailliet, L.	Carnaval	Leb
Cailliet, L.	Fantasy and Fugue on O' Susanna	SM
Cailliet, L.	Quartet for Saxophones. *2asax, tsax, bar sax*	B-M
Caix d'Hervelois, L. de-Classens	La Marche du Czar	EPC
Casseday, A.	Quartet, g. *2asax, tsax, bar sax*	Bou
Casto-Holmes	Heart Strings Intermezzo. *2asax, tsax, bar sax*	Bar
Cheyette, I.	Viennese Lullaby. *2asax, tsax, bar sax*	Sha
Chopin, F.-Dedrick	Chopin Favorites. *sop sax(asax), asax, tsax, bar sax*	Ken
Christensen, J.	Comedy for Saxophones. *2asax, tsax, bar sax*	NK
Clarke, S.-Williams	Belgian March. *2asax, tsax, bar sax*	SM
Clementi, M.-Evertse	Canon	T-M

Four Saxophones

Clérisse, R.	Cache-cache	ALe
Clérisse, R.	Caravan	ALe
Clérisse, R.	Chanson du rouet	ALe
Clérisse, R.	Introduction and Scherzo	ALe
Clérisse, R.	Polka Valaisane	EdR
Clérisse, R.	Sérénade mélancolique	ALe
Cohen, S.	Novelette. *2asax, tsax, bar sax*	B-M
Conley	Song and Caprice. *2asax, tsax, bar sax*	Ken
Corelli, A.-Johnson	Sarabande and Courante. *2asax, tsax, bar sax*	Rub
Cowell, H.	Sailor's Hornpipe. *2asax, tsax, bar sax*	SMP
Croley, R.	Tre Espressioni (1969)	ArM
Dakin, C.	Prelude and Dance (1956)	HE
Danks, H.	Silver Threads Among the Gold. *2asax, tsax, bar sax, opt pf*	GFB
Debussy, C.-Mule	The Little Negro	ALe
Dedrick, A.	Waltz for Four. *2asax, tsax, bar sax*	Ken
Dedrick, C.	Sensitivity. *sop sax(asax), asax, tsax, bar sax*	Ken
Dedrick, R.	Impressionism (The Modern Art Suite). *sop sax(asax), asax, tsax, bar sax*	Ken
Dedrick, R.	Mysticism (The Modern Art Suite). *sop sax(asax), asax, tsax, bar sax*	Ken
Dedrick, R.	Purism & Surrealism (The Modern Art Suite). *sop sax (asax), asax, tsax, bar sax*	Ken
Dedrick, R.	Realism (The Modern Art Suite). *sop sax(asax), asax, tsax, bar sax*	Ken
Delamont, G.	3 Entertainments. *sop sax(asax), asax, tsax, bar sax*	Ken
Delbecq, L.	A bâtons rompus	EdR
Delbecq, L.	4 saxos en récréation	EdR
Delbecq, L.	Impromptu	EdR
Delbecq, L.	A saute-mouton	EdR
Desenclos, A.	Quartet	ALe
Dillon, H.	Nightshade. *2asax, tsax, bar sax*	B&H
Donizetti, G.-Dietze	Sextet (Lucia). *2asax, tsax, bar sax*	Rub
Drdla, R.-Harger	Souvenir. *2asax, tsax, bar sax*	B-M
Dubois, P.	Quartet	ALe
Dury, M.	Divertissement, op. 5	EMb
Dvorak, A.-Delbecq	Humoresque	EdR
Dvorak, A.-Vereecken	Humoresque. *2asax, tsax, bar sax*	CF
Dvorak, A.-Gordon	Largo (New World Symphony). *2asax, tsax, bar sax*	SM

Four Saxophones

Dvorak, A.	Songs My Mother Taught Me.	GFB
	2asax, tsax, bar sax, opt pf	
Dyck, V.	Quatuor Moderne "Leblanc"	Bil
Elgar, E.-Brooke	Salut d'Amour.	CF
End, J.	2 Modern Saxophone Quartets.	Ken
	2asax, tsax, bar sax	
Erickson, F.	Rondino. *2asax, tsax, bar sax*	B-M
Eymann	Prelude and Fugue. *4asax*	CF
Farhart, H.	Divertimento	Leb
Fauré, J.-Brooke	The Palms. *2asax, tsax, bar sax*	*CF*
Fiala, G.	First Saxophone Quartet (1955; rev. 1962)	Can
Fiala, G.	Second Saxophone Quartet (1961)	Can
Ficher, J.	Quartet	SMP
Foster, S.	2 Stephen Foster Melodies.	GFB
	2asax, tsax, bar sax, opt pf	
Frackenpohl, A.	Fanfare, Air and Finale	JB
Francaix, J.	Kleines Quartett	SS
Franck, C.	Panis Angelicus.	GFB
	2asax, tsax, bar sax, opt pf	
Frangkiser, C.	Jennadean. *2asax, tsax, bar sax*	B&H
Frangkiser, C.	**Luxury Lane.** *2asax, tsax, bar sax*	B-M
Frangkiser, C.	Song of the Orchid.	B&H
	2asax, tsax, bar sax	
Frank, M.	Conversation Piece.	Ken
	2asax, tsax, bar sax	
Frescobaldi, G.-Aaron	Gagliarda. *asax, 2tsax, bar sax*	Sch
Gabelles, G.	3 Pieces	EdR
Gabelles, G.	2 pieces	EdR
Gade, N.-Gee	Novellette. *2asax, tsax, bar sax*	Reb
Galuppi, B.	Toccata. *2asax, tsax, bar sax(tsax)*	EdM
Garcia, R.	Miniatury Symphony	EMo
Gastyne, S. de	Saxophone Quartet, op. 53	Fer
Gibbons, O.-Hemke	Fantazia	SM
Gilet	Promenade	EdR
Gilet	Quartet-valse	EdR
Glaser, W.	4 Pieces (1934)	STI
Glazounov, A.-Gee	Canzona, 2 Variations and Scherzo	B&H
Glazounov, A.	Quartet, op. 109	B&H
Gluck, C.-Johnson	Air de Ballet (Alceste).	Rub
	2asax, tsax, bar sax	
Gluck, C.-Classens	Iphigenie en Tauride	EPC
Godard, B.-Brooke	Berceuse. *2asax, tsax, bar sax*	CF
Gounod, C.	Marche Pontificale.	GFB
	2asax, tsax, bar sax, opt pf	
Gretry, A.	3 Danses Villagoises	MM
Grieg, E.	Ase's Death (Peer Gynt).	GFB
	2asax, tsax, bar sax, opt pf	
Grieg, E.-Taylor	Elegie. *2asax, tsax, bar sax*	B-M
Grieg, E.-Johnson	March of the Dwarfs.	Rub
	2asax, tsax, bar sax	
Grieg, E.-Brooke	Norwegian Dance.	CF

130

Four Saxophones

	2asax, tsax, bar sax	
Handel, G.-Hervig	Adagio and Allegro (Concerto Grosso, B♭).	Rub
	2asax, tsax, bar sax	
Handel, G.-Skolnik	Air. *2asax, tsax, bar sax*	SM
Handel, G.	Bourree, Air en Gavotte	MM
Handel, G.-Evertse	Koraalbewerking (St. John's Passion)	T-M
Handel, G.-Brooke	Largo. *2asax, tsax, bar sax*	CF
Handel, G.-Lemarc	Menuet (Berenice)	T-M
Handel, G.-Williams	Sarabanda. *2asax, tsax, bar sax*	SM
Handel, G.-Johnson	Sarabande and Air.	Rub
	2asax, tsax, bar sax	
Handel, G.	Sarabande et menuet	MM
Harris, A. (arr)	Farewell to Cucullain.	CF
	2asax, tsax, bar sax	
Harris, A. (arr)	4 Heart Songs.	CF
	2asax, tsax, bar sax	
Harris, F.	Vesper Moods.	Lud
	2asax, tsax, bar sax	
Haubiel, C.	For Louis XVI.	B-M
	2asax, tsax, bar sax	
Hawthorne, A.	Whispering Hope.	GFB
	2asax, tsax, bar sax, opt pf	
Haydn, F.-Hervig	Finale (Quartet, op. 9/3).	Rub
	2asax, tsax, bar sax	
Haydn, F.-Johnson	Third Movement (Symphony No.100).	Rub
	2asax, tsax, bar sax	
Heppener, R.	Canzona	SD
Herbert, V.-Briegel	Ocean Breezes.	GFB
	2asax, tsax, bar sax	
Hervig, R.	Divertimento No. 3.	Rub
	2asax, tsax, bar sax	
Hilliard, J.	Saxonata. *2asax, tsax, bar sax*	MCA
Holmes, G.	Little Ione Waltz.	Bar
	2asax, tsax, bar sax	
Holmes, G.	Master Builder March.	Bar
	2asax, tsax, bar sax	
Holmes, G. (arr)	Memories of Stephen Foster.	Bar
	2asax, tsax, bar sax	
Holmes, G.	Primrose Intermezzo.	Bar
	2asax, tsax, bar sax	
Holmes, G.	Spiritual Fantasia.	Rub
	2asax, tsax, bar sax	
Howland, R.	Quartet No. 1	YM
Humperdinck, E.-Johnson	Children's Prayer.	Rub
	2asax, tsax, bar sax	
Ibert, J.	3 Histoires	ALe
Jarnefelt, A.-Thompson	Praeludium. *2asax, tsax, bar sax*	Alf
Jeanjean, P.	Quartet	EdS
Johnson, W.	Chorale-Fantasy.	Fit
	2asax, tsax, bar sax	

Four Saxophones

Johnson, W.	Impromptu. *2asax, tsax, bar sax*	B-M
Johnson, W.	Pastorale. *2asax, tsax, bar sax*	B-M
Johnson, W.	Valse Mignonne. *2asax, tsax, bar sax*	B-M
Johnston, M.-Bonnell	Deep River. *2asax, tsax, bar sax*	SHM
Johnston, M.-Bonnell	Procession of the Sardar. *2asax, tsax, bar sax*	SHM
Jongbloed, D.	Romance	T-M
Jongen, J.	Quatuor, op. 122 (1942)	CBD
Jongen, L.	Divertissement (1937)	CBD
Kaderavek, M.	Introduction and Allegro	TP
Karlins, M.	Blues. *2asax, tsax, bar sax*	JB
Karlins, M.	Quartet. *2asax, tsax, bar sax*	CoF
Kéler-Béla-Holmes	Lustpiel. *2asax, tsax, bar sax*	Bar
Kesnar, M.	Capriccio. *2asax, tsax, bar sax*	CF
Keuris, T.	Quartet	SD
King, K.-Holmes	Night in June. *2asax, tsax, bar sax*	Bar
Klingsor, T.	Serenade	ChM
Koch, E.	Miniatyrer (1970)	STI
Korte, K.	Facets	ArM
Krieger, S.	Johann Krieger Suite	MM
Lacour, G.	Quatuor	Bil
Lange, G.-Brooke	Flower Song. *2asax, tsax, bar sax*	CF
Lantier, P.	Andante et Scherzzeto	Bil
Lebeirre, O.	Styrienne	T-M
Leclercq, E.	Introduction et scherzando	Mau
Leclercq, E.	Prélude et mouvement perpétuel	Mau
Leduc, J.	Suite en quatuor	SS
Legley, V.	5 miniatures, op. 54 (1958)	CBD
Liadow, A.-Harger	Musical Snuff Box. *2asax, tsax, bar sax*	B-M
Linn, R.	Prelude and Dance	Wes
Linn, R.	Quartet	Wes
Liszt, F.	Dream of Love. *2asax, tsax, bar sax, opt pf*	GFB
Liszt, F.-Holmes	Rhapsodie Hongroise No. 11. *2asax, tsax, bar sax*	Bar
Loup & Francois	Quatuor, g	EdR
Macbeth, A.-Brooke	Intermezzo "Forget Me Not." *2asax, tsax, bar sax*	CF
MacDowell, E.-Patrick	2 Woodland Sketches. *2asax, tsax, bar sax*	TP
Maganini, Q.	Beginner's Luck. *2asax, tsax, bar sax(tsax)*	EdM
Maganini, Q.	Double Canon. *2asax, tsax, bar sax(tsax)*	EdM
Manzo, S.	2 Tempi	GZ
Marie, G. [Gabriel-Marie]-Thompson	Golden Wedding. *2asax, tsax, bar sax*	Alf
Marshall, J.	Goldrush Suite	Sha
Mascagni, P.-Holmes	Intermezzo. *2asax, tsax, bar sax*	Bar

Four Saxophones

Massenet, J.-Thompson	Air de Ballet (Scenes Pittoresques). *2asax, tsax, bar sax*	Alf
Massenet, J.-Thompson	Marche (Scenes Pittoresques). *2asax, tsax, bar sax*	Alf
Maurice, R.	Aurore	Mau
Maury, L.	Cock of the Walk	Wes
McCarty, F.	5 Situations	ArM
McKay, G.	American Panorama. *4 equal saxes*	CF
McKay, G.	Fiesta Mejicana. *4 equal saxes*	CF
Mellish (arr)	Drink to Me Only with Thine Eyes. *2asax, tsax, bar sax, opt pf*	GFB
Mendelssohn, F.	Faith, op. 102/6. *2asax, tsax, bar sax, opt pf*	GFB
Mendelssohn, F.-Brooke	Spring Song. *2asax, tsax, bar sax*	CF
Mendelssohn, F.-Johnson	War March of the Priests (Athalie). *2asax, tsax, bar sax*	Rub
Menichetti, F.	Bouquet oriental (1934)	EdR
Meulemans, A.	Quatuor (1953)	CBD
Mielenz, H.-Voxman	Scherzo. *2asax, tsax, bar sax*	Rub
Miller, R.	Quartet No. 2. *2asax, tsax, bar sax*	PrA
Millöcker, K.	Herinneringen	MM
Molloy, J.	Love's Old Sweet Song. *2asax, tsax, bar sax, opt pf*	GFB
Moritz, E.	Quartet. *2asax, tsax, bar sax*	SM
Moskowski, M.-Harger	Spanish Dance. *2asax, tsax, bar sax*	B-M
Moulaert, R.	Andante, fugue et final (1907)	CBD
Mourant, W.	Quartet	CoF
Mourant, W.	Scherzo	CoF
Mozart, W.	Adagio and Menuet	HeE
Mozart, W.	Allegro (Piano Sonata, C)	HeE
Mozart, W.	Ave Verum *2asax, tsax, bar sax, opt pf*	GFB
Mozart, W.	Berceuse	MM
Mozart, W.-Lang	First Movement (Eine Kleine Nachtmusik). *2asax, tsax, bar sax*	Lan
Mozart, W.-Houtvast	Menuet Favorite	MM
Mozart, W.-Classens	Petite musique de nuit	EPC
Mozart, W.	Sonate	MM
Murphy, L.	Prelude & Canon	Wes
Murphy, L.	Rondino	Wes
Murphy, L.	Suite	Wes
Mussorgsky, M.	Mushrooms. *2asax, tsax, bar sax(tsax)*	EdM
Nelhybel, V.	3 Pieces. *2asax, tsax, bar sax*	B-M
Nestico, S.	A Study in Contrasts. *sop sax(cl), asax, tsax, bar sax*	Ken
Nevin, E.-Thompson	Narcissus. *2asax, tsax, bar sax*	Alf
Offenbach, J.	Barcarolle (Tales of Hoffman). *2asax, tsax, bar sax*	CF

Four Saxophones

Offenbach, J.-Holmes	Orpheus Overture. *2asax, tsax, bar sax*	Bar
Ostling, A.	Quar-tete-a-tete. *2asax, tsax, bar sax*	B-M
Otten, L.	Quartet	SD
Ottoson, D.	Svit. *2asax, tsax, bar sax*	STI
Paderewski, I.-Holmes	Minuet. *2asax, tsax, bar sax*	Bar
Palestrina, G.	Alma Redemptoris	EdR
Parera, A.-Walters	El Capeo. *2asax, tsax, bar sax*	Rub
Pascal, C.	Quatuor	Dur
Paschedag/Buchtel	First Ensemble. *2asax, tsax, bar sax*	NK
Pelemans, W.	Saxophone Quartet	Mau
Perrault, M.	Quatuor (1953)	Can
Petersen, T.	Miniature Suite. *2asax, tsax, bar sax*	Ken
Petersma, W.	Saxophone Quartet	SD
Pierné, G.-Mule	Chanson d'autrefois	ALe
Pierné, G.-Mule	Chanson de la Grand'maman	ALe
Pierné, G.	Introduction and Variations	ALe
Pierné, G.-Mule	La veillée de l'ange gardien	ALe
Pierné, G.-Nelson	The Guardian Angel & Song of the Grandmother. *2asax, tsax, bar sax*	Lud
Pierné, G.-Mule	March of the Little Tin Soldiers, op. 14/6	ALe
Pierné, P.	3 Conversations	Bil
Pitts	The Church in the Wildwood. *2asax, tsax, bar sax, opt pf*	GFB
Planquette, R.	Cloches de Corneville	MM
Poot, M.	Scherzo (1941)	CBD
Presser, W.	Waltz and Scherzo. *2asax, tsax, bar sax*	SM
Prokofiev, S.-Johnson	Romance and Troika. *2asax, tsax, bar sax*	Rub
Quinet, M.	Pochades	Bil
Ramsoe, W.-Voxman	Quartet No. 5, First Movement. *2asax, tsax, bar sax*	Rub
Raphling, S.	Concert Suite. *4asax*	EdM
Rascher, S. & L. Patrick	5 Centuries for Saxophone Quartet. *2asax, tsax, bar sax*	Bou
Rascher, S. & L. Patrick	Masterpieces for Saxophone Quartet. *2asax, tsax, bar sax*	Bou
Rea, J.	Fantaisies and/et Allusions (1969)	Can
Reber H.-Foret	Berceuse	Bil
Regt, H. de	Musica per 4 sassofoni	SD
Rex, H. (arr)	Shenandoah. *2asax, tsax, bar sax*	B-M
Ricard, C.	Badinerie	SM
Rimsky-Korsakov, N.-Mule	Le Vol du Bourdon	Bil
Rivier, J.	Grave et Presto	Bil
Rodney-Holmes	Calvary. *2asax, tsax, bar sax*	Bar

Four Saxophones

Roussakis, N.	21 Quartets for Saxophones. *2asax, tsax, bar sax*	CoF
Rueff, J.	Concert en quatuor	ALe
Ruelle, F.	Prelude	Mau
Saint-Saens, C.-Brooke	My Heart At Thy Sweet Voice. *2asax, tsax, bar sax*	CF
Saint-Saens, C.-Brooke	The Swan. *2asax, tsax, bar sax*	CF
Scarlatti, A.-Schmidt	Prelude & Fugue	Wes
Scharwenka, X.-Brooke	Polish Dance. *2asax, tsax, bar sax*	CF
Schmidt, W.-Van den Brink	Finale (Quartet No. 4)	MM
Schmidt, W.	Suite	Wes
Schmitt, F.	Quatuor, op. 102	Dur
Schmutz, A.	Introduction, Recitative & Chorale. *2asax, tsax, bar sax(tsax)*	AMP
Schmutz, A.	Prelude & Finale. *2asax, tsax, bar sax(tsax)*	AMP
Schrijver, K. de	Drie - Delige Suite	T-M
Schubert, F.-Gilet	Célèbre marche militaire	EdR
Schubert, F.-Thompson	Moment Musical. *2asax, tsax, bar sax*	Alf
Schubert, F.-Holmes	Serenade. *2asax, tsax, bar sax*	Bar
Schubert, F.-Ostling	Symphonic Theme. *2asax, tsax, bar sax*	B-M
Schumann, R.-Rascher	4 Short Pieces. *2asax, tsax, bar sax*	B-M
Schuman, W.-Rascher	Quartettino. *2asax, tsax, bar sax*	SMP
Schwarz, I.	Canzone. *2asax, tsax, bar sax*	Rub
Serebrier, J.	Quartet	SMP
Sibelius, J.-Beeler/Rope	Andante Festivo. *2asax, tsax, bar sax*	SMP
Sibelius, J.	Finlandia. *2asax, tsax, bar sax, opt pf*	GFB
Singelee, J.-Lefèvre	Allegro de Concert. *2asax, tsax, bar sax*	CF
Singer, S.	Orientale. *2asax, tsax, bar sax*	CF
Singer, S.	Theme and Little Fugue. *2asax, tsax, bar sax*	CF
Smetsky, J. de-Whear	March of the Spanish Soldiery. *2asax, tsax, bar sax*	Lud
Smith, C.-Holmes	Life's Lighter Hours. *2asax, tsax, bar sax*	Bar
Soderlundh, L.	Idea I and II. *2asax, tsax, bar sax*	STI
Sorensen-Holmes	With the Colors. *2asax, tsax, bar sax*	Bar
Sousa, J.-Harger	The Thunderer March. *2asax, tsax, bar sax*	B-M
Spears, J.	Episode	SM
Spears, J.	Quartet '66. *2asax, tsax, bar sax*	SM
Stein, L.	Suite (1962). *2asax, tsax, bar sax*	SM
Strauss, R.-Johnson	Allerseelen, op. 10/8. *2asax, tsax, bar sax*	Rub

Four Saxophones

Stults, R.	The Sweetest Story Every Told. *2asax, tsax, bar sax, op, pf*	GFB
Tchaikovsky, P.	Lieder ohne Worte	MM
Tchaikovsky, P.	Nuits bizarre en Barcarolle	MM
Telemann, G.-Johnson	Menuet and Polonaise (Suite, a). *2asax, tsax, bar sax*	Rub
Telemann, G.-Johnson	Overture Baroque (Suite, a). *2asax, tsax, bar sax*	Rub
Tufilli, W.	Rose Blush. *2asax, tsax, bar sax*	B-M
Tuthill, B.	Quartet. *2as x, tsax, bar sax*	SM
Vecchi, O.	The Cricket. *2asax, tsax, bar sax(tsax)*	EdM
Vellones, P.	Au jardin des bêtes sauvages	Dur
Vellones, P.	Les Cavaliers Andalous	HLe
Verdi, G.-Holmes	Anvil Chorus (Il Trovatore). *2asax, tsax, bar sax*	Bar
Verdi, G.	Celeste Aida. *2asax, tsax, bar sax*	CF
Verdi, G.-Holmes	Miserere (Il Trovatore). *2asax, tsax, bar sax*	Bar
Verdi, G.	Quartet (Rigoletto). *2asax, tsax, bar sax*	CF
Verdi, G.-Holmes	Rigoletto. *2asax, tsax, bar sax*	Bar
Violeau, R.	Suite Chinoise	Bil
Vivaldi, A.	Giga. *2asax, tsax, bar sax(tsax)*	EdM
Von Suppé, F.-Holmes	Light Cavalry Overture. *2asax, tsax, bar sax*	Bar
Von Suppé, F.-Holmes	Poet and Peasant Overture. *2asax, tsax, bar sax*	Bar
Wagner, R.-Gordon	March (Tannhauser). *2asax, tsax, bar sax*	NK
Wagner, R.	Pilgrim Chorus (Tannhauser). *2asax, tsax, bar sax, opt pf*	GFB
Wagner, R.-Holmes	Tannhauser March. *2asax, tsax, bar sax*	Bar
Wahlberg, R.	Prisma	STI
Walker, R.	4 Fancies. *2asax, tsax, bar sax*	B-M
Walker, R.	Suite. *2asax, tsax, bar sax*	Ken
Walters, H.	Fair and Warmer. *2asax, tsax, bar sax*	Rub
Walters, H.	I'm On My Way. *2asax, tsax, bar sax*	Rub
Walters, H.	Pizza Party. *2asax, tsax, bar sax*	Rub
Weber, C.M. von-Thompson	Oberon Overture. *2asax, tsax, bar sax*	Alf
Westendorf	I'll Take You Home Again Kathleen. *2asax, tsax, bar sax, opt pf*	GFB
Williams, V.	Prelude and Beguine. 2asax, tsax, bar sax	CF
Yoder, P. (arr)	Dry Bones. *2asax, tsax, bar sax, perc opt*	NK
Yoder, P. (arr)	Jericho. *2asax, tsax, bar sax*	NK

Four Saxophones

Yoder, P.	Relax!	NK
	2asax, tsax, bar sax, perc opt	
Yoshioka, E.	Aria (Aria & Allegro)	ArM
Yradier, C.-Brooke	La Paloma. *2asax, tsax, bar sax*	CF

FOUR SAXOPHONES - COLLECTIONS

Arnold, J. & C. Lindsay	Saxophone Quartets.	MS
	2asax, tsax, bar sax	
Cailliet, L.	Quartet Album.	B-M
	2asax, tsax, bar sax	
Clerisse, R. (arr)	Recueil de quatuors classiques	EdR
Hautvast (arr)	Meister Perlen	T-M
Holmes, G. & Long	Symphony Ensemble Series.	Rub
	2asax, tsax, bar sax	
Hudadoff, I. (arr)	24 Saxophone Quartets.	PrA
	2asax, tsax, bar sax	
Voxman, H.	Quartet Repertoire.	Rub
	2asax, tsax, bar sax	

FOUR BASSOONS

Bottje, W.	Dances: Solemn & Joyous	CoF
Childs, B.	Quartet	CoF
Dubensky, A.	Prelude and Fugue	FrC
Dubois, P.	Scherzo	ALe
Goviksman, B.	Prelude & Fugue	MR
Haba, A.	Quartet	CHF
Josten, W.	Concertante Music	HeE
Maxwell	Idyls of Four Goblins	Wes
Prokofiev, S.	Humorous Scherzo	M&M
Prokofiev, S.	Humorous Scherzo, op. 12/9	Spr
Schuman, W.	Quartettino	SMP
Weait, C. (arr)	Suite of Early American Tunes	CP

FOUR WOODWINDS

Alemann, E.	3 Micropoems. *fl, ob, cl, bsn*	SMP
Alexandrov, H.	Suite. *fl, ob, cl, bsn*	MR
Allgen, C.	Fuga. *fl, ob, cl, bsn*	STI
Artot, J.-Harris	12 Quartettes. *fl, ob, cl, bsn*	CF
Artot, J.-Harris	12 Quartets.	CF
Artot, J.-Harris	12 Quartets. *2cl, asax(cl, acl), bsn(bcl, asax)*	CF
Artot, J.-Harris	12 Quartets. *cl, 3asax*	CF
Augenblick, L.	Scherzo, C. *fl, ob, cl, bsn*	Wes
Bach, J.C.-Maganini	Allegro Brillante. *fl, ob, cl, bsn*	CF
Bach, J.S.-Banquer	Ach Gott und Herr, Wie Gross und Schwer. *fl, ob(cl), cl, bsn*	CF
Bach, J.S.-Hekker	Air (Suite No. 3). *cl, cl(asax), cl(tsax), bar sax*	War
Bach, J.S.-Damm	Bourree. *fl, ob, cl, bsn*	CF
Bach, J.S.-Banquer	Chorale and Prelude on Auch Gott und Herr. *fl, 2cl, bcl(bsn)*	CF
Bach, J.S.-Wilkinson	4 Pieces. *fl, ob, cl, bsn*	Nov
Bach, J.S.-Cafarella	Fughetta. *fl, ob, cl, bsn*	Vol
Bach, J.S.-McKay	Fugue No. 4. *fl, ob, cl, bsn(bcl)*	Bar
Bach, J.S.-Seay	Fugue, c. *fl, ob, cl, bsn*	Spr
Bach, J.S.-Hahn	Fugue, g. *fl, 2cl, bsn*	CF
Bach, J.S.-Kessler	Fugue XIV, Vol. II. *fl, ob, cl, bsn*	Rub
Bach, J.S.-Cox	Gavotte (French Suite No. 5). *fl, ob, cl, bsn*	B&H
Bach, J.S.-Grisez	Loure. *fl, ob, cl, bsn*	CF
Bach, J.S.-Organn	Minuet, G. *2ob, 2bsn*	Reb
Bach, J.S.-Houseknecht	Quartet No. 5. *fl, ob, cl, bsn*	SM
Bach, J.S.-Reed	Sarabande and Double. *ob, cl, cl(hn), bsn*	Ken
Bagley-Harris	Thistledown. *fl, ob, cl, bsn*	CF
Bagley-Harris	Thistledown. *2cl asax(cl, acl), bsn(bcl, asax)*	CF
Baird, T.	Divertimento (1956). *fl, ob, cl, bsn*	AP
Barbier, R.	Petite suite, op. 108 (1964). *fl, ob, cl, bsn*	CBD
Bartolozzi, B.	Concertazioni a Quattro (1969). *fl, ob, cl, bsn*	ESZ
Beckwith, J.	Quartet (1951). *fl, ob, ehn, bsn*	Can
Beethoven, L. van-Hahn	Contra Dance. *fl, ob(cl), cl, bsn*	CF
Beethoven, L. van-Toll	Excerpt from Rondo (Sonata Pathetique). *2cl, asax(cl, acl), bsn(bcl, asax)*	CF
Beethoven, L. van-Laube	Menuet (First Symphony). *fl, ob, cl, bsn*	CF
Beethoven, L. van-Tarlow	Menuetto (op. 10/3). *fl, 2cl, bsn*	War
Beethoven, L. van-Dahm	Minuet (Septet, op. 20). *fl, ob, cl, bsn*	CF
Beethoven, L. van-Cafarella	Minuet (Sonata, op. 22). *fl, ob, cl, bsn*	Vol
Beethoven, L. van-Hahn	Scene at the Brook (Symphony No. 6). *fl, ob, cl, bsn(bcl)*	CF

Four Woodwinds

Bentley, A. (arr)	16th Century Quartets. *4 ww instr*	Cha
Berbiguier, B.-Wienandt	Theme and Variations. *fl, 3cl*	PrA
Berger, A.	Quartet, C. *fl, ob, cl, bsn*	Pet
Berlinski, H.	Canons and Rounds. *4ob*	TP
Bertouille, G.	Prelude et fugue (1959). *fl, ob, cl, bsn*	CBD
Bitsch, M.	Divertissement. *fl, ob, cl, bsn*	ALe
Bizet, G.-Brooke	Andante and Minuet (L'Arlesienne). *3fl, acl*	CF
Bjelinski, B.	Scherzi di notte. *fl, ob, cl, bsn*	HG
Blacher, B.	Divertimento (1951). *fl, ob, cl, bsn*	B&B
Blatny, J.	Suite. *2fl, cl, bsn*	CHF
Blin, L.	Grupettino. *2cl, asax, tsax*	GaM
Boeringer, J.	Dance Suite. *fl, ob, cl, bsn*	AMP
Böhm, C.-Hamilton	Calm as the Night. *2cl, 2bsn*	GaM
Bottenberg, W.	Quartet (1960). *fl, 2cl, bsn*	Can
Bottje, W.	Threesome for Four. *2fl, cl, bsn*	CoF
Bozza, E.	Serenade. *fl, ob, cl, bsn*	ALe
Bozza, E.	Sonatine. *fl, ob, cl, bsn*	ALe
Bozza, E.	3 Pièces pour une musique de nuit. *fl, ob, cl, bsn*	ALe
Brahms, J.-Hunter	3 Easy Quartets. *fl, ob, cl, bsn*	SS
Bridge, F.	Divertimenti. *fl, ob, cl, bsn*	B&H
Butterworth, N. (arr)	Tudor Suite. *fl(ob, cl), ob(cl), asav, bsn*	Cha
Cabus, P.	Houtblazerskwartet. *fl, ob, cl, bsn*	Mau
Cambert, R.	An Overture. *2ob, ehn, bsn*	CP
Carter, E.	8 Etudes and a Fantasy (1950). *fl, ob, cl, bsn*	AMP
Casterede, J.	Music for the Oboe Family. *ob, ob d'amore, ehn, heckelphone*	Pet
Castle, A.	Summer Sketches. *2fl, 2cl*	Ken
Cazden, N.	Insistence, op. 40/2. *2ob, 2bsn*	Spr
Cazden, N.	Waltz, op. 40/1. *fl, ob, cl, bsn*	Spr
Cervetti, S.	Divertimento. *ob, cl, bcl, bsn*	SMP
Chagrin, F.	Renaissance Suite. *fl, ob, cl, bsn*	Nov
Chaminade, C.-Guenther	Scarf Dance. *4ww*	B-M
Chopin, F.-Trinkhaus	Polonaise Militaire. *2cl, 2bsn*	GaM
Christlieb, D. (arr)	3 Pieces. *2ob, ehn, bsn*	CP
Clementi, M.-Evertse	Canon. *cl, cl(tsax), cl(asax), bar sax*	T-M
Colin, G.	Quatuor. *fl, ob, cl, bsn*	Mau
Coppola, D.	Quartet for Winds. *fl, ob, cl, bsn*	Ken
Corbeel, R.	Andante. *fl, ob, cl, bsn*	Mau
Corelli, A.	Allemanda. *fl, ob, cl, bsn*	EdM
Corelli, A.	Gavotte and Gigue. *fl, ob, cl, bsn*	EdM
Corelli, A.-Harris	Gigue. *fl, ob, cl, bsn*	CF
	Gigue. *fl, ob, cl, bsn*	EdM
Corelli, A.-Harris.	Gigue. *2cl, asax(acl), bsn(bcl)*	CF
Corroyez, G. (arr)	Nouvelle petite collection facile en quatuors. *4ww*	EdR
Corroyez, G. (arr)	Petite Collection populaire,	EdR

139

	artistique et facile en quatuors. *4ww*	
Corroyez, G. (arr)	20 petites pieces concertantes. *4ww*	EdR
Cox, N.	Menuet. *fl, ob, cl, bsn*	B&H
Cray, R. (arr)	6 Easy Transcriptions. *fl, ob, cl, bsn*	SF
Csonka, P.	French Suite. *4ww*	SMP
Cui, C.	Orientale. *fl, ob, cl, bsn*	CF
Cui, C.-Harris	Orientale. *2cl, asax(acl), bsn(bcl)*	CF
Debras, L.	Rotationen (1967). *fl, ob, cl, bsn*	See
De Filippi, A.	Hornpipe for a Gay Dolphin. *fl, ob, cl, bsn*	HeE
De Filippi, A.	In a Nostalgic Mood. *fl, ob, cl, bsn*	HeE
De Filippi, A.	March of the Little Tumblers. *fl, ob, cl, bsn*	HeE
De Lassus, O.-Corbeel	Domineconvertere. *fl, ob, cl, bsn*	Mau
De Lassus, O.-Corbeel	Soyons joyeus. *fl, ob, cl, bsn*	Mau
Delbecq, L. (arr)	Quatuors favoris. *4ww*	EdR
Delvaux, A.	Sonata a quattro (1964). *fl, ob, cl, bsn*	CBD
Denza, L.-Harris	Funiculi-Funicula. *fl, ob, cl, bsn*	CF
Denza, L.-Harris	Funiculi-Funicula. *2cl, asax (cl, acl), bsn(bcl, asax)*	CF
Dewit, A.-Harris	Harvest Dance. *fl, ob, cl, bsn*	CF
Dewit, A.-Harris	Harvest Dance. *2cl, asax(acl), bsn(bcl)*	CF
Dewit, A.-Harris	Hungarian Fantasie. *fl, ob, cl, bsn*	CF
Dewit, A.-Harris	Hungarian Fantasie. *2cl, asax (cl, acl), bsn(bcl, asax)*	CF
Dewit, A.-Harris	On the Lake. *fl, ob, cl, bsn*	CF
Dewit, A.-Harris	On the Lake. *2cl, asax(acl), bsn(bcl)*	CF
Dewit, A.-Harris	Polonaise No. 1. *fl, ob, cl, bsn*	CF
Dewit, A.-Harris	Polonaise No. 1. *2cl, asax(acl), bsn(bcl)*	CF
Dewit, A.	Spanish Waltz. *fl, ob, cl, bsn*	CF
Dewit, A.	Spanish Waltz. *2cl, asax (cl, acl), bsn(bcl, asax)*	CF
Dewit, A.	Summertime. *fl, ob, cl, bsn*	CF
Dewit, A.	Summertime. *2cl, asax(cl, acl), bsn(bcl, asax)*	CF
Donovan, R.	Quartet. *fl, ob, cl, bsn*	NVM
Doppelbauer, J.	Quartet. *fl, ob, cl, bsn*	LDo
Dubois, P.	TheThree Musketeers. *ob, cl, asax(cl), bsn*	ALe
Eckhardt-Gramatte, S.	Wind Quartet (1946). *fl, co, bsn, bcl*	Can
Elgar, E.	Salut d'amour, op. 12. *3fl, acl*	CF
Engelmann, H.	Permutazioni (1959), op. 20a. *fl, ob, cl, bsn*	A&S

Four Woodwinds

Erbse, H.	Quartet, op. 20. fl, ob, cl, bsn	Pet
Erdmann, D.	Divertimento. *fl, ob, cl, bsn*	S-V
Erdmann, D.	Improvisation. *fl, ob, cl, bsn*	HG
Erdmann, D.	Variations. *fl, ob, cl, bsn*	S-V
Erickson, F.	Scherzino. *4ww*	B-M
Eriksson, N.	Quartetto. *fl, ob, cl, bsn*	STI
Farrenc, J.-Brooke	Andante. *3fl, acl*	CF
Ferneyhough	Sonatina. *3cl, bsn*	Pet
Fishman, M.	6 Studies in Sonorities. *fl, ob, cl, bsn*	CF
Flegier, A.	Quatuor. *2ob, 2bsn*	E&C
Fragale, F.	Sprightly Flight. *fl, ob, cl, bsn*	AMC
Francaix, J.	Quartet. *fl, ob, cl, bsn*	SS
Frank, M.	Canon and Fugue. *fl, ob, cl, bsn(bcl)*	Ken
Frank, M.	Prelude and Fuguette. *fl, ob, cl, bsn*	Sh
Freistadt, M.	Woodwind Quartet. *fl, ob, cl, bsn*	AMC
Frescobaldi, G.-Rocerato	Fugue, c. *fl, ob, cl, bsn*	Vol
Fricker, P.	5 Kanons. *2fl, 2ob(2cl)*	BrH
Fuleihan, A.	Acrobatics (Humoristic Preludes). *fl, ob, cl, bsn*	SMP
Fuleihan, A.	Exit (Humoristic Preludes). *fl, ob, cl, bsn*	SMP
Fuleihan, A.	In a Barnyard (Humoristic Preludes). *fl, ob, cl, bsn*	SMP
Fuleihan, A.	Overture (Humoristic Preludes). *fl, ob, cl, bsn*	SMP
Fuleihan, A.	A Serenade for Judy (Humoristic Preludes). *fl, ob, cl, bsn*	SMP
Fürst, P.	Bläserquartett, op. 40. *fl, ob, cl, bsn*	LDo
Gabrielsky, W.-DeCaprio	Adagio. *fl, ob, cl, bsn*	NK
Gabrielsky, W.-DeCaprio	Finaletto. *fl, ob, cl, bsn*	NK
Garlick, A.	Quartet. *fl, ob, cl, bsn*	See
German, E.-Dahm	Pastorale Dance. *fl, ob, cl, bsn*	CF
Gerschefski, E.	"America" Variations for Winds, op. 44/6. *fl, cl, asax, bsn*	CoF
Gerschefski, E.	"America" Variations for Winds, op. 44/13. *fl, cl, asax, bsn*	CoF
Ghent, E.	Quartet. *fl, ob, cl, bsn*	OxU
Gibbons, O.-Cruft	2 Corantos. *fl, ob, cl, bsn*	B&H
Gideon, M.	Divertimento. *fl, ob, cl, bsn*	CoF
Glazounov, A.	In Modo Religioso. *fl, ob, cl, bsn*	CF
Glazounov, A.-Bettoney	In Modo Religioso. *2cl, asax (acl), bsn(bcl)*	CF
Goepfart, C.-Andraud	Quartet, op. 93. *fl, ob, cl, bsn*	SM
Grieg, E.-Taylor	3 Little Pieces. *fl, ob, cl, bsn*	CF
Grünauer, I.	Bläserquartett. *fl, ob, cl, bsn*	LDo
Gyring, E.	Fugue in Old Style. *fl, ob, cl, bsn*	CoF

Four Woodwinds

Gyring, E.	10 Canons for Two and Three Woodwinds. *fl, ob, cl, bsn*	CoF
Gyring, E.	Woodwind Quartet No. 1. *fl, ob, cl, bsn*	CoF
Handel, G.-Stang	How Beautiful are the Feet (Messiah). *fl, ob, cl, bsn*	CF
Handel, G.-Stang	How Beautiful Are the Feet (Messiah). *2cl, asax(cl, acl), bsn(bcl, asax)*	CF
Handel, G.-Stang	Largo (Xerxes). *fl, ob, cl, bsn*	CF
Handel, G.-Stang	Largo (Xerxes). *2cl, asax (cl, acl), bsn(bcl, asax)*	CF
Handel, G.-Ostling	Petite Fugue. *4ww*	B-M
Handel, G.-Grisez	Rinaldo's Aria. *fl, ob, cl, bsn*	C₁
Handel, G.-**Stang**	Sinfonia (Messiah). *fl, ob, cl, bsn*	CF
Handel, G.-**Stang**	Sinfonia (Messiah). *2cl, asax (cl, acl), bsn(bcl, asax)*	CF
Handel, G.-Cox	3 Movements. *fl, ob, cl, bsn*	Nov
Harris, A. (arr)	Farewell to Cucullain. *cl, 3asax*	CF
Harris, A. (arr)	Farewell to Cucullain. *fl, ob(cl), cl, bsn*	CF
Harris (arr)	Farewell to Cucullain. *2cl, asax (cl, acl), bsn(bcl, asax)*	CF
Harris, A. (arr)	4 Heart Songs. *fl, ob(cl), cl, bsn*	CF
Harris, A. (arr)	4 Heart Songs. *2cl, asax(cl, acl), bsn(bcl, asax)*	CF
Harris, A. (arr)	4 Heart Songs. *cl, 3asax*	CF
Harris, A. (arr)	Sacred Melodies. *fl, ob, cl, bsn*	CF
Harris, A. (arr)	Sacred Melodies. *2cl, asax (cl, acl), bsn(bcl, asax)*	CF
Harris, A. (arr)	Scottish Airs. *fl, ob, cl, bsn*	CF
Harris, A. (arr)	Scottish Airs. *2cl, asax(cl, acl), bsn(bcl, asax)*	CF
Harris, A. (arr)	Songs of America. *fl, ob, cl, bsn*	CF
Harris, A. (arr)	Songs of America. *2cl, asax (cl, acl), bsn(bcl, asax)*	CF
Harris, A.	Diversion. *ww quartet*	BB
Hartley, W.	Woodwind Quartet. *fl, ob, cl, bsn*	Cre
Haydn, F.-Tarlow	Adagio (op. 64/5). *fl, 2cl, bsn*	War
Haydn, F.-Geiger	Adagio (Piano Sonata). *fl, ob, cl(asax), bsn*	CF
Haydn, F.-Speets	Adagio (Quartet No. 29). *fl, ob(cl), asax, tsax*	T-M
Haydn, F.-Hahn	Allegro con Brio (String Quartet No. 4). *fl, ob(cl), cl, bsn*	CF
Haydn, F.-Speets	Andante (op. 33/6). *fl(E♭ cl), cl(asax), cl, tsax*	T-M
Haydn, F.-Ostling	Andante (Surprise Symphony). *4ww*	B-M
Haydn, F.	Flute Clock Sonatas. *2fl, 2cl*	OxU
Haydn, F.-Seay	Menuet. *fl, ob, cl, bsn*	Spr

Four Woodwinds

Haydn, F.-Kreisler	Menuetto and Scherzando. *fl, ob, cl, bsn*	SM
Haydn, F.-Banquer	Presto Scherzando (op. 20/4). *fl, ob, cl, bsn*	MCA
Haydn, F.-Hahn	Theme and Variations (Emperor Quartet). *fl, ob, cl, bsn(bcl)*	CF
Hekster, W.	Relief No. 4. *fl, ob, cl, bsn*	SD
Helm, E.	Quartet. *fl, ob, cl, bsn*	Sim
Hennign, E.	Badinage. *fl, ob, cl, bsn*	TP
Heussenstamm, G.	Callichoreo, op. 23. *fl, ob, cl, bsn*	See
Hounsell, H.	Suite. *fl, ob, cl, bsn*	Tem
Hurnik, I.	Esercizi. *fl, ob, cl, bsn*	UE
Hurrell, C.	2 Impressions. *fl, ob, cl, bsn(bcl)*	GFB
Ibert, J.	2 mouvements. *fl, fl(ob), cl, bsn*	ALe
Jelinek, H.	Divertimento. *E♭ cl, cl, basset hn, bcl*	UE-
Jones, C.	Lyric Waltz Suite. *fl, ob, cl, bsn*	Pet
Josquin des Près	Vive le Roy. *ehn, 3bsn*	Heu
Kabalevsky, D.-Seay	Childrens Suite, op. 27. *fl, ob, cl, bsn*	Spr
Kabalewski, W.	5 Pieces (1960). *fl, ob, cl, bsn*	AP
Kantor, J.	Serenade. *fl, ob, cl, bsn*	Wes
Kellam, I.	Cassation. *fl, ob, cl, bsn*	Gal
Kersters, W.	Variations, op. 49 (1969). *fl, ob, cl, bsn*	CBD
Kingman	4 Miniatures. *fl, ob, cl, bsn*	Wes
Kohn, K.	Divertimento. *fl, ob, cl, bsn*	AMC
Kondorossy, L.	Little Suite. *fl, ob, cl, bsn*	AMC
Kouguell, A.	Suite for Woodwinds. *fl, ob, cl, bsn*	AMC
Kozenykov	2 Pieces. *fl, ob, cl, bsn*	MR
Kudo, E.	Study for Woodwinds. *fl, ob, cl, bsn*	CoA
Kuhlau, F.-Cafarella	Allegretto Grazioso (Sonatina, op. 55/3). *fl, ob, cl, bsn*	Vol
Kurka, R.	7 Moravian Folk-Songs. *fl, ob, cl, bsn*	MS
La Capria, V.	Notturnino. *fl, ob, cl, bsn*	Fit
Lajtha, L.	4 Homages. *fl, ob, cl, bsn*	ALe
Landry-Grisez	Musette. *fl, ob, cl, bsn*	CF
Laube, P.-Harris	Alsatian Dance. *fl, ob, cl, bsn*	CF
Leeuwen, A. van	4 Miniatures. *2fl, 2cl*	SM
Leichtling, A.	Quartet No. 2, op. 25. *fl, ob, cl, bsn*	AMC
Limmert, E.	Griechische Essays (1965). *fl, ob, cl, bsn*	BrH
Lindbom, A.	Kvartett (1948). *fl, ob, cl, bsn*	STI
Lipatti, D.	Aubade. *ww quartet*	BB
Lloyd	Puzzle canon. *ob, ehn, 2bsn*	Heu
Lorenzo, L. de	I Quattro Virtuosi, op. 80. *fl, ob, cl, bsn*	Pet
Lully, J.-Taylor	Courant. *fl, ob, cl, bsn*	B-M

Four Woodwinds

Lully, J.	Military Marches. *2ob, ehn, bsn*	MR
Maasz, G.	Finckenschlag. *fl, ob, cl, bsn*	HSM
Macbeth, A.-Harris	Intermezzo "Forget Me Not." *fl, ob, cl, bsn*	CF
Macbeth, A.-Harris	Intermezzo "Forget Me Not." 2cl, *asax(cl, acl), bsn(bcl, asax)*	CF
Malipiero, G.	Sonata a quattro (1954). *fl, ob, cl, bsn*	UE
Maniet, R.-Rulst	Habanera. *2cl, asax, tsax*	EMb
Manson, E.	Fugue. *fl, ob, cl, bsn*	AMP
Martin, D.	Rondo for Woodwinds (1960). *fl, ob, cl, bsn*	Can
Martini, J.	Plaisir d'Amour. *fl, ob, cl, bsn*	EdM
Massenet, J.-Harris	Last Slumber of the Virgin. *2cl, asax(cl, acl), bsn(bcl, asax)*	CF
Massias, G.	Variations. *ob, cl, asax, bsn*	Bil
Mazellier, J.	10 Fugues. *fl, ob, cl, bsn*	E-V
McBride, R.	Interwoven. *2cl, 2bsn*	CoF
McClellan, R.	3 Modes. *fl, 2cl, bcl*	Wes
McKay, F.	Green Meadows. *fl, ob, cl, bsn(bcl)*	Bar
McKay, F.	Musette. *fl, ob, cl, bsn(bcl)*	Bar
McKay, F.	Novellette. *fl, ob, cl, bsn(bcl)*	Bar
McKay, G.	3 Nautical Characters. *fl, ob, cl, bsn(bcl)*	Bar
McNicol, R.	Quartet. *fl, ob, cl, bsn*	Pet
McNicol, R.	3 Dances. *fl(cl), cl, ob(cl), bsn*	HE
Meulemans, A.	Quatuor (1962). *fl, ob, cl, bsn*	CBD
Meyerbeer, G.-Harris	Coronation March (The Prophet). *fl, ob, cl, bsn*	CF
Meyerbeer, G.-Harris	Coronation March (The Prophet). *2cl, asax(cl, acl), bsn(bcl, asax)*	CF
Mielenz, H.	Scherzo. *fl, ehn, cl, bsn*	R&E
Molloy, J.-Harris	Kerry Dance. *fl, ob, cl, bsn*	CF
Molloy, J.-Harris	Kerry Dance. *2cl, asax(cl, acl), bsn(bcl, asax)*	CF
Montanari, N.	5 Invenzioni. *ww quartet*	Edi
Moyse, L.	Suite in C. *2fl, cl, bsn*	SM
Mozart, W.-Richter	Adagio. *fl, ob, cl, bsn*	War
Mozart, W.-Laube	Adagio (Clarinet Concerto). *2cl, asax(acl), bsn(bcl)*	CF
Mozart, W.	Adagio, K. 580a. *ehn, 2hn(2basset hn, 2cl), bsn*	EK
Mozart, W.-Wojciechowski	Adagio, K.V. 580a. *ehn, 2basset hn, bsn*	HSM
Mozart, W.	Alleluia. *fl, ob, cl, bsn*	EdM
Mozart, W.-Langenus	Andante and Menuetto (String Quartet No. 21). *fl, ob, cl, bsn*	CF
Mozart, W.-Pillney	Andante in Rondoform, K. 616. *fl, ob, cl, bsn*	BrH
Mozart, W.-Gee	Divertimento (K. 251). *fl, ob(fl), cl, bsn(bcl)*	PrA

Four Woodwinds

Mozart, W.-Harris	Excerpt (Piano Sonata No. 10). *fl, ob, cl, bsn*	CF
Mozart, W.-Toll	Excerpt (Sonata No. 4). *2cl, asax(cl, acl), bsn(bcl, asax)*	CF
Mozart, W.-Stephens	Minuet (Symphony, E♭). *fl, ob, cl, bsn*	CF
Mozart, W.-Stephens	Minuet (Symphony, E♭). *2cl, asax(acl), bsn(bcl)*	CF
Mozart, W.-Lentz	Quartet (K. 298). *fl, ob, cl, bsn*	Tem
Mozart, W.	Quintet, K. 581; Divertimento No. 11, K. 251. *ww quartet*	EdK
Mozart, W.-Kesnar	Rondo. *fl, ob, cl, bsn(bcl)*	CF
Mozart, W.-Toll	Rondo (Piano Sonata No. 1). *fl, ob, cl, bsn*	CF
Mozart, W.-Toll	Rondo (Piano Sonata No. 1). *2cl, asax(cl, acl), bsn(bcl, asax)*	CF
Mueller, F.	Suite for Four. *fl(ob, cl, tsax), fl(ob, cl, tsax), cl(acl, asax), bsn(bcl)*	Uni
Mozart, W.-Bellison	Suite No. 2, G. *2cl, basset hn (cl), bcl*	FrC
Mussorgsky, M.-Skolnik	Mushrooms. *fl, ob, cl, bsn*	EdM
Naumann, S.	Ruoli (1959). 2cl, bcl, basset hn	STI
Nemiroff, I.	4 Treble Suite. *2fl, 2cl*	M&M
Niehaus, L.	Conversation Piece. *2fl, 2cl*	Wes
Niehaus, L.	Woodwind Nocturne. *2fl, 2cl*	Wes
Nilsson, B.	Déjà vu (1968). *fl, ob, cl, bsn*	Che
Organn, R.	Air and Variations. *2ob, 2bsn*	Reb
Organn, R.	Autumn. *2ob, 2bsn*	Reb
Organn, R.	Autumn. *2ob, 2cl*	Reb
Organn, R.	In a Garden. 2ob, 2bsn	Reb
Organn, R.	Reverie. *fl, ob, cl, bsn*	Reb
Organn, R.	Serenade to a Young Lady. *2ob, 2bsn*	Reb
Organn, R. (arr)	3 Short Dances. *2ob, 2bsn*	Reb
Orland, H.	Fuga. *fl, ob, cl, bsn*	See
Parkinson	Air de Ballet. *fl, ob, cl, bsn(bcl)*	GFB
Pasquini, B.-Rocereto	Sonata II. *fl, ob, cl, bsn*	Vol
Paulson, G.	Liten serenad, op. 22. *fl, ob, cl, bsn*	STI
Pelemans, W.	Blazerskwartet. *fl, ob, cl, bsn*	Mau
Pelemans, W.	Onder de appelbomen. *fl, ob, cl, bsn*	Mau
Pierné, G.	March of the Little Tin Soldiers. *fl, ob, cl, bsn*	CF
Pillin, B.	Scherzo. *fl, ob, cl, bsn*	Wes
Pisk, P.	Elegy and Scherzino. op. 70/2. *ww quartet*	CoF
Pisk, P.	A Little Woodwind Music. *ob, 2cl, bsn*	AMP
Pleyel, I.	Andante and Rondo, op. 48/1. *fl, ob, cl, bsn*	CF

Four Woodwinds

Pleyel, I.	Andante and Rondo, op. 48/1. *2cl, asax(cl, acl), bsn(bcl, asax)*	CF
Pleyel, I.	Quartet, E♭. *fl, 2cl, bsn*	MR
Poldini, E.-Mueller	Poupée Valsante (Dancing Doll). *fl, ob, cl, bsn*	CF
Poot, M.	Musique (1964). *fl, ob, cl, bsn*	CBD
Poot, M.	Petite marche de fete (1938). *fl, ob, cl, bsn*	CBD
Praag, H. van	Kwartet (1947). *fl, ob, cl, bsn*	SD
Praag, H. van	3 Schetsen (1958). *fl, ob, cl, bsn*	SD
Prokofiev, S.	Fleeting Moments, op. 22. *fl, ob, cl, bsn*	CF
Prokofiev, S.	Gavotta (Classical Symphony). *fl, ob, cl, bsn*	EdM
Prokofiev, S.	Gavotta (Classical Symphony). *fl, ob, 2cl*	EdM
Prokofiev, S.	Gavotta (Classical Symphony). *2fl, 2cl*	EdM
Prokofiev, S.	Gavotta (Classical Symphony). *2fl, cl, bsn*	EdM
Prokofiev, S.	Visions Fugitives. *fl, ob, cl, bsn*	M&M
Provinciali, E.	Danse Villageoise. *fl, ob, cl, bsn*	EME
Puccini, G.-Leidzen	Musetta's Waltz (La boheme). *fl, ob, cl, bsn*	FrC
Puccini, G.-Leidzen	One Fine Day(Madama Butterfly). *fl, ob, cl, bsn*	FrC
Puccini, G.-Leidzen	They Call Me Mimi (La Bohème). *fl, ob, cl, bsn*	FrC
Puccini, G.-Leidzen	Vissi d'arte (Tosca). *fl, ob, cl, bsn*	FrC
Purcell, H.-Edmunds	Dioclesian. *fl, ob, cl, bsn*	CF
Purcell, H.-Elkan	I Attempt from Love's Sickness to Fly. *fl, ob, cl, bsn*	B-M
Purcell, H.-Edmunds	King James II Suite. *fl, ob, cl, bsn*	CF
Quinet, M.	Quatuor (1964). *fl, ob, cl, bsn*	CBD
Rameau, J.-Soeller	Gavotte. *fl, ob, cl, bsn*	Fit
Rameau, J.-Corbeel	Gavotte en rondeau. *fl, ob, cl, bsn*	Mau
Rameau, J.-Dawn	Rigaudon. *fl, ob, cl, bsn*	B&H
Raphael, G.	Quartet, op. 61 (1945). *fl, ob, cl, bsn*	B&N
Raphling, S.	Concert Suite. *4ob*	EdM
Raphling, S.	Square Dance. *fl, ob, cl, bsn*	EdM
Rathburn, E.	Second Waltz for Winds (1949). *fl, ob, cl, bsn*	Can
Rathburn, E.	Waltz for Winds (1949; rev 1955). *fl, ob, cl, bsn*	Can
Ravin, I.	Sonatina for Woodwinds. *fl, ob, cl, bsn*	AMC
Renzi, A.	5 Bagatelle. *fl, ob, cl, bsn*	EDS
Riegger, W.	3 Canons, op. 9 (1930). *fl, ob, cl, bsn*	TP
Riisager, K.	Quartet, op. 40a (1941). *fl, ob, cl, bsn*	SPD

Four Woodwinds

Roland-Manuel, A.	2 Rondels de Péronnelle d'Armentières. *2fl, cl, bsn*	Dur
Rousakis	March, Song and Dance. *fl, ob, cl, bsn*	B-M
Roy, K.	Sterlingman Suite. *fl, ob, cl, bsn*	TP
Rubbra, E.	Nocturno. *pic, fl, ob, cl*	AlL
Sadler, H.	Quartettino. *fl, ob, cl, bsn*	B&N
Salome, T.-Taylor	Canon Marziale. *fl, ob, cl, bsn*	B-M
Samonov	Suite. *fl, ob, cl, bsn*	ChM
Scarlatti-Rosenthal	Scarlattiana. *fl, ob(fl), cl, bsn(bcl)*	Wes
Scarlatti-Rocereto	Sonata VIII, F. *fl, ob, cl, bsn*	Vol
Scarmolin, A.	Danse Grotesque. *fl, ob, cl, bsn(bcl)*	Bar
Scarmolin, A.	Mirth. *fl, ob, cl, bsn(bcl)*	Bar
Scarmolin, A.	Scherzo. *fl, ob, cl, bsn*	CF
Scarmolin, A.	Will o' the Wisp. *fl, ob, cl, bsn(bcl)*	Bar
Schenk, J.-Steinbeck	Quartet. *fl, 2ehn, bsn*	LDo
Schickele, P.	7 Bagatelles. *fl, ob, cl, bsn*	E-V
Schilling, H.	Metamorphosen über ein altes Liebeslied. *fl, ob, cl, bsn*	BrH
Schmit, C.	Burlesques (1964-65). *fl, ob, cl, bsn*	CBD
Schmitt (arr)	Alte Bläsersätze. *4 winds in any combination*	SS
Schubert, F.-Hahn	Minuetto (Fantasia, op. 78). *fl, ob(cl), cl, bsn*	CF
Schumann, R.-Grisez	Allegretto (Sonata No. 1). *fl, ob, cl, bsn*	CF
Schumann, R.-Williams	A-Maying. *fl, ob, cl, bsn*	SM
Schumann, R.-Corbeel	Lentelied. *fl, ob, cl, bsn*	Mau
Schumann, R.-Holer	3 Pieces (Album for the Young). *fl, ob, cl, bsn*	Byr
Schumann, R.	Traumerei. *3fl, acl*	CF
Schuyt, N.	Alla Notturna. *2ob, ob d'amore, ehn*	SD
Scott, S.	Woodwind Quartet. *fl, ob, cl, bsn*	CoA
Sehlbach, E.	Quartet. *fl, ob, cl, bsn*	MV
Silcher, F.-Harris	Lorely-Paraphrase. *fl, ob, cl, bsn*	CF
Silcher, F.-	Loreley-Paraphrase. *2cl, asax (cl, acl), bsn(bcl, asax)*	CF
Sontag, H.	Quartet on Old Tunes. *fl, ob, cl, bsn*	TP
Sorce, R.	Theme and Variations. *fl, ob, cl, bsn*	StM
Souris, A.	Concert flamand (1965). *fl, ob, cl, bsn*	CBD
Spino, P.	Woodwind Quartet. *ob, fl, cl, bsn*	StM
Spisak, M.	Quartet (1938). *ob, 2cl, bsn*	AP
Stamitz-Kesnar	Andante. *2cl, asax(acl), bsn(bcl)*	CF

Four Woodwinds

Steiner, H.	Ich hatt' einen Kameraden. *2cl, 2bsn*	**B&B**
Stevens, H.	8 Pieces. *fl, ob, cl, bsn*	CoF
Stone, D.	The Minstrel's Gallery. *fl, ob, cl, bsn*	B&H
Strang, G.	Variations. *fl(ob), ob(cl), cl(ehn), bsn(bcl)*	ACA
Stravinsky, I.	Pastorale. *fl, ob, cl, bsn*	EdM
Stringfield, L.	An Old Bridge. *4ww*	MCA
Stroud, R.	Sketch. *fl, ob, cl, bsn*	CoA
Tardos, B.	Divertimento. *fl, ob, cl, sn*	B&V
Tardos, B.	Quartettino. fl, ob, cl, bsn	EMB
Tausinger, J.	Colloquium. *fl, ob, cl, bsn*	Art
Taylor	3 Little Pieces from Grieg. *fl, ob, cl, bsn(bcl)*	CF
Tchaikovsky, P.-Hamilton	Chanson Triste. *2cl, 2bsn*	GaM
Telemann, G.-Polnauer	6 Minuets (Sept fois Sept et Un). *fl, ob, cl, bsn*	CF
Thomè, F.-Harris	Pizzicato. *fl, ob, cl, bsn*	CF
Thomè, F.-Harris	Pizzicato. *2cl, asax(cl, acl), bsn(bcl, asax)*	CF
Tseiger, H.	Suite on Estonian Themes. *fl, ob, cl, bsn*	MR
Turechek, E.	Divertissement, f. *fl, ob, cl, bsn*	War
Tustin, W.	Improvisation. *fl, ob, cl, bsn(bcl)*	Bar
Tuthill, B.	Divertimento. *fl, ob, cl, bsn*	CF
Uber, D.	3 Sketches. *fl, ob, cl, bsn*	SMP
Van de Vate	Woodwind Quartet. *fl, ob, cl, bsn*	SM
Van Leeuwen, A.	4 Miniatures. *2fl, 2cl*	SM
Vellère, L.	Quartetto. *fl, ob, cl, bsn*	Mau
Verdi, G.-Harris	Quartet (Rigoletto). *fl, ob, cl, bsn*	CF
Verdi, G.-Harris	Quartet (Rigoletto). *2cl, asax (cl, acl), bsn(bcl, asax)*	CF
Villa-Lobos, H.	Quartet. *fl, ob, cl, bsn*	EME
Vivaldi, A.	Giga. *fl, ob, cl, bsn*	EdM
Walckiers, E.-Brooke	Rondo. *3fl, cl*	CF
Walckiers, E.-Harris	Rondo. *2cl, asax(cl, acl), bsn(bcl, asax)*	CF
Waters, C.	2 Miniatures. *fl, ob, cl, bsn*	Pet
Watson, W.	Scherzo. *fl, ob, cl, bsn*	CoA
Weigl-Dancla-Harris	Air Varie. *fl, ob, cl, bsn*	CF
Weigl-Dancla-Harris	Air Varie. *2cl, asax(cl, acl), bsn(bcl, asax)*	CF
Weisgall, H.	Lines. *fl, ob, cl, bsn*	TP
Weis gall, H.	Pastorale. *fl, ob, cl, bsn*	TP
Welin, K.	Ancora (1969). *pic, fl, afl, bfl*	STI
Wesley, S.-Dawn	Gavotte. *fl, ob, cl, bsn*	B&H
Wieslander, I.	Missologi: liten svit. *2cl, 2bsn*	STI
Wilkinson, P.	Suite. *fl(ob, cl), ob(cl), cl, bsn(cl)*	Nov
Wilson, K.	Nocturne. *4ww*	B-M
Wittinger, R.	Concentrationi (1965), op. 7. *fl, ob, cl, bsn*	BrH

Four Woodwinds

Wuorinen, C.	Sonatina. *fl, ob, cl, bsn*	TP
Wyman	Les Clarinets Joyeux. *3cl, bsn*	War
Zonn, P.	Compositions for Quartet. *fl, ob, cl, bsn*	CoF
Zonn, P.	Divertimento No. 3. *ob, cl, bcl, bsn*	CoF

THREE FLUTES - KEYBOARD

Andersen, J.-Walters	Scherzino	Rub
Barnard, G.	The Pals	NK
Beethoven, L. van-Klaus	Menuet	Ken
Boismortier, B.-Ruf	Sonate, g. *3fl, bc*	B&N
Bond, C.-Buchtel	I Love You Truly	NK
Bonner	Over the Hills	EdM
Buchtel, F.	Azure Skies	NK
Buchtel, F.	Coquette	NK
Buchtel, F.	Dancing Nymphs	NK
Buchtel, F.	Elf in Dance	NK
Buchtel, F. (arr)	The Rosary	NK
Corelli, A.	Allemanda	EdM
Corrette, M.	Concerto Comique. *3fl, bc*	WIN
Course, W.	Happy-Go-Lucky	Rub
Cunningham, M.	Haiku	CoA
Delibes, L.-Erickson	Caprice	SHM
Erickson, F.	Carnival of Venice	SHM
Filas, T.	'Round & 'Round She Goes	AMC
Filas, T.	The Chase	AMC
Fote, R.	Tutti Fluti	Ken
Grundman, C.	Flutation	B&H
Harris, F.	Petite Mazurka	Lud
Hurrell, C.	Galway Pipers	Rub
Hurrell, C.	The Girl Friends	Rub
Johnson, C.	The Debonaires	Rub
Jordan, J.	Little Red Monkey	AMC
Kennedy-Harris	Star of the East	Lud
Koepke, P.	Aubade	Rub
Koepke, P.	Harlequinade	Rub
McKay, F.	The Dancer	Bar
McKay, F.	Hallowe'en Time	Bar
McKay, F.	Siciliano	Bar
Moyse, L.	4 Pieces	Sch
Oliver-Lubetkin	Tropical Serenade	Hal
Oliver, R.	American Folk Song	Hal
Osterling, E.	Beguine for Flutes	Lud
Osterling, E.	Samba for Flutes	Lud
Ostransky, L.	Arabesques	Rub
Ostransky, L.	Spanish Rondo	Rub
Paulson	Impromptu	GFB
Purcell, H.-Ring	Chaconne. *3fl, pf, vc ad lib*	S&C

Three Flutes, Keyboard

Rimsky- Korsakoff, N.-Walters	Flight of the Bumblebee	Rub
Rorich, C.	Burleske, op. 64	WZ
Salieri, A.	Danse (Tarare)	EdM
Scarlatti, A.	Quartet, F. *3fl, pf, bsn ad lib*	Pet
Scarlatti, A.-Woehl	Quarttitino. *3fl, pf, vc ad lib*	Pet
Siennicki, E.	Ponytail Polka	NK
Simeone, H.	Flute Cocktail	Sha
Taylor, L.	Trio	Hal
Tchaikovsky, P.-Magini	Dance of the Reed Flutes	CF
Tchaikovsky, P.-Hummel	Danse des Mirlitons	Rub
Tchaikovsky, P.-Finlayson	Nutcracker Suite. *3fl, pf, opt bells*	B&H
Vivaldi, A.	Giga	EdM
Walker, R.	Capriccio	Bar
Walker, R.	Cortege	Bar
Walters, H.	Safari	Rub
Whitney, M-Walters	Mosquitoe's Parade	Rub

THREE CLARINETS - KEYBOARD

Barnard, G.	Merriment Polka	CF
Barnard, G.	Merriment Polka	Wat
Barnett, W.	Waltz for Three	Ken
Beethoven, L. van	Theme (Symphony No. 2)	Cen
Bizet, G.	Carillon	EdM
Brahmstedt, N.	Frivolities	Rub
Buchtel, F.	Azure Skies	NK
Buchtel, F.	Coquette	NK
Buchtel, F.	Elfin Dance	NK
Buchtel, F.	Soft Shoe Dance	NK
Cailliet, L.	Divertissement	HeE
Campo, F.	Concertino, op. 32. $E\flat$ *cl, cl, bcl, pf*	Wes
Chaminade, C.	Scarf Dance	Cen
Chedeville, N.	Scherzo	EdM
Chopin, F.	Preludes, op. 28/7, 20	Cen
Colby, C.	Three Blind Mice	War
Corelli, A.	Air and Dance	EdM
Corelli, A.	Gavotte and Gigue	EdM
Corelli, A.	Gigue	EdM
Dahm, P.	Concert Album	EdM
Dieterich, M.	Chanson Joyeuse	Rub
Dieterich, M.	Chanson Triste	Rub
Estes, A.	Claristhenics	Ken
Fabre, C.-Harris	Second Reverie	CF
Ghys, J.-Harris	Amaryllis & Country Gardens	Lud
Grieg, E.	Watchman's Song, op. 12/3	Cen
Handel, G.	Sonata No. 2	MR
Harris, F.	Andante & Gavotte	Lud
Heuberger, R.-Kreisler/Leidzen	Midnight Bells	CFo

Three Clarinets, Keyboard

Hummel (arr)	Clarinet Polka	Rub
Iljinsky, A.	Berceuse	Cen
Johnson, C.	Caprice Gracieuse	Rub
Johnson, C.	Serenade Impromptu	Rub
Klauss, N.	Cape Kennedy Sketches	Ken
Koepke, P.	Evensong	Rub
Koepke, P.	Shivaree	Rub
Kreisler, F.-Leidzen	Liebesfreud	CFo
Kreisler, F.-Leidzen	Rondino on a theme of Beethoven	CFo
Kreisler, F.-Leidzen	Schön Rosmarin	CFo
Lotti, A.	Arietta	EdM
Maganini, Q.	Concert Album	EdM
Maganini, Q.	Milady's Fan	EdM
Martini, J.	Plaisir d'Amour	EdM
Mazas, J.-Paulson	Rondo	PrA
McKay, F.	Hallowe'en Time	Bar
Mendelssohn, F.	Song Without Words No. 48	Cen
Mozart, W.	Minuet and Trio	Cen
	(Symphony in E$\flat$)	
Nardini, P.	Shepherd's Pipes	EdM
Olivadoti, J.	Air and Tarantella	Rub
Olivadoti, J.	Dance in Olden Style	Rub
Ostransky, L.	Pastorale and Scherzo	Rub
Ostransky, L.	Waltz and Burlesk	Rub
Rachmaninoff, S.	Vocalise	EdM
Raphling, S.	Square Dance	EdM
Rimsky-Korsakoff, N.-Walters	Flight of the Bumblebee	Rub
Rugolo, P.	Bach and Fourth	Wes
Savage	Momento Giojoso	CF
Scarmolin, A.	Barcarolle & Petite Humoresque.	Lud
	2cl, bcl, pf	
Scholtes	We Three	Wat
Schumann, R.	Soldier's March, op. 68/2	Cen
Siennicki, E.	Ponytail Polka	NK
Taylor, L.	Polka-A-Poco	Hal
Tchaikovsky, P.-Davis	Danse des Mirlitons	Rub
Vivaldi, A.	Giga	EdM
Whitney-Walters	The Mosquitoes' Dance	Rub

THREE SAXOPHONES, KEYBOARD

Arditi, L.	Il Bacio (The Kiss). asax, tsax (asax), tsax (asax), pf	Cen
Barnard, G.	The Pals. 3 asax, pf	NK
Barnes, C.	3 Debonairs. 3 sax, pf	Vol
Beaumont	Con Amore. asax, tsax (asax), tsax (asax), pf	Cen
Beethoven, L. van	Minuet in G. asax tsax (asax) tsax (asax), pf	Cen

Three Saxophones, Keyboard

Beethoven, L. van	Moonlight Sonata (Adagio). *asax, tsax (asax), tsax (asax), pf*	Cen
Bond, C.-Buchtel	I Love You Truly. *3 asax, pf*	NK
Briegel, G.	Soloette. *2 asax, tsax, pf*	GFB
Briegel, G.	3 Stars. *2 asax, tsax, pf*	GFB
Briegel-Tucker	Triplets. *2 asax, tsax, pf*	GFB
Buchtel, F.	Azure Skies. *3 asax, pf*	NK
Buchtel, F.	Coquette. *3 asax, pf*	NK
Buchtel, F.	Soft Shoe Dance. *3 asax, pf*	NK
Buchtel, F. (arr)	Southern Fantasy. *2 asax, tsax, pf*	NK
Buchtel, F. (arr)	The Rosary. *3 asax, pf*	NK
Di Capua, E.	O Sole Mio (My Sunshine). *asax, tsax (asax), tsax (asax), pf*	Cen
Dvorak, A.	Humoreske. *asax, tsax (asax), tsax (asax), pf*	Cen
Frank	Minka, Minka. *2 asax, tsax, pf*	Rub
Grieg, E.	To Spring. *asax, tsax (asax), tsax (asax), pf*	Cen
Grooms, C.	Two Guitars (Russian Song). *asax, tsax (asax), tsax (asax), pf*	Cen
Harris, F.	Gallant Brigadiers. *2 asax, tsax, pf*	Bar
Harris, F. (arr)	The Old Refrain & Dark Eyes. *2 asax, tsax (asax), pf*	Lud
Harris, F.	3 Cadets. *2 asax, tsax, pf*	Lud
Harris, F.	3 Cubs. *2 asax, tsax, pf*	Lud
Harris, F.	3 For The Show. *2 asax, tsax (asax), pf*	Lud
Harris, F.	3 Syncopators. *2 asax, tsax, pf*	Lud
Herbert, V.-Harris	Gypsy Love Song. *2 asax, tsax, pf*	Lud
Heuberger, R.-Kreisler-Leidzen	Midnight Bells. *3 asax, pf*	CFo
Heuberger, R.-Kreisler-Leidzen	Midnight Bells. *2 asax, tsax, pf*	CFo
Jahrl	Frolic of the Keys. *2asax, tsax, pf*	GFB
Kennedy	Star of Hope (Reverie). *asax, tsax (asax), tsax (asax), pf*	Cen
Lemare, E.	Cathedral Meditation. *asax, tsax (asax), tsax (asax), pf*	Cen
Leybach, I.	Fifth Nocturne, G. *asax, tsax (asax), tsax (asax), pf*	Cen
Liszt, F.	Love Dreams (Liebestraum). *asax, tsax (asax), tsax (asax), pf*	Cen
McCall, H.	Valse Elise. *2 asax, tsax, pf*	Lud
McKay, F.	Anita. *2 asax, tsax, pf*	*Bar*
McKay, F.	Carmela. *2 asax, tsax (asax), pf*	Bar
McKay, F.	Chiquita. *2 asax, tsax (asax), pf*	Bar
McKay, F.	Hallowe'en Time. *2 asax, tsax, pf*	Bar
McKay, F.	3 Amigos. *2 asax, tsax (asax), pf*	Bar
McKay, F.	3 Cadets. *2 asax, tsax (asax), pf*	Bar
McKay, F.	3 Jesters. *2 asax, tsax (asax), pf*	Bar
Ravel, M.-Walters	Pavane. *2 asax, tsax, pf*	Rub

Three Saxophones, Keyboard

Richards, J.	Triad. *2 asax, tsax, pf*	Bar
Rimsky-Korsakoff, N.	Song of India. *asax, tsax (asax), tsax (asax), pf*	Cen
Saint-Saens, C.	My Heart At Thy Sweet Voice. *asax, tsax (asax), tsax (asax), pf*	Cen
Scarmolin, A.	3 Swingsters. *2 asax, tsax, pf*	Lud
Schaefer, A.	Troubadours. *3 asax (2 asax, tsax), pf*	CF
Siennicki, E.	Ponytail Polka. *3 asax, pf*	NK
Tchaikovsky, P.-Harris	Sweet Dreams. *2 asax, tsax, pf*	Lud
Walters, H.	Fantasy for Three. *2 asax, tsax, pf*	Rub
Walters, H.	Jim Dandies. *2 asax, tsax, pf*	Rub
Wood	Let 'Er Go. *asax, tsax (asax), tsax (asax), pf*	Cen

THREE WOODWINDS, KEYBOARD

Abbado, M.	Riverberazioni. *fl, ob, bsn, pf*	Ric
Asplund, G.	Kvartett, Op. 6. *ob, cl, bsn, pf*	STI
Balada, L.	Cuatris. *fl, cl, bsn, pf*	Gen
Barati, G.	Quartet. *fl, ob, bsn, pf*	Pet
Bizet, G.	3 Pieces. *fl, cl (ob), bsn, pf*	SM
Bodinus, S.-Fischer	Sonate. *2 ob, bsn, pf*	Pet
Bonner	Over the Hills. *fl, ob, cl, pf*	EdM
Chedeville, N.	Scherzo. *fl, cl, bsn, pf*	EdM
Chedeville, N.	Scherzo. *fl, ob, cl, pf*	EdM
Corelli, A.	Air and Dance. *fl, cl, bsn, pf*	EdM
Corelli, A.	Air and Dance. *fl, ob, cl, pf*	EdM
Corelli, A.	Allemanda. *fl, cl, bsn, pf*	EdM
Corelli, A.	Gavotte and Gigue. *fl, cl, bsn, pf*	EdM
Corelli, A.	Gavotte, and Gigue. *fl, ob, cl, pf*	EdM
Corelli, A.	Gigue. *fl, ob, cl, pf*	EdM
Couperin, F.	Concerto No. 1. *ob, cl, bsn, pf*	GaM
	fl, ob, cl, pf	CBD
Delvaux, A.	5 Impromptus (1949). *fl, ob, cl, pf*	CBD
Depelsenaire, J.	Concerto Grosso, e. *fl, ob, cl, pf*	GaM
Dressel, E.	Concerto. *ob, cl, bsn, pf*	R&E
Evans	5 Variations on an Olde Englishe Ayre. *fl, cl, bsn (bcl), pf*	Sha
Fasch, J.-Wojciechowski	Sonata, d. *2 ob, bsn bc*	HSM
Fesch, W. de-Schroeder	Sonata, D, op. 7/2. *2 fl, bsn, bc*	Hei
Fesch, W. de-Schroeder	Sonata, e, op. 7/8. *2 fl, bsn, bc*	Hei
Fesch, W. de-Schroeder	Sonata, g, op. 7/4. *2 fl, bsn, bc*	Hei
Garscia, J.	Miniatures. *ob, 2 bsn, pf*	EBM
Gerschefski, E.	"America" Variations for Winds, op. 44/1. *fl, cl, bsn, pf*	CoF

Three Woodwinds, Keyboard

Glanville-Hicks, P.	Concertina da Camera.	
	fl, cl, bsn, pf	EdL
Goeb, R.	Concertant Ib. *fl, ob, cl, pf*	CoF
Grunenwald, J.	Fantasie arabesque.	
	ob, cl, bsn, pf	EdS
Handel, G.-Seiffert	Chamber Trio No. 4, F.	
	2 ob, bsn, pf	BrH
Handel, G.-Seiffert	Chamber Trio No. 1, B♭.	
	2 ob, bsn, pf	BrH
Handel, G.-Seiffert	Chamber Trio No. 2, d.	
	2 ob, bsn, pf	BrH
Handel, G.	Kammertrio No. 8, g. *2 fl,*	
	(2 ob, 2 vn), bsn (vc), pf	BrH
Handel, G.	Kammertrio No. 14, g. *2 fl,*	
	(2 ob, 2 vn), bsn (vc), pf	BrH
Handel, G.	Kammertrio No. 6, D.	
	2 ob, bsn (vc), pf	BrH
Holmboe, V.	Quartetto Medico. *fl, ob, cl, pf*	Che
Honegger, A.	Rhapsody. *2 fl, cl, pf*	EdS
Kosma, J.	Divertissement. *fl, cl, bsn, pf*	EME
Lemare, E.-Long	Andantino. *3 ww, pf*	Vxl
Maganini, Q.	Trio Album. *fl, ob, cl, pf*	EdM
Martini, J.	Plaisir d'Amour. *fl, ob, cl, pf*	EdM
McBride, R.	Rudiments of Rugcutting.	
	2 ob, bsn, pf	ACA
Milhaud, D.	Sonate. *fl, ob, cl, pf*	Dur
Nardini, P.	Shepherd's Pipes. *fl, ob, cl, pf*	EdM
Paganini, N.-Tustin	Moto Perpetuo. *fl, ob, cl, pf*	Spr
Quinet, M.	Concertino. (1960). *ob, cl, bsn, pf*	CBD
Rieti, V.	Sonate. *fl, ob, bsn, pf*	UE
Rimsky-Korsakov, N.-Horsfall	Flight of the Bumblebee.	
	fl, ob, cl, pf	CF
Rovics, H.	Quartet. *fl, ob, bsn, hpcd*	CoF
Saint-Saens, C.	Caprice on Danish and Russian	
	Airs, op. 79. *fl, ob, cl, pf*	Int
Saint-Saens, C.	Caprice on Danish and Russian	
	Airs, op. 79. *fl, ob, cl, pf*	M&M
Saint-Saens, C.	Caprice sur des airs danois et	
	russes, op. 79. *fl, ob, cl, pf*	Dur
Salieri, A.	Danse (Tarare). *fl, ob, cl, pf*	EdM
Schmitt, F.	A Tour d'Anches, op. 97.	
	ob, cl, bsn, pf	Dur
Schneider, W.	Hohenheimer Tänze.	
	ob, cl, bsn, pf	Pet
Schubert, F.	Entr'acte (Rosamunde).	
	fl, ob, (cl), cl, pf	CF
Schubert, F.-Jospe	Impromptu, op. 142/2.	
	fl, ob, cl, pf	CF
Shores, R.	Mulholland Suite. *2 fl, cl, pf*	Wes
Siennicki, E.	Ponytail Polka. *2 cl, bsn, pf*	NK
Stam, H.	Sonate (1959). *fl, ob, bsn, hpcd*	SD

Three Woodwinds, Keyboard

Stamitz	Andantino. *fl, cl, bsn, pf*	EdM
Telemann, G.-Seiffert	Quartet, d (Tafelmusik).	
	bsn, 2 fl, bc	BrH
Telemann, G.-Hinnenthal	Quartet, d. *2 fl, bsn, bc*	B&N
Uggen, E.	Playwell Trio and Quartet Folio.	
	3 cl, pf	SHM
Uggen, E.	Playwell Trio and Quartet Folio.	
	3 fl, pf	SHM
Uggen, E.	Playwell Trio and Quartet Folio.	
	3 sax, pf	SHM
Vivaldi, A.	Concerto, g. *fl, ob, bsn, bc*	B&V
Vivaldi, A.	Giga. *fl, ob, cl, pf*	EdM
Vivaldi, A.-Ghedini	Sonata, g. *fl, ob, bsn, pf*	Int
Zelenka, J.-Schoenbaum	Triosonate No. 5, F. *2 ob, bsn, bc*	B&N
Zelenka, J.-Schoenbaum	Triosonate No. 4, g. *2 ob, bsn, bc*	B&N
Zelenka, J.-Schoenbaum	Triosonate No. 3, B♭.	
	2 ob, bsn, bc	B&N
Zelenka, J.-Schoenbaum	Triosonate No. 2, g. *2 ob, bsn, bc*	B&N
Zonn, P.	Liberata I. *fl/pic,*	
	ob/ehn, cl/bcl, pf	CoF

WOODWINDS, BRASS

Apostel, H.	Quartet, op. 14. *fl, cl, bsn, hn*	UE
Bach, J.S.-Hirsch	Fugue, E♭. *fl, cl, bsn, hn*	CF
Bach, J.S.-Catelinet	Kunst der Fuge (Contrapunctus I).	
	ob, cl, hn, bsn	Pet
Birtwistle, H.	Refrains and Choruses.	
	fl, ob, bsn, hn	UE
Boustead, A.	3 Madrigale. *fl, cl, bsn, hn*	BrH
Butt, J.	Winsome's Folly. *ob, cl, bsn, hn*	B&H
Chavez, C.	Soli. *ob, cl, bsn, tpt*	B&H
Dedrick, C.	Sensitivity. *ob, cl, hn, bsn*	Ken
DiLasso, O.-Cheyette	Matona, Lovely Maiden. *2cl, hn*	
	(acl, asax, ehn, bsn),	
	bsn (bar sax)	GaM
Ehrenberg, C.	Quartet, op. 40. *ob, cl, bsn, hn*	ABe
Eler, A.-Leloir	Quartet, op. 10/1. *2 cl, hn, bsn*	Kaw
Eler, A.-Leloir	Quartet, op. 10/2. *2 cl, hn, bsn*	Kaw
Eler, A.-Leloir	Quartet, op. 10/3. *2 cl, hn, bsn*	Kaw
Eröd, I.	Ricercare ed Aria. *fl, ob, bcl, hn*	LDo
Fink, R.	4 Modes for Winds.	
	fl, cl, bsn (bcl), hn	S-B
Frescobaldi, G.-Aaron	Gagliarda. *ob (cl),*	
	cl, hn, bsn (bcl)	Sch
Fuchs, G.	3 Quartets. *cl, 2hn, bsn*	Wes
Gerschefski, E.	"America" Variations for Winds,	
	op. 44/10. *fl, cl, bsn, tpt*	CoF
Grafe, P.	March. *2 ob, bsn, tpt*	WIN

Woodwinds, Brass

Grainer	Discussions. *fl, cl, hn, bsn*	Cha
Grieg, E.-Cafarella	Norwegian Dance, op. 47/28.	
	fl, ob, cl, hn	Vol
Handel, G.-Aaron	Chaconne, *ob, cl, hn*	
	(trb), bsn (bcl)	Sch
Hartley, W.	Sonata da Camera.	
	ob, cl, bsn trb	Cre
Haydn, F.-Aaron	Capriccio. *ob (cl), cl,*	
	hn (trb), bsn (bcl)	Sch
Haydn, F.-Landon	Divertimento No. 4, Hob. II: 14 (C).	
	2 cl, 2 hn	LDo
Haydn, F.-Höckner	Divertimento. *2 cl, 2 hn*	WH
Haydn, F.-Paterson-Moore	Largo (Quartet, op. 76/5).	
	2 cl, bsn, hn	Gal
Haydn, F.-Paterson-Moore	Poco Adagio Cantabile	
	(op. 76/3). *2 cl, bsn, hn*	Gal
Haydn, F-Nakagawa	Quartet No. 18, op. 3/5.	
	fl, cl, bsn, hn	AMP
Haydn, F.-Janetzky	12 Nocturnos, D, Hob II:5.	
	2 fl, 2 hn	PrM
Haydn, M.-Lauschmann	Divertimento, D. *fl, ob, hn, bsn*	FrH
Henneberg, A.	Liten kvartett, op. 36.	
	fl, ob, hn, bsn	STI
Hermann, F.	Zur Ubung im Zusammenspiel,	
	Bk. 1. *ob, cl, bsn, hn*	BrH
Hertel, J.-Sallagar	Sonata a Quattro. *2 bsn, 2 hn*	OHN
Hoddinott, A.	Divertimento. *ob, cl, bsn, hn*	OxU
Holzbauer, I.-Janetzky	Divertimento. *2 bsn, 2 hn*	FrH
Hovhaness, A.	Divertimento, op. 61/5. *ob (cl),*	
	hn (cl), bsn (bcl)	Pet
Jadin, L.	Nocturne No. 3. *fl, cl, bsn, hn*	EK
Kammel, A.	Serenata, G. *ob, bsn, 2 hn*	M&M
Kapp, B.	Suite. *fl, ob, bsn, hn*	MR
Karkoff, M	Divertimento, op. 29 (1957).	
	fl, ob, bsn, hn	STI
Kauder, H.	Quartet (1948). *ob, cl, bsn, hn*	Pre
Kauder, H.	Quartet. *ob, cl, bsn, hn*	SM
Kay, N.	Miniature Quartet. *fl, cl, bsn, hn*	OxU
Korda, V.	Quartettino. *fl, cl, hn, tpt*	LDo
Krejci, M.	Divertimento. *fl, cl, bsn, tpt*	Art
Kunz, A.	Emanation No. 2 (1964).	
	fl, cl, bsn, hn	Can
Kuusisto, I.	Cassazione (1961). *2 cl, 2 hn*	MT
Locke, M.	Music For His Majesty's Sackbuts	
	and Cornets. *2 cl, bsn, hn*	OxU
Lutgen	Quartet. *2 fl, 2 hn*	Wes
McBride, R.	Television Special. *2 cl, 2 hn*	CoF
Mozart, W.	Cassazione. *ob (fl), cl, hn, bsn*	SM
Mazart, W.	Divertimento No. 11, K. 251.	
	fl, ob, cl, bsn	EdK
Mozart, W.-Schneider	Kegel-Divertimento.	
	ob, cl, hn, bsn	OHN

Woodwinds, Brass

Mozart, W.	Konzertantes Quartette, K.V. 19.	
	ob, cl, bsn hn	CF
Nowak, L.	Suite. *fl, ob, cl, hn*	CoF
Padovano, A.	Rondo. *ob (fl), cl, hn, bsn*	GZ
Pearson, W.	The Hunt. *fl, ob, cl, hn (bsn)*	Cha
Petyrek, F.	Gute Nacht, o Welt.	
	ob, cl, hn, bsn	LDo
Placheta, H.	Quartet, op. 10. *ob, cl, bsn hn*	LDo
Regner, H.	Serenade. *ob, cl, bsn, hn*	OHN
Riisager, K.	Divertimento. *fl, ob, bsn hn*	Pet
Rossini, G.	Andante e Variazioni.	
	fl, cl, hn, bsn	Heu
Rossini, G.-Oubradous	Quartet No. 1. *fl, cl, bsn, hn*	EMT
Rossini, G.-Zachert	Quartette, 2 vols. *fl, cl, bsn, hn*	SS
Ryan, P.	A Haydn Movement (Sonata No. 5).	
	fl, ob, cl, hn (bsn, bcl)	Cha
Sabatini, G.	Quartet. *ob, cl, bsn, hn*	Cor
Schneider, W.	Kleines Quartett. *fl, ob, cl, hn*	MV
Schneider, W.	Variationen über ein Sommerlied.	
	ob, cl, hn, bsn	MV
Schubert, F.-Busto	Waltz, a. *fl, cl, bsn, hn*	CF
Schurtz, F.	Divertimento. *ob, cl, hn, bsn*	MV
Schurtz, F.	Kleine Musik. *ob, cl, hn, bsn*	MV
Schwegler, J.	Quartet, E♭. *2fl, 2 hn*	Wes
Stamitz, C.-Rosenthal	Quartet. *ob, cl, hn, bsn*	Wes
Stamitz, C.-Weigelt	Quartet, e♭, op. 8/2.	
	ob, cl, bsn, hn	Leu
Stamitz, C.-Schuller	Quartet, op. 8/2. *ob, cl, bsn, hn*	M&M
Stringfield, L.	An Old Bridge. *ob, cl, bsn, hn*	MCA
Sutermeister, H.	Serenade. *2 cl, bsn, tpt*	SS
Swift, R.	Folk Song Suite. *fl, cl, bcl, hn*	Ken
Tchaikovsky, P.-Aaron	Humoresque, op. 10.	
	ob, cl, hn, bsn (bcl)	Sch
Tenaglia, A.-Cheyette	Aria. *2 cl, hn (acl, asax,*	
	ehn, bsn), bsn (bar sax)	GaM
Vellère, L.	Prelude *ob, cl, hn, bsn*	Mau
Walker, R.	Caprice. *2 cl, bsn, hn*	Tem

WOODWINDS, STRINGS

Abel, C.	Quartet, A, op. 12/2.	MR
	fl(ob), vn, va, vc	
Abel, C.	Quartet A. *fl, vn, va, vc*	Sch
Abel, C.-Hunt	Quartet, G. *fl, vn, va, vc*	SS
Aitken, H.	Quartet. *cl, vn, va, vc*	AMC
Almenraeder, K.	Variations on an Ancient Melody.	Spr
	bsn, vn, va, vc	
Ames, W.	Quartet. *ob, vn, va, vc*	ACA

Woodwinds, Strings

Angerer, P.	Konzertantes Quartet. *ob, hn, va, vc*	LDo
Arnold, M.	Oboe Quartet, op. 61 (1957). *ob, vn, va, vc*	Fab
Babbitt, M.	Composition for Four Instruments (1947-48). *fl, cl, vn, vc*	TP
Bach, J.C.	Quartet, A. *fl, vn, va, vc*	MR
Bach, J.C.	Quartet, C. *fl, vn, va, vc*	MR
Bach, J.C.-Dameck	Quartet, C, op. 8/1. *fl(ob), vn, va, vc*	B&B
Bach, J.C.-Erbrecht	Quartet, C. *2fl, va, vc*	Kis
Bach, J.C.-Erbrecht	Quartet, C. *2fl, vn, vc*	Kis
Bach, J.C.	Quartet, D. *fl, vn, va, vc*	MR
Bach, J.C.-Ermeler	Quartet, D, op. 20/2. *2fl, va, vc*	B&N
Bach, J.C.-Erbrecht	Quartet, D. *2fl, va, vc*	Kis
Bach, J.S.-Nagel	Quartet, E♭, op. 8/6. *fl, vn, va, db*	SS
Bach, J.C.-Hillemann	Quartet, F, op. 8/4. *fl, vn, va, vc*	B&N
Bach, J.C.-Erbrecht	Quartet, G. *2fl, va, vc*	Kis
Bach, J.C.	Quartet, op. 8/2. *fl, vn, va, vc*	MR
Bach, J.C.	3 Quartettes, op. 8/1, 3, 5. *fl(ob, cl), vn, va, vc*	CF
Bach, J.C.	2 Quartets, op. 19/1, 3. *fl, fl(vn), va, vc*	MR
Bach, J.S.-Davis	Prelude and Fugue, g. *ob, cl, va, vc*	Wes
Bach, J.S.	Sonate No. 4. *fl, vn, va, vc*	Ham
Ballou, E.	Fantasia Brevis. *ob, vn, va, vc*	CoF
Ben-Haim, P.	Serenade. *fl, vn, va, vc*	Hei
Berkeley, L.	Oboe Quartet (1967). *ob, vn, va, vc*	Che
Bertouille, G.	Quartet No. 4 (1948). *fl, vn, va, vc*	CBD
Boccherini, L.-Rampal	Quartet. *fl, vn, va, vc*	Int
Bois, R. du	Kwartet (1965). *ob, vn, va, vc*	SD
Borris, S.	Oboe Quartet, op. 17/1. *ob, vn, va, vc*	S-V
Britten, B.	Phantasy Quartet. *ob, vn, va, vc*	B&H
Buczynski, W.	Divertimento, op. 15 (1957). *cl, bsn, vn, vc*	Can Can
Cannabich, C.	Quartet, B♭. *ob, vn, va, vc*	LDo
Cannabich, C.-Walther	Quartet, G. *fl, vn, va, vc*	Hei
Carlstedt, J.	Divertimento, op. 17 (1962). *ob, vn, va, vc*	STI
Catel, S.	Quartet. *cl, vn, va, vc*	MR
Chevreuille, R.	Musique de salon, op. 49 (1951). *fl, vn, va, vc*	CBD
Childs, B.	Interbalances I. *ob, ehn, bcl/asax, db*	ACA
Coker, W.	Concertino. *bsn, vn, va, vc*	UE
Colaco Osorio-Swaab, R.	Kwartet No. 1 (1952). *fl, vn, va, vc*	SD

Woodwinds, Strings

Cole, H.	Quartet. *ob, vn, va, vc*	Nov
Cooke, A.	Quartet. *ob, vn, va, vc*	Nov
Cruft, A.	Fantasy. *ob, vn, va, vc*	Gal
Crusell, B.-Bellison	Quartet, E♭. *cl, vn, va, vc*	FrC
Crusell, B.	Quartet, op. 4. *cl, vn, va, vc*	EK
Crusell, B.	Quartet, op. 7. *cl, vn, va, vc*	EK
Danzi, F.-Sonntag	Quartet, d, op. 56/2. *fl, vn, va, vc*	Hei
Danzi, F.	Quartet, op. 40/1. *bsn, vn, va, vc*	MR
Danzi, F.	Quartet, B♭, op. 40/2. *bsn, vn, va, vc*	MR
Danzi, F.	Quartet, B♭, op. 40/3. *bsn, vn, va, vc*	MR
David, T.	Flute Quartet. *fl, vn, va, vc*	EMo
Delden, L.	Quartetto, op. 58 (1957). *fl, vn, va, vc*	SD
Delvaux, A.	Cassazione (1966). *ob, cl, vn, vc*	CBD
Devienne, F.	Quartet, C, op. 73/1. *bsn, vn, va, vc*	MR
Devienne, F.	Quartet, G, op. 11/1. *fl, vn, va, vc*	MR
Devienne, F.	Quartet, G, op. 11/1. *fl, vn, va, vc*	Sch
Devienne, F.	Quartet, G, op. 2/1. *fl, vn, va, vc*	B&V
Devienne, F.	Quartet, op. 11/1. *fl, vn, va, vc*	Pet
Di Domenica, R.	Quartet. *fl, vn, va, vc*	EBM
Donato, A.	Drag and Run. *cl, 2vn, vc*	See
Donovan, R.	Serenade. *ob, vn, va, vc*	TP
Doran, M.	Quartet. *ob, cl, va, bsn*	Wes
Druschetzky, G.-Vécsey	Quartet, E♭. *ob, vn, va, vc*	EMB
Druschetzky, G.-Vécsey	Quartet, F. *ob, vn, va, vc*	EMB
Druschetzky, G.-Vécsey	Quartet, g. *ob, vn, va, vc*	EMB
Duvernoy, F.	Quartet. *cl, vn, va, vc*	MR
Eder, H.	Quartet (1955). *cl, vn, va, vc*	BrH
Eisma, W.	Diaphonia (1962). *ob, vn, va, vc*	SD
Eisma, W.	World within World. *ob, vn, va, vc*	Pet
Etler, A.	Quartet. *ob, cl, bsn, va*	NVM
Fernstrom, J.	Liten serenad, op. 73. *fl, cl, bsn, vc*	EMF
Fiala, J.-Klement	Quartette, E♭, F. *ob, vn, va, vc*	B&N
Fiala, J.	2 Quartets. *ob, vn, va, vc*	ES
Foster	A Village Festival. *fl, 2vn, db*	Edm
Francaix, J.	Quartet. *ehn, vn, va, vc*	SS
Fuchs, F., Jr.	Little Suite. *fl, 2vn, va*	AMP
Fuchs, G.	Quartet. *cl, vn, va, vc*	MR
Gassmann, F.-Schroeder	Quartet, B♭. *ob, va, 2vc*	MRL
Gassmann, F.-Klement	3 Divertimenti. *ob, 2va, vc*	B&N
Gatti, L.	Quartet, F. *ob, vn, va, vc*	RS
Gebauer, F.	First Quartet. *ob, vn, va, vc*	M&M
Gebauer, F.	3 Quartets. *cl, vn, va, vc*	M&M
Giordani, T.	Flute Quartet, D, op. 2/5. *fl, vn, va, vc*	MR
Giordano, T.	Quartet, D, op. 2/5. *fl, vn, va, vc*	B&V
Giardini, T.-Steinbeck	Quartet, op. 25/3. *ob, vn, va, vc*	BrH

Giordani, T.	Quartet, op. 2/5. *fl, vn, va, vc*	Pet
Goeb, R.	Oboe Quartet. *ob, vn, va, vc*	CoF
Griesbach, K.	Musik. *fl, vn, va, vc*	BrH
Grosskopf, E.	Sonata No. 3 (1967). *fl, vn, va, vc*	B&B
Gursching, A.	Quartet (1962). *ob, vn, va, vc*	EMo
Gyring, E.	Fugue No. 11. *cl, vn, va, vc*	CoF
Gyring, E.	Fugue No. 15. *cl, vn, va, vc*	CoF
Gyring, E.	Fugue No. 5. *cl, vn, va, vc*	CoF
Gyring, E.	Fugue No. 4. *cl, vn, va, vc*	CoF
Gyring, E.	Fugue No. 14. *cl, vn, va, vc*	CoF
Gyring, E.	Fugue No. 9. *cl, vn, va, vc*	CoF
Gyring, E.	Fugue No. 1. *cl, vn, va, vc*	CoF
Gyring, E.	Fugue No. 7. *cl, vn, va, vc*	CoF
Gyring, E.	Fugue No. 6. *cl, fn, va, vc*	CoF
Gyring, E.	Fugue No. 16. *cl, vn, va, vc*	CoF
Gyring, E.	Fugue No. 10. *cl, vn, va, vc*	CoF
Gyring, E.	Fugue No. 13. *cl, vn, va, vc*	CoF
Gyring, E.	Fugue No. 3. *cl, vn, va, vc*	CoF
Gyring, E.	Fugue No. 12. *cl, vn, va, vc*	CoF
Gyring, E.	Fugue No. 2. *cl, vn, va, vc*	CoF
Gyrowetz, A.	Dritte Nachtmusik, op. 26. *fl, vn, va, vc*	WZ
Gyrowetz, A.-Botsch	Quartet, D. *fl, vn, va, vc*	Hei
Gyrowetz, A.-Hollanders	Quartet, g, op. 19/2. *fl, vn, va, vc*	B&V
Hanschke, H.	Variations on a Children's Song. *fl, vn, va(vn), vc*	SS
Haydn, F.	Divertissement. *ob, vn, va da gamba, db, opt hpcd*	OxU
Haydn, F.	Husband and Wife or the Birthday. *fl, vn, va, vc*	Pet
Haydn, F.-Koelbel	Quartet, C. *fl, vn, va, vc*	B&N
Haydn, F.-Koelbel	Quartet, C. *fl, vn, va, vc*	Pet
Haydn, F.-Sonntag	Quartet, D. *fl, vn, va, vc*	MRL
Haydn, F.	Quartet, D, op. 5/1. *fl, vn, va, vc*	MR
Haydn, F.	Quartet, D, op. 5/1. *fl, vn, va, vc*	Sch
Haydn, F.	Quartet, G, op. 5/2. *fl, vn, va, vc*	MR
Haydn, F.	Quartet, G, op. 5/2. *fl, vn, va, vc*	Sch
Haydn, F.	Quartet (Man and Wife). *fl, vn, va, vc*	Ton
Haydn, F.-Rampal	6 Quartets, 2 vols. *fl, vn, va, vc*	Int
Haydn, M.-Rainer	Quartet, C. *ehn, vn, vc, db*	LDo
Heiden, B.	Serenade (1955). *bsn, str trio*	AMP
Helm, E.	Quartet. *fl, vn, va, vc*	AMC
Hennessy, S.	4 Celtic Pieces, op. 59. *ehn, str trio*	EME
Hennessy, S.	Variations on a Six-Note Theme, op. 58. *fl, str trio*	EME
Hermans, N.	Serenade, op. 3 (1948). *ob, vn, va, vc*	SD
Hindemith, P.	Abendkonzert No. 2. *fl, 2vn, vc*	SS
Hindemith, P.	Abendkonzert No. 4. *cl, vn, va, vc*	SS
Hockner, W. (arr)-Mlynarczyk	Das Flötenquartett. *fl, vn, va, vc*	B&N

Woodwinds, String

Höffer, P.	Serenade "Innsbruck, ich muss dich lassen." *ob, vn, va, vc*	Pet
Hoffmeister, F.-Ermeler	Quartet, c, op. 16/2. *fl, vn, va, vc*	Hei
Hoffmeister, F.-Sonntag	Quartet, G. *fl, vn, va, vc*	HSM
Hoffmeister, F.-Höckner	2 Quartets. *cl, str trio*	ABe
Honegger, A.	Canon sur basso obstinée à 4 voix (Trois Contrepoints No. 3). *fl, ob(eh), vn, vc*	Che
Horowitz	Quartet. *ob, vn, va, vc*	B-M
Huggler, J.	Quartet, op. 47. *bsn, vn, va, vc*	CoF
Huggler, J.	Quartet, op. 38. *ehn, vn, va, vc*	ACA
Huggler, J.	Quartet, op. 27. fl, vn, va, vc	CoF
Hummel, J.N.	Quartet. *cl, vn, va, vc*	MR
Hummel, J.N.	Quartet. *cl, vn, va, vc*	Sch
Hye-Knudsen, J.	Quartet. *fl, ob/eh, vn, vc*	Che
Jacob, G.	Quartet. *ob, vn, va, vc*	Nov
Kahn, E.	7 Chansons populaires de la Bretagne. *fl, cl, bsn, vn*	CoF
Karlins, M.	Fantasy & Passacaglia. *fl, bsn, va, db*	CoF
Karlins, M.	Variations (1963). *cl, vn, va, vc*	CoF
Kasbergen, M.	3 Episodes. *fl, vn, va, vc*	SD
Kaufmann, A.	Quartet, op. 17. *fl, vn, va, vc*	LDo
Kingma, P.	Serenata Gemini. *fl, ob, vn, vc*	HU
Komma, K.	First Quartet. *fl, vn, va, vc*	I-V
Komma, K.	Second Quartet. *fl, vn, va, vc*	I-V
Kramář-Krommer, F.	2 Quartets. *ob, vn, va, vc*	B&N
Krommer-Kramar, F.-Racek-Pohanka	Concerto, F. *ob, vn, va, vc*	ES
Krommer, F.	Quartet B♭, op. 46/1. *bsn, vn(va), va, vc*	MR
Krommer-Kramar, F.	Quartet. *ob, vn, va, vc*	ES
Krommer, F.	Quartet, op. 94. *fl, vn, va, vc*	FrH
Krull, D.	Kvartett. *cl, 2vn, vc*	EMF
Kruyf, T. de	Mosaico, op. 24. *ob, vn, va, vc*	B&B
LeFanu, N.	Oboe Quartet. *ob, vn, va, vc*	Nov
Lefevre, X.	3 Quartets. *cl, vn, va, vc*	M&M
Lessel, F.-Tauros	Quartet. *fl, vn, va, vc*	AP
Lidholm I.	Concertino. *fl, ob, ehn, vc*	EMF
Lowman, K.	Los Angeles Sketches. *ob, cl, va, bsn*	Wes
Malipiero, G.	Epodi e Gambi. *ob, bsn, vn, va*	Che
Martino, D.	Quartet. *cl, vn, va, vc*	CoF
Martinu, B.	Mazurka-Nocturne, op. posth. *ob, 2vn, vc*	EME
Masséus, J.	Serenade, op. 31 (1958). *ob, bsn, vn, va*	SD
McAfee, D.	Quartet. *fl, cl, vn, vc*	AMC
McCabe, J.	Quartet (1968). *ob, vn, va, vc*	Nov
Mechem, K.	Divertimento, op. 12. *fl, vn, va, vc*	ECS
Mica, J.A.-Steinbeck	Quartet, C. *ob, vn, va, vc*	LDo
Mieg, P.	Divertimento. *ob, vn, va, vc*	EMo

Woodwinds, Strings

Miller, R.	Lively Mood. *cl, 2vn, vc*	B-M
Miller, R.	Martial Spirit. *cl, 2vn, vc*	B-M
Milner, A.	Quartet. *ob, vn, va, vc*	Nov
Moeran, E.	Fantasy Quartet. *ob, vn, va, vc*	Che
Moeschinger, A.	Images. *fl, sax, vn, vc*	Bil
Mortari, V.	3 danze antiche. *fl, ob, va, vc*	Car
Moryl, R.	Improvisations. *fl, cl, vn, vc*	Bow
Most, A.	Miniature Suite (1966). *ob, cl, bsn, va*	CP
Mozart, W.	Concertino. *ob, vn, va, vc*	SM
Mozart, W.	4 Quartets. *fl, vn, va, vc*	Int
Mozart, W.	Oboe Quartet, K. 370. *ob, vn, va, vc*	B&H
Mozart, W.-Rothwell	Oboe Quartet, K.V. 370. *ob, vn, va, vc*	Che
Mozart, W.	Quartet, A. *fl, vn, va, vc*	CF
Mozart, W.	Quartet, A, K. 298. *fl, vn, va, vc*	BrH
Mozart, W.	Quartet, C. *fl, vn, va, vc*	CF
Mozart, W.	Quartet, D. *fl, vn, va, vc*	CF
Mozart, W.	Quartet, D, K. 285. *fl, vn, va, vc*	BrH
Mozart, W.-Pohanka	Quartet, F, K. 370. *ob, vn, va, vc*	B&N
Mozart, W.	Quartet, F.K. 370. *ob, vn, va, vc*	BrH
Mozart, W.	Quartet, F, K. 370. *ob, vn, va, vc*	Pet
Mozart, W.-Einstein	Quartet, G, K. 285a. *fl, vn, va, vc*	Pet
Mozart, W.	Quartet, K. 370. *ob, vn, va, vc*	Int
Mozart, W.	Quartet, K. 370. *ob, vn, va, vc*	SM
Mozart, W.-Pohanka	Quartets, K.V. 285, 285a, 285b, 298. *fl, vn, va, vc*	B&N
Mozart, W.-Schwedler	3 Quartets, K. 285, 285b, 298. *fl, vn, va, vc*	Pet
Müller, I.	Deuxième Quatuor. *cl, vn, va, vc*	M&M
Müller, L.	12 Veränderungen. *fl, vn, va, vc*	BrH
Nowak, L.	Quartet. *ob, vn, va, vc*	CoF
Osieck, H.	Sonatine (1961). *ob(cl), vn, va, vc*	SD
Park, S.	Pastorale. *fl, vn, va, vc*	See
Pinkham, D.	Prelude. *fl, vn, va, vc*	CoF
Pisk, P.	Music. *cl, bsn, vn, vc*	CoF
Pleyel, I.-Albrecht	Quartet, B♭, op. 20/2. *fl, vn, va, vc*	Kis
Pleyel, I.-Albrecht	Quartet, C, op. 20/3. *fl, vn, va, vc*	Kis
Pleyel, I.-Albrecht	Quartet, G, op. 20/1. *fl, vn, va, vc*	Kis
Praag, H. van	3 Movements (1958). *ob, vn, va, bsn(vc)*	SD
Prévost, A.	Mobiles (1959). *fl, vn, va, vc*	Can
Raasted, N.	Serenade, op. 40. *fl, ob, va, vc*	SPD
Rainier, P.	Quanta. *ob, vn, va, vc*	S&C
Rameau, J.-Urban	Tambourin. *ob, vn, va, vc*	B-M
Randolph, D.	Prelude & Variations. *cl, vn, va, vc*	AMC
Rautavaara, E.	Quartet (1965). *ob, vn, va, vc*	MT
Regt, H. de	Musica. *ob, vn, va, vc*	SD
Reicha, A.-Racek-Janetzky	3 Quartets, op. 98/1-3.	ES

Woodwinds, Strings

	fl, vn, va, vc	
Reuter, F.	Spielmusik, F, op. 30.	FrH
	fl, 2vn, vc(va)	
Reiti, V.	Variations. *fl, cl, vn, vc*	Gen
Riisager, K.	Sonata. *fl, cl, vn, vc*	Che
Roetscher, K.	Divertimento, op. 22. *fl, cl, vn, vc*	B&B
Rohwer, J.	Quartet. *fl, vn, va, vc*	MV
Sammartini, G.-Rhau	Notturno a quartro. *fl, 2vn, vc*	BrH
Sarai, T.	Quartet (1961-62). *fl, vn, va, vc*	EMB
Schibler, A.	Epitaph, Furioso und Epilog,	A&S
	op. 65. *fl, vn, va, vc*	
Schroeder, H.	Quartet, op. 38. *ob, vn, va, vc*	SS
Schubert, F.-Urban	Cradle Song. *fl, vn, va, vc*	B-M
Schwartz, E.	Quartet. *ob, vn, va, vc*	Gen
Schwindl, F.	Quartet, G. *fl, vn, va, vc*	Pet
Searle, H.	Quartet, op. 12. *cl, bsn, vn, va*	Pet
Seiber, M.	Pastorale. *fl, vn, va, vc*	SS
Semiatin, L.	Encore. *cl, vn, va, vc*	AMC
Shield, W.	Quartet, F, op. 3/2. *ob, vn, va, vc*	SS
Simons, N.	Quartet. *fl, vn, va, vc*	CoF
Sims, E.	From an Oboe Quartet.	ACA
	ob, vn, va, vc	
Sims, E.	Sonate Concertante. *ob, vn, vc, db*	CoF
	Played simultaneously with	
	"Sonate" for string quartet	
Sperger, J.-Malaric	Quartet, D. *fl, va, vc, db*	LDo
Stamitz, C.	2 Quartets. *fl, vn, va, vc*	M&M
Stamitz, C.-Ott	Quartet, A, op. 4/6. *cl, vn, va, vc*	Leu
Stamitz, C.-Ott	Quartet, A, op. 4/6.	Leu
	fl(ob, cl), vn, va, vc	Leu
Stamitz, C.	Quartet, B♭, op. 19/5.	MR
	bsn, vn, va, vc	
Stamitz, C.-Mönkmeyer	Quartet, C. *fl, 2vn, vc*	SS
Stamitz, C.-Upmeyer	Quartet, D, op. 8/1.	B&N
	fl(ob), vn, hn(va), vc	
Stamitz, C.	Quartet, E♭. *cl(ob), vn, va, vc*	CF
Stamitz, C.-Höckner	Quartet, E♭. *cl, vn, va, vc*	Hei
Stamitz, C.-Steins	Quartet, E♭, op. 8/4.	B&B
	cl(ob), vn, va, vc	
Stamitz, C.	Quartet, E♭, op. 8/4.	Int
	cl(ob), vn, va, vc	
Stamitz, C.	Quartet, E♭, op. 8/4. *cl, vn, va, vc*	MR
Stamitz, C.	Quartet, E♭, op. 19/1.	MR
	cl, vn, va, vc	
Stamitz, C.	Quartet, E♭, op. 19/3.	MR
	cl, vn, va, vc	
Stamitz, C.-Mönkmeyer	Quartet, F. *fl, 2vn, vc*	SS
Stamitz, C.	Quartet, F, op. 8/3.	MR
	ob(cl), vn, va(hn), vc	
Stamitz, C.	Quartet, F, op. 19/6. *bxn,*	MR
	bsn, vn, va, vc	
Stamitz, C.	Quartet, op. 19/2. *cl, vn, va, vc*	MR

Woodwinds, Strings

Stamitz, C.-Marx	2 Quartets. *cl, vn, va, vc*	M&M
Stamitz, C.	2 Quartets. *ob, vn, va, vc*	M&M
Straesser, J.	Muziek (1962). *ob, vn, va, vc*	SD
Sydeman, W.	Quartet (1962). *ob, vn, va, vc*	See
Tamas, J.	Quartet, B♭. *cl, vn, va, vc*	Pet
Toch, E.	Quartet. *ob, cl, bsn, va*	B-M
Tremblay, G.	5 Pieces (1966). *ob, cl, bsn, va*	CP
Trowbridge, L.	Pensively. *cl, vn, va, vc*	See
Ullman, B.	Kvartett (1956). *fl, cl, va, vc*	EMF
Verhaar, A.	Divertimento, op. 12 (1937). *fl, vn, va, vc*	SD
Viecenz, H.	Quartet. *fl, vn, va, vc*	Pet
Viotti, G.	Flute Quartet, B♭, op. 22/1. *fl, vn, va, vc*	MR
Vogel, J.	Quartet, op. 5/1. *bsn, vn, va, vc*	MR
Vogel, W.	"inspiré par jean arp." *fl, cl, vn, vc*	Hei
Vogel, W.	12 Varietudes (1942). *fl, cl, vn, vc*	ESZ
Vogler, G.-Zöller	Quartet, B♭. *fl, vn, va, vc*	HSM
Wagner, J.	Theme and Variations. *fl, cl, vn, vc*	SMP
Wailly, P. de	Serenade. *fl, vn, va, vc*	EdS
Wanhal, J.-Schroeder	Notturno, C. *fl, 2vn, vc*	MRL
Wanhal, J.	Quartet. *cl, vn, va, vc*	MR
Wanhal, J.	Quartet, G, op. 7/3. *ob, vn, va, vc*	MR
Wendling, J.-Bopp	Quartet, G, op. 10/4. *fl, vn, va, vc*	B&N
Whettam, G.	Oboe Quartet. *ob, vn, va, vc*	Sch
Whitney, M.	Adagio and Fugue. *fl, vn, va, vc*	SM
Wildberger, J.	Quartetto. *fl, cl, vn, vc*	EMo
Wilson, D.	Doubles. *cl, bsn, va, db*	Pet
Winter, P. von	Quartet, E♭. *cl, vn, va, vc*	MR
Wirén, D.	Kvartett, op. 31. *fl, ob, cl, vc*	CGM
Wolf, E.-Höckner/Tischer	Quartet, G. *fl, ob, bsn, vc*	Hei
Woollen, R.	Quartet. *fl, vn, va, vc*	CoF
Wordsworth, W.	Oboe Quartet, op. 44. *ob, vn, va, vc*	AlL
Wuorinen, C.	Bearbeitungen über das Glogauer Liederbuch. *fl/pic, cl/bcl, vc, db*	Pet
Yun, I.	Images (1968). *fl, ob, vn, vc*	B&B
Zielche, H.-Höckner/Mlynarczyk	Quartet, G. *fl, 2vn, vc*	Hei
Zonn, P.	Concert Piece. *bsn, vn, va, vc*	CoF
Zonn, P.	Microditties. *ob, vn, va, vc*	CoF

WOODWIND, BRASS, STRING

Angerer, P.	Konzertantes Quartett (1951). *ob, hn, va, vc*	LDo
Angerer, P.	Serenata (1951). *vn, va, hn, bsn*	LDo

Woodwind, Brass, String

Boatwright, H.	Serenade. *cl, hn, vn, vc*	OxU
Dobrowolski, A.	8 Studies (1959). *ob, bsn, tpt, db*	AP
Gaburo, K.	Line Studies. *fl, cl, va, trb*	AMC
Haworth, F.	The Glory and the Dream (1957). *cl, hn(va), vn, vc*	Can
Kruyf, T. de	Quartetto. *fl, bsn, tpt, vn*	SD
Kubizek, A.	Vergnügliche Miniaturen, op. 28a *cl, bsn, vn, trb*	LDo
Rattenbach, A.	Serenata. *fl, cl, tpt, vc*	SMP
Stearns, P.	Chamber Set II. *asax, tpt, vn, db*	CoF
Sydeman, W.	Quartet (1955). *cl, vn, db, tpt*	See
Tanenbaum, E.	Music for Three Chamber Groups. *fl/alf, fl/pic, vc, trb(db)*	CoF
Wyner, Y.	Passover Offering. *fl, cl, trb, vc*	CoF

WOODWIND, BRASS, KEYBOARD

Beethoven, L. van-Phillips	Rondino, E♭. *ob (cl), cl, hn (cl), pf*	OxU
Berwald, F.	Quartet, E♭. *cl, hn, bsn, pf*	CGM
Breval, J.	Concertante, op. 38. *cl, hn, bsn, pf*	Kaw
Crusell, B.-Weelink	Concertante, op. 3. *cl, bsn, hn, pf*	Kaw
Döhl, F.	Toccata (1962-63). *fl, tpt, cemb, pf*	HG
Drew, J.	Collage I. *fl, tpt, trb, pf*	CoF
Hubeau, J.	Sonatine Humoresque. *fl, cl, hn, pf*	Bil
Kupferman, M.	Curtain Raiser. *fl, cl, hn, pf*	Gen
Pfeiffer, G.-Lauschmann	Sonata. *fl, hn, bsn, pf*	FrH
Roland-Manuel, A.	Suite dans le goût espagnol. *ob, bsn, tpt, pf*	Dur
Skalkottas, N.	Quartet. *ob, bsn, tpt, pf*	UE
Starer, R.	Concerto a Tre. *cl, tpt, trb, pf*	MCA

WOODWINDS, STRINGS, KEYBOARD

-Johanson	Greensleeves. *fl, vn, vc, pf*	BM
Andriessen, J.	Suite de Noel (1944). *fl, vn, va, pf*	SD
Antoniou, T.	Quartetto giocoso, op. 26 (1965). *ob, vn, vc, pf*	B&N
Bach, J.C.-Ruf	Quartet, C. *fl, vn, va, bc*	Hei
Bach, C.P.E.	Quartet, G, Wq 95. *fl, va, vc, pf*	B&N
Bach, C.P.E.-Schmid	Quartet No. 1, a, Wq 93. *fl, va, vc, pf*	B&N
Bach, C.P.E.-Schmid	Quartet No. 3, G, Wq 94. *fl, va, vc, pf*	B&N

Woodwind, String, Keyboard

Bach, C.P.E.-Schmid	Quartet No. 2, D, Wq 94.	
	fl, va, vc, pf	B&N
Bach, J.C.-Nagel	Quartet, op. 8/VI.	
	fl, vn, va, bc	SS
Bach, J.S.-Gounod, C.	Meditation (Ave Maria).	
	fl (of, cl), vn, vc, pf	Pet
Bach, J.S.	Sonata a 3. *fl, vn, vc, pf*	Sch
Bach, J.S.-Seiffert	Trio (Musical Offering).	
	fl, vn, vc, pf	BrH
Bach, J.S.-Seiffert	Trio Sonata (S. 1039). *2 fl, vc, pf*	BrH
Bach, J.S.-Hindermann	Triosonate, b.	
	2 ob d'amore, vc, bc	B&N
Barati, G.	Quartet. *fl/afl,*	
	ob/ehn, db (vc), hpcd	Pet
Bentzon, N.	Mosaique Musicale, op. 54.	
	fl, vn, vc, pf	Che
Berkeley, L.	Concertino, op. 49.	
	fl, vn, vc, hpcd (pf)	Che
Beversdorf, T.	Divertimento da Camara.	
	fl/pic, ob/ehn, db, hpcd	Sch
Beyer, J.-Gronefeld	Partita, C. *fl, vn, vc, pf*	Leu
Bizet, G.	Adagietto. *fl, vn, va, pf*	EdM
Bizet, G.	Adagietto. *fl, vn, vc, pf*	EdM
Britten, B.	Gemini Variations, op. 73 (1965).	
	fl, vn, pf (2 players)	Fab
Burkhard, W.	Lyrische Musik, op. 88.	
	fl, va, vc, pf	B&N
Carter, E.	Sonata (1952). *fl, ob, vc, hpcd*	AMP
Castaldi, P.	Clausola (1961/68).	
	pic/fl, vn, va, pf	ESZ
Castera, R. de	Concert. *fl, cl, vc, pf*	EdS
Corelli, A.	Gavotte and Gigue. *fl, vn, va, pf*	EdM
Corelli, A.	Gavotte and Gigue. *fl, vn, vc, pf*	EdM
Corrette, M.-Ruf	Concerto, e, op. 4/6.	
	fl, 2 vn, bc	SS
Corrette, M.	Sonata en Trio, No. 5.	
	fl, vn, vc, pf	EMT
Fasch, J.-Hechler	Concerto, G. *ob, 2 vn, bc*	Hei
Fasch, J.-Woehl	Sonate, B♭. *fl, ob, vn, bc*	B&N
Fasch, J.	Sonata, D. *fl, vn, bsn, bc*	B&V
Fasch, J.F.-Gerlach	Sonate, D. *fl, vn, bsn (vc), bc*	B&N
Feldman, M.	Durations I. *alf, vn, vc, pf*	Pet
Finkbeiner, R.	Quartet (1966). *cl, vn, vc, pf*	BrH
Finney, R.	Divertissement. *cl, vn, vc, pf*	Bow
Fontyn, J.	Musica a Quatro. *cl, vn, vc, pf*	ECh
Fortner, W.	New-Delhi-Musik. *fl, vn, vc, pf*	SS
Foster	A Village Festival. *fl, vn, vc, pf*	EdM
Franken, W.	Divertimento (1948). *fl, va, vc, pf*	SD
Fux, J.-Hillemann	Sonata a tre, d. *fl, vn, vc, pf*	Pet
Fux, J.-Hillemann	Sonata a tre, d. *ob, vn, vc, bc*	Pet
Gassmann, F.-Töttcher & Hartig	Quartet, B♭. *ob, va, vc, bc*	HSM
Giordani, T.	An Eighteenth Century Air.	

Woodwind, String, Keyboard

	fl, vn, vc, pf	EdM
Giordani, T.-Ruf	Quartet, G. *fl, vn, vc, pf*	SS
	Quartet, G, op. 3/1.	
	fl, vn, vc, pf	MR
Godron, H.	Sonatine (1948). *fl, vn, va, pf*	SD
Goossen, J.	Quartet. *cl, vn, va, pf*	AMC
Gow, D.	Quartet, op. 28. *fl, ob, vc, hpcd*	MR
Graun, J.-Brinckmann-Mohr	Concerto, e. *fl, 2 vn, c*	B&N
Graun, J.-Schroeder	Concerto, F. *fl, 2 vn, bc*	HMo
Green, R.	Holiday for Four - Chamber	
	Quartet. *cl, bsn, va, pf*	JB
Greenberg, L.	Quartet (1964). *afl, bsn, vn, pf*	Can
Guillemain, L.-Klengel	Conversation galante et amusante,	
	op. 12/1. *fl, vn, vc, pf*	BrH
Guillemain, L.-Winschermann	Quartet, C, op. 12/6.	
	fl (ob), vn, va, bc	HSM
Guillemain, L.-Petit	Sonate No. 3. *fl, vn, vc, bc*	EMT
Guillou, J.	Colloques No. 1. *fl, ob, vn, pf*	ALe
Guyonnet, J.	Polyphonie III. *fl, va, 2 pf*	UE
Hagerup-Bull, E.	Ad Usum Amicorum.	
	fl, vn, vc, pf	Bil
Handel, G.-Zobeley	Concerto No. 1, d. *fl, vn, vc, bc*	SS
Handel, G.-Monkemeyer	8 Psalmouvertüren, 2 vols.	
	ob, 2 vn, bc	Pel
Handel, G.	Kammertrio No. 19, G.	
	2 fl, vc, pf	BrH
Hasse, J.-Mohr	Concerto, A. *fl, 2 vn, bc*	B&N
Hasse, J.-Sonntag	Concerto, D. *fl, 2 vn, bc*	SS
Haubiel, C.	In Praise of Dance. *ob, vn, vc, pf*	HeE
Haubiel, C.	Masks. *ob, vn, vc, pf*	See
Haubiel, C.	Partita. *ob, vn, vc, pf*	See
Haydn, F.-Upmeyer	Quartet, G, op. 5/4.	
	fl, vn, va, bc	B&N
Heinichen, J.	Concerto, G. *fl (ob), 2 vn, bc*	CFV
Heinichen, J.-Hausswald	Sonate. *fl, ob, vc, pf*	BrH
Heiss, J.	Quartet (1971). *fl, cl, vc, pf*	Bow
Hindemith, P.	Quartet (1938). *cl, vn, vc, pf*	SS
Hosmer, J.	7/4 Serenade (1966).	
	fl, ob, db, hpcd	M&M
Hovhaness, A.	Quartet No. 1, op. 97.	
	fl, ob, v, hpcd	Pet
Hovhaness, A.	Quartet No. 2, op. 112.	
	fl, ob, vc, pf	Pet
Huber, N.	Chronogramm (1966).	
	cl, vn, vc, pf	B&N
Hurnik, I.	Sonata da camera.	
	fl, ob (cl), vc, pf	Art
Janitsch, J.-Wolff	Chamber Sonata, op. 8, "Echo".	
	fl, ob (fl), va, bc	BrH
Janitsch, J.-Winschermann	Quartet, c. *ob, vn, va, bc*	HSM
Janitsch, J.	Sonata, C, op. 4. *fl, ob, vn, bc*	MR

Woodwind, String, Keyboard

Janitsch, J.	Sonata da camera, op. 4.	
	fl, ob, vn, bc	B&V
Kapr, J.	5 Testimonies. *cl, vn, vc, pf*	ES
Karkoff, M.	Quartetto piccolo, op. 53.	
	fl, vn, vc, pf	EMF
King, H.	A fleur d'eau (1964).	
	fl, vn, pf, vc	SD
Kolman, P.	Due Casti, op. 2. *fl, cl, vn, pf*	SHF
Krebs, J.	Trio, D. *fl (va), vn, vc, pf*	BrH
Krommer, F.-Spindler	Concertante. *fl, ob, vn, pf*	FrH
Kupferman, M.	Infinities 13. *fl, cl, vn, pf*	Bow
Lee, N.	Variations. *fl, ob, vc, pf*	AMC
Linicke, J.-Schroeder	Concerto, G. *fl, vn, va, bc*	Pet
Loeillet, J.-Ruf	Concerto, D. *fl, 2 vn, bc*	B&N
Maasz, G.	Concertino. *fl, vn, vc, pf*	B&N
Maasz, G.	Hamburgische Tafelmusik.	
	fl, vn, vc, pf	R&E
Maganini, Q.	Trio Album. *fl, vn (va), vc, pf*	EdM
Martinu, B.	Quartet (1947). *ob, vn, vc, pf*	EME
Messiaen, O.	Quatuor pour la fin du Temps.	
	cl, vn, vc, pf	Dur
Michael, E.	Petite Suite Antique. *fl, vn, vc, pf*	Pet
Mortensen, O.	Quatuor Concertant. *fl, vn, vc, pf*	Che
Moss, L.	Patterns. *fl, cl, va, pf*	See
Müntzig, A.	Kvartett. *cl, va, vc, pf*	EMF
Müntzig, A.	Sommarmusik. *cl, 2 vc, pf*	EMF
Naudot, J.-Ruf	Concerto, G, op. 17/5.	
	fl (ob), 2 vn, bc	B&N
Naumann, J.-Bormann	Quartet, E♭, op. 1/5.	
	fl, vn, vc, pf	HSM
Orrego-Salas, J.	Sonata a Quattro.	
	fl, ob, db, hpcd	SMP
Pergolesi, G.	Sicilian Air. *fl, vn, vc, pf*	EdM
Pinchard, M.	Tombeau de Marin Marais.	
	fl, vn, vc, pf	EMT
Pousseur, H.	Madrigal II. *fl, vn,*	
	va da gamba, hpcd	UE
Rachmaninoff, S.	Vocalise. *fl, vn, va, pf*	EdM
Rachmaninoff, S.	Vocalise. *fl, vn, vc, pf*	EdM
Rochberg, G.	Contra mortem et tempus	
	(1965). *fl, cl, vn, pf*	UE
Salieri, A.-Wojciechowski	Triple Concerto, D. *ob, vn, vc, pf*	HSM
Sammartini, G.-Mönkemeyer	Sonata, D. *fl, 2 vn, bc*	Hei
Samonov, A.	Rhapsody. *cl, vn, vc, pf*	MR
Scarlatti, A.-Woehl	Quartet, F. *fl, 2 vn,*	
	pf, vc ad lib	Pet
Schickhard, J.-Peter	Sonate. *fl, ob, vc, pf*	MRL
Schilling, H.	Concerto piccolo. *fl, ehn, va, pf*	BrH
Schmelzer, J.	Sonata ad tabulam. *fl, vn, vc, org*	ES
Schmitt, F.	Pour presque tous les temps,	
	op. 134. *fl, vn, vc, pf*	Dur
Schwartz, E.	Soliloquies. *fl, cl, vn, pf*	Bow

Woodwind, Strings, Keyboard

Sköld, Y.	Kvartett. 2 *fl, vc, pf*	EMF
Smith, W.	Quartet. *cl, vn, vc, pf*	MJQ
Stamitz	Andantino. *fl, va, vc, pf*	EdM
Stamitz, K.	Triosonate, op. 14/5.	
	fl, vn, vc, pf	BrH
Stölzel, G.	Sonata a 3. *fl (ob), vn, vc, pf*	BrH
Stölzel, G.	Sonate. *ob, vn, vc, pf*	BrH
Sydeman, W.	Haus Music. *fl, vn, vc, pf*	See
Sydeman, W.	Quartet. *cl, vn, vc, pf*	See
Sydeman, W.	Quartet (1963). *fl, cl, vn, pf*	See
Telemann, G.-Veyron-Lacroix	Concerto a 4. *fl, ob, vn, pf*	Int
Telemann, G.	Concerto, B♭. 2 *fl, vc, pf*	EMT
Telemann, G.-Richter	Concerto, D. *fl, vn, vc, pf*	SS
Telemann, G.	Concerto, E. *fl, ob d'Amore,*	
	va d'Amore, pf	Pet
Telemann, G.-Upmeyer	Concerto, G. *fl, 2 vn, bc*	B&N
Telemann, G.	Concerto Primo, G (Pariser	
	Quartette). *fl, vn, vc, bc*	B&N
Telemann, G.	Concerto Secondo, D (Pariser	
	Quartette). *fl, vn, vc, bc*	B&N
Telemann, G.-Dohrn	Quartet, b (Parisian	
	Quartet). *fl, vn, vc, bc*	B&N
Telemann, G.	Quartet, D. *fl, vn, vc, pf*	WZ
Telemann, G.-Dohrn	Quartet, e (Parisian	
	Quartet). *fl, vn, vc, bc*	B&N
Telemann, G.-Seiffert	Quartet, e (Tafelmusik 1733, III	
	No. 2). *fl, vn, vc, pf*	BrH
Telemann, G.-Bergmann	Quartet, F. *fl, ob, vn,*	
	pf, vc ad lib	SS
Telemann, G.-Hinnenthal	Quartet, G. *fl, ob, vn, bc*	B&N
Telemann, G.-Grabe	Quartet, G. *fl, vn, vc, bc*	HSM
Telemann, G.	Quartet, g. *fl, vn, vc, pf*	WZ
Telemann, G.-Winschermann &		
Buck	Quartet. g. *ob (fl), vn, va, bc*	HSM
Telemann, G.-Töttcher & Grebe	Quartet, G (Tafelmusik I).	
	fl, ob, vn, bc	HSM
Telemann, G.-Richter	Sonata, a. *fl, vn, va, bc*	SS
Telemann, G.	Sonata Prima, A (Pariser	
	Quartette). *fl, vn, vc, bc*	B&N
Telemann, G.-Kolbel	Sonata (Quartet), G.	
	fl, 2 va da gamba, bc	HSM
Telemann, G.-Braun	Suite. *fl, vn (ob), vc,*	
	pf, va ad lib	Pet
Telemann, G.-Ermeler	Suite, e. *fl, vn, vc, bc*	B&N
Telemann, G.-Schneider	3 Trietti methodichi & 3 Scherzi,	
	3 vols. 2 *fl, vc, pf*	BrH
Thilman, J.	Das kleine Requiem, op. 27	
	(1945). *ehn, asax, va, pf*	Bar
Vivaldi, A.-Schroeder	Concerto. *fl, 2 vn, bc*	HMo
Vivaldi, A.-Ruf	Concerto, a. *fl (ob), 2 vn, bc*	SS
Vivaldi, A.	Concerto, d, FXII, 42.	
	fl, vn, bsn, bc	MR

Woodwind, String, Keyboard

Vivaldi, A.	Concerto, g, P. 404.	
	fl, bsn, vn, bc	MR
Weber, B.	Variations, op. 11a.	
	cl, vn, vc, pf	CoF
Webern, A.	Quartet, op. 22. *cl, tsax, vn, pf*	UE
Werner, G.-Moder	Concerto a quattro, A.	
	fl, 2 vn, bc	LDo
Wiesner, H.	Quartet. *fl, ob, vc, hpcd*	CoA
Young (arr)	King James' Pleasure.	
	2 ob, db, pf	Pet
Young (arr)	17th-Century Suite. *2 ob, db, pf*	Pet
Young, W.	19 Tanzsätze.	
	2 fl (2 ob), vc, bc	UE
Zelenka, J.-Schoenbaum	Triosonate No. 5, F.	
	2 ob, bsn (vc), bc	B&N
Zelenka, J.-Schoenbaum	Triosonate No. 4, g.	
	2 ob, bsn (vc), bc	B&N
Zelenka, J.-Schoenbaum	Triosonate No. 1, F.	
	2 ob, bsn (vc), bc	B&N
Zelenka, J.-Schoenbaum	Triosonate No. 6, c.	
	2 ob, bsn (vc), bc	B&N
Zelenka, J.-Schoenbaum	Triosonate No. 3, B♭.	
	2 ob, bsn (vc), bc	B&N
Zelenka, J.-Schoenbaum	Triosonate No. 2, g.	
	2 ob, bsn (vc), bc	B&N

WOODWIND, STRING, BRASS, KEYBOARD

Bancquart, A.	Ecorces II. *vn, cl, hn, pf*	Job
Casella, A.	Sinfonia (1932), op. 54	B&N
	cl, tpt, vc, pf	
Czerny, C.	Serenade, E♭. *cl, hn, vc, pf*	MR
Delannoy, M.	Rhapsodie. *asax, tpt, vc, pf*	Heu
Di Domenica, R.	Quartet. *fl, hn, vn, pf*	MJQ
Dobrowolski, A.	Krabogapa. *cl, trb, vc, pf*	JB
Dodge, C.	Composition. *ob, hn, vn, pf*	CoF
Doppler, F.-Rampal	Nocturne, op. 19. *fl, vn, hn(vc), pf*	Int
Fasch, J.-Töttcher & Spannagel	Sonata a 4. *ob, hn, vn, bc*	HSM
Kotonski, W.	Pour quatre. *cl, trb, vc, pf*	EBM
Meale, R.	Las Alboradas. *fl, vn, hn, pf*	JB
Serocki, K.	Swinging Music. *cl, trb, vc(db), pf*	HMo
Szalonek, W.	Improvisations sonoristiques.	EBM
	cl, trb, vc, pf	
Townsend, D.	Eight by Eight, op. 3/1.	Pet
	fl, tpt(cl, ob), vc(bsn), pf	
Welin, K.	Manzit. *cl, vc, trb, pf*	A&S

170

FOUR INSTRUMENTS INCLUDING HARP

Amy, G.	Inventions I and II. *fl, pf, perc, hp*	TP
Arnell, R.	Music for Harp. *fl, vn, va, hp*	SMP
Beecroft, N.	Contrasts for Six Performers (1962). *ob, va, hp, perc*	Can
Bijl, T. van der	Concert in F (1954). *fl, vn, va, hp*	SD
Cabus, P.	Sonate. *3cl, hp*	Mau
El-Dabh, H.	A Look at Lightning. *fl, ob, ehn, hp*	Pet
Glanville-Hicks, P.	Musica Antiqua No. 1. *fl, hp, marimba, perc*	CoF
Goldberg, T.	Quartet (1962). *afl, va, vc, hp*	Can
Hambraeus, B.	Mikrogram. *afl, vib, va, hp*	EMF
Homs, J.	Sonata (1955). *fl, ob, cl, hp*	See
Hovhaness, A.	The Flowering Peach. *cl, asax, hp, cel*	Sch
Hovhaness, A.	Orbit No. 1, op. 92/2. *fl, cel, hp, dr*	Pet
Hovhaness, A.	Upon Enchanted Ground, op 90/1. *fl, vc, hp, dr*	Pet
Jones, C.	Serenade. *fl, vn, vc, hp*	AMC
Klebe, G.	7 Bagatellen, op. 35. *basset hn, trb, hp, perc*	B&B
Leeuw, T. de	Krishna en Radha (1964). *fl, hp, timp, perc*	SD
Louel, J.	Suite (1967). *fl, vc, hp, vib*	CBD
Maconchy, E.	Reflections. *ob, cl, va, hp*	OxU
Malec, I.	Miniatures pour Lewis Carroll. *fl, vn, hp, perc*	HG
Migot, G.	Quartet. *fl, vn, cl, hp(pf)*	ALe
Mulder, E.	Quartet (1946). *ob, bsn, vc, hp*	SD
Otten, L.	Prelude en koraal (1959). *fl, va, vc, hp*	SD
Pedersen, P.	Serial Composition (1965). *bsn, hn, vn, hp*	Can
Petric, I.	Game for three - Game for four. *fl, E♭ cl, hp, perc*	EdD
Prosperi, C.	4 Invenzioni (1952/53). *cl, vn, va, hp*	ESZ
Schuller, G.	Densities I. *cl, vib, hp, db*	MjQ
Sheinkman	Divertimento. *cl, tpt, trb, hp*	Pet
Stahl, E.	Nocturne, op. 66. *fl, vn, vc, hp*	WZ
Vellones, P.	Rapsodie, op. 92. *asax, hp, cel, perc*	E-V
Wildberger, J.	Quartet (1967). *fl/afl/bfl, ob/ehn, hp, pf*	HG HG

FOUR INSTRUMENTS INCLUDING GUITAR

Beethoven, L. van-Schmidt	Adagio. *fl, vn, guit, pf*	B&N
Delden, L. van	Ballet, op. 14 (1946). *fl, bsn, va, guit*	SD

Four Instruments including Guitar

Erdmann, D.	Notturno. *fl, 3guit*	HG
Haydn, F.-Brojer	Quartette, op. 5/4. *fl, vn, va, guit*	LDo
Kotonski, W.	Selection I. *cl, asax, tsax, guit*	AP
Kubizek, A.	Quartetto da Camera, op. 24. *ob, cl, trb(bsn), guit*	LDo
Monteverdi, C.	5 Instrumental-Canzonetten. *fl, va da braccio, va da gamba, lute*	HSM
Santorsola, G.	Quartet No. 2. *fl, va, vc, guit*	SMP
Schubert, F.-Kinsky	Guitar Quartet, g. *fl, va, vc, guit*	Pet
Schubert, F.-Behrend	Quartet (Notturno, op. 21 by Matiegka). *fl, va, vc, guit*	B&B
Sydeman, W.	Music. *fl, va, guit, perc*	Pet
Truhlar, J.	Quartet, op. 14. *fl, vn, vc, guit*	Art
Wernick, R.	Stretti (1965). *cl, vn, va, guit*	B-M
Wolff, C.	Electric Spring I. *hn, cbsn, db, guit*	Pet

FOUR INSTRUMENTS INCLUDING PERCUSSION

Back, S.	Favola. *cl, vc, pf, perc*	Sch
Bowles, P.	Music for a Farce. *cl, tpt, perc, pf*	MS
Brown, E.	Hodograph I. *fl, pf, cel, perc*	AMP
Buczynski, W.	Two and a Half Squares in a Circle (1967). *fl, vn, vc, timp*	Can
Childs, B.	Quartet. *fl, ob, db, perc*	CoF
Corghi	Stereofonie x 4. *fl, vc, org, perc*	Ric
Diaz, F.	Meu Bem. *sax, tpt, trb, perc*	PMP
Diemente, E.	Quartet (1967). *asax, trb, db, perc*	See
Diemente, E.	Quartet (1966). *fl, cl, db, vib*	See
Denisow, E.	Concerto. *fl, ob, pf, perc*	UE
Dreifus, G.	The Seasons. *fl, va, vib, perc*	SS
Dubois, P.	Lou Cascarelet. *3ob, tambourine*	ALe
Endo, R.	Dessein Improvisation (1961). *fl, ob, pf, perc*	ESZ
Foss, L.	Echoi for Four Virtuosi (1961/63). *cl, vc, pf, perc*	SS
Fürst, P.	Beat the Beat. *cl, trb, db, perc*	EMo
Fussell, C.	Dance Suite (1963). *fl, tpt, va, perc*	Can
Guinjoan, J.	Miniaturas (1966). *cl, vn, pf, perc*	See
Hambraeus, B.	Introduzione-Sequenze-Coda (1958-59). *3fl, perc*	Nor
Hambraeus, B.	Mikrogram. *afl, vib, va, hp*	EMF
Herman, V.	Variante. *2cl, pf, perc*	EMU
Hibbard, W.	Gestures. *fl, db, perc, mar*	ACA

Four Instruments including Percussion

Hodkinson, S.	Interplay (1967). *alf/pic, cl/asax, db, perc*	Can
Hovhaness, A.	Dance of Black-Haired Mountain Storm. *fl, 3perc*	Pet
Hovhaness, A.	Orbit No. 1, op. 92/2. *fl, cel, hp, dr*	Pet
Hovhaness, A.	Upon Enchanted Ground, op. 90/1. *fl, vc, hp, dr*	Pet
Katz, E.	Toy Concerto. *pic, fl, cel, perc*	SF
Klebe, G.	Gratulations-Tango, op. 40a. *asax, tpt, pf, perc*	B&B
Klebe, G.	7 Bagatellen, op. 35. *basset hn, trb, hp, perc*	B&B
Lawson, P.	Valentia Extramaterial. *fl, pf, 2perc*	JB
Louel, J.	Suite (1967). *fl, vc, vib, hp*	CBD
Lu, Y.	Quartet. *cl, tu, 2perc*	See
Lunden, L.	Svart lek (1957). *2fl, bcl, perc*	STI
Mamlok, U.	Concert Piece for Four. *fl, ob, va, perc*	CoF
Matuszczak, B.	Musica da camera (1967). *3fl, perc*	HMo
Nordgren, E.	6 Movements (1966), op. 64. *fl, bsn, hn, dr*	STI
Petric, I.	Game for three - Game for four. *fl, E♭ cl, hp, perc*	EdD EdD
Pier, G.	3 Etüden. *cl, tpt, pf, dr*	LDo
Pinkham, D.	Eclogue. *fl, hpcd, 2perc*	JB
Pleskow, R.	3 Bagatelles (1967). *fl, cl, db, vib(pf)*	See
Reif, P.	Interpolations. *fl, cl, bsn, perc*	Gen
Rorem, N.	Lovers. *ob, v, hpcd, perc*	B&H
Rosenboom, D.	Pocket Pieces. *fl, asax, va, perc*	CoA
Schat, P.	2 stukken (1959). *fl, vn, tpt, perc*	SD
Shimoyama, H.	Structure (1961). *bcl, vn, tpt, perc*	ESZ
Simeone, H.	Creole Clarinet. *cl, db, pf, perc*	Sha
Stockhausen, K.	Kreuzspiel (1951). *ob, bcl, pf, perc*	UE
Subotnick, M.	Serenade II. *cl, hn, perc, pf*	M&M
Sydeman, W.	Music. *fl, va, guit, perc*	Pet
Tippett, M.	"Crown of the Year": No. 8 - Prelude. *ob, cl, dr, pf*	S&C
Ullman, B.	Racconto II. *cl, vc, pf, perc*	EMF
Wegner-Regeny, R.	Divertimento. *fl, cl, bsn, perc*	BrH
Westergaard, P.	Quartet (1960). *cl, vn, vc, vib*	SS
Wilkinson, M.	Variants of Glass. *2fl, ob, perc*	UE
Wolpe, S.	Quartet No. 1 (1950). *tsax, tpt, perc, pf*	M&M
Wolpe, S.	Quartet. *ob, vc, pf, perc*	M&M
Zender, H.	Quartet (1964-65). *fl, vc, pf, perc*	B&B
Zonn, P.	Turnaround. *ob, E♭ cl/bcl, vib, tape*	ACA

FOUR INSTRUMENTS INCLUDING RECORDER

Fasch, J.-Moeck	Sonata, G. *fl, 2rec, bc*	HMO
Loeillet, J.-Poulteau	Sonate en trio, g. *rec, ob, vc, pf*	ALe
Poglietti, A.	Sonata a tre, C. *rec, ob, bsn, pf*	Pet
Schickhardt, J.	Sonata, B♭. *rec, ob, vc, pf,* *vc ad lib*	Pet
Telemann, G.-Töttcher & Grebe	Concerto, a. *a rec, ob, vn, bc*	HSM
Thybo, L.	Quartet "Non si Levava Ancor." *rec, ehn, hn, bsn*	Che

FOUR INSTRUMENTS INCLUDING TAPE

Reynolds, R.	Traces. *fl, vc, pf, tape*	Pet
Wahren, K.	L'art pour l'art (1968). *fl, vc, pf, tape*	B&B
Zonn, P.	Turnaround. *ob, E♭ cl/bcl, vib, tape*	ACA

MISCELLANOUS

Becher, H.	Ansbacher Quartett. *ob, ob d'amore, ehn, bsn*	PG
Benker, H.-Hohner	2 Tänze. *fl, vn, vc, accordeon*	Hoh
Hovhaness, A.	Hanna, op. 101. *2cl, 2pf*	Pet
Klebe, G.	Gratulations, op. 40a. *asax, tpt, cemb, harmonium*	B&B
Klebe, G.	7 Bagatellen, op. 35. *basset hn, trb, hp, glock*	B&B
Mayuzumi, T.	Metamusic. *sax, vn, pf, conductor*	Pet
Moulaert, R.	Andante, Fugue et Final. *ob, ob d'amour, ehn, heckelphone*	CBD
Zagwijn, H.	Suite (1951). *2ob, ehn, heckelphone*	SD

FIVE INSTRUMENTS

FIVE FLUTES

Boismortier, J.B. de-Spindler	6 Concerti, Nos. 4-6	FrH
Boismortier, J.B. de-Glasenapp	6 Concerti, Nos. 1-3	FrH
Bottje, W.	Quintet	CoF
Brown, R.	3 Fugues	Wes
Cunningham, M.	Glorification	AMC
Cunningham, M.	Pastel Design. *3fl, afl(cl), bfl(cl)*	CoA
Frank, M.	Introduction and Scherzo	SF
Giltray	Divertimento	SD
Lorenzo, L. de	Sinfonietta, op. 75	Pet
Praag, H. van	Sonata	SD

FIVE OBOES

Globokar	Discours III	Pet

FIVE CLARINETS

Bach, J.C.-Voxman	Allegro (Sinfonia II). *3cl, acl, bcl*	Rub
Bach, J.S.-Johnson	Celebrated Air (Suite No. 3). *3cl, acl, bcl*	Rub
Bach, J.S.-Dansby	Terzetto (Cantata No. 38). *4cl, bcl(cl)*	Ken
Bargiel, W.-Harris	Meditation. *cl(fl), cl(ob), cl, acl(cl, hn), bcl(bsn)*	CF
Beethoven, L. van-Johnson	Adagio Cantabile (Sonata No. 8). *3cl, acl, bcl*	Rub
Beethoven, L. van-Johnson	Scherzo (Octet, op. 103). *3cl, acl, bcl*	Rub
Bizet, G.-Freedman	5 Pieces from "Carmen." *3cl, acl, bcl*	MCA
Davis, V.	The Spinning Wheel	Sha
Dvorak, A.-Johnson	Menuetto (Serenade, op. 44). *3cl, acl, bcl*	Rub
Fox	Pavanne. *4cl, bcl*	SF
Glaser, W.	Musik (1964).	STI
Grieg, E.-Voxman	Lyric Piece No. 2. *3cl, acl, bcl*	Rub
Handel, G.-Voxman	Sarabande and Allegro (Concerto Grosso No. 3). *3cl, acl, bcl*	Rub
Harmon	First Suite	Wes
Haydn, F.-Johnson	Second Movement (Symphony No. 100). *3cl, acl, bcl*	Rub
Haydn, F.-Johnson	Third Movement (Symphony No. 94). *3cl, acl, bcl*	Rub
Johnson, C.	Scherzo Capriccio. *3cl, acl, bcl*	Rub
Marie, G.-Harris	Berceuse	CF
Maganini, Q.-Harris	Reverie	CF

175

Five Clarinets

McBride	Melody by Chopin. *4cl, bcl*	SF
McBride	Melody by Grieg. *4cl, bcl*	SF
Moffitt, D.	Frisky	CF
Mozart, W.	Adagio, B♭, K. 411. *3cl, acl, bcl(bsn)*	Pre
Mozart, W.-Voxman	Adagio, K. 411. *3cl, acl, bcl*	Rub
Mozart, W.-Johnson	Menuetto (Eine Kleine Nachtmusik). *3cl, acl, bcl*	Rub
Mozart, W.-Voxman	Menuetto (Serenade No. 1). *3cl, acl, bcl*	Rub
Mussorgsky, M.	Ballet of the Chicks in their Shells	EdM
Nestico, S.	A Study in Contrasts. *3cl, acl(cl), bcl*	Ken
Schubert, F.-Johnson	Menuet and Trio (Sonata, op. 78). *3cl, acl, bcl*	Rub
Schumann, R.-Milano	Fuga. *4cl, bcl*	SF
Schwarz, I.	Capriccio. *3cl, acl, bcl*	Rub
Tchaikovsky, P.-Johnson	Andante Cantabile (Quartet, op. 11). *3cl, acl, bcl*	Rub
Verrall, J.	Serenade. *3cl, acl(cl), bcl(bsn)*	TP
Weber, C.M. von	Minuet (Quintet, op. 34). *3cl, acl(asax), bcl(bsn)*	CF

FIVE SAXOPHONES

Bach, J.S.-Schmidt	Fugue XXII. *sop sax, 2asax, tsax, bar sax*	Wes
Cazden, N.	No. 4 Formation (6 Discussions)	Spr
Clark, S.-Williams	Belgian March	SM
Harger, E.	Beguine for Five. *2asax, 2tsax, bar sax*	B-M
Haydn, F.-Johnson	Third Movement (Symphony No. 100)	Rub
Lake, M.	Andantino. *2asax, 2tsax, bar sax*	Lud
Lake, M.	Cleveland March. *2asax, 2tsax, bar sax*	Lud
Lake, M.	Iron Mountain. *2asax, 2tsax, bar sax*	Lud
Lake, M.	Long, Long Ago. *2asax, 2tsax, bar sax*	Lud
Lake, M.	Louisiana. *2asax, 2tsax, bar sax*	Lud
Lake, M.	Madeline. *2asax, 2tsax, bar sax*	Lud
Lakey, C.	Saxet No. 1-5. *sop sax, 2asax, tsax, bar sax* Published separately	SM
Moratin	Quintette	EdR
Mussorgsky, M.	Ballet of the Chicks in Their Shells. *3asax, tsax, bar sax*	EdM
Sary, L.	Incanto	EMB
Schmaltz, E.	Strictly for Saxes. *2asax, 2tsax, bar sax*	Byr
Schumann, R.-Williams	2 Kinderscenen, op. 15/8, 9	SM
Toselli, E.-Harger	Serenade. *2asax, 2tsax, bar sax*	B-M
Waele de	Quintette	EdR

WOODWIND QUINTET (fl, ob, cl, hn, bsn)

Absil, J.	Danses Bulgares, op. 103	HLe
Absil, J.	Quintette, op. 16 (1934)	CBD
Adler, S.	Intrada	OxU
Agay, D.	5 Easy Dances	TP
Aitken, H.	8 Studies	E-V
Altmann, E.	Kleine Tanzsuite	FrH
Ambrosi, D. d'	Introduzione e Allegro	Edi
Ambrosius, H.	Suite, op. 57 (1925)	FrH
Amram, D.	Fanfare and Processional	Pet
Amram, D.	Quintet	Pet
Andersen, J.	Quintet (1939)	SPD
Anderson, T., Jr.	5 Etudes and a Fancy	CoF
Andriessen, H.	Quintet (1951)	SD
Andriessen, J.	Sciarada spagnuloa (1962)	SD
Angerer, P.	Quintet	LDo
Antonini, A.	20th Century Doll	Cha
Arma, P.	7 Transparencies	Elk
Arne, T.-Collins	Suite of Dances	ShB
Arnell, R.	Cassation, op. 45	HE
Arnold, M.	3 Shanties	Pat
Arrieu, C.	Quintette, C	Bil
Avni, T.	Quintet	B-M
Baaren, K. van	Quintetto a fiati (1963)	SD
Bacewicz, G.	Quintet (1933)	AP
Bach, J.C.-Maros	Quintet No. 3	EMB
Bach, J.C.	Sinfonia, No. 1	TP
Bach, J.S.-Mickens	Bourrée (Suite No. 3)	B&H
Bach, J.S.-Orem	Bouree (Overture No. 3)	TP
Bach, J.S.-Waln	Classical Quintet	NK
Bach, J.S.-Brahms-Cantrell	4 Transcriptions	Wes
Bach, J.S.-Hirsh	Fugue, c	TP
Bach, J.S.-Von Kreisler	Prelude and Fugue	SM
Bach, J.S.-Cantrell	Prelude and Fugue, D	Wes
Bach, J.S.-Rosenthal	Prelude and Fugue, e	Wes
Bach, J.S.-Rosenthal	Prelude and Fugue, g	Wes
Bach, J.S.-Rosenthal	Prelude and Fugue, G	Wes
Bach, J.S.	Prelude and Fugue XXI	AMP
Bach, J.S.-Nakagawa	Prelude and Fugue XXII	JB
Bach, J.S.-Gordon	Prelude to Cantata No. 106	SM
Bach, J.S.-Kessler	Prelude XXII, Vol. I	Rub
Bach, J.S.-Mickens	Sarabande (French Suite No. 1)	B&H
Bach, J.S.-Henschel	Sarabande (French Suite No. 1)	B&H
Bach, J.S.-Gordon	Sarabande and Gavotte	CF
Bach, J.S.-Brearley	3 Chorale Preludes	Nov
Bach, J.S.-Catelinet	2 Bach Fugues	HE
Badings, H.	Quintet No. 2 (1929)	SD
Badings, H.	Quintet No. 4 (1948)	SD
Baeyens, A.	Quintette (1950)	CBD
Balassa, S.	Quintet, op. 9	EMB
Balay, G.	L'aurore sur la Forêt	ALe
Balay, G.	Little Miniature Suite in 18th Century Style	ALe

Woodwind Quintet

Balay, G.-Waln	Menuet & Rondo (Little Miniature Suite)	NK
Balfe, M.	Kvintett, op. 2	STI
Ballif, C.	Quintet, op. 10	B&B
Bamert, W.	Woodwind Quintet	Sch
Barati, G.	Woodwind Quintet	AMC
Barber, S.	Summer Music, op. 31	Sch
Barboteu, G.	Caricatures	ECh
Barboteu, G.	Prélude et Divertissement	ECh
Barraine, E.	"Ouvrage de dame"	ChM
Barrows, J.	March	Sch
Barthe, A.	Passacaille	ALe
Barthe, A.-Waln	Passacaille	NK
Barthe, A.	Passacaille	Rub
Barthe, A.-Andraud	Passacaille	SM
Bartos, F.	Büger als Edelmann (1934)	Art
Bartow	Divertimento	Sha
Bartsch, C.	3 Mouvements	Mau
Bassett, L.	Woodwind Quintet	CoF
Bauer, M.	Quintet, op. 48	CoF
Baumann, M.	Kleine Kammermusik	S-V
Baur, J.	Quintetto sereno (1958)	BrH
Beach, B.	Scherzo	Leb
Beach, H.	Pastorale	See
Beck, J.	Quintet	MV
Becker, G.	Serpentinata (1968)	HG
Beckler, S.	Five	CoA
Beckler, S.	Little Suite	CoA
Beekhuis, H.	Elegie en humoreske (1939)	SD
Beekhuis, H.	Quintet (1935)	SD
Beethoven, L. van	Adagio and Allegro for the Musical Clock	UE
Beethoven, L. van-Holmes	Allegro (Symphony No. 6)	Bar
Beethoven, L. van-Brearley	Bagatelle, op. 119/1	Nov
Beethoven, L. van-DeBueris	Country Dance No. 1	CF
Beethoven, L. van-DeBueris	Country Dance No. 3	GFB
Beethoven, L. van-DeBueris	Gavotte, F	CF
Beethoven, L. van-Thornton	Octet, op. 103	SM
Beethoven, L. van-Scott	Piano Sonata, op. 49/1	Wat
Beethoven, L. van-Stark	Quintet, op. 71 (Sextet)	SM
Beethoven, L. van-Philadelphia ww Quintet	Quintet, op. 71, E♭	TP
Beethoven, L. van-Taylor	Rondo, F (Piano Sonata, op. 10/2)	CF
Beethoven, L. van-Taylor	Rondo, F (Sonata, op. 10/3). fl, ob, cl, hn, bsn (bcl)	CF
Beethoven, L. van-Filas	6 Variations on a Theme by Paisiello	PMP
Beethoven, L. van-Bellison	Variations on a Theme form "Don Giovanni" by Mozart	FrC
Benguerel, X.	Successions (1960)	EMo
Bennett, D.	Rhapsodette	CF

Woodwind Quintet

Bennett, R.R.	Quintet	UE
Benson, W.	Marche	Sha
Berezowsky, N.	Suite No. 2	B-M
Berge, S.	Yang-Guan (1967)	Nor
Berger, J.	6 Short Pieces	WZ
Bergmann, W.	Musik für Bläserquintett (1961)	LDo
Bergsma, W.	Concerto	GaM
Beyer, J.	Movement	AMC
Bezanson, P.	Woodwind Quintet, Homage to Great Americans	CoF
Biggs, J.	Scherzo	AMC
Birtwistle, H.	Refrains and Choruses (1957)	UE
Bissell	Folk Song Suite	B&H
Bitsch, M.	Sonatine	ALe
Bizet, G.-Williams	Berceuse, op. 22/3	SM
Bizet, G.-Holmes	Minuetto (L'Arlesienne Suite)	Bar
Bizet, G.-Elkan	Quintet (Carmen)	HeE
Bjelik, M.	Mobile	LDo
Blank, A.	Quintet	See
Bloch, W.	Serenade (1966)	LDo
Blumenfeld, H.	Expansions	MCA
Blumer, T.	Quintet, op. 52	WZ
Blumer, T.	Swiss Quintet	HSM
Bobescu, C.	Parafraza pe motivul "Horei staccato"	EMU
Boedijn, G.	Kwintet concertante, op. 150 (1957)	SD
Boely, A.-Taylor	Andante	GFB
Bois, R. du	Chants et contrepoints (1962)	SD
Bois, R. du	Reflexions sur le jour ou Perotin Grand ressuscitera	SD
Bon, W.	Quintet	SD
Bonsel, A.	Kwintet No. 1 (1949)	SD
Bonsel, A.	Quintet No. 2 (1953)	SD
Booren, J. van	Spectra (1967)	SD
Borowski, F.	Madrigal to the Moon	B&H
Borris, S.	Woodwind Quintet, op. 25/2	S-V
Bosmans, A.	Diabelliana	HeE
Bottje, W.	Fluctuations	CoF
Bottje, W.	Quintet	AMC
Bourguignon, F.	2 pièces, op. 71 (1941)	CBD
Bozay, A.	Quintet (1962)	EMB
Bozza, E.	Pentaphonie	ALe
Bozza, E.	Scherzo, op. 48	ALe
Bozza, E.	Variations sur un thème libre, op. 42	ALe
Brahms, J.-Rosenthal	Capriccio	Wes
Brana, H.	Cinco Entradas	Gen
Brana, H.	Estribillo	Gen
Brana, H.	Filigrana	Gen
Brana, H.	Lunes Azul	Gen
Brana, H.	Metamorphosis	Gen

Woodwind Quintet

Brana, H.	Tema	Gen
Brant, H.	Requiem in Summer	CoF
Bravnicar, M.	4 Pieces	EdD
Bredow, E.	Serenade of Franconia	ABe
Brehm, A.	Divertimento	EBM
Brenta, G.	Le Soldat Fanfaron	CBD
Bresgen, C.	Salzburger Divertimento	LDo
Brickman, J.	Suite	StM
Bright, H.	3 Short Dances	Sha
Brod, H.-Schuller	Quintet, op. 2/1	M&M
Brod, H.-Schuller	Quintet, op. 2/2	M&M
Brons, C.	Balletto (1961)	SD
Brons, C.	Mutazione (1964)	SD
Brown, C.	Quintet	ECh
Brugk, H.	Serenade, op. 22	HSM
Bruns, V.	Bläserquintett, op. 16	FrH
Buczynski, W.	Suite, op. 13 (1955)	Can
Buicliu, N.	Quintet	EMU
Bull, J.-Moortel	Preludio e Canzone	EMb
Bull-Byrd-Gibbons-Cantrell	4 Elizabethan Pieces	Wes
Bush, G.	Quintet	GaM
Butt, J.	Winsome's Folly: Suite No. 2	Nov
Cacavas, J.	Windette	SF
Cage, J.	Music for Wind Instruments (1937)	Pet
Cailliet, L.	Concertino	HeE
Calabro, L.	Divertimento	E-V
Cambini, G.	Quintet No. 1	M&M
Cambini, G.	Quintet No. 3, op. 4	M&M
Cammarota	Introduction, Chromatic Fugue, and Finale	EdB
Carion, F.	Fantaisie Concertante	EMb
Carlstedt, J.	Kvintett, op. 19 (1962)	STI
Carlstedt, J.	Sinfonietta	STI
Carter, E.	Woodwind Quintet (1948)	AMP
Castérède, J.	Quintet	ALe
Cazden, N.	3 Constructions, op. 38	Spr
Cellier, A.	Images Médiévales	EMT
Chagrin, F.	Divertimento	GaM
Chagrin, F.	Serenade "Jottings for Jeremy"	Nov
Chailley, J.	Barcarolle	ALe
Chaynes, C.	Sérénade	ALe
Chemin-Petit, H.	Quintet (1948)	MRL
Cherney, B.	Interlude and Variations (1965)	Can
Cherney, B.	Quintet (1965)	Can
Chevreuille, R.	Divertissement, op. 21 (1942)	CBD
Chevreuille, R.	Sérénade, op. 65 (1956)	CBD
Childs, B.	First Wind Quintet (1962)	CoF
Childs, B.	Second Wind Quintet	CoF
Childs, B.	Third Wind Quintet	CoF
Childs, B.	Fourth Woodwind Quintet	CoF
Childs, B.	Wind Quintet	AMC

Woodwind Quintet

Christensen, J.	5 for the Fun of It. *fl, ob (cl),* *cl, hn (tsax), bsn (bcl)*	Ken
Clapp, P.	Prelude and Finale	B&H
Clarke, H.	Saraband for the Golden Goose	CoF
Cohen, S.	Forest Lullaby (Suite). *fl, ob, cl,* *hn, bsn (bcl)*	CF
Cohen, S.	March-Militaire (Suite). *fl, ob, cl* *hn, bsn (bcl)*	CF
Cohen, S.	March-Miniature	CF
Cohen, S.	Minuet-Fantasy (Suite). *fl, ob,* *cl, hn, bsn (bcl)*	CF
Coker, W.	Quintet in Three Movements	TP
Colaco Osorio-Swaab, R.	Suite (1948)	SD
Comes, L.	Divertisment (1970)	EMU
Coursey, R. de	Fugue a la Rumba (1958)	Can
Cowell, H.	Ballad (1956)	AMP
Cowell, H.	Suite	TP
Croley, R.	Microespressioni I (1969)	JB
Cruft, A. (arr)	2 English Keyboard Pieces	GaM
Cui, C.	Orientale	CF
Custer, A.	2 Movements	Gen
Dahl, I.	Allegro and Arioso (1942)	M&M
Damase, J.	17 Variations, op. 22	ALe
Danzi, F.-Maganini	Gypsy Dance	CF
Danzi, F.-Weigelt	Quintet, B♭, op. 56/1	Leu
Danzi, F.-Weigelt	Quintet, g, op. 56/2	Leu
Danzi, F.-Waln	Allegretto (op. 56/2)	NK
Danzi, F.-Kneusslin	Bläserquintett, F, op. 56/3	Leu
Danzi, F.-Rottler	Bläserquintett, G, op. 67/1	Leu
Danzi, F.-Kneusslin	Quintet, op. 67/2, e	EK
Danzi, F.-Rampal	Quintet, op. 67/2, e	Int
Danzi, F.-Kneusslin	Quintet, op. 68/1, A	EK
Danzi, F.	Quintet, op. 68/2	EK
Danzi, F.-Vester	Quintet, d, op. 68/3	MR
Dávid, G.	Quintet No. 1 (1949)	EMB
Dávid, G.	Quintet No. 3 (1964)	EMB
David, T.	Bläserquintett (1966)	LDo
David, T.	Quintet (1966)	LDo
Déak, C.	Kvintett (1965)	STI
Debussy, C.-Elkan	Arabesque No. 1	HeE
Debussy, C.-Elkan	Arabesque No. 2	HeE
Debussy, C.-Rosenthal	Arabesque No. 2	Wes
Debussy, C.-Frank	Reverie	SF
Debussy, C.-Bozza	The Little Negro	ALe
Dedrick, R.	My Baby's Smile. *fl, ob (cl),* *cl, hn, bsn (bcl)*	Ken
Dela, M.	Petite Suite Maritime (1946)	Can
Dela, M.	Suite (1963)	Can
Delaney, R.	Suite	SM
Delvaux, A.	Walliser suite (1966)	CBD
Demuth, N.	Pastorale and Scherzo	HE
Denisow, E.	Quintet	UE

Woodwind Quintet

Deslandres, A.-Andraud	3 pièces en quintette	SM
Despic, D.	Vignette, op. 43b	HG
Desportes, Y.	Prelude, Variations and Finale	SM
Diamond, D.	Quintet (1957)	SMP
Diemer, E.	Woodwind Quintet No. 1 (1962)	B&H
Diercks, J.	Wind Quintet (1955)	TP
Dimov, B.	Composition III (1968)	EMo
Dobias, V.	Quintetto Pastorale (1953)	Pan
Dohl, F.	Klangfiguren (1962)	HG
Domazlicky, F.	Bläserquintett I	CHF
Donato, A.	Quintet	Cam
Domenico, O. di	Quintetto	ALe
Doppelbauer, J.	Bläserquintett	LDo
Douglas, R.	Dance Caricatures (1939)	HE
Dragan, R.	Aus der Jugend	Isr
Drejsl, R.	Bläserquintett	CHF
Dubois, P.	Fantasia	ALe
Dubois, T.	First Suite	Heu
Dupont, P.	3 Pièces Brèves	Bil
Durey, L.	Les Soirées de Valfère	Bil
Durkó, Z.	Improvisation	EMB
Dvorak, A.-Haufrecht	Serenade, op. 44	CoF
Eben, P.	Bläserquintett (1965)	ES
Eckhardt-Gramatté, S.	Woodwind Quintet (1962-63)	Can
Eder, H.	Quintet, op. 25	LDo
Eder, H.	Septuagesima instrumentalis, op. 51	LDo
Eder de Lastra, E.	Wind Quintet	LDo
Eisman, W.	Fontamara (1966)	SD
Eisman, W.	Quintet (1955)	SD
Eklund, Hans	Improvisata (1958)	STI
Eklund, Hans	Sommarparafras (1968)	STI
Epstein, A.	Quintet	See
Erdlen, H.	Kleine Variationen über ein Frühlingslied, op. 27/1	WZ
Errante, B.	Schizzo Moderno. *fl, ob (fl, cl), cl, hn (acl), bsn (bcl)*	PrA
Escher, R.	Quintet (1967)	SD
Essex, K.	Wind Quintet (1941)	HE
Etler, A.	Quintet No. 1 (1955)	AMP
Etler, A.	Quintet No. 2 (1957)	AMP
Evans, R.	Prelude & Fugue	AMP
Farberman, H.	Quintessence	Gen
Farkas, F.	Antiche Danze Ungheresi (1953)	EMB
Farkas, F.	Divertissement (1967)	EMB
Farkas, F.	Régi Magyar Táncok	EMB
Farkas, F.	Serenade (1951)	EMB
Fauré, G.-Williams	Berceuse (Dolly), op. 51/1	SM
Ferguson, S.	Overture for Winds	CoA
Fernstrom, J.	Kvintett, op. 59 (1943)	STI
Ferrari, D.	Pastorale	Cor
Fiala, G.	Musique de chambre (1948)	Can

Woodwind Quintet

Fine, I.	Partita	B&H
Fine, I.	Romanza	B-M
Finke, F.	Quintet	BrH
Folprecht, Z.	Wind Quintet, op. 17	CHF
Fortner, W.	5 Bagatellen (1960)	SS
Francaix, J.	Quintette	SS
Franco, J.	Canticle (1958)	CoF
Franzen, O.	Spel (1969)	STI
Freed, I.	Quintet	AMC
Freedman, H.	Quintet (1962)	Can
Freistadt, M.	Woodwind Quintet No. 1	AMC
Freistadt, M.	Woodwind Quintet No. 2	AMC
Freyer, J.	Divertimento	BrH
Fricker, P.R.	Quintet, op. 5 (1947)	SS
Furer, A.	Bläserquintett, op. 21	Pel
Fürst, P.	Konzertante Musik, op. 25	LDo
Fürst, P.	Quintet No. 3, op. 29	LDo
Futterer, C.	Quintet, B♭ (1922)	EK
Gaal, J.	Bläserquintett	B&V
Gaal, J.	Quintet No. 2	EMB
Gabaye, P.	Quintet (1959)	ALe
Gade, N.-Elkan	Merry-Go-Round	HeE
Garrido-Lecca, C.	Divertimento	SMP
Gayfer, J.	Suite (1947)	B&H
Gebauer, F.-Sirker	Bläserquintett, No. 2, E♭	Leu
Gebauer, F.-Sirker	Bläserquintett, No. 3, c	Leu
Gebauer, F.-Sirker	Quintet No. 3, c	Leu
Gee, H. (arr)	Bransle	Byr
Geissler, F.	Heitere Suite	BrH
Genzmer, H.	Bläser-Quintett (1956-57)	Lit
Geraedts, J.	Kleine watermuziek (1951)	SD
Gerhard, R.	Quintet (1928)	B-M
Gerster, O.	Heitere Musik	SS
Gillis, D.	And Mr. Tortoise Wins the Race	B-M
Gillis, D.	Br'er Rabbit Dreams	B-M
Gillis, D.	Five Piece Combo	B-M
Gillis, D.	Frolic in B-Bop Major	B-M
Gillis, D.	Sermonette (Southern Style)	B-M
Gillis, D.	They're Off	B-M
Giltay, B.	Divertimento (1963)	SD
Gipps, R.	Seascape	SF
Gluck, C.-Josep	Gavotte (Paris and Helena)	CF
Goeb, R.	Prairie Songs	SMP
Goeb, R.	Quintet for Winds No. 1	CoF
Goeb, R.	Quintet for Woodwinds II	CoF
Gonzalez-Zuleta, F.	Quinteto 1960	SMP
Goode, D.	Symphonia, Woodwind Quintet No. 2	AMC
Goodenough, F.	Woodwind Quintet	CoF
Goodman, J.	Woodwind Quintet (1954)	AlB
Gottlieb, J.	Twilight Crane	Sch

183

Woodwind Quintet

Grabócz, M.	Alte ungarische Tänze des 18. Jahrhunderts	B&N
Grainger, P.	Walking Tune	S&C
Granados, E.-Elkan	Oriental, op. 5	HeE
Grandert, J.	Pour Philippe (1970)	STI
Grant, W.	Soliloquy and Jubilation	CoF
Gretry, A.-Sabatini	Tambourine	Cor
Grieg, E.-Trinkhaus	Erotikon, op. 43/4	MS
Grieg, E.-Trinkaus	Morning Mood (op. 46/1)	War
Grieg, E.-Trinkhaus	Rigaudon	MS
Grimm, C.-Andraud	A Little Serenade, op. 36	SM
Groot, H. de	Burla Ritmica	B&V
Groot, H. de	Variatiesuite (1944)	B&V
Guenther, R.	Rondo	CF
Guentzel, G.	Bas-bleu	Bar
Guentzel, G.	In the Meadow	Bar
Guentzel, G.	Scherzo	Bar
Guentzel, G.	Tarantella	Bar
Guilmant, A.-Taylor	Canzonetta	War
Guinjoan, J.	Triptico (1965)	See
Guion, D.-Waln	The Harmonica Player (Alley Tunes)	NK
Gyring, E.	Quintet	AMC
Haas, P.	Quintet, op. 10 (1929)	M&M
Haddad, D.	Blues au Vent. *fl, ob, cl, bsn, hn, perc opt*	Sha
Haddad, D.	Encore "1812"	Sha
Haddrill, P.	Recitation	PrA
Hahnel, H.	Quintet	Hei
Hall, P.	Quintet (1944)	Pet
Hamerik, E.	Quintet (1942)	SPD
Handel, G.-Bauer	6 Little Fugues	AMP
Hanus, J.	Suita domestica, op. 57	Art
Hartley, G.	Divertissement	AMP
Hartley, W.	2 Pieces	Cre
Hasse, J.	Chamber Music	ABe
Haubiel, C.	5 Pieces	See
Haufrecht, H.	A Woodland Serenade	BB
Haufrecht, H.	From the Hills	CoF
Haworth, F.	Glenrose Suite (1960)	Can
Haydn, F.-Holmes	Allegretto (Symphony No. 11)	Bar
Haydn, F.-Perry	Divertimento [B♭]	B&H
Haydn, J.-Phila. Quintet	Divertimento No. 1, B♭	TP
Haydn, F.-Haufrecht	Divertimento, C	CoF
Haydn, F.-Long	Divertimento, C	Sch
Haydn, F.-McCathren	Finale (Sonata, C)	Ken
Haydn, F.-Meek	Largo (op. 76/5)	TP
Haydn, F.-Andraud	Menuet and Presto	SM
Haydn, F.-Holmes	Minuetto (Symphony No. 2)	Bar
Haydn, F.-Von Kreisler	Menuetto and Scherzo	SM
Haydn, F.-Skowronek	Musical Clock Pieces	M&M
Haydn, F.	Quintet	Cor

Woodwind Quintet

Haydn, F.-Kesztler	Quintet	EMB
Haydn, F.-Andraud	Quintet (Klavier Trio)	SM
Haydn, F.-Long	Quintet No. 1	SM
Haydn, F.-Long	Quintet No. 4	SM
Haydn, F.-Cutler	7 German Dances	Cor
Haydn, F.-Andraud	2 Short Quintets	SM
Heiden, B.	Sinfonia (1949)	SS
Heiden, B.	Woodwind Quintet (1965)	AlB
Hekster, W.	Pentagram	SD
Hekster, W.	Quintet	SD
Helm, E.	Woodwind Quintet	SS
Hempel, R.	Movimento (1966)	B&N
Henkemans, H.	Quintet No. 1	SD
Henkemans, H.	Quintet No. 2 (1962)	SD
Henze, H.	Quintet (1952)	SS
Hermann, F.	Zur Ubung im Zusammenspiel, Bk. 2	BrH
Herrmann, H.	Pastorale Phantasietten, op. 51	Sim
Hess, W.	Divertimento, op. 51	HE
Hetu, J.	Quintet, op. 13 (1967)	Can
Heussenstamm, G.	Instabilities, op. 21	See
Hewitt-Jones, T.	Theme and Variations	Nov
Hilfiger	Mirage	Ken
Hindemith, P.	Kleine Kammermusik, op. 24/2	SS
Hirsch, H.	Quintetto sereno	Pet
Hirsch, H.	Nocturne	GFB
Hirner, T.	Wind Quintet (1960)	SHF
Hlobil, E.	Wind Quintet, op. 20	CHF
Höffer, P.	Bläserquintett (1947)	Mit
Hofmann, W.	Serenade	S-V
Hofmann, W.	Bläserquintett, D	BrH
Höller, K.	Serenade, op. 42a	WMS
Holm, M.	Sonata, op. 25	WH
Holm, P.	2 Pieces	Che
Holmes, G.	Castillia (Bolero)	Bar
Hosmer, J.	Fugue, C	War
Hovaness, A.	Wind Quintet, op. 159	Pet
Hovland, E.	Quintett	Nor
Hrisanide, A.	Directions (1970)	HG
Huber, K.	3 Sätze in 2 Teilen (1958-59)	B&N
Hummel, B.	Quintet	ABe
Hunter, E.	Dance Humoresque, op. 1/3	CF
Hurnik, I.	Die vier Jahreszeiten	CHF
Huse, P.	Recurrences (1966)	Can
Huybrechts, A.	Quintette (1936)	CBD
Ibert, J.	3 pièces brèves	ALe
Ioannidis, Y.	Actinia (1969)	HG
Ivey, J.	Androcles & the Lion	AMC
Jacobi, F.	Scherzo	CF
Jacoby, H.	Quintet (1946)	Isr
James, P.	Suite in Four Movements	CF

Woodwind Quintet

Jardanyi, P.	Phantasy and Variations on a Hungarian Folk Song (1955)	EMB
Jersild, J.	Music-making in the Forest	WH
Jettel, R.	Quintet	LDo
Jirko, I.	Suite (1956)	Pan
Jirkova, O.	Variationen	CHF
Joachim, O.	Divertimento (1962)	Can
Johanson, S.	Kvintett (1964)	STI
Johansson, B.	Concertino (1963)	STI
Johnson, H.	Quintet, C	CF
Jolivet, A.	Sérénade	Bil
Jones, K.	Quintet (1968)	Can
Jones, W.	Quintet	AMC
Jong, M. de	Aphoristisch triptiek, op. 82bis (1953)	CBD
Jongen, J.	Concerto, op. 124	SM
Josephs, W.	Wry Rumba	B&H
Jungk, K.	Chaconne	HSM
Kadosa, P.	Quintet, op. 49a (1954)	EMB
Kalabis, V.	Divertimento	CHF
Kalabis, V.	Kleine Kammermusik, op. 27 (1967)	Art
Kallstenius, E.	Divertimento, op. 29 (1943)	STI
Kantor, J.	Woodwind Quintet No. 1	Wes
Karkoff, M.	Kvintett, op. 24 (1956-57)	STI
Karkoff, M.	Serenata piccola, op. 34c	EMF
Karkoschka, E.	Antinomie (1968)	EdT
Kauffmann, L.	Quintet	UE
Kaufmann, W.	Partita	Sha
Keetbaas, D.	Quintet (1961)	Can
Keldorfer, R.	Musik	LDo
Kelemen, M.	Entrances	Pet
Kelemen, M.	Etudes contrapuntiques	SS
Kelly, R.	Passacaglia and Fugue	CoF
Kelterborn, R.	7 Bagatellen	EMo
Ketting, O.	Quintet "A Set of Pieces"	SD
King, H.	Kwintet (1949)	SD
Kingman, D.	Quintet	Wes
Kjellberg, J.	Kvintett	STI
Klimko, R.	Quintet	CoA
Klughardt, A.	Quintet, op. 79	WZ
Knab, A.	Serenade	Pet
Koch, F.	Scherzo for Five Winds	Gen
Kocśar, M.	Variazioni (1968)	EMB
Kodaly, Z.-Elkan	Zongora Muszika No. 2	HeE
Koetsier, J.	Divertimento, op. 16/1 (1937)	SD
Koetsier, J.	Divertimento No. 2, op. 35/1 (1947)	SD
Kohout, J.	6 Miniaturen	FrH
Kohoutek, C.	Suite (1959)	Art
Kohs, E.	Woodwind Quintet	AMC
Komme, K.	Divertimento (1955)	I-V
Kont, P.	Quintet in memoriam Fr. Danzi	LDo

Woodwind Quintet

Kopp, F.	Passacaglia in the Olden Style	See
Kopp, F.	3 Movements	See
Korda, V.	Divertimento	LDo
Korn, P.	Quintet for Winds	JB
Kotonski, W.	Quintet (1964)	AP
Kötschau, J.	Bläserquintett, op. 14	WZ
Kounadis, A.	"Wer Ohren hat zu hören, der höre," (1970)	B&B
Kraft, L.	Partita No. 3	Gen
Krasko, J.	Sit down sun	SHF
Krause-Graumnitz, H.	Bläserquintett, No. 1	BrH
Krejči, I.	Dechovy kvintet	Art
Krek, U.	Episodi concertanti	EdD
Krenek, E.	Pentagramm (1952/57)	B&N
Kubizek, A.	Kammerquintett	LDo
Kunad, R.	Musik für Bläser (1965)	Deu
Kunert, K.	Zweites Bläserquintett, op. 17	FrH
Kunert, K.	Divertimento No. 2, op. 18	FrH
Kunz, A.	Quintet (1964)	Can
Kuri-Aldana, M.	Candelaria	MR
Kurtág, G.	Quintet (1959)	EMB
Kurtág, G.	Quintet, op. 2	EMB
Lacerda, O.	Variations and Fugue	SMP
Lachner, F.	Quintet	MR
Ladmirault, P.	Choral et Variations	E-V
Landré, G.	Kwintet (1960)	SD
Landré, G.	Quintetto (1930)	SD
Lang, I.	Quintet No. 1 (1964)	EMB
Lang, I.	Quintet No. 2 (1965)	EMB
Lantz, J.	5 Miniatures	Sha
Larsson, L.	4 Tempi, op. 55 (1968)	CGM
Laudenslager, H.	Woodwind Quintet	Cor
Lazarof, H.	Concertino da Camera	Isr
Leduc, J.	Quintett à vent	Mau
Lefèbvre, C.	Canon (Suite, op. 57)	PrA
Lefèbvre, C.-Waln	Prélude for Quintet (from 2nd Suite)	NK
Lefèbvre, C.	Suite, op. 57	CF
Lefèbvre, C.	Suite, op. 57	E-V
Lefèbvre, C.	Suite, op. 57	Ham
Lefèbvre, C.	Suite, op. 57	Int
Lefèbvre, C.-Andraud	Suite, op. 57	SM
Legley, V.	Quintette, op. 58 (1961)	CBD
Lehmann, D.	Woodwind Quintet	AMC
Lehmann, H.	Episoden (1963/64)	SS
Leichtling, A.	Quintet No. 2, op. 24	AMC
Leichtling, A.	Quintet, op. 33	AMC
Leichtling, A.	Quintet No. 3	See
Lemare, E.-Trinkhaus	Andantino	MS
Lessard, J.	Partita	Gen
Leukauf, R.	Bläserquintett, op. 25	LDo
Lewis, P.	Contrasts	CoF

Woodwind Quintet

Lewis, P.	5 Movements	CoF
Liadov, A.	8 Russian Folksongs	MR
Liadov, A.	8 Russian Folksongs	Wes
Lickl, J.-Kneusslin	Quintetto Concertante, F	EK
Liedbeck, S .	Impromptu	STI
Ligeti, G.	10 Stücke	SS
Lilge, H.	Variationen und Fuge über ein eigenes Thema, op. 67	Kis
Lilien, I.	Quintetto No. 2 (1952)	SD
Lilien, I.	Voyage au printemps (1952)	SD
Linke, N.	Bläserquintett in einem Satz	HG
Linn, R.	Quintet	Wes
Liszt, F.-Hamilton	Pastorale (Les Préludes)	GaM
Liszt, F.-Seay	Weihnachtslied	Spr
Lohse, D.	Quintet	Pet
London, E.	Quintet	MJQ
Lonquich, H.	Missa (1971)	HG
Lora, A.	6 Dances, Old and New	CoF
Louel, J.	Quintette (1958)	CBD
Luigini, A.-Holmes	Ballet Egyptian	Bar
Lunden, L.	Variationer on "Byssan lull"	Nor
Lundkvist, P.	Kvintett	STI
MacDowell, E.-Trinkaus	Idyl, op. 28/2	War
Maganini, Q.-Harris	Reverie. *fl, ob, cl, hn, bsn(bcl)*	CF
Maganini, Q.	Simple Aveu. *fl, ob, cl, hn, bsn(bcl)*	CF
Malipiero, R.	Musica da camera (1959)	ESZ
Mamlok, U.	Quintet	CoF
Maniet, R.	Quintette à ven, No. 1	Mau
Mann, L.	4 Studies in the Blues Idiom, op. 23 (1969)	Can
Marckhl, E.	Sonate	LDo
Marechal, H.	Air du Guet	Heu
Marez Oyens, T. de	2 Sketches (1963)	SD
Marie, G.-Harris	Berceuse. *fl, ob, cl, hn, bsn(bcl)*	CF
Maros, R.	Consort (1970)	SMP
Maros, R.	Musica Leggiera (1956)	EMB
Martino, D.	Concerto	JB
Martinon, J.	Domenon	Bil
Massis, A.	Thème et Variations	Bil
McBride, Robert	Cuatro Milpas	CoF
McBride, R.	5 Winds Blowing	CoF
McBride, R.	Home on the Range	CoF
McBride, R.	Jam Session	See
McBride, R.	Mexican Dance	CoF
McBride, R.	Rock 'em Cowboy	CoF
McBride, R.	Serenade to Country Music	CoF
McCall, H.	2 Tunes from Mother Goose	SM
McIntyre, P.	Fantasy on an Eskimo Song (1962)	Can
McKay, F.	Bainbridge Island Sketches	Bar
McKay, G.	Joyful Dance	TP
McKay, G.	3 Nautical Characters	Bar
McKay, G.	3 Sea Sketches	Bar

Woodwind Quintet

McPeek, B.	Woodwind Quintet (1961)	Can
Mederacke, K.	Böhmische Suite, op. 43	FrH
Meester, L. De	Divertimento (1946)	CBD
Mendelssohn, F.	Figurate Hymn	CF
Mendelssohn, F.-Boyd	Intermezzo (Midsummer Night's Dream)	CF
Mendelssohn, F.	Krakowiak	GFB
Mendelssohn, F.-Seay	Scherzetto, op. 102/3	Spr
Mendelssohn, F.-Jospe	Scherzo, op. 110	CF
Mendelssohn, F.-Cafarella	Song without Words, op. 62/4	Vol
Mengelberg, M.	Omrent een Componisten-actie	SD
Mersson, B.	Musik, op. 20	BrH
Meulemans, A.	Quintet No. 1 (1931)	CBD
Meulemans, A.	Quintet No. 2 (1932)	CBD
Meulemans, A.	Quintet No. 3 (1958)	CBD
Meyer-Tormin, W.	Kleines Quintett (1951)	B&B
Michael, F.	Serenata piccola (1966/67)	BrH
Migot, G.	Quintette	ALe
Milhaud, D.	Divertissement in Three Parts	Heu
Milhaud, D.	La Cheminée du Rou René (1939)	SM
Milhaud, D.	2 Sketches	TP
Miller, K.	Ode to Spring	Byr
Miller, L.	Sonatina (1962)	Can
Mills, C.	Sonata Fantasia	CoF
Monteverdi, C.-Townsend	Sinfonia	Ric
Moore, C.	Quintet (1964)	B-M
Moore, D.	Quintet	AMC
Moritz, E.	Quintet, op. 41	WZ
Moritz, E.	Quintet, op. 169	WZ
Mortensen, F.	Quintet, op. 4	WH
Mortensen, O.	Quintet	WH
Moulaert, P.	Passepied en rondo (1940)	CBD
Moussorgsky, M.-Kessler	Ballet of the Chickens in Their Shells	Rub
Moyse, L.	Quintet	M&M
Moyzes, A.	Wind Quintet, op. 17	SHF
Mozart, W.	Adagio, K. 411	CF
Mozart, W.	Adagio, B♭, K.V. 411	FrH
Mozart, W.-Weigelt	Adagio, B♭, K. 411	Leu
Mozart, W.-Meyer	Andante, K. 616	HSM
Mozart, W.-Vester	Andante für eine Orgelwalze, K. 616	B-M
Mozart, W.-Maros	Divertimento	EMB
Mozart, W.-Weigelt	Divertimento No. 8, F, K.V. 213	Leu
Mozart, W.-Weigelt	Divertimento No. 9, B♭, K.V. 240	Leu
Mozart, W.-Rottler	Divertimento No. 12, E♭, K.V. 252	Leu
Mozart, W.-Bryant	Divertimento No. 12, K. 252	Gal
Mozart, W.-Weigelt	Divertimento No. 13, F, K.V. 253	Leu
Mozart, W.-Baines	Divertimento No. 14, K. 270	OxU
Mozart, W.-Maros	Divertimento, B♭, K.V. 270	EMB
Mozart, W.-Moortel	Divertimento No. 14, K.V. 270	EMb

Woodwind Quintet

Mozart, W.-Weigelt	Divertimento No. 14, B♭, K.V. 270	Leu
Mozart, W.-Rottler	Divertimento No. 16, E♭ K.V. 289	Leu
Mozart, W.-Meyer	Fantasy, f, K. 594	HSM
Mozart, W.-Pillney	Fantasie, f, K. 594	BrH
Mozart, W.-Meyer	Fantasy, f, K. 608	HSM
Mozart, W.-Vester	Fantasie für eine Orgelwalze, K. 608	B-M
Mozart, W.-Waln	Menuet	NK
Mozart, W.-Andraud	Minuet and German Dance	SM
Mozart, W.-Cailliet	Quintet, F, K.V. 370	E-V
Mozart, W.-Rottler	Quintet, c K.V. 406	Leu
Mozart, W.-Nakagawa	Sonata, B♭, K. 358	AMP
Mozart, W.-Andraud	2 Short Quintets	SM
Muczynski, R.	Movements, Op. 16	Sha
Mueller, F.	5 Pieces	Cor
Mueller, F.	3 Transcriptions	Cor
Mueller, P.	Quintet No. 1, E♭	MR
Mueller, P	Quintet No. 2, E♭	MR
Mueller, P.	Quintet No. 3, A	MR
Müller-Medek, W.	Woodwind Quintet No. 1	Pet
Mulder, H.	Kwintet, op. 119 (1961)	SD
Negel, R.	Divertimento (1951)	CoF
Necke, H.-Taylor	Mill of Sans Souci	B-M
Nelhybel, V.	Woodwind Quintet No. 2	Gen
Nelhybel, V.	Quintet No. 3	Gen
Neubert, G.	Musik (1968/69)	BrH
Nevin, E.-Gordon	Gondolieri	TP
Nero, P.	Monsoon. *fl, ob, cl, hn, bsn (bcl)*	CF
Nielsen, C.	Quintet, op. 43	WH
Novak, J.	Concertino	CHF
Olsen, S.	Quintet, op. 35	HL
Onslow, G.-Redel	Quintet, F, op. 81/3	Leu
Onslow, G.	Quintet	M&M
Osokin, M.	Quintet, op. 37	MR
Otten, L.	Blaaskwintet No. 2 (1954)	SD
Otten, L.	Movements for Wind Quintet (Blaaskwintet No. 3)	SD
Ottoson, D.	Svit	STI
Oubradous, F.	Fantaisie Dialoguée	EdL
Paciorkiewicz, T.	Quintet (1951)	AP
Papineau-Couture, J.	Fantaisie (1963)	Can
Parchman, G.	Sonata	See
Parris, H.	Woodwind Miniatures	HeE
Parris, R.	5 Easy Canons & a Fugue	CoF
Parris, R.	Sonatina for Winds	CoF
Partos, O.	Nebulae (1966)	Isr
Patterson, P.	Quintet	JoW
Pauer, J.	Bläserquintett (1960)	Art
Pedersen, P.	Wind Quintet (1959)	Can
Pelemans, W.	Blaaskwintet No. 1	Mau
Pelemans, W.	Quintet No. 2	EMe

Woodwind Quintet

Pelz, W.	A Light Touch of Blue	Reb
Perle, G.	Quintet No. 2, op. 4	TP
Persichetti, V.	Pastoral, op. 21 (1943)	Sch
Pessard, E.	Aubade, op. 6	CF
Peterson, W.	Metamorphoses	See
Petric, I.	Woodwind Quintet No. 1	EdD
Petric, I.	Woodwind Quintet No. 2	EdD
Petrovics, E.	Wind Quintet (1964)	EMB
Phillips, D.	Lullabic Digressions	CoA
Phillips, P.	Little Prelude and Blues	MJQ
Pierce, E.	Allegro Piacevole and Scherzo	War
Pierce, E.	Romance	PrA
Pierce, E.	Short Quintet, B♭	War
Pierné, G.-Andraud	March of the Little Tin Soldiers, op. 14/6. *pf and drum ad lib*	ALe
Pierné, G.	Pastorale, op. 14/1	ALe
Pierné, G.	Pastorale, Op. 14/1	CF
Pierné, G.-Andraud	Pastorale, Op. 14/1	SM
Pierné, P.	Suite pittoresque	ALe
Pietsch, Edna-McCathren	Miniature Sweet	SHM
Pijper, W.	Quintet (1929)	SD
Pilss, K.	Serenade	LDo
Pisk, P.	Woodwind Quintet, op. 96	CoF
Piston, W.	Quintet (1956)	AMP
Placheta, H.	Divertimento, op. 8	LDo
Poldini, E.-Elkan	General Boom-Boom	HeE
Poldowski, D.-Barrere	Suite Miniature	GaM
Ponse, L.	Kwintet, op. 32 (1961)	SD
Ponse, L.	2 pieces (1943)	SD
Poot, M.	Concertino	ALe
Porsch, G.	Suite Modique	War
Porter, Q.	Divertimento (1960)	Pet
Powell, M.	Divertimento	AMC
Praag, H. van	Quintet No. 1 (1938)	SD
Praag, H. van	Quintet No. 2 (1948)	SD
Praag, H. van	Sonata (1963)	SD
Presser, W.	Minuet, Sarabande and Gavotte	TP
Purdie, H.	Canon Apertus	PrA
Quinet, M.	8 petites pièces (1946)	CBD
Quinet, M.	Quintet (1949)	CBD
Rackley, L.	2 Madrigals and a Jig	CoA
Radulescu, M.	Bläserquintett	LDo
Rainier, P.	6 Pieces	S&C
Rajter, L.	Wind Quintet (1946)	SHF
Rameau, J.-Desormière	Ballet Music (Ascante et Céphise)	ALe
Rameau, J.-Nakagawa	L'Agacante & L'Indiscrète	AMP
Rameau, J.-Oubradous	Symphonies and Dances	ALe
Rameau, J.-Lockhart	Tambourin	War
Ránki, G.	Pentaerophonia (1958)	EMB
Rathaus, K.	Galante Serenade	B&H
Ravel, M.-Jones	Tombeau de Couperin	Dur
Ravel, M-Kessler	Pièce en forme de habanera	ALe

Woodwind Quintet

Read, G.	Scherzino, op. 24 (1935)	SMP
Reed	Symphonic Dance	B-M
Reicha, A.-Waln	Andante and Menuetto Allegro (Op. 91)	NK
Reicha, A.-Smith	Introduction and Allegro (Op. 88/4)	TP
Reicha, Anton	Quintet No. 3	FrH
Reicha, A.-Weigelt	Quintet, E♭, op. 88/2	Leu
Reicha, A.-Wise	Quintet, op. 88/2	Wes
Reicha, A.-Hertl-Smetacek	3 Quintets, op. 88/3, op. 91/9, 11	ES
Reicha, A.-Seydel	Quintet, B♭, op. 88/5	Leu
Reicha, A.-Kneusslin	Quintet, op. 91/1, C	EK
Reicha, A.	Quintet, op. 91/2, a	EK
Reicha, A.	Quintet, op. 91/3, D	EK
Reicha, A.	Quintet, g, op. 91/4	Bil
Reicha, A.-Kneusslin	Quintet, op. 91/5, A	EK
Reicha, A.-Vester	Quintet, op. 99/2	MR
Reicha, A.	Quintet, op. 100/4, e	EK
Reicha, A.	3 Quintetti	Art
Reicha, A.	2 Andantes and Adagio	B&V
Reif, P.	Wind Spectrum (1966)	See
Reiner, K.	Dvanact. Suita	Art
Reinhold, O.	Bläserquintett (1962)	Lit
Reiter, A.	Musik	LDo
Reizenstein, F.	Quintet	B&H
Reynolds, R.	Gathering	Pet
Reynolds, V.	Woodwind Quintet	MCA
Rhodes, P.	Suite	CoF
Riegger, W.	Bläserquintett, op. 51	SS
Riegger, W.	Bläserquintet	AMC
Rieti, V.	Quintet (1957)	AMP
Rieti, V.	Silografie (Woodcuts)	Gen
Rimsky-Korsakov, N.-Atkins	Flight of the Bumble Bee	Wes
Rinck, J.	Woodwind Quintet	Cor
Rivier, J.	Capriccio	Bil
Roetscher, K.	Quintet, op. 41	B&B
Rogers, J.	Rotational Arrays	Bow
Roos, R. de	Incontri	SD
Ropartz, J.	2 pièces	Dur
Rorich, C.	Quintet, op. 58	WZ
Rosenberg, H.	Kvintett (1959)	STI
Rosenthal, L.	Commedia	Cha
Rosetti, F.-Kneusslin	Quintet, E♭	EK
Rosetti, F.-Philadelphia Ww Quintet	Quintet, E♭	TP
Rosseau, N.	Quintet, Op. 54 (1955)	CBD
Rota, N.	Petite offrande musicale	ALe
Roussakis, N.	Woodwind Quintet No. 1	CoF
Rousseau, J.-Haufrecht	Airs pour Joues a la proupe Marchant	CoF
Rossum, F.	Pyrogravures, op. 19 bis (1968)	CBD
Rugolo, P.	Bossa Waltz	Wes

Woodwind Quintet

Russell, R.	Woodwind Quintet	Gen
Ruyneman, D.	Nightengale quintet (1949)	SD
Ruyneman, D.	Reflexions No. 4 (1961)	SD
Rychlik, J.	Quintet	ES
Sachsse, H.	Bläsersuite, op. 32	ABS
Salmenhaara, E.	Quintet (1964)	See
Santa Cruz, D.	Quintet	SMP
Santoliquido, F.	Nocturne & Pastorale	Cof
Saveliev, B.	Suite	MCA
Scarlatti, D.-Herder	Sonata	AMP
Scarlatti, D.	Suite, F	Cof
Scarmolin, A.	Rustic Dance	Bar
Scarmolin, A.	By the Sleeping Nile	AMC
Schat, P.	Improvisations and symphonies (1960)	SD
Schibler, A.	Kaleidoskop (1954), op. 41	A&S
Schierbeck, P.	Capriccio, op. 53	WH
Schiffman, H.	Allegro con Spirito di San Niccolo	B&B
Schilling, H.	Quintet, op. 67	BrH
Schilling, H.	Zeacis Hafis. Quintet 76	BrH
Schindler, G.	Divertimento notturno	EMo
Schiske, K.	Quintet, op. 24 (1945)	LDo
Schlemm, G.	Bläser-Quintett	PG
Schmid, H.	Quintet, op. 28	SS
Schmidek, K.	Sonatine, op. 31	LDo
Schmitt, F.	Chants Alizés, op. 125	Dur
Schmutz, A.	Scherzo Poetique	CF
Schneider, W.	Quintet	MV
Schoenberg, A.	Quintet, op. 26	UE
Schönberg, S.	Litet stycke (1957)	STI
Schouwman, H.	Nederlandse suite, op. 40b (1953)	SD
Schramm, H.	Woodwind Quintet	AMC
Schröder, H.	Divertimento	Pet
Schubert, F.-Holmes	Allegretto	Bar
Schubert, F.-Taylor	Marche Hongroise	B-M
Schubert, F.-Schoenbach	Shepherd Melody No. 6 (Rosamunde)	TP
Schubert, F.-Elkan	Valse Sentimentale	HeE
Schubert, M.	Moments musicaux (1967)	Deu
Schuller, G.	Woodwind Quintet (1958)	AMP
Schuller, G.	Suite	M&M
Schumann, R.-Filas	5 Pieces	PMP
Schwaen, K.	Mährisches Holzbläserquintett	Pet
Schwertsik, K.	Querschnitt durch eine Operette	LDo
Scott, S.	Woodwind Quintet	CoA
Sehlbach, E.	Bläserquintett (1968)	B&V
Sehlbach, E.	Kortum-Serenade, op. 30	MV
Seiber, M.	Permutazioni a Cinque (1958)	SS
Seletsky, H.	Woodwind Quintet, op. 14 (1967)	See
Senaille, J.-Taylor	Rondo Serioso	B-M
Serebrier, J.	Little Suite	SMP
Sibelius, J.-Langenus	Pastorale (Pelleas et Melisande)	CF

Woodwind Quintet

Siennicki, E.-Hite	Allegro	B&H
Siennicki, E.	Diversion	LMP
Sirulnikoff, J.	The Doctor in Spite of Himself (1961)	Can
Skorzeny, F.	Eine Nachtmusik (1963)	LDo
Slowinski, W.	Quintet (1958)	AP
Smith, L.	Wind Quintet	CoF
Sobeck, J.	Allegretto Giojoso (op. 11)	B-M
Sobeck, J.	Allegro Mosso (op. 14)	B-M
Sobeck, J.	Andante Sostenuto (op. 11)	B-M
Sobeck, J.	Larghetto	B-M
Sobeck, J.	Tarantella	B-M
Sokoloff, N.	Quintet	AMC
Somis, G.-Henried	Adagio and Allegro	CF
Sörenson, T.	Music on "Veni redemptor gentium" (1965)	STI
Sonninen, A.	Divertimento (1970)	MT
Sorrentino, C.	Beneath the Covered Bridge	B-M
Souris, A.	Rengaines (1937)	ALe
Sowerby, L.	Pop Goes the Weasel	Fit
Spencer, O.	Playtime	GFB
Spisak, M.	Quintet (1949)	AP
Sprongl, N.	Bläserquintett, op. 90	LDo
Stainer, C.	Scherzo, op. 27	B&H
Stamitz, K.	Quintet, E♭, op. 8/2	Leu
Stearns, P.	Quintet	CoF
Steel, C.	Divertimento	Nov
Stein, H.	Sour Suite	Wes
Stein, L.	Quintette	CoF
Stewart, R.	5 Visions	CoF
Stewart, R.	3 Pieces	CoF
Stewart, R.	2 Movements	CoF
Stockhausen, K.	Adieu	UE
Stoker, R.-Brain	Quintet	HE
Stone, D.	Prelude and Scherzetto. fl, cl(ob), cl, hn(cl), bsn	Nov
Storp, S.	Kammermusik	MV
Stradella, A.	Sonata, G	Cor
Stringfield, L.	A Moonshiner Laughs	Bro
Stutschewsky, J.	4 Movements (1967)	See
Suchon, E.	Serenade, op. 5	SHF
Surdin, M.	Piece (1969)	Can
Swack, I.	Woodwind Quintet	AMC
Sweelinck, J.-Lubin	Variations on a Folksong	B&H
Sydeman, W.	Quintet	AMC
Sydeman, W.	Quintet No. 2	AMC
Sydeman, W.	Texture Studies (1966)	See
Sylvan, S.	Kvintett	STI
Szalonek, W.	Aarhus Music	See
Szalowski, A.	Wind Quintet	SF
Szekely, E.	Quintet No. 1	B-M
Szekely, E.	Wind Quintet No. 2 (1961)	EMB

194

Woodwind Quintet

Szekely, E.	Wind Quintet No. 3	EMB
Szeligowski, T.	Quintet (1950)	AP
Szervansky, E.	Quintet No. 1 (1953)	EMB
Szervansky, E.	Quintet No. 2 (1957)	EMB
Taffanel, P.	Quintet	ALe
Taffanel, P.	Quintet	Int
Taffanel, P.-Andraud	Quintet	SM
Takács, J.	Eine kleine Tafelmusik, op. 74	LDo
Tal, J.	Quintet (1966)	Isr
Tanenbaum, E.	Sonatina	CoF
Tanenbaum, E.	Woodwind Quintet No.2	CoF
Taranov, G.	Quintet	ChM
Tartini, G.-Trinkhaus	Arioso, e	MS
Tartini, G.-Trinkhaus	Evening Song	MS
Tartini, G.-Trinkhaus	Largo (Violin Sonata, g)	War
Taylor, L. (arr)	Petite Suite	B-M
Tchaikovsky, P.-Trinkaus	Andante Cantabile (String Quartet, op. 11)	CF
Tchaikovsky, P.-Trinkhaus	April, op. 37/4	MS
Tchaikovsky, P.-Seay	Chant sans paroles, op. 40/6	Spr
Tchaikovsky, P.	Fragments (Sleeping Beauty)	MR
Tchaikovsky, P.-Trinkhaus	June, op. 37/6	MS
Tchaikovsky, P.-Lychenheim	Melodie, op. 42/3. *fl, ob, cl, hn, bsn (bcl)*	CF
Tchaikovsky, P.-Nakagawa	3 Tänze, op. 39/8, 10, 14	SS
Telcs, A.	Kvintett	Reu
Telemann, G.-Weigelt	Ouvertüren-Suite	Leu
Templeton, A.-Rhoads	Passepied	TP
Tepper, A.	Dance Souvenirs	See
Teuber, F.	Introduction Piece	JB
Thilman, J.	Aphorismen	BrH
Thilman, J.	Quintet, op. 44a	Mit
Thomas, A.-Trinkhaus	Gavotte (Mignon)	MS
Thomsen, Muchova, G.	Serenada	Art
Tiessen, H.	Kleine Suite, op. 51	Kis
Tisne, A.	Disparates	Bil
Toebosch, L.	Sarabande en allegro, op. 71 (1959)	SD
Toews, T.	Music	CoA
Tomasi, H.	5 danses profanes et sacrées	ALe
Tomasi, Q	Quintette	HLe
Tomasi, H.	Variations sur un thème Corse	ALe
Trede, Y.	Le Chant des Oiseaux	Pet
Tremblay, G.	Wind Quintet	CoF
Trexler, G.	Spitzweg-Suite	BrH
Trojan, V.	Quintet, op. 8 (1937)	Art
Tsouyopoulos, G.	Musik	HG
Tull, F.	Suite	Sha
Turner, R.	Serenade (1960)	Can
Tuthill, B.	Sailor's Hornpipe, Op. 14/1 (1935)	CF
Uber, D.	Suite No. 1	CoA

Woodwind Quintet

Uray, E.	Musik für Bläserquintet	LDo
Urbanner, E.	Etude für Bläser (1965)	LDo
Vachey, H.	Quintette a vent	ALe
Valen, O.	Serenade, op. 42 (1947)	HL
Vandor, I.	Winds 845 (1969)	ESZ
Van Hulse, C.	Quintet, op. 3	Sha
Vazzana, A.	Quintet	AMC
Veerhoff, C.	Bläser-Quintett	B&B
Velden, R. van der	1ste Concert	Mau
Velden, R. Van der	Concerto No. 2	EMe
Verrall, J.	Serenade (1944)	TP
Verrall, J.	Serenade No. 2	CoF
Vetessy, G.	Serenade	EMo
Vilec, M.	Wind Quintet	SHF
Vincze, I.	Divertimento (1962)	EMB
Vinter, G.	2 Miniatures	B&H
Vlijmen, J.	Quintetto (1960)	SD
Von Kreisler, A.	Andante and Allegro	SM
Von Kreisler, A.	Chorale, Prelude and Fugue	SM
Von Kreisler, A.	Fable (Music for Woodwind Quintet)	SM
Von Kreisler, A.	Humouous March (Music for Woodwind Quintet)	SM
Von Kreisler, A.	Pastorale (Music for Woodwind Quintet)	SM
Von Kreisler, A.	Possum Trot (Music for Woodwind Quintet)	SM
Von Kreisler, A.	Quintet	SM
Von Kreisler, A.	Triptych	SM
Von Kreisler, A.	2 Portraits	SM
Voss, F.	Capriccioso (1965)	BrH
Vredenburg, M.	Au pays des vendages (1951)	SD
Wagner, R.-Boyd	An Album Leaf	CF
Walker, R.	Adagio and Allegro	Bar
Walker, R.	In Joyous Mood	Bar
Walker, R.	Rigaudon	Ken
Walzel, L.	Quintetto impetuoso, op. 42	LDo
Ward, W.	Little Dance Suite	B-M
Ward-Steinman, D.	Montage	MJQ
Washburn, R.	Quintet	OxU
Washburn, R.	Suite (1960)	TP
Weber, A.	Quintette	ALe
Weber, L.	Quintet	MV
Weigel, E.	Short, Slow & Fast	AMC
Weigl, V.	Mood Sketches	CoF
Weinzweig, J.	Woodwind Quintet (1963-64)	Can
Weiss, F.	Serenade	WH
Weiss, A.	Quintet	CoF
Welin, K.	Etwas für...(1966)	STI
Wellejus, A.	Bläserkvintet	SPD
Wellesz, E.	Suite, op. 73	HSM
Werner, S.	Jubilus (1968)	Che

Woodwind Quintet

Wesley, C.-Dawn	Gavotte	B&H
Weston, P.	Arbeau Suite	Gal
Whear, P.	Quintet (1956)	Leb
White, D.	3 for 5	Sha
Wijdeveld, W.	Quintet (1934)	SD
Wilder, A.	Woodwind Quintet No. 3	Sch
Williams, C.	Concerto Suite	SM
Winkel Holm, M.	Sonate, op. 25	WH
Wirth, H.	Kleine Clementiade	HSM
Wisse, J.	Limitazioni No. 2 (1962)	SD
Woollen, R.	Woodwind Quintet	CoF
Wuensch, G.	Quintet No. 2, op. 34	Can
Wuorinen, C.	Movement	TP
Wuorinen, C.	Wind Quintet	CoF
Yoder, P. (arr.)	Dry Bones. *perc opt*	NK
Yoder, P.	Relax! *perc opt*	NK
York, W.	Neo Gothics	Roc
Zafred, M.	Quintet	Ric
Zagwijn, H.	Quintetto (1948)	SD
Zamecnik, J.	Allegro Guibiloso	SF
Zamecnik, J.	La Gondoliera	SF
Zaninelli, L.	Dance Variations	Sha
Zaninelli, L.	Musica Drammatica. *fl, ob, cl,*	
	bsn, hn, perc opt	Sha
Zender, H.	Quintet (1950), op. 3	B&B
Zilcher, H.	Quintet, op. 91	B&N
Zillig, W.	Lustspielsuite (1934)	B&N
Zimmer, J.	Wind Quintet, op. 61	SHF
Zipp, F.	Serenade	MV
Zuckert, L.	Little Prince in Montreal (1968)	Can

WOODWIND QUINTET (Collections)

Andraud, A.	Collection of 4 Quintets	SM
Andraud, A.	3 Little Pieces	SM
Andraud, A. (comp)	22 Woodwind Quintets	SM
Andraud, A. (comp)	2 Short Classic Quintets	SM
Barnes, C. (arr)	Robbins Collection of Classics	Big
Gordon, P. (arr)	Elkan-Vogel Woodwind Ensemble Folio	E-V
John, F.	Sammlung klassischer Stücke alter Meister	FrH
Rameau, J.-Nakagawa	Gavotte with 6 Doubles	AMP
Taylor, R.	18 Woodwind Quintets	SM
Tchaikovsky, P.-Taylor	Music for the Young, 3 Suites	Wes
Ulrich, H. (arr)	Ensemble Music for Five Instruments.	
	fl(ob, cl), fl(ob, cl), cl, cl(hn), bcl(bsn)	BM
Voxman, H. & Hervig, R.	Ensemble Repertoire	Rub

FIVE WOODWINDS (not including fl, ob, cl, hn, bsn)

Aschenbrenner, J.	Quintet. *fl, ob, bcl, bsn, hn*	EMo
Ascough, R.	Quintet. *fl, ob, cl, sop sax, bsn*	ExM
Aspelmayr, F.-Pulkert	Partita, D. *2ob, 2hn, bsn*	Leu
Aspelmayr, F.-Pulkert	Partita, F. *2ob, 2hn, bsn*	Leu
Bach, J.C.-Stein	Bläser-Sinfonien, 2 vols. *2cl, 2hn, bsn*	FrH
Bach, J.C.	4 Quintets, 2 vols. *2cl, 2hn, bsn*	B&H
Bach, J.C.-Wojciechowski	3 Marches. *2ob(2fl), 2hn, bsn*	HSM
Bach, J.S.-Banquer	Badinerie (Suite No. 2). *fl, 3cl, bcl*	MCA
Bacon, E.	Old Airs from Many Countries. *fl, ob, 2cl, bsn, perc opt*	Sch
Barrow, R.	Suite. *fl, ob, acl, bsn, hn*	CoA
Beethoven, L. van-Greist	Menuetto (op. 18/5). *fl, 3cl, bcl*	MCA
Beethoven, L. van-Hess-Zellner	Quintet. *ob, bsn, 3hn*	SS
Beethoven, L. van-Draper	Scherzo (Violin Sonata, op. 24). *4cl, bsn*	OxU
Bissell, K.	A Folk-Song Suite (1960). *2fl, 2cl, bcl(bsn)*	B&H
Björklund, S.	Pastoral (1970). *fl, ehn, cl, bsn, hn*	STI
Boellmann, L.	Menuet gothique. *ob, ehn, cl, bsn, hn*	Dur
Bottje, W.	Diversions. *fl/pic, ob, ehn, cl, bsn*	CoF
Bottje, W.	Quintet. *fl, ob, ehn, cl, bsn*	CoF
Briegel, G.	Morning in the Forest. *fl, 2cl, acl, bcl*	GFB
Chattelun, M.	Suite inchoative. *fl, ehn, cl, hn, bsn*	EMT
Childs, B.	Take 5. *any 5 instruments*	TP
Cone, E.	Stanzas. *fl, ehn, cl, bsn, hn*	EBM
Daquin, C.-Gordon	The Cuckoo. *fl, ob, 2cl, bsn*	War
De Bueris, J.	Petite Pastorale. *fl, ob, 2cl, bsn*	GFB
Désormière, R.	6 Danseries du XVI siècle. *fl, cl, ehn, hn, bsn*	ALe
Ditters, K.-Rhau	3 Partien, F, A, D. *2ob, 2hn, bsn*	BrH
Dittersdorf, K.-Wojciechowski	Divertimento. *2ob, 2cl, bsn*	HSM
Dittersdorf, K. von-Haas	Partia, D. *2ob, 2hn, bsn*	MR
Druschetzky, G.	Partita No. 9, F. *2ob, 2hn, bsn*	BrH
Druschetzky, G.	Partita No. 10, F. *2ob, 2hn, bsn*	BrH
Druschetzky, G.	Partita No. 13, B♭. *2ob, 2hn, bsn*	BrH
Druschetzky, G.	Partita No. 21, G. *2ob, 2hn, bsn*	BrH
Dussek, F.	Parthia. *2ob, bsn, 2hn*	M&M
Fiala, J.-Janetzky	3 Quintets, E♭, B♭, E♭. *2ehn, 2hn, bsn*	FrH
Fitelberg, J.	Capriccio. *fl, ob, cl, bcl, bsn(trb)*	SF
Flothuis, M.	Quintet, op. 13 (1942). *fl, ob, cl, bcl, bsn*	SD
Frid, G.	Serenade, op. 4 (1928). *fl, 2cl, bsn, hn*	SD
Gastyne, S. de	Partita for Winds (1956). *2fl, 2cl, bsn*	Fer
Golabek, J.-Ochlewski	Partita. *2cl, bsn, 2hn*	AP
Handel, G.	2 Arias. *2ob, 2hn, bsn*	MR
Hansen, T.	Toccata. *2fl, ob, cl, bsn*	CoA
Harris	Whistlin' Joe. *pic, 2cl, acl, bcl*	GFB
Harris	Whistlin' Joe. *pic, 2cl, ob, bsn*	GFB
Haydn, F.-Janetzky	Parthia, F, Hob II: F. 12. *2ob, 2hn, bsn*	MR

Five Woodwinds

Haydn, F.-Banquer	Rondo (op. 33/3). *fl, 3cl, bcl*	MCA
Holborne, A.	Suite for Brass. *2cl(2ob), hn, 2bsn*	OxU
Horvit, M.	Concert Music. *fl, 3cl, bcl*	AMC
Hughes, L.	Allegro Scherzoso, op. 92. *2fl, ob, cl, bsn*	BM
Hugues, L.-Cavally	Allegro Scherzoso. *2fl, ob, cl, bsn*	SM
Karg-Elert, S.	Quintet, op. 30. *ob, 2cl, bsn, hn*	FrH
Knab, A.	Serenade. *fl, ob, 2cl, bsn*	Lit
Le Fleming, C.	Homage to Beatrix Potter. *fl, ob, 2cl, bsn*	Che
Le Jeune, C.-Banquer	Revecy Venir du Printans. *fl, 3cl, bcl*	MCA
Locke, M.	Music for His Majesty's Sackbuts and Cornets. *3cl, 2bsn*	OxU
Lunden, L.	Rondino. *fl, ob, 2cl, bsn*	Nor
Lunden, L.	The Wheatear. *fl, ob, 2cl, bsn*	Che
Lunden, L.	3 Swedish Tunes. *fl, ob, 2cl, bsn*	Che
Maganini, Q.-Harris	Reverie. *fl(cl), ob(cl), cl, acl(asax, cl), bcl(bsn)*	CF
Mann, L.	Wind Quintet, op. 19 (1961). *fl, ehn, cl, bsn, hn*	Can
Marie, G.-Harris	Berceuse. *fl(cl), ob(cl), cl, acl(asax, cl), bcl(bsn)*	CF
Meulemans, A.	Rapsodie (1961). *3cl, bcl, asax*	CBD
Moritz, C.	Heitere Suite, op. 12. *fl, ob, 2cl, bsn*	R&E
Mozart, W.	Adagio, B♭, K. 411. *2cl, 3basset hn*	BrH
Mozart, W.	Adagio, K. 411. *2cl, 2cl(2ob), bsn*	OxU
Mozart, W.	Adagio and Allegro, K. 594. *2cl, 2ob(2fl), bsn*	OxU
Mozart, W.-Banquer	Andante Cantabile (K. 330). *fl, 3cl, bcl*	MCA
Mozart, W.-Spies	Andante (für eine Orgelwalze), K. 616. *2fl, fl(ob, cl), 2cl*	Pet
Mozart, W.-Draper	4 Movement (Les Petit Riens). *4cl, bsn*	OxU
Mozart, W.-Caputo	Minuet. *ob, 2cl, bsn, hn*	Vol
Prowo, P.-Koch	Concerto a 5, No. 1, F. *3ob, 2bsn*	MV
Ralston, A. (arr)	7 Norwegian Miniatures. *fl, ob, 2cl, bsn(bcl)*	B&H
Regner, H.	Eine kleine Waldmusik. *ob, cl, 2hn, bsn*	MV
Reicha, A.-Vester	2 Andantes and Adagio "pour le cor anglais." *fl, ehn, cl, hn, bsn*	UE
Rieti, V.	Valsette. *2fl, 2cl, bsn*	Gen
Roussakis, N.	March, Song and Dance. *fl, ob, bsn, 2cl*	FrC
Schumann, R.	Romanza (4th Symphony). *fl, 4cl*	GFB
Schumann, R.	Romanza (4th Symphony). *fl, 2cl, acl, bcl*	GFB
Schumann, R.-Williams	2 Kinderscenen, op. 15/8, 9. *2ob, 2bsn, ehn*	SM
Schumann, R.-Banquer	2 Pieces (Album for the Young). *fl, 3cl, bcl*	MCA
Schwertsik, K.	Eichendorff-Quintet. *pic, ob, cl, hn, bsn*	UE
Seter, M.	Diptyque (1955). *fl, ehn, cl, bsn, hn*	Isr
Sorrentino, C.	Rialto Serenade. *ob, 2cl, hn, bsn*	Ken
Stamitz, K.-Lebermann	12 Serenades. *2fl, 2hn, bsn*	HSM
Stockhausen, K.	Zeitmasse. *ob, ehn, cl, bsn, hn*	UE
Stone, D.	Prelude and Scherzetto. *fl, cl(ob), cl, hn(cl), bsn*	Nov
Telemann, G.-Hinnenthal	Overture-Suite, D. *2ob, 2hn, bsn*	Leu

Five Woodwinds

Ulrich, H. (arr)	Ensemble Music for Five Instruments. *fl(ob, cl), fl(ob, cl), cl, cl(hn), bcl(bsn)*	BM
Villa-Lobos, H.	Quintet in Form eines Chores (1928). *fl, ob, ehn, cl, bsn*	EME
Vivaldi, A.-Banquer	Allegro (Concerto, D). *fl, 3cl, bcl*	MCA
Vogel, W.	Ticinella (1941). *fl, ob, cl, asax, bsn*	ESZ
Wanhal, J.	Divertimento. *2ob, bsn, 2hn*	Pet
Zelenka, I.	Chronologie (1965). *fl, ob, bcl, bsn, hn*	LDo

WOODWIND, KEYBOARD

Beethoven, L. van	Quintet, E♭, op. 16. *ob, cl, bsn, hn, pf*	BrH
Beethoven, L. van	Quintet, op. 16. *ob, cl, bsn, hn, pf*	EdK
Beethoven, L. van	Quintet, E♭, op. 16. *ob, cl, bsn, hn, pf*	Int
Beethoven, L. van- Kross	Quintet, E♭, op. 16. *ob, cl, hn, bsn, pf*	JB
Beethoven, L. van	Quintet, E♭, op. 16. *ob, cl, bsn, hn, pf*	MR
Beethoven, L. van	Quintet, op. 16. *ob, cl, bsn, hn, pf*	Pet
Bennett, D.	Sax-Soliloquy. *2asax, 2tsax (ten, bari), pf*	SM
Bonneau, P.	Divertissement. *4fl, pf*	ALe
Carle-Wheeler	Enchantment. *3cl, bcl, pf*	Vol
Carle-Wheeler	Enchantment. *4sax, pf*	Vol
Carle-Wheeler	Enchantment. *4bsn, pf*	Vol
Corelli, A.	Gavotte and Gigue. *2fl, 2cl, pf*	EdM
Corrette, M.	Concerto. *4bsn, hpcd*	CP
Dahm, P.	Parade of the Scouts. *4cl, pf*	Vol
Danzi, F.	Quintet, d, op. 41. *ob, cl, bsn, hn, pf*	B&V
Danzi, F.	Quintet, d, op. 41. *ob, cl, bsn, hn, pf*	MR
Danzi, F.	Quintet, op. 41. *ob, cl, bsn, hn, pf*	Pet
Danzi, F.	Quintet, d, op. 41. *ob, cl, hn, bsn, pf*	Sch
Danzi, F.	Quintet, op. 53. *fl, ob, cl, bsn, pf*	MR
Danzi, F.	Quintet, op. 54. *fl, ob, cl, bsn, pf*	MR
Danzi, F.	Sinfonia Concertante. *fl, ob, bsn, hn, pf*	MR
Darnley, C. (arr)	8 Easy Pieces. *fl, ob, cl, bsn, pf*	Che
Delibes, L.-Groff	Pizzicato polka. *4fl, pf*	Sch
Denza, L.-Harris	Funiculi-Funicula. *4cl, pf*	CF
Eklund, H.	Zodinai (1966). *fl, 2cl, bsn, pf*	STI
Elgar, E.-Holmes	Salut d'Amour. *2asax, tsax, bar sax, pf*	Rub
Escudié, L.	Andante. *4sax, pf*	EdR
Fischer, J.C.F.	Suiten. *4ww, bc*	B&N
Fritsch, J.	September 70, Grand quatuor. *4fl, pf*	Fab
Ghedini, G.	Concerto a cinque. *fl, ob, cl, bsn, pf*	Ric
Grieg, E.	Watchman's Song, op. 12/3. *4cl, pf*	Cen
Gyrowetz, A.	Sinfonia Concertante. *cl, ob, bsn, hn, pf*	MR
Handel, G.-Joosen	Menuet. *4ww, pf*	HU
Hekster, W.	Diversities. *fl, cl, bsn, hn, pf*	SD
Herzogenberg, H.	Quintet, op. 43. *ob, cl, bsn, hn, pf*	MR
Huybrechts, A.	Suite (1929). *fl, ob, cl, bsn, pf*	CBD
Iljinsky, A.	Berceuse. *4cl, pf*	Cen

Jongen, L.	Quintuor (1958). *fl, cl, bsn, hn, pf*	CBD
Joosen, B.	Spiritual Quartet I. *4ww, pf*	HU
Joosen, B.	Welsh Dances. *4ww, pf*	HU
Josten, W.	Canzona Seria. *fl, ob, cl, bsn, pf*	HeE
Kálmán, E.	Un Coin sous les Toits. Tango. *2cl, acl, bcl, pf*	EME
Keller, G.-Tilmouth	Quintet, d. *2fl, 2ob, bc*	SS
Kiellish, F.	Serenade Impromptu. *2asax, 2tsax, pf*	Ken
Lanoy, E.	Quintet, op. 2. *ob, cl, bsn, hn, pf*	MR
Laube, P.	Alsatian Dance. *fl, ob, cl(asax), bsn, pf*	CF
Laube, P.	Alsatian Dance. *fl, ob, asax, hn, pf*	CF
Lee, N.	Quintet. *fl, ob, cl, bsn, pf*	AMC
Lees, B.	3 Variables. *ob, cl, bsn, hn, pf*	B&H
Longo, A.	Scenetta pastorale. *fl, ob, cl, bsn, pf*	Edi
Lundquist, T.	4 Rondeaux (1969). *fl, ob, cl, bsn, pf*	STI
Magnard, A.	Quintet. *fl, ob, cl, bsn, pf*	EdS
Massenet, J.-Holmes	Angelus (Scenes Pittoresques).	
	2asax, tsax, bar sax, pf	Rub
Matêj, J.	Musik. *4ww, pf*	Art
Maw, N.	Chamber Music. *ob, cl, bsn, hn, pf*	Che
McCall, H.	Annie Laurie. *2asax, tsax, bar sax, pf*	Lud
McCall, H.	2 Spirituals. *2asax, tsax, bar sax, pf*	Lud
McKay, G.F.	American Street Scenes. *4sax, pf*	CoA
Mendelssohn, F.	Song Without Words No. 48. *4cl, pf*	Cen
Meyerbeer, G.-Holmes	Coronation March (The Prophet).	
	2asax, tsax, bar sax, pf	Rub
Moffitt, D.	In the Spotlight. *2cl, acl, bcl, pf*	CF
Molloy, J.-Harris	Kerry Dance. *4cl, pf*	CF
Molloy, J.-Sears	Kerry Dance. *4cl, pf*	PrA
Monger (arr)	First Ensemble Album. *4fl, pf*	TP
Monger (arr)	First Ensemble Album. *4cl, pf*	TP
Mozart, W.-Stark	Konzertantes Quartett, E♭, KV Anhang 9.	
	ob, cl, bsn, hn, pf	BrH
Mozart, W.	Minuet and Trio (Symphony in E♭). *4cl, pf*	Cen
Mozart, W.-Federhofer	Quintet, E♭, K.V. 452. *ob, cl, hn, bsn, pf*	B&N
Mozart, W.-Leech	Quintet, K. 452. *ob, cl, bsn, hn, pf*	HE
Mozart, W.	Quintet, E♭, K. 452. *ob, cl, bsn, hn, pf*	Int
Mozart, W.	Quintet, E♭, K. 452. *ob, cl, hn, bsn, pf*	MR
Mozart, W.	Quintet, K. 452. *ob, cl, hn, bsn, pf*	SM
Mozart, W.	Sinfonia Concertante, K. 297b.	
	ob, cl, bsn, hn, pf	Int
Mozart, W.	Sinfonia Concertante, E♭, K. 297B.	
	ob, cl, hn, bsn, pf	MR
Offenbach, J.-Guy	Orpheus Overture. *2asax, tsax, bar sax, pf*	Rub
Papineau-Couture, J.	Suite (1947). *fl, cl, bsn, hn, pf*	Can
Passani, E.	Quintet (1954). *fl, ob, cl, bsn, pf*	EMT
Pleyel, I.	Quintet, C. *ob, cl, hn, bsn, pf*	MR
Pleyel, I.	Sinfonia Concertante. *fl, ob, bsn, hn, pf*	MR
Pleyel, I.	5th Symphonie Concertante.	
	fl, ob(cl), bsn, hn, pf	EMT
Quinet, M.	Concerto grosso (1964). *4cl, pf*	CBD
Rawsthorne, A.	Quintet. *cl, ob, bsn, hn, pf*	OxU

Woodwinds, Keyboard

Rieti, V.	Sonata a Cinque. *fl, ob, cl, bsn, pf*	Gen
Rimsky-Korsakov, N.	Quintet. *fl, cl, hn, bsn, pf*	B&H
Rimsky-Korsakov, N.	Quintet, B♭. *fl, cl, bsn, hn, pf*	Be
Rimsky-Korsakov, N.	Quintet, B♭. *fl, cl, bsn, hn, pf*	Int
Rose, D.	Holiday for Flutes. *4fl, pf*	BVC
Schubert, F.-Holmes	Marche Militaire. *2asax, tsax, bar sax, pf*	Rub
Schwertsik, K.	Eichendorff Quintet. *ob, cl, bsn, hn, pf*	UE
Short, J.	Flirty Flutes. *4fl, pf*	Ken
Sixta, J.	Kvinteto. *fl, ob, cl, bsn, pf*	SHF
Spohr, L.	Quintet, op. 52. *fl, cl, bsn, hn, pf*	AlB
Spohr, L.-Schmitz	Quintet, c, op. 52. *fl, cl, hn, bsn, pf*	B&N
Sugár, R.	Frammenti musicali. *fl, cl, hn, bsn, pf*	EMB
Taylor, L.	Clarinet Calypso. *4cl, pf*	Hal
Toll, R. (arr)	6 Little Gems from the Masters. *4cl, pf*	CF
Tower, J.	Prelude for 5 Players. *fl, ob, cl, bsn, pf*	ACA
Turner, R.	Lament (1951). *fl, ob, cl, bsn, pf*	Can
Uggen, E.	Playwell Trio and Quartet Folio. *4fl, pf*	SHM
Uggen, E.	Playwell Trio and Quartet Folio. *4cl, pf*	SHM
Uggen, E.	Playwell Trio and Quartet Folio. *4sax, pf*	SHM
Verdi, G.-Harris	Quartet (Rigoletto). *4cl, pf*	CF
Verhey, T.	Quintet, op. 20. *ob, cl, bsn, hn, pf*	BrH
Volbach, F.	Quintet, op. 24. *ob, cl, bsn, hn, pf*	BrH
Weber, C.M. von-Holmes	Der Freischutz Selection. *2asax, tsax, bar sax, pf*	Rub
Weigl, K.	4 Short Pieces. *4cl, pf*	CoF

WOODWIND, BRASS

Benguerel, X.	Successions. *fl, ob, cl, bsn, tpt*	EMo
Brown, N.	Pastorale and Dance. *fl, cl, sax, tpt, trb*	CoA
Handel, G.	Marches. *2cl(2ob), 2tpt, bass instr*	TP
Hartley, W.	Suite for Five Winds. *fl, ob, cl, asax, trb*	Cre
Hertel, J.-Sallagar	Concerto a cinque. *tpt, 2ob, 2bsn*	OHN
Macero, T.	Canzona No. 1. *2asax, tsax, bar sax, tpt*	TP
Miller, J.	Settignano (1968). *afl, ob, cl, bsn, tpt*	See
Powell, M.	Divertimento. *fl, ob, cl, bsn, tpt*	CF
Premru, R.	Concertino (1954). *fl, ob, cl, bsn, trb*	MR
Revueltas, S.	First Little Serious Piece. *pic, ob, cl, bar sax, tpt*	SMP
Revueltas, S.	Second Little Serious Piece. *pic, ob, cl, bar sax, tpt*	SMP
Seeger, P.	Kleine Jagdgeschichte. *4 winds with tpt*	PG
Uray, E.	Schladminger Tänze. *fl, cl, bsn, hn, tpt*	LDo
Weckman, M.-Binkerd	Now Dance & Sing. *ob, ehn, bsn, 2trb*	AMP

WOODWINDS, STRINGS

Adolphus, M.	Elegy, op. 80. *cl, hn, vn, va, vc*	CoF
Albert, K.	Quintette. *fl, ob, vn, va, vc*	EMe
Aitken, H.	Quintet. *ob, 2vn, va, vc*	AMC
Ames, W.	Quintet. *cl, 2vn, va, vc*	CoF
Andriessen, J.	Hommage à Milhaud (1948). *fl, 2vn, va, vc*	SD
Arnold, M.	Quintet. *fl, bsn, hn, vn, va*	CF
Bach, J.S.	Pastorale. *ob, 2vn, va, db*	Cor
Ballif, C.	Quintet, op. 34. *bsn, 2vn, va, vc*	B&B
Ballif, C.	Quintet, op. 24a. *fl, ob, vn, va, vc*	B&B
Balorre, C.	Quintette. *cl, 2vn, va, vc*	Ham
Ballou, E.	Fantasia Brevis II. *ob, 2vn, va, vc*	CoF
Barati, G.	Quintet. *ob, 2vn, va, vc*	CoF
Beecke, I.-Gottron	Quintetto, G. *fl, ob, vn, va, vc*	B&N
Ben-Haim, P.	Quintet. *cl, 2vn, va, vc*	HE
Bentzon, J.	Variazioni Interrotti. *cl, bsn, vn, va, vc*	Che
Blackwood, E.	Concertino, op. 5. *fl, ob, vn, va, vc*	Sch
Bliss, A.	Conversations. *fl, ob, vn, va, vc*	Fab
Bliss, A.	Quintet. *cl, 2vn, va, vc*	Nov
Boccherini, L.	Quintet, D, op. 21/1. *fl, 2vn, va, vc*	MR
Boccherini, L.	Quintet, G, op. 21/5. *fl(ob), 2vn, va, vc*	MR
Boccherini, L.	Quintet, E♭, op. 21/6. *fl(ob), 2vn, va, vc*	MR
Boccherini, L.-Haas	Quintet, E♭, op. 21/6. *fl, 2vn, va, vc*	Nov
Boccherini, L.-Lebermann	Quintets, op. 45/1-3. *ob, 2vn, va, vc*	Pet
Boccherini, L.	Quintetto, C. *fl, ob, vn, va, vc*	MR
Boccherini, L.	Quintetto, op. 21/6. *fl, 2vn, va, vc*	EDS
Boccherini, L.-Geigling	3 Quintets, op. 45/4-6. *ob(fl), 2vn, va, vc*	HSM
Boguslawski,	Metamorphosen. *fl, cl, vn, va, vc*	HMo
Bottje, W.	Concertino. *ehn(asax), 2vn, va, vc*	AMC
Bottje, W.	Quintet. *fl, 2vn, va, vc*	CoF
Bourguignon, F. de	Quintet, op. 100 (1952). *ob, 2vn, va, vc*	CBD
Brahms, J.	Clarinet Quintet, op. 115. *cl, 2vn, va, vc*	B&H
Brahms, J.	Quintet, b. *cl, 2vn, va, vc*	Ric
Brahms, J.	Quintet, b, op. 115. *cl, 2vn, va, vc*	BrH
Brahms, J.	Quintet, b, op. 115. *cl, 2vn, va, vc*	Int
Brahms, J.	Quintet, b, op. 115. *cl, 2vn, va, vc*	MR
Brahms, J.	Quintet. *cl, 2vn, va, vc*	CF
Brahms, J.	Quintet, op. 115. *cl, 2vn, va, vc*	Pet
Braun, R.	Suite. *cl, 2vn, va, vc*	YM
Bräutigam, H.	Fröhliche Musik. *fl, ob, 3vn*	BrH
Brautigam, H.-Wagner	Tänzerische Spielmusik. *2fl, 2vn, vc(db)*	SS
Brings, A.	Suite. *fl, ob, cl, hn, db*	AMC
Chagrin, F.	4 Lyric Interludes. *fl, 2vn, va, vc*	Nov
Chagrin, F.	4 Lyric Interludes. *ob, 2vn, va, vc*	Nov
Cherney, B.	Quintet (1962). *asax, 2vn, va, vc*	Can
Coleridge-Taylor, S.	Quintet. *cl, 2vn, va, vc*	M&M
Coleridge Taylor, S.	Quintet. *cl, 2vn, va, vc*	MR
Crusell, B.	Divertimento, C. *ob, 2vn, va, vc*	MT
Crusell, B.	Quintet I, E♭. *cl, 2vn, va, vc*	MT
Crusell, B.	Quintet II, C. *cl, 2vn, va, vc*	MT
Crusell, B.	Quintet III, D. *cl, 2vn, va, vc*	MT

WOODWINDS, STRINGS

David, T.	Quintet. *cl, vn, va, vc, db*	LDo
Diamond, D.	Quintet. *cl, 2va, 2vc*	SMP
Di Domenica, R.	Quintet. *cl, 2vn, va, vc*	EBM
Donovan, R.	Ricercare. *ob, 2vn, va, vc*	AMC
Dushkin, D.	Quintet for Amanda. *cl, 2vn, va, vc*	NVM
Dushkin, D.	Quintet for Amanda. *fl, 2vn, va, vc*	NVM
Dushkin, D.	Quintet for Amanda. *ob, 2vn, va, vc*	NVM
Elliot, W.	Poem. *bsn, 2vn, va, vc*	Cor
Finzi, G.	Interlude. *ob, 2vn, va, vc*	B&H
Franco, J.	Divertimento. *fl, 2vn, va, vc*	CoF
Frankel, B.	Quintet. *cl, 2vn, va, vc*	Che
Fromm-Michaels, I.	Musica larga. *cl, 2vn, va, vc*	HSM
Fuchs, R.	Quintet, op. 102. *cl, 2vn, va, vc*	JB
Gal, H.	Concertino, op. 82. *fl, 2vn, va, vc*	UE
Gastyne, S. de	Suite Rhetaise, op. 26. *asax, 2vn, va, vc*	Fer
Ginastera, A.	Impressions of Puna. *fl, 2vn, va, vc*	SMP
Giuffre, J.	Clarinet Quintet No. 1. *cl, 2vn, va, vc*	MJQ
Glazunov, A.	Oriental Reverie. *cl, 2vn, va, vc*	Cor
Goeb, R.	Concertant IIb. *bsn, 2vn, va, vc*	CoF
Goldberg, T.	Quintet, op. 7 (1952). *cl, 2vn, va, vc*	B&B
Golz, W.	For Flute and Muted String Quartet. *fl, 2vn, va, vc*	See
Gyring, E.	Concertino. *cl, 2vn, va, vc*	CoF
Harris, R.	Four Minutes and Twenty Seconds. *fl, 2vn, va, vc*	B-M
Hartig, H.	Composition, op. 50. *fl, ob, vn, va, vc*	B&B
Hartley, W.	Quintet Movement. *cl, 2vn, va, vc*	Cre
Hartmann, R.	Variationen über ein Thema von Paganini, op. 1. *fl, ob, vn, va, vc*	B&B
Haydn, M.-Hockner	Divertimento a 5, G. *fl, vn, va, hn, bsn*	Sim
Haydn, M.-Strassl	Divertimento, B♭. *ob, bsn, vn, va, db*	LDo
Haydn, M.-Strassl	Divertimento, G. *fl, hn, vn, va, db*	LDo
Haydn, M.-Balassa	Quintetto. *cl, bsn, hn, vn, va*	EMB
Hemel, O. van	Clarinet Quintet (1958). *cl, 2vn, va, vc*	SD
Henning, E.	Quintet. *fl, hn, vn, va, vc*	AMC
Heussenstamm, G.	Mini-Variations, op. 25. *fl, ob, vn, va, vc*	See
Hindemith, P.	Quintet, op. 30. *cl, 2vn, va, vc*	SS
Höller, K.	Clarinet Quintet, op. 46. *cl, 2vn, va, vc*	B&N
Jacob, G.	Quintet. *cl, 2vn, va, vc*	Nov
Jacob, G.	Suite. *bsn, 2vn, va, vc*	MR
Kallstenius, E.	Klarinettkvintett. *cl, 2vn, va, vc*	EMF
Kilpatrick, J.	Clarinet Quintet, g. *cl, 2vn, va, vc*	CoF
Koerppen, A.	Serenade (1952). *fl, 2vn, va, vc*	BrH
Koetsier, J.	Quintet, op. 43 (1955). *ehn, 2vn, va, vc*	SD
Kont, P.	Concerto lirico, op. 61/2. *fl, cl, vn, va, vc*	LDo
Kopp, F.	October '55. *cl, 2vn, va, vc*	See
Kornauth, E.	Clarinet Quintet, op. 33. *cl, 2vn, va, vc*	LDo
Korte, K.	Quintet (1959). *ob, 2vn, va, vc*	Can
Kraus, J.	Quintet, D (1783). *fl, 2vn, va, vc*	BrH
Kraus, J.-Hoffman	Wiener Flötenquintett, D. *fl, 2vn, va, vc*	MV
Krieger, J.-Seiffert	Partie, F. *2ob, ehn, va, bsn*	Kis
Kuhlau, F.-Winkel	Quintet, op. 51/1 (1823). *fl, vn, 2va, vc*	SPD

Woodwinds, Strings

Kupferman, M.	Quintet. *bsn, 2vn, va, vc*	Gen
Landré, G.	4 miniaturen (1950). *cl, 2vn, va, vc*	SD
Lemeland, A.	Mouvement Concertant. *fl, ob, vn, va, vc*	Bil
Leukauf, R.	Quintet, op. 32a. *fl, ob, vn, va, vc*	LDo
Levy, F.	Quintet. *fl, 2vn, va, vc*	Cor
Lewis, P.	Serenade. *fl, 2vn, va, vc*	CoF
Lipscomb, H.	Design. *cl, 2vn, va, vc*	TP
Lockwood, N.	Clarinet Quintet. *cl, 2vn, va, vc*	ACA
Loshkin, A.	Quintet. *cl, 2vn, va, vc*	MR
Lourié, A.	Pastorale de la Volga. *ob, bsn, 2va, vc*	EME
Maasz, G.	Divertimento. *fl(ob), 2vn, va, vc*	HSM
Macero, T.	Electrique. *asax, 2vn, va, vc*	AMC
Martinu, B.	Serenata I. *hn, 2vn, va, vc*	Art
Martinu, B.	Serenade. *2cl, vn, va, vc*	EME
McBride, R.	Comfortable Flight. *ehn, 2vn, va, vc*	CoF
McBride, R.	Quintet. *ob, 2vn, va, vc*	Sch
Meyer, E.	Kleine Eröffnungsmusik. *cl, 2vn, va, vc*	BrH
Meyers, E.	Suite. *cl, 2vn, va, vc*	AMC
Mezö, I.	Quintet. *2fl, cl, bsn, db*	EMB
Milhaud, D.	Les Rêves de Jacob. *ob, vn, va, vc, db*	Heu
Mills, C.	Piece. *fl, rec, vn, va, vc*	CoF
Moore, D.	Quintet. *cl, 2vn, va, vc*	CF
Mourant, W.	Burletta. *cl, 2vn, va, vc*	CoF
Mozart, W.-Levin	Allegro, B♭ (K.V. Anh. 91). *cl, 2vn, va, vc*	B&N
Mozart, W.	Clarinet Quintet. *cl, 2vn, va, vc*	B&H
Mozart, W.	Clarinet Quintet, K. 581. *cl, 2vn, va, vc*	EdK
Mozart, W.-Schmid	Quintet, A, K.V. 581. *cl, 2vn, va, vc*	B&N
Mozart, W.	Quintet, A, K. 581. *cl, 2vn, va, vc*	BrH
Mozart, W.	Quintet, A, k. 581. *cl(va), 2vn, va, vc*	Int
Mozart, W.	Quintet. *cl, 2vn, va, vc*	Bil
Mozart, W.	Quintet. *fl, 2vn, va, vc*	Bil
Mozart, W.	Quintet, K. 581. *cl, 2vn, va, vc*	Deu
Mozart, W.	Quintet, K. 581. *cl, 2vn, va, vc*	Pet
Mozart, W.	Quintet, K. 581. *cl, 2vn, va, vc*	Ric
Mozart, W.-Christmann	Quintet, K. 581. *cl, 2 vn, va, vc*	Sch
Mozart, W.	Quintet No. 6. *cl, 2vn, va, vc*	CF
Mul, J.	Kwintet (1957). *cl, bsn, vn, va, vc*	SD
Neukomm, S. von	Quintet, op. 8. *cl, 2vn, va, vc*	Sim
Park, S.	Pastorale. *fl, 2vn, va, vc*	SM
Parris, R.	Quintet. *fl, ob, bsn, vn, vc*	CoF
Partos, O.	Maqamat. *fl, 2vn, va, vc*	He
Pedersen, P.	Chorale Prelude No. 2 (1958). *fl(ob, cl), 2vn, va, vc*	Can
Pelemans, W.	3rd Concertino. *fl, cl, vn, va, vc*	Mau
Petric, I.	3 esquisses. *fl, 2vn, va, vc*	EdD
Piston, W.	Quintet. *fl, 2vn, va, vc*	AMP
Pleyel, I.	Quintet, E♭, op. 10/3. *fl, ob, vn, va, vc*	LDo
Ponse, L.	Kwintet, op. 25 (1956). *fl, ob, vn, va, vc*	SD
Porter, Q.	Quintet. *fl, 2vn, va, vc*	CoF
Porter, Q.	Quintet. *cl, 2vn, va, vc*	CoF
Presser, W.	Passacaglia. *cl, vn, va, vc, hn*	See
Prokofiev, S.	Quintet. *ob, cl, vn, va, db*	B&H

Woodwinds, Strings

Prokofiev, S.	Quintet. *ob, cl, vn, va, db*	EdK
Prokofiev, S.	Quintet, g, op. 39. *ob, cl, vn, va, db*	Int
Prokofiev, S.	Quintet, op. 39. *ob, cl, vn, va, db*	MR
Randolph, D.	Prelude & Variations. *cl, 2vn, va, vc*	AMC
Raphael, G.	Quintet, op. 4. *cl, 2vn, va, vc*	Sim
Rathburn, E.	Pastorella (1949). *ob, 2vn, va, vc*	Can
Reger, M.	Quintet, op. 146. *cl, 2vn, va, vc*	Pet
Reicha, Anton	Quintet, B♭. *cl, 2vn, va, vc*	MR
Reicha, A.	Quintet, B♭. *cl, 2vn, va, vc*	Pet
Reicha, A.	Quintet. *cl, 2vn, va, vc*	B&V
Reicha, A.	Quintet, F. *ob, 2vn, va, vc*	MR
Reicha, A.-Merka	Quintet, F, op. 107. *cl, 2vn, va, vc*	GZ
Reicha, A.	Quintetto, op. 107. *ob, 2vn, va, vc*	M&M
Reizenstein, F.	Theme, Variations and Fugue. *cl, 2vn, va, vc*	AlL
Roche, G.	Ballade. *ob, 2vn, va, vc*	E&C
Romberg, A.	Quintet, op. 57. *cl, vn, 2va, vc*	M&M
Rubbra, E.	Suite: The Buddha. *fl, ob, vn, va, vc*	AlL
Rudzinski, W.	Quintet (1954). *fl, 2vn, va, vc*	AP
Scarmolin, L.	Quintet. *cl, hn, vn, va, vc*	AMC
Schäfer, G.	Quintet. *cl, 2vn, va, vc*	ABe
Schäfer, G.	Quintet. *cl, 2vn, va, vc*	Sim
Schwantner, J.	Consortium. *fl, cl, vn, va, vc*	ACA
Schwartz, E.	Miniconcerto. *fl, ob, vn, va, vc*	CF
Shaughnessy, R.	Bolotowsky. *fl, 2vn, va, vc*	See
Siegel, A.	Country Churchyard. *fl, 2vn, va, vc*	AMC
Siegl, O.	Quintet-Serenade. *cl, bsn, vn, va, vc*	LDo
Simons, N.	Quintet (1953). *fl, ob, cl, bsn, db*	CoF
Simpson, R.	Clarinet Quintet. *cl, 2vn, va, vc*	AlL
Smith, L.	Quintet. *bsn, 2vn, va, vc*	CoF
Smith, J.	Quintet. *ob(cl), 2vn, va, vc*	CF
Sokorski, J.	Little Quintet (1963). *cl, 2vn, va, vc*	AP
Sollberger, H.	Solos for Five Instruments. *fl, cl, hn, vn, db*	CoF
Stallaert, A.	Quintet. *asax, 2vn, va, vc*	Bil
Stamitz, K.-Höckner	Quintet. *ob, hn, 2va, vc*	Sim
Stamitz, K.-Winschermann-Buck	3 Quintets, op. 11/1, 2. *ob, hn, 2va, vc*	HSM
Sterans, P.	Nocturne, Dance & Aubade. *cl, bcl, vn, va, vc*	AMC
Stein, L.	Quintet. *asax, 2vn, va, vc*	Cor
Stein, L.	Quintet. *cl, 2vn, va, vc*	Cor
Still, R.	Clarinet Quintet. *cl, 2vn, va, vc*	AlL
Stock, D.	Quintet, op. 12. *cl, 2vn, va, vc*	ACA
Stock, D.	Serenade for 5 Instruments. *fl, cl, hn, va, vc*	ACA
Stout, A.	Quintet, op. 12. *cl, 2vn, va, vc*	CoF
Strategier, H.	3 Stukken (1937). *ob, 2vn, va, vc*	SD
Strauss, R.-Hasenoehrl	Till Eulenspiegel einmal anders! *cl, bsn, hn, vn, db*	Pet
Stravinsky, I.	Pastorale. *vn, ob, ehn, cl, bsn*	SS
Süssmayer, F.-Steinbeck	Quintet. *fl, ob, vn, va, vc*	LDo
Tarp, S.	Serenade (1930). *fl, cl, vn, va, vc*	SPD
Taylor, S.	Quintet. *cl, 2vn, va, vc*	M&M

Woodwinds, Strings

Thilman, J.	Clarinet Quintet, op. 73. *cl, 2vn, va, vc*	Pet
Tosatti	Divertimento. *cl, bsn, vn, va, vc*	FrC
Trede	Quintett in einem Satz. cl, 2vn, va, vc	Pet
Van Vactor, D.	Quintet. *fl, 2vn, va, vc*	TP
Weber, C.M. von	Grand Quintet, op. 34. *cl, 2vn, va, vc*	MRL
Weber, C.M. von-Kohl	Introduktion, Thema und Variationen. *cl, 2vn, va, vc*	B&B
Weber, C.M. von	Quintet, B♭, op. 34. *cl, 2vn, va, vc*	Int
Weber, C.M. von	Quintet, B♭, op. 34. *cl, 2vn, va, vc*	MR
Weber, C.M. von	Quintet, op. 34. *cl, 2vn, va, vc*	BrH
Weber, C.M. von	Quintet, op. 34. *cl, 2vn, va, vc*	CF
Weiss, A.	Concerto. *bsn, 2vn, va, vc*	CoF
Wellesz, E.	Quintet, op. 81. *cl, 2vn, va, vc*	Hei
Werdin, E.	Concertino. *2fl, 2vn, vc*	SS
Whitney, M.	Adagio and Fugue. *fl, cl, vn, va, vc*	See
Wilson, D.	Quintet. *cl, 2vn, va, vc*	GaM
Wordsworth, W.	Quintet, op. 50. *cl, 2vn, va, vc*	AlL
Ziems, H..	Quintet (1965). *cl, 2vn, va, vc*	B&B

WOODWINDS, BRASS, STRINGS

Casella, A.	Serenata. *cl, bsn, tpt, vn, vc*	UE
Haieff, A.	Dance Suite. *fl, bsn, tpt, vn, vc*	Be
Smith, L.	Introduction and Divertimento. *cl, tpt, vn, va, vc*	CoF
Thomson, V.	Sonata da Chiesa. *E♭ cl, tpt, hn, trb, va*	AMC

WOODWINDS, BRASS, STRINGS, KEYBOARD

Delannoy, M.	Rapsodie. *sax, va, vc, tpt, pf*	Heu
Feldman, M.	Projection II. *fl, vn, vc, tpt, pf*	Pet
Glick, S.	Dance Concertante No. 2 (1964). *fl, cl, tpt, vc, pf*	Can
Hindemith, P.	3 Stücke (1925). *cl, tpt, vn, db, pf*	SS
Ives, C.	Scherzo, all the way around and back. *cl(fl), vn, tpt, hn, pf*	PIC
Stewart, R.	5 Movements. *bsn, fl, flugelhorn, db, pf*	CoF
Weckmann, M.	Sonata a 4. *ob, vn, trb, bsn, bc*	MR

WOODWINDS, STRING, KEYBOARD

Adaskin, M.	Cassenti Concertante (1963). *ob, cl, bsn, vn, pf*	Can
Albright, W.	Danse Macabre. *fl, cl, vn, vc, pf*	Bow
Bach, J.C.	Quintet, A, op. 11/5. *fl, ob, vn, va, bc*	MR
Bach, J.C.	Quintet, C, op. 11/1. *fl, ob, vn, va, bc*	MR
Bach, J.C.-Ermeler	Quintet, D. *fl, ob, vn, vc, pf*	B&N
Bach, J.C.-Erhart	Quintet, F. *ob, vn, va, vc, pf*	SS
Bach, J.C.	Quintet, F, op. 11/3. *fl, ob, vn, va, bc*	MR
Bach, J.C.	Quintet, G, op. 11/2. *fl, ob, vn, va, bc*	MR
Bach, J.C.-Steglich	Quintet, op. 11/1, C. *fl, ob, vn, va, bc*	B&N
Bach, J.C.-Steglich	Quintet, op. 11/2, G. *fl, ob, vn, va, bc*	B&N
Bach, J.C.-Steglich	Quintet, op. 11/3, F. *fl, ob, vn, va, bc*	B&N
Bach, J.C.-Steglich	Quintet, op. 11/4, E♭. *fl, ob, vn, va, bc*	B&N
Bach, J.C.-Steglich	Quintet, op. 11/5, A. *fl, ob, vn, va, bc*	B&N
Bach, J.C.-Steglich	Quintet, op. 11/6, D. *fl, ob, vn, va, bc*	B&N
Bach, J.C.F.-Ruf	Sonate, D. *fl, vn, va, vc, pf*	B&N
Badings, H.	Fuga (1938). *fl, ob, vn, va, org*	SD
Beyer, F.	Concerto (1968). *fl, cl, vn, vc, pf*	B&B
Boismortier, J.-Ruf	Concerto, e. *fl, ob, bsn, vn, bc*	Ric
Bolcom, W.	Duets for Quintet. *fl, cl, vn, vc, pf*	Bow
Bolcom, W.	Whisper Moon. *afl, cl, vn, vc, pf*	Bow
Burge, D.	Aeolian Music. *fl, cl, vn, vc, pf*	Bow
Cordero, R.	Quinteto. *fl, cl, vn, vc, pf*	SMP
Corelli, A.	Gavotte and Gigue. *fl, 2vn, va, pf*	EdM
Couperin, F.-Boulay	La Sultane. *fl(ob), vn(fl), 2va da gamba (vc), pf*	EMT
Couperin, F.-Désormière	Quartrième Concert Royal. *fl, ob, bsn, vn, hpcd*	EdL
Diamond, D.	Quintet. *fl, vn, vc, vc, pf*	SMP
Donatoni, F.	Etwas ruhiger im Ausdruck (1967). *fl, cl, vn, vc, pf*	ESZ
Dubois, F.	Quintet. *ob, vn, va, vc, pf*	Heu
Fasch, J.-Sallagar	Concerto. *bsn, 2vn, va, bc*	Pet
Gandini, G.	Musica Nocturna. *fl, vn, va, vc, pf*	SMP
Glick, S.	Suite Hebraique No. 2 (1969). *cl, vn, va, vc, pf*	Can
Graupner, C.-Angerhofer	Concerto. *bsn, 2vn, va, pf(hpcd)*	FrH
Hallnäs, H.	Kvintett. *fl, ob, va, vc, pf*	EMF
Hambraeus, B.	Diptychon (Tabu-Manu), op. 30. *fl, ob, va, cel, hpcd*	EMF
Handel, G.	Einleitungen zu 3 Anthems. *ob, 2vn, vc, bc*	MV
Hasse, J.A.-Kölbel	Sinfonia a 5, G. *2fl, 2vn, bc*	B&N
Haydn, F.-Sitt	Sinfonie Concertante. *ob, bsn, vn, vc, pf*	Int
Haydn, F.-Sitt	Sinfonie Concertante, op. 84. *ob, bsn, vn, vc, pf*	BrH
Haydn, F.	Symphony Concertante, op. 84. *ob, bsn, vn, vc, pf*	EdK
Hedwall, L.	Kvintett (1965). *fl, ob, vn, vc, hpcd*	STI
Heinichen, J.	Concerto, G. *fl, 2vn, vc, pf*	Pet
Höller, K.	Divertimento, op. 11. *fl, vn, va, vc, pf*	B&N
Holzbauer, I.-Schroeder	Quintet, G. *fl, vn, va, vc, pf*	BrH
Ives, C.	Adagio Sostenuto. *ehn(fl), 3vn, vc ad lib, pf(hp)*	SMP

208

Woodwinds, String, Keyboard

Janitsch, J.-Wolff	Kammersonate "Echo," op. 8.	
	fl, ob(fl), va, vc, pf	BrH
Joubert, J.	Sonata a cinque, op. 43. *fl, 2vn, vc, hpcd*	Nov
Karkoschka, E.	Aus Dreien (1969). *fl, cl, vn, vc, pf*	HG
Kenins, T.	Concertino a cinque (1968). *fl, ob, va, vc, pf*	Can
Kilpatrick, J.	Waiting for Godot. *fl, cl, hn, vn, pf*	CoF
Kopelent, M.	Musik für Fünf. *ob, cl, bsn, va, pf*	HG
Kreutzer, C.	Quintet. *fl, cl, vn, vc, pf*	MR
Luti, V.	Mixed Quintet. *fl, cl, vn, vc, pf*	Bow
Malipiero, G.	Sonata a cinque. *fl, vn, va, vc, pf*	Ric
Marx, K.	Divertimento, op. 21a. *fl, vn, va, vc, pf*	B&N
Miereanu, C.	Sursum Corda I. *cl, vn, va, vc, pf*	SS
Miroglio, F.	Phases. *fl, vn, va, vc, pf*	UE
Mozart, W.	Adagio and Rondo, c. K. 617. *fl, ob, va, vc, pf*	Int
Mozart, W.-Moyse	3 Quartets. *fl, vn, va, vc, pf*	Sch
Musgrave, T.	Chamber Concerto No. 2.	
	fl/pic/afl, cl/bcl, vn/va, vc, pf	Che
Oliveros, P.	Aeolian Partitions. *fl, cl, vn, vc, pf*	Bow
Palmer, R.	Quintet. *cl, vn, va, vc, pf*	SMP
Pousseur, H.	Quintette a la Memoire d'Anton Webern	
	(1955). *cl, bcl, vn, vc, pf*	ESZ
Ratiu, A.	Concerto per la "Musica Nova."	
	cl, vn, va, vc, pf	EMU
Regamey, K.	Quintet (1944). *cl, bsn, vn, vc, pf*	AP
Rosseau, N.	Pentaphonium, op. 164 (1964).	
	fl, ob, va, vc, pf	CBD
Ruyneman, D.	Divertimento (1927). *fl, cl, hn, va, pf*	Che
Samuel-Rousseau	Bergers et Mages. *ob, bsn, vn, vc, pf*	Heu
Sauguet, H.	Près du bal. *fl, cl, bsn, vn, pf*	EdS
Scarlatti, A.-Roy	Sonata, A. *2fl, 2vn, bc*	HMo
Schickhard, J.-Peter	3 Sonatas. *fl, 2ob, vc, pf*	MRL
Schmidt, F.	Quintet, A. *cl, vn, va, vc, pf*	JoW
Schmidt, F.	Quintet, B♭. *cl, vn, va, vc, pf*	JoW
Schoenberg, A.-Webern	Kammersymphonie, op. 9	
	fl, cl, vn, vc, pf	UE
Shifrin, L.	Serenade. *ob, cl, hn, va, pf*	Pet
Spitzmuller, A.	Divertimento, op. 6. *2vn, va, bsn, pf*	UE
Stevens, H.	Quintet. *fl, vn, va, vc, pf*	AMC
Stölzel, G.-Hausswald	Sonate, F. *ob, hn, vn, vc, pf*	BrH
Telemann, G.-Seiffert	Quartet, d (Tafelmusik II Nr. 2).	
	bsn, 2fl, vc, pf	BrH
Vivaldi, A.	Concerto, C, P. 81. *fl, ob, 2vn, bc*	MR
Vivaldi, A.	Concerto, C, P. 82. *fl, ob, vn, bsn, bc*	MR
Vivaldi, A.-Schroeder	Concerto, D, "La Pastorella."	
	fl, ob, bsn, vn, bc	Hei
Vivaldi, A.	Concerto, D, P. 155. *fl, ob, bsn, vn, bc*	MR
Vivaldi, A.	Concerto, F, P. 323. *fl, ob, bsn, vn, bc*	MR
Vivaldi, A.-Ghedini	Concerto, g. *fl, ob, bsn, vn, pf, vc & db ad lib*	Int
Vivaldi, A.	Concerto, g, P. 342. *fl, bsn, 2vn, bc*	MR
Vivaldi, A.	Concerto, g, P. 360. *fl, ob, bsn, vn, bc*	MR
Vivaldi, A.-Ghedini	Sonata, D. *fl, vn, bsn, vc (db), pf*	Int
Weigel, E.	Quintet. *cl, vn, va, vc, pf*	AMC

Woodwinds, Strings, Keyboard

Wendel, E.	Interferenze. *cl, vn, va, vc, pf*	HG
Werner, G.-Moder	Concerto a 4. *fl, 2vn, vc, hpcd*	LDo
Widdoes, L.	From a Time of Snow (1970). *fl, cl, vn, vc, pf*	Bow
Widor, C.	Serenade, op. 10. *fl, pf, vn, vc, harmonium*	Ham
Williamson, M.	Serenade. *fl, vn, va, vc, pf*	JoW
Wuorinen, C.	Concertante. *ob, vn, va, vc, hpcd*	M&M
Zeljenka, I.	Klavirne Kvinteto (1956). *cl, vn, va, vc, pf*	SHF

FIVE INSTRUMENTS INCLUDING HARP

Absil, J.	Concert à cinq, op. 38 (1939). *fl, vn, va, vc, hp*	CBD
Anderberg, C.	"Höstens hökar." *cl, bsn, vn, vc, hp*	EMF
Badings, H.	Capriccio. *fl, vn, va, vc, hp*	SD
Badings, H.	Kwintet No. 3 (1936). *fl, vn, va, vc, hp*	SD
Cras, J.	Quintette. *fl, vn, va, vc, hp*	EdS
Damase, J.	Quintet. *fl, vn, va, vc, hp*	E-V
Demarquez, S.	Sonatina. *fl, vn, va, vc, hp*	EMT
Dinerstein, N.	Serenade (1963). *ob, cl, vn, vc, hp*	Can
Denisow, E.	Romantische Musik. *ob, vn, va, vc, hp*	UE
Francaix, J.	Quintet. *fl, vn, va, vc, hp*	SS
Gerschefski, E.	Song Without Words. *fl, 2vn, va, hp(pf)*	CoF
Girnatis, W.	Serenade. *ob, vn, va, vc, hp*	HSM
Grkovic, B.	Contemplation. *fl, cl, vc, hp, pf*	Kaw
Hovhaness, A.	The World beneath the Sea, op. 133/1. *sax, vib, hp, 2perc*	Pet
Hovhaness, A.	The World beneath the Sea (II), op. 133/2. *cl, db, hp, 2perc*	Pet
Indy, V. d'	Suite en parties. *fl, vn, va, vc, hp*	Heu
Jolivet, A.	Chant de Linos. *fl, vn, va, vc, hp(pf)*	ALe
Kalmar, L.	Triangoli. *cl, vn, vc, hn, hp*	EMB
Kelemen, M.	Radiant. *fl, va, pf, hp, perc*	Pet
Lajtha, L.	Marionnettes. *fl, vn, va, vc, hp*	EdS
Lajtha, L.	Second Quintet, op. 46. *fl, vn, va, vc, hp*	ALe
Lazarof, H.	Tempi Concertati. *fl, pf, hpcd, hp, cel*	Sch
Lesur, D.	Suite médiévale. *fl, vn, va, vc, hp*	Dur
Liedbeck, S.	Fantasi. *ob, fl, vn, vc, hp*	EMF
Malipiero, G.	Sonata a cinque. *fl, vn, va, vc, hp*	Ric
Monnikendam, M.	Suite in C (1960). *fl, ob, cl, bsn, hp*	SD
Mozart, W.-Stout	Fantasia, C, K.V. 616a. *fl, ob, va, vc, hp*	CoF
Musgrave, T.	Serenade. *fl, cl, va, vc, hp*	Che
Petric, I.	Nuances en couleur. *fl/pic, bsn, vc, pf, hp*	EdD
Pierné, G.	Variations Libres et Final. *fl, vn, va, vc, hp*	EdS
Pierné, G.	Voyage au Pays du Tendre. *fl, vn, va, vc, hp*	ALe
Pillois, J.	Cinq Hai-Kai. *fl, vn, va, vc, hp*	Dur
Rands, B.	Actions for Six. *fl, va, vc, hp, perc*	UE
Rieti, V.	Concertino. *fl, va, vc, hp, hpcd*	EMo
Rocca	Storiella. *bsn, 2tpt, pf, hp*	Ric
Rpoartz, J.	Prélude, Marine et chansons. *fl, vn, va, vc, hp*	Dur

Five Instruments including Harp

Rota, N.	Quintet. *fl, ob, va, vc, hp*	Ric
Roussel, A.	Serenade, op. 30. *fl, vn, va, vc, hp*	Dur
Schmitt, F.	Suite en rocaille, op. 84. *fl, vn, va, vc, hp*	Dur
Smit, L.	Quintet (1928). *fl, vn, va, vc, hp*	SD
Thilman, J.	Ostinati. *fl, va, vc, hp, perc*	Pet
Thorarinsson, L.	Kadensar. *ob, cl, bcl, bsn, hp*	M&M
Tocchi, G.	Arlecchino. *fl, cl, vn, va, hp*	Car
Tournier, M.	Suite. *fl, vn, va, vc, hp*	E-V
Villa-Lobos, H.	Quintet. *fl, vn, va, vc, hp*	EME
Zagwijn, H.	Nocturne (1918). *fl, ehn, cl, bsn, hp*	SD
Zagwijn, H.	Quintet (1954). *fl, vn, va, vc, hp*	SD

FIVE INSTRUMENTS INCLUDING GUITAR

Bartolozzi, B.	Concertazioni (1965). *ob, va, db, guit, perc*	ESZ
Buhé, K.	Europäische Volks-und Tanzweisen.	
	fl, accordeon, guit, db, perc	SS
Buhé, K.	Volks-und Tanzweisen aus Amerika.	
	fl, accordeon, guit, db, perc	SS
Ettore, E.	Flippin' Around. *2cl, db, guit, pf*	CoA
Feld, J.	Capriccio. *fl, ob, cl, bsn, guit*	Art
Ferritto, J.	Diffusione. *bcl, vn, db, guit, perc*	ACA
Hespos, H.	frottages. *asax, vc, hp, perc, mandoline*	EMo
Kraft, K.	Musik unterm Fenster, op. 14. *2vn, cl, db, lute*	ABS
Spinner, L.	Quintet, op. 14. *cl, bsn, hn, guit, db*	B&H
Sternberg (arr)	Variations on German Folk Songs, 2 vols.	
	cl(sax), db, guit, pf, perc	Deu
Strange, A.	Chamber Piece. *fl, cl, vn, db, guit*	CoA
Welin, K.	Renovationes (1960).	
	fl, vn, vc, perc, mandoline	EdT

FIVE INSTRUMENTS INCLUDING PERCUSSION

Adamis, M.	Anakyklesis. *fl, ob, va, vc, cel*	EMo
Bartolozzi, B.	Concertazioni (1965). *ob, va, db, guit, perc*	ESZ
Benguerel, X.	Arguments (1966). *fl, cl, vn, pf, vib*	See
Blomdahl, K.	Dans-svit nr 1. *fl, vn, va, vc, perc*	EMF
Bolcom, W.	Session III. *E$\flat$ cl, vn, vc, pf, perc*	TP
Buhé, K.	Europäische Volks-und Tanzweisen.	
	fl, accordeon, guit, db, perc	SS
Buhé, K.	Volks-und Tanzweisen aus Amerika.	
	fl, accordeon, guit, db, perc	SS
Castiglioni, N.	Tropi (1959). *fl, cl, vn, vc, perc*	ESZ
Christlieb, D. (arr)	4 Pieces. *2ob, ehn, bsn, sdr* ·	CP
Cowell, H.	26 Simultaneous Mosaics. *cl, vn, vc, pf, perc*	Pet

Five Instruments including Percussion

Denisov, E.	Concerto. *fl, ob, pf, timp, perc*	UE
Ehle, R.	5 Pieces for Instruments with Prepared Electronics. *cl, vn, pf, perc, tape*	CF
Ferritto, J.	Diffusione. *bcl, vn, db, guit, perc*	ACA
Fink, S.	Serenade in Percussion. *cl, db, 3perc*	B&N
Fisher, A.	Five Time Prisms. *sop sax, tsax, bass sax, vib, pf*	CoA
Gehlhaar, R.	Helix (1967). *sax, trb, db, pf, perc*	Fab
Hartwell, H.	"Matinée d'Ivresse" (1966). *cl, vn, vc, pf, perc*	Can
Heininen, P.	Quintetto (1961). *fl, sax, pf, vib, perc*	MT
Hellerman, W.	Formata. *fl, cl, trb, pf, perc*	CoF
Hespos, H.	frottages. *asax, vc, hp, perc, mandoline*	EMo
Holewa, H.	Kvintett (1962). *cl, vc, trb, pf, perc*	EMF
Hovhaness, A.	The World beneath the Sea, op. 133/1. *sax, vib, hp, 2perc*	Pet
Hovhaness, A.	The World beneath the Sea (II), op. 133/2. *cl, db, hp, 2perc*	Pet
Kelemen, M.	Radiant. *fl, va, pf, hp, perc*	Pet
Lathrop, G.	Piece 4-5. *asax, tpt, vc, db, perc*	CoA
Lazarof, H.	Tempi Concertati. *fl, pf, hpcd, hp, cel*	Sch
Linda, B.	Musica per sylvanum. *fl, bsn, vn, hn, xyl*	EMF
Mellnäs, A.	Per caso. *asax, trb, vn, db, perc*	EdT
Mercure, P.	Tetrachromie (1963). *cl, asax, bcl, perc, electronics*	Can
Mestres-Quadreny, J.	Musica de Cambra I (1960). *fl, vn, db, pf, perc*	See
Miroglio, F.	Phases. *fl, pf, 3perc*	UE
Parris, R.	St. Winefred's Well. *fl, 2vc, pf, perc*	CoF
Pennisi, F.	Quintetto in 4 Parti (1965). *fl, tpt, trb, pf, perc*	ESZ
Petrassi, G.	Serenata (1958). *fl, va, db, hpcd, perc*	ESZ
Pololanik, Z.	Musica concisa. *fl, bcl, perc, hpcd, pf*	Art
Pousseur, H.	Madrigal III. *cl, vn, vc, pf, perc*	UE
Rabe, F.	Impromptu 1962. *bcl, trb, vc, pf, perc*	EMF
Rands, B.	Actions for six. *fl, va, vc, hp, perc*	UE
Rytterkvist, H.	Tre satirer. *cl/bcl, vib, xyl, pf, vc*	EMF
Schröder, H.	Musik in 7 Sätzen. *ob, 3vn, dr*	MRL
Sternberg (arr)	Variations on German Folk Songs, 2 vols. *cl(sax), db, guit, pf, perc*	Deu
Stroud, R.	Quintet. *cl, 4perc*	CoA
Sydeman, W.	Quintet (1960). *cl, hn(trb), db, pf, perc*	See
Tanenbaum, E.	Chamber Piece No. 1. *fl, cl, vc, pf, perc*	CoF
Thilman, J.	Ostinati. *fl, va, vc, hp, perc*	Pet
Welin, K.	Renovationes (1960). *fl, vn, vc, perc, mandoline*	EdT
Widmer, E.	Coco 1961 (Divertimento No. 3). *fl, cl, hn, pf, perc*	Hei
Wilkinson, M.	Variants of Glass. *pic, fl, ob, 2perc*	UE
Williams, J.	Continuum. *fl, cl/bcl, vn, vc, perc*	ACA
Wrochem, K. von	Limelight. *fl, vn, 2db, perc*	CoA
Zonn, P.	One Slow Turn of the World. *fl/pic, ob, cl/bcl, db, perc*	ACA

FIVE INSTRUMENTS INCLUDING RECORDER

Boismortier, J.-Ruf	Concerto, e. *rec(fl), ob, bsn, vn, bc*	FrC
Loeillet, J.-Ermeler	Quintet, b. *2fl, 2rec, bc*	B&N
Mills, C.	Piece. *fl, rec, vn, va, vc*	ACA
Schickhardt, J.	Sonatas. *rec, 2ob(2fl), vc, pf, vc, ad lib*	Pet
Vivaldi, A.	Concerto, D, P. 201. *rec, ob, vn, bsn, bc*	MR
Vivaldi, A.	Concerto, D, P. 204. *rec, ob, vn, bsn, bc*	MR

FIVE INSTRUMENTS INCLUDING TAPE

Bottje, W.	Modalities. *4sax, tape*	ACA
Claflin, A.	Pastoral-The Oriole. *2fl, 2cl, tape*	ACA
Davidovsky, M.	Synchronisms No. 2 (1964). *fl, cl, vn, vc, tape*	M&M
Ehle, R.	5 Pieces for Instruments with Prepared Electronics. *cl, vn, pf, perc, tape*	CF
Fennelly, B.	Evanescences. *afl, cl, vn, vc, tape*	ACA
Hellermann, W.	Columbus Circle. *3ww, pf, electronics*	ACA
Mercure, P.	Tetrachromie (1963). *cl, asax, bcl, perc, electronics*	Can
Ott, J.	Aeolian Harp. *fl, cl, vn, vc, tape*	CBP
Subotnick, M.	Serenade No. 3. *fl, cl, vn, pf, tape*	Bow

SIX INSTRUMENTS

SIX SAXOPHONES

Dallin, L.	Aubade in Blue	B-M
Dvorak, A.-Johnson	First Movement (Serenade, op. 44). *6sax*	Rub
Gomez, A.-Johnson	Il Guarany. *6sax*	Rub
Guilmant, A.-Taylor	Cantilène Pastorale. *3asax, 2tsax, bar sax*	B-M
Haydn, F.-Johnson	Third Movement (Symphony No. 100). *6sax*	Rub
Johnson, W.	Concert Overture	B-M
Kramer, M.	Lawd. *sax sextet*	MCA
Massenet, J.-Johnson	Phèdre Overture. *6sax*	Rub
Ostransky, L.	Poem and Dance. *6sax*	Rub
Ostransky, L.	3 Pieces. *6sax*	Rub
Tallmadge, I.	Saxophone Sextet No. 1.	B-M
Walters, H.	Moonrise. *6sax*	Rub

SIX WOODWINDS

Adler, S.	7 Epigrams. *2fl, ob, cl, bcl, bsn*	OxU
Allers, H.	Suite. *fl, ob, cl, 2hn, bsn*	MV
Altmann, E.	Kleine Tanzsuite. *fl, ob, cl, 2hn, bsn*	FrH
Amy, G.	Alpha-Beth. *fl, ob, cl, bcl, bsn, hn*	Heu
Beckerath, A. von	Volksweisen aus Böhmen. 6 *wind instr*	PG
Beethoven, L. van-Kahn	Minuet and March. *2cl, 2bsn, 2hn*	EBM
Beethoven, L. van-Schoenfeld	Scherzo (op. 27/2). *fl, ob, 2cl, hn, bsn*	War
Beethoven, L. van-Schoenfeld	Scherzo (op. 2/3). *fl, ob, 2cl, hn, bsn*	War
Beethoven, L. van	Sextet, E♭, op. 71. *2cl, 2bsn, 2hn*	BrH
Beethoven, L. van	Sextet, E♭, op. 71. *2cl, 2bsn, 2hn*	Int
Beethoven, L. van	Sextet, op. 71. *2cl, 2bsn, 2hn*	HE
Bissell, K.	A Folk-Song Suite. *2fl, 2cl, bcl, bsn*	B&H
Bozza, E.	Lucioles. *Ebcl, 2cl, basset hn, bcl, cbcl*	ALe
Braun, R.	An Air from Erin. *fl, cl, cl(asax), cl, cl(tsax), cl*	YM
Braun, R.	Angevin Carol. *fl, cl, cl(asax), cl, cl(tsax), cl*	YM
Briegel, G.	Morning in the Forest. *fl, ob, 2cl, bsn, hn*	GFB
Cadow, P.	Pastorale im alten Stil. *2ob, ehn, 2bsn, hn*	PG
Carmichael, H.-Klickmann	Star Dust. *fl, ob, 2cl, hn, bsn*	B-M
Castil-Blaze, F.	Sextet. *2cl, 2bsn, 2hn*	MR
Chagrin, F.	7 Petites Pièces. *pic, fl, ob, cl, hn, bsn*	Nov
Childs, B.	Interbalances V. *fl, ob, cl, asax, bsn, hn*	CoF

214

Six Woodwinds

Danzi, F.-	Sextet, E♭. *2cl, 2bsn, 2hn*	
Wojciechowski		HSM
Davies, P.	Alma Redemptoris Mater. *fl, ob, 2cl, bsn, hn*	S&C
Druschetzky, G.	Partita, E♭. *2cl, 2bsn, 2hn*	EK
Druschetzky, G.	Sestetto. *2cl, 2bsn, 2hn*	SS
Dubois, P.	Sinfonia da camera. *fl, ob, cl, asax(cl), bsn, hn*	ALe
Froschauer, H.	Sextet. *fl, ob, 2cl, bsn, hn*	LDo
Gossec, F.	La chasse de Chantilly. *2cl, 2hn, 2bsn*	Heu
Genzmer, H.	Sextet. *2cl, 2bsn, 2hn*	Lit
Gyrowetz, A.	Notturno. *2cl, 2bsn, 2hn*	MR
Hartley, W.	Chamber Music (1959-60).	
	asax, fl, ob, cl, bsn, hn	Cre
Haydn, F.-Spiegel	Divertimento, F.	
	2fl(2ob), 2hn(2cl), cl(bsn), bsn	OxU
Haydn, F.-Landon	Divertimento No. 8, D. *2ob, 2bsn, 2hn*	LDo
Haydn, F.-Landon	Divertimento No. 5, Hob. II: D 18.	
	2ob, 2bsn, 2hn	LDo
Haydn, F.-Landon	Divertimento No. 1, Hob. II: 15.	
	2ob, 2bsn, 2hn	LDo
Haydn, F.-Landon	Divertimento No. 7, G. *2ob, 2bsn, 2hn*	LDo
Haydn, F.-Landon	Divertimento No. 6, Hob. II: 3. *2ob, 2bsn, 2hn*	LDo
Haydn, F.-Landon	Divertimento No. 3, Hob. II: 7. *2ob, 2bsn, 2hn*	LDo
Haydn, F.-Landon	Divertimento No. 2, Hob. II: 23.	
	2ob, 2bsn, 2hn	LDo
Haydn, F.-Haas	Feldpartie, C. *2ob, 2bsn, 2hn*	MR
Haydn, F.	March, G. *2ob, 2bsn, 2hn*	MR
Haydn, F.-Lumsden	Parthia, F. Hob. II: 23. *2ob, 2bsn, 2hn*	MR
Haydn, M.-Rainer	Divertimento D. *2ob, 2hn, 2bsn*	LDo
Hazzard, P.	Music in Counterpoint. *2fl, 2cl, bcl, hn*	See
Heiden, B.	Intrada. *fl, ob, cl, bsn, hn, asax*	SM
Henning, E.	Fugue. *fl, ob, cl, 2bsn, hn*	AMC
Janáček, L.	Mladi (Youth). *fl, ob, cl, bcl, bsn, hn*	Art
Kabeláč, M.	Sextett, op. 8 (1940). *fl, ehn, 2cl, bsn, hn*	Art
Kelterborn, R.	Meditationen. *2cl, 2bsn, 2hn*	OHN
Kleinsinger, G.	Design for Woodwinds. *fl, ob, 2cl, hn, bsn*	AMP
Krommer, F.-Gutte	Partita. *2cl, 2hn, 2bsn*	Frh
Lagrenze, G.	La Buscha. *4ob, 2bsn*	CP
Locke, M.	3 Works. *2ob, ehn, 3bsn*	CP
Loucheur, R.	En Famille. *6cl*	Bil
Lully, J.	5 Works. *2ob, 2ehn, 2bsn*	CP
Lunden, L.	Quadrille. *2fl, 2cl, bcl(sax), bsn*	Che
Lunden, L.	Queen Christina's Song. *2fl, 2cl, bcl(sax), bsn*	Che
MacKinnon, R.	Suite. *2fl, 2cl, bcl, bsn*	Uni
Manicke, D.	Sextet. *2cl, 2hn, 2bsn*	Sim
Maschek, V.	Allegretto and Variations. *fl(ob), 2cl, 2hn, bsn*	WIN
Melnik	Clarinet Holiday. *6cl*	SF
Michael, D.-Hall	Parthia IV. *2cl, 2hn, 2bsn*	B&H
Michael, D.-McCorkle	Parthia VI. *2cl, 2bsn, 2hn*	B&H
Michael, D.-Hall	Parthia II. *fl, 2cl, 2hn, bsn*	B&H
Missal, J.	Rondo Caprice. *6fl*	Leb
Mozart, W.-Brearley	Adagio, K. 516. *fl, ob, 2cl, hn, bsn*	HE
Mozart, W.-Kahn	Contradance in Rondo Form. *2ob, 2bsn, 2hn*	EBM

Six Woodwinds

Mozart, W.-Spiegel	Divertimento, B♭, K.V. 196f.	
	2cl, 2hn, 2bsn, 2ob ad lib	SS
Mozart, W.	Divertimento, K. 240. 2ob, 2bsn, 2hn	EdK
Mozart, W.	Divertimento, K. 213. 2ob, 2bsn, 2hn	EdK
Mozart, W.	Divertimento No. 8, F, K. 213. 2ob, 2hn, 2bsn	BrH
Mozart, W.	Divertimento No. 14, B♭, K. 270.	
	2ob, 2hn, 2bsn	BrH
Mozart, W.	Divertimento No. 14, K. 270. 2ob, 2bsn, 2hn	EdK
Mozart, W.	Divertimento No. 9, B♭, K. 240. 2ob, 2hn, 2bsn	BrH
Mozart, W.	Divertimento No. 16, E♭, K. 289.	
	2ob, 2hn, 2bsn	BrH
Mozart, W.	Divertimento No. 16, K. 289. 2ob, 2bsn, 2hn	EdK
Mozart, W.	Divertimento No. 13, F, K. 253. 2ob, 2hn, 2bsn	BrH
Mozart, W.	Divertimento No. 13, K. 253. 2ob, 2bsn, 2hn	EdK
Mozart, W.	Divertimento No. 12, E♭, K. 252.	
	2ob, 2hn, 2bsn	BrH
Mozart, W.	Divertimento No . 12, K. 252. 2ob, 2bsn, 2hn	EdK
Mozart, W.-Brearley	Menuetto & Trio, K. 516. fl, ob, 2cl, hn, bsn	HE
Mozart, W.-de Smet	Romanze, Menuetto & Trio (Eine kleine	
	Nachtmusik, K. 525). 2ob, 2cl, 2bsn	HE
Mozart, W.-Haas	Serenade, E♭, K. 375. 2cl, 2bsn, 2hn	MR
Nelhybel, V.	Impromptus for 6 Woodwinds. 2fl, ob, 2cl, bsn	BM
Nordenstrom, G.	Palm Springs Sextet. fl/pic, ob, cl, bcl, hn, bsn	B&N
Parchman, G.	Sextet (1966). fl, ob, cl, 2bsn, hn	See
Phillips, I.	3 Hunting Songs.	
	2ob(2cl), 2cl(2hn), cl(bsn), bsn	OxU
Pleyel, I.	Sextet, E♭. 2cl, 2bsn, 2hn	MR
Praetorius, M.-	Terpsichore. A Suite of Dances.	
Davenport	2ob, 2ehn, 2bsn	AMP
Rebner, W.	Sextett. fl, ob, cl, bcl, hn, bsn	EMo
Righini, V.	Sextet. 2cl, 2bsn, 2hn	MR
Ringbom, N.	Wind Sextet (1959). ob, ehn, cl, bcl, bsn, hn	MT
Rosetti, A.	Parthia, D. ob, 2cl, bsn, 2hn	B&B
Schubert, F.-	Shepherd Melody No. 6 (Rosamunde).	
Schoenbach	2ob, 2bsn, 2hn	TP
Schumann, R.-Briegel	Romanza (4th Symphony). fl, ob, 2cl, bsn, hn	GFB
Seiber, M.	Serenade. 2cl, 2bsn, 2hn	WH
Socor, M.	3 Salviri. 6ww	EMU
Stearns, P.	Octet. pic, fl, ob, ehn, bcl, cbsn	CoF
Stein, L.	Sextet. asax, fl, ob, cl, bsn, hn	Cor
Stravinsky, I.-Stone	Napolitana. fl, ob, 2cl, hn, bsn	DGo
Svensson, Sven	Sextet. fl, ob, cl, bcl, bsn, hn	EMF
Templeton, A.-Rhoads	Passepied. fl, ob, ehn, cl, bcl, bsn	TP
Thomson, V.	Barcarolle. fl, ob, ehn, cl, bcl, bsn	TP
Tomasi, H.	Printemps. fl, ob, cl, bsn, asax, hn	ALe
Vaughan Williams, R.	Household Music (3 Preludes). 3cl, sax, 2hn	OxU
Vinter, G.	Dance of the Marionettes.	
	fl, fl/pic, ob/ehn, 2cl, bsn	B&H
Wanhal, J.	Divertimento, C. 2ob, 2hn, 2bsn	JB
Waters, C.	Solemn Minuet. fl, ob, 2cl, 2bsn	HE
Weber, C.M. von-	Adagio and Rondo. 2cl, 2hn, 2bsn	
Dobrée		MR

Six Woodwinds

Zehm, F.	Musica Pastorale. *2fl, ob, ehn, 2bsn*	Sim

WOODWIND QUINTET, KEYBOARD

Andriessen, J.	L'incontro di Cesare e Cleopatra (1956)	SD
Arrieu, C.	Concerto	Ric
Badings, H.	Sextet (1952)	SD
Beckler, S.	Songs and Dances	CoA
Bezanson, P.	Sextet	CoF
Bizet, G.-Wilson	Quintet (Carmen). *fl, ob, cl, hn, bsn(bcl), pf*	CF
Blumer, T.	Sextet, op. 92	R&E
Boccherini, L.	Menuet. *fl, ob, cl, hn, bsn(bcl), pf*	CF
Boisdeffre, R. de	Scherzo (Septet, op. 49).	
	fl, ob, cl, hn, bsn(bcl), pf	CF
Casadesus, R̩.	Sextuor, op. 58	Dur
Coulthard, J.	Divertimento (1968)	Can
Cruft, A.	Dance Movement	Gal
Custer, A.	Sextet	CoF
David, J.-Bohle	Kume, kumgeselle min, op. 24, Divertimento	BrH
Di Domenica, R.	Sextet	EBM
Diemer, E.	Sextet	CoA
d'Indy, V.	Sarabande and Minuet, op. 24 bis	Int
Indy, V. d'	Sarabande & Minuet, op. 72	Int
Dionisi, R.	Divertimento	GZ
Dresden, S.	Kleine suite, C (1913)	SD
Dresden, S.	Suite naar Rameau (1916)	SD
Dresden, S.	3rd Suite (1920)	SD
Dvorak, A.-Harris	Humoreske. *fl, ob, cl, hn, bsn(bcl), pf*	CF
Francaix, J.	L'Heure du berger	SS
Frensel-Wegener, E.	Sextet (1927)	SD
Frid, G.	Sextet	SD
Godron, H.	Godron, H.	
Godron, H.	Serenade (1947)	SD
Görner, H.	Kammerkonzert, op. 29	Pet
Greenberg, L.	Sextet (1963)	Can
Hemel, O. van	Sextet (1962)	SD
Hill, E.	Sextet, op. 39	TP
Husa, K.	Serenade. *fl, ob, cl, bsn, hn, pf(hp)*	ALe
Husa, K.	Serenade	B&N
Jacob, G.	Sextet	MR
Jentsch, W.	Kleine Kammermusik, op. 5	R&E
Jongen, J.	Rhapsodie, op. 70 (1922)	CBD
Juon, P.	Divertimento, op. 51. *fl, ob, cl, hn, bsn, pf*	MRL
Kahowez, G.	Structures	LDo
Keith, G.	Journey of the Swagmen	War
Koetsier, J.	Introduction et folatrerie avec un thème (1961)	SD
Kohn, K.	Serenade. *fl/pic, ob, cl, hn, bsn, pf*	CF
Kox, H.	Sextet No. 4 (1960)	SD
Kox, H.	Sextet No. 3 (1959)	SD
Lakner, Y.	Sextet (1951)	Isr
Margola, F.	Sonatina a sei	EdB

Woodwind Quintet, Keyboard

Mendelssohn, F.	Intermezzo (Midsummer Night's Dream).	
	fl, ob, cl, hn, bsn(bcl), pf	CF
Mendelssohn, F.-Jospe	Scherzo, op. 110. *fl, ob, cl, hn, bsn(bcl), pf*	CF
Meulemans, A.	Aubade (1934)	CBD
Miller, R.	3 American Dances, op. 25.	
	fl, ob, cl, hn, bsn(bcl), pf	CF
Mozart, W.	Sextet	Cor
Mozart, W.-Pijper	Sextet, K. 608	SD
Mulder, E.	Sextet (1946)	SD
Nordgren, E.	Serenad, op. 64 (1965)	STI
Onslow, G.	Sextuor, op. 77	Heu
Osieck, H.	Divertimento (1950)	SD
Pijper, W.	Phantasie (1927)	SD
Pijper, W.	Sextet (1923)	SD
Poulenc, F.	Sextet (1932/39)	WH
Pouwels, J.	Sextet (1958)	SD
Reed, A.	Symphonic Dance	B-M
Riegger, W.	Concerto, op. 53	AMP
Roldan, A.	Ritmica No. 1	SMP
Roos, R. de	Sextuor (1935)	SD
Roussel, A.	Divertissement, op. 6	EdK
Roussel, A.	Divertissement, op. 6	EdS-
Schroeder, H.	Sextet, op. 36	SS
Schubert, F.	Rosamunde. *fl, ob, cl, hn, bsn(bcl), pf*	CF
Smit, L.	Sextuor (1933)	SD
Strategier, H.	Sextet (1951)	SD
Sugár, R.	Frammenti musicali (1958)	EMB
Tansman, A.	Dance of the Sorceress	EME
Thuille, L.	Gavotte (Sextet, op. 6).	
	fl, ob, cl, hn, bsn(bcl), pf	CF
Thuille, L.	Sextet, B♭, op. 6	BrH
Thuille, L.	Sextet, B♭, op. 6	Int
Tuthill, B.	Variations on "When Johnny Comes	
	Marching Home"	GaM
Ultan, L.	Piano Sextet	ACA
Van der Velden, R.	Sextet	EMe
Wagner, R.-Boyd	An Album Leaf. *fl, ob, cl, hn, bsn(bcl), pf*	CF
Weiss, A.	Sextette	CoF
Zagwijn, H.	Scherzo (1946)	SD
Zagwijn, H.	Suite (1912)	SD

WOODWINDS, KEYBOARD

Boccherini, L.	Menuet.	
	fl(cl), ob(cl), cl, acl(asax, cl), bcl(bsn), pf	CF
Boccherini, L.	Menuet. *5cl, pf*	CF
Denza, L.-Harris	Funiculi-Funicula.	
	fl(cl), ob(cl), cl, acl(asax, cl), bcl(bsn), pf	CF
Denza, L.-Harris	Funiculi-Funicula. *5cl, pf*	CF
Dvorak, A.-Harris	Humoreske. *5cl, pf*	CF
Dvorak, A.-Harris	Humoreske. *3cl, acl(asax), bcl(bsn), pf*	CF
Harvey, J.	Tryptich. *fl, ob, 2cl, bsn, pf*	SS
Martinu, B.	Sextet. *fl, ob, cl, 2bsn, pf*	B&N

Woodwinds, Keyboard

Pleyel, I.-Harris	Rondo. *5cl, pf*	CF
Pleyel, I.-Harris	Rondo.	
	fl(cl), ob(cl), cl, acl(asax, cl), bcl(bsn), pf	CF
Schubert, F.	Rosamunde Ballet Music. *5cl, pf*	CF
Schubert, F.	Rosamunde.	
	fl(cl), ob(cl), cl, acl(asax, cl), bcl(bsn), pf	CF
Seidel, F.	Sextet. *fl, ob, bsn, 2hn, hpcd(pf)*	M&M
Wagner, R.-Boyd	An Album Leaf. *fl, 2cl, hn, bsn, pf*	CF

WOODWINDS, BRASS

Achron, J.	Sextet. *fl, ob, cl, bsn, hn, tpt*	AMC
Albam, M.	Escapade. *trb solo, fl, ob, cl, bsn, hn*	Ken
Bereau, J.	Sextuor. *fl, ob, cl, bsn, hn, tpt*	ECh
Crosse, G.	Canto. *fl, ob, cl, bsn, hn, trb*	OxU
Gabrieli, G.-Shuman	Canzoni a 6. *cl, 2tpt, 2trb, tu*	SMP
Gerschefski, E.	"America" Variations for Winds, op. 45/2.	
	fl, ob, cl, bsn, tpt, tu	CoF
Gwinner, V.	6 niederdeutsche Volkstänze. *2cl, tpt, 2hn, trb*	MV
Patzig, G. (ed)	Milaärmärsche des 18. Jahrhunderts, Vol. 3.	
	ob, 2cl, 2bsn, tpt	B&N
Read, G.	Nine by Six. *fl/pic, ob/ehn, cl/bcl, bsn, hn, tpt*	Pet
Schwertsik, K.	Proviant. *fl, ob, cl, bsn, hn, tpt*	LDo
Stewart, R.	Divertimento. *fl, ob, cl, bsn, hn, tpt*	CoA
Sutermeister, H.	Serenade No. 2. *fl, ob, cl, bsn, hn, tpt*	SS
Zettler, R.	Allgäuer Skizzen. *cl, tpt, 2hn, bar, trb*	MV

WOODWINDS, STRINGS

Ames, W.	Sextet. *ob, 2vn, 2va, vc*	CoF
Anderson, R.	Prelude & Rondo. *fl, str quintet*	AMC
Bach, W.F.E.-Janetzky	Sextet, E♭. *cl, 2hn, vn, va, vc*	Pet
Ballif, C.	Doppeltrio, op. 35/2, 3. *fl, ob, cl, hn, vn, vc*	B&B
Berkeley, L.	Sextet. *cl, hn, 2vn, va, vc*	Che
Balorre, C.	Allegro Appassionato. *ob, cl, 2vn, va, vc*	Ham
Boccherini, L.-	Sextet, B♭. *ob, bsn, 2vn, va, vc*	FrH
Janetzky		FrH
Boccherini, L.-	Sextet, E♭, op. 42/2. *ob(fl), hn, bsn, vn, va, db*	HSM
Bormann		HSM
Boccherini, L.-Haas	Sextet, E♭, op. 42/2. *ob, bsn, hn, vn, va, vc*	Nov
Boguslawski, E.	Metamorphoses (1967). *ob, cl, 2vn, va, vc*	AP
Butting, M.	Festschrift for Bach, op. 77.	
	fl, ehn, bsn, vn, va, vc	Pet
Engel, J.	Suite I. *cl, 2vn, va, vc, db*	UE
Erlanger, G.	Sextet, op. 41. *cl, bsn, hn, vn, va, vc*	Kis
Etler, A.	Sextet (1959). *ob, cl, bsn, vn, va, vc*	AMP
Gerhardt, C.	Sextet, G. *fl, ehn, bsn, vn, va, vc*	MRL

219

Woodwinds, Strings

Flothuis, M.	Divertimento, op. 46 (1952).	
	cl, bsn, hn, vn, va, db	SD
Giuliani, V.	Divertimento. *fl, ob, cl, vn, va, vc*	Edi
Gluck, C.	Marche religieuse (Alceste). *fl, str quintet*	Dur
Goeb, R.	Declarations. *fl, ob, cl, hn, bsn, vc*	CoF
Gyring, E.	Sextet-Fantasy. *fl, cl, hn, vn, va, vc*	CoF
Handel, G.-Gevaert	Andante. *ob, str quintet*	Dur
Hartley, W.	Divertimento. *vc, fl, ob, cl, bsn, hn*	Cre
Hartley, W.	Serenade. *fl, ob, cl, bsn, hn, db*	Cre
Haydn, F.-Landon	Divertimento, C, Hob. II: 11. *fl, ob, 2vn, vc, db*	LDo
Haydn, F.-Janetzky	Sextet No. 14, E♭, Hob. II: 40.	
	ob, hn, bsn, vn, va, vc	MR
Haydn, M.-Rainer	Divertimento, G. *ob, 2hn, bsn, va, vn*	LDo
Heiller, A.	Sextet. *ob, cl, bsn, vn, va, vc*	UE
Hoddinott, A.	Sextet. *fl, cl, bsn, vn, va, vc*	OxU
Hoffmeister, F.-	Serenata, F, op. 9. *fl, vn, va, vc, 2hn*	
Höckner		Hei
Homs, J.	Sextet (1959). *fl, ob, cl, vn, va, vc*	See
Ireland, J.	Sextet. *cl, hn, 2vn, va, vc*	Gal
Kilpatrick, J.	Sextet, op. 143. *fl, hn, 2vn, va, vc*	CoF
Landré, G.	Sextet (1959). *fl, cl, 2vn, va, vc*	SD
Leeuw, T. de	5 Schetsen (1952). *ob, cl, bsn, vn, va, vc*	SD
Levy, F.	Sextet. *fl, cl, bsn, vn, va, vc*	Cor
Martinu, B.	Serenade No. 1 (1932). *cl, hn, 3vn, vc*	Art
McKay, H.	6 Minutes for Six Pieces. *fl, cl, bsn, vn, va, vc*	Wes
McKay, G.	Sonatine. *cl, 2vn, va, vc, db*	CoA
Mulder, E.	Fuga No. 3 (1940). *ob, cl, bsn, vn, va, vc*	SD
Pablo, L. de	Cesuras (1963). *fl, ob, cl, vn, va, vc*	EdT
Papineau-Couture, J.	Sextuor (1967). *ob, cl, bsn, vn, va, vc*	Can
Pisk, P.	Envoy, op. 104. *ob, cl, bsn, vn, va, vc*	CoF
Poser, H.	Kleine Spielmusik after Silesian Folksongs.	
	fl(ob), 2vn, va, vc, db	HSM
Praag, H. van	4 réflexions (1950). *fl, ob, cl, bsn, hn, vn*	SD
Quintet, M.	Ballade (1962). *vn, fl, ob, cl, hn, bsn*	CBD
Rathaus, K.	Allegro concertante. *cl, 2vn, va, vc, db*	Hei
Rosetti, F.-	Notturno, D. *fl, 2hn, vn, va, vc*	
Belsky-Racek		ES
Scarmolin, L.	Suite. *cl, hn, vn, va, vc, db*	AMC
Schaub, H.	Spielmusik. *fl, ob, cl, bsn, vn, va*	Sim
Seiber, M.	Fantasia (1945). *fl, hn, 2vn, va, vc*	ESZ
Sorge, E.	Komm, der Völker Heiland. *ob, 5str*	S-V
Sperger, J.-Malaric	Rondo. *fl, 2hn, vn, va, db*	LDo
Stearns, P.	Sextet. *fl, cl, hn, vn, va, db*	CoF
Telemann, G.	Concerto. *vn, fl, ob, cl, bsn, hn*	Cam
Wagner, R.	Adagio. *cl, 2vn, va, vc, db*	
[H. Baermann]		BrH
Wagner, R.	Adagio. *cl, 2vn, va, vc, db*	
[H. Baermann]		EdK
Wagner-Regeny, R.	Kleine Gemeinschaftsmusik.	
	ob, cl, bsn, vn, va, vc	Pet
Welin, K.	Visoka 12 (1965). *2fl, 2vn, 2vc*	STI
Whittenberg, C.	Sextet. *fl/pic, cl, bsn, vn, vc, db*	ACA

WOODWINDS, BRASS, STRINGS

Ardevol, J.	Musica de Camera. *fl, cl, bsn, tpt, vn, vc*	SMP
Bolcom, W.	Session I. *fl/pic/afl, ob/ehn, bsn, va, vc, trb*	TP
Bottje, W.	Concertino. *ehn, tpt, 2vn, va, vc*	CoF
Feldman, M.	2 Pieces. *fl, afl, hn, tpt, vn, vc*	Pet
Haieff, A.	Dance Suite. *fl, bsn, tpt, pf, vn, vc*	Be
Jacob, W.	Komposition 5/7. *fl, bcl, tpt, vn, va, db*	BrH
Kelterborn, R.	Varianti. *fl, cl/bcl, tpt, vn, va, vc*	OHN
Macero, T.	Canzona No. 1. *sax, 2vn, va, vc, tpt*	TP
Salmenhaara, E.	Elegie I, 1965. *3fl, 2tpt, db*	See
Sanner, L.	Sextett. *ob, tpt, 2vn, va, vc*	EMF

WOODWINDS, BRASS, KEYBOARD

Albinoni, T.- Wojciechowski	Concerto, C. *tpt, 3ob, bsn, bc*	HSM
Gerschefski, E.	"America" Variations for Winds, op. 44/14a. *fl, cl, asax, bsn, tpt, pf*	CoF
Vlijmen, J. van	Serie per sei strumenti (1960). *fl, ob, cl, bsn, tpt, pf*	SD

WOODWINDS, STRINGS, KEYBOARD

Achron, J.	Children's Suite, op. 57. *cl, 2vn, va, vc, pf*	UE
Bach, J.C.	Sextet, C. *ob, vn, vc, 2hn, hpcd*	MR
Copland, A.	Sextet. *cl, 2vn, va, vc, pf*	B&H
Delden, L. van	Introduzione e Danza, op. 26 (1950). *fl, cl, vn, va, vc, pf*	SD
Dijk, J. van	Pastorale (1938). *fl, 2vn, va, vc, pf*	SD
Dohnanyi, E.	Sextet, C, op. 37. *cl, hn, vn, va, vc, pf*	AlL
Eberl, A.	Sextet. *cl, hn, vn, va, vc, pf*	MR
Eder, H.	Musica semplice, op. 23/1. *fl, 2vn, va, vc, pf*	BrH
Eisler, H.	14 Arten den Regen zu beschreiben. *fl, cl, vn, va, vc, pf*	Pet
Escher, R.	Le tombeau de Ravel (1952). *fl, ob, vn, va, vc, hpcd*	SD
Falla, M. de	Concerto (1926). *hpcd(pf), fl, ob, cl, vn, vc*	EME
Fauconier, C.	Sextuor facile. *fl, 2vn, vc, db, pf*	ScF
Fesch, W. de-Ruf	Concerto, B♭, op. 3/2. *2ob(2fl), bsn, 2vn, bc*	Ric
Galuppi, B.-Schroeder	Concerto, e. *2fl, 2vn, va, bc*	Pet
Goeb, R.	Concertant IVb. *cl, pf, 2vn, va, vc*	CoF
Hambraeus, B.	Kammarmusik. *fl, ob, cl, asax, va, hpcd*	EMF
Harris, R.	Concerto, op. 2. *cl, 2vn, va, vc, pf*	AMP
Hasse, J.-Englander	Concerto, G. *fl, 2vn, va, vc, pf*	NV
Hasse, J.	Konzert, b. *fl, 2vn, va, vc, pf*	BrH
Hertel, J.	Sinfonia a 6. *2fl, 2vn, va, bc*	MV
Hier, E.	Suite for Chamber Ensemble. *fl, ob, vn, va, vc, pf*	AMC

Woodwinds, Strings, Keyboard

Ives, C.	Adagio Sostenuto. *ehn, 3vn, vc, pf*	JB
Ives, C.	Allegretto Sombreoso. *fl, ehn, 3vn, pf*	SMP
Kox, H.	Sextet (1957). *fl, ob, vn, va, vc, hpcd*	SD
Kraft, L.	Sextet. *cl, 2vn, va, vc, pf*	AMC
Lesur, D.	Sextuor. *fl, ob, vn, va, vc, pf*	Amp
Lewis, P.	Septet. *fl, cl, bsn, vn, va, pf*	AMC
Mozart, W.-Hartmann	Eine kleine Nachtmusik. *2vn, va, vc, pf, cl*	H-P
Orrego-Salas, J.	Sextet. *cl, 2vn, va, vc, pf*	SMP
Pleskow, R.	Sextet (1963). *fl, ob, cl, vn, vc, pf*	See
Ponse, L.	Sextet, op. 27 (1958). *fl, ob, vn, va, vc, hpcd*	SD
Prokofiev, S.	Overture on Hebrew Themes. *cl, 2vn, va, vc, pf*	EdK
Prokofiev, S.	Overture on Hebrew Themes, op. 34. *cl, 2vn, va, vc, pf*	Int
Prokofiev, S.	Overture on Jewish Themes. *cl, 2vn, va, vc, pf*	B&H
Roussakis, N.	Sextet. *fl, cl, vn, va, vc, pf*	CoF
Sarri, D.-Meylan	Sonata, a. *fl, 2vn, va, vc, pf*	Leu
Schiske, K.	Sextett. *cl, 2vn, va, vc, pf*	UE
Sollberger, H.	Solos for Violin and Five Instruments. *vn, fl, cl, hn, db, pf*	M&M
Stamitz, J.-Kölbel	Concerto, C. *fl, 2vn, va, vc, bc*	B&N
Stewart, R.	Hydra. *fl, ob, bsn, vn, vc, pf*	CoF
Strang, G.	Concerto for Cello. *fl, ob, cl, bsn, vc, pf*	ACA
Weber, B.	Serenade, op. 39. *fl, ob, vn, va, vc, hpcd(pf)*	ACA
Woollen, R.	Sextet. *cl, 2vn, va, vc, pf*	CoF
Zagwijn, H.	Entrata e Fuga (1950). *fl, ob, vn, va, vc, hpcd*	SD

WOODWINDS, BRASS, STRINGS, KEYBOARD

Aitken, H.	Partita. *ob, cl, tpt, va, vc, pf*	AMC
Anderberg, C.	Hexafoni. *cl, tpt, trb, vn, db, pf*	ESu
Donovan, R.	Music for Six. *ob, cl, tpt, vn, vc, pf*	Pet
Erb, D.	Hexagon (1963). *fl, asax, tpt, trb, vc, pf*	Can
Martinu, B.	La revue de cuisine. *vn, vc, cl, bsn, tpt, pf*	ALe
Weber, B.	Ballet, op. 26, The Pool of Darkness. *fl, bsn, tpt, vn, vc, pf*	CoF

SIX INSTRUMENTS INCLUDING HARP

Addison, J.	Serenade. *fl, ob, cl, bsn, hn, hp*	OxU
Ahlberg, G.	Exercitio III (1964). *fl, vn, va, vc, hp, vib*	STI
Boutry, R.	2 Pieces en Sextuor. *fl, ob, cl, bsn, hn, hp(pf)*	JB
Chou, Wen-Chung	Suite. *fl, ob, cl, bsn, hn, hp*	Pet
Christov, D.	Concerto. *fl, 2vc, hp, pf, perc*	EMo
Druckman, J.	Divertimento (1950). *cl, hn, hp, str trio*	MCA

Six Instruments including Harp

Goehr, A.	Suite, op. 11. *vn/va, vc, fl, cl, hn, hp*	S&C
Haydn, F.-Tocchi	Capriccio. *fl, cl, vn, va, vc, hp*	EDS
Holewa, H.	Concertino (1960). *cl, va, hn, pf, hp, perc*	EMF
Hovhaness, A.	The Flowering Peach (1954).	
	cl, asax, timp, perc, hp, cel	AMP
Lachenmann, H.	Introversion II (1964). *cl, tpt, db, hp, org, perc*	EdT
Lanjean, M.	Souleibrado, Petite Suite Provencale.	
	fl, ob, 2cl, vc, hp	EMT
Mason, D.	3 Pieces. *fl, 2vn, va, vc, hp*	TP
Moran, R.	4 Visions. *fl, 2vn, va, vc, hp*	TP
Moulaert, R.	Concert (1950). *fl, ob, cl, hn, bsn, hp*	CBD
Perrault, M.	Sextuor (1955). *cl, hp, 2vn, va, vc*	Can
Petric, I.	Mosaics. *cl, trb, vc, hp, 2perc*	EdD
Soler, J.	Quetzalcoatl (1966). *fl, cl, vn, vc, pf, hp*	See
Soler, J.	Sonatina (1964). *fl, cl, vn, vc, pf, hp*	See
Surinach, C.	3 Berber Songs. *fl, ob, cl, va, vc, hp*	SMP
Togni, C.	Aubade (1965). *fl, cl, vib, vc, hp, hpcd*	ESZ
Vandor, I.	Serenata (1964). *fl, bcl, hn, va, vc, hp*	ESZ
Villa-Lobos, H.	Sextuor Mystique (1917).	
	fl, ob, asax, guit, hp, cel	EME
Wolpe, S.	Sextet. *cl, tpt, vn, vc, hp, pf*	M&M
Wuorinen, C.	Chamber Concerto. *ob, tu, hp, pf, db, perc*	CoF

SIX INSTRUMENTS INCLUDING GUITAR

Gerhard, R.	Libra. *fl, cl, vn, pf, guit, perc*	AlB
Glick, S.	Divertissement (1968).	
	cl, vib, guit, mandoline, vc, db	Can
Richter, N.	Serenade (1934). *fl, ob, vn, va, vc, guit*	SD
Subotnick, M.	Serenade No. 1. *fl, cl, vc, vib, pf, mandoline*	M&M
Tomasi, H.	Recuerdos de las Baleaus. *ob, 3guit, pf, perc*	E-V
Villa-Lobos, H.	Sextuor Mystique (1917).	
	fl, ob, asax, guit, hp, cel	EME
Zelenka, I.	Fruh-Stuck. *afl, bcl, hn, trb, va, guit*	EMo

SIX INSTRUMENTS INCLUDING PERCUSSION

Ahlberg, G.	Exercitio III (1964). *fl, vn, va, vc, hp, vib*	STI
Albright, W.	Danse Macabre (1971).	
	fl, cl/bcl, vn, vc, pf, perc	Bow
Ames, W.	Henry IV, Incidental Music. *ob, 5perc*	ACA
Back, S.	Favola. *cl, 5perc*	WH
Balada, L.	Geometrias (1966). *fl, ob, cl/bcl, tpt, bsn, perc*	Gen
Barbe, H.	Miniaturen zu einem Lustpiel von	
	Shakespeare (1959).	
	cl, tpt, trb, db, perc, pf	B&N

Six Instruments including Percussion

Barkin, E.	Refrains. *fl, cl, vn, va, vc, cel*	ACA
Bentzon, N.	Sinfonia Concertante, op. 100.	
	cl, vn, va, vc, brass instr, perc	WH
Castiglioni, N.	Tropi. *fl, cl, vn, vc, pf, perc*	ESZ
Christlieb, D. (arr)	3 Pieces. *2ob, ehn, bsn, 2sdr*	CP
Christov, D.	Concerto. *fl, 2vc, hp, pf, perc*	EMo
Donovan, R.	Soundings. *tpt, bsn, 4perc*	ACA
Farberman, H.	3 States of Mind. *fl, vn, vc, tpt, pf, perc*	Gen
Fine, V.	Divertimento. *3ww, tpt, pf, perc*	AMC
Gerhard, R.	Libra. *fl, cl, vn, pf, guit, perc*	AlB
Gilbert, A.	Intoit, Gradual and 2 Chorals.	
	cl, hn, tpt, trb, vc, perc	SS
Glanville-Hicks, P.	Masque of the Wild Man. *fl, perc, 2vn, va, vc*	CoF
Glick, S.	Divertissement (1968).	
	cl, vib, guit, mandolin, vc, db	Can
Glodeanu, G.	Inventiuni (1967). *fl, ob, cl, bsn, hn, perc*	EMU
Grandis, R. de	Canti sulle pause (1961).	
	tsax, vn, trb, vib, cel, perc	EdT
Hartwell, H.	Soul-Piece (1967). *asax, tsax, tpt, db, pf, perc*	Can
Hazzard, P.	Expression. *fl, cl, 2tpt, bcl, perc*	See
Heininen, P.	Musique d'été (1963). *fl, cl, vn, vc, hpcd, perc*	MT
Hespos, H.	EN-KIN. *sop sax/tsax, tpt, vn, vc, db, perc*	EMo
Holewa, H.	Concertino (1960). *cl, va, hn, pf, hp, perc*	EMF
Homs, J.	Music for Six (1962). *fl, cl, bsn, db, pf, perc*	See
Jackson, D.	Chamber Suite. *fl, cl, 2vn, vc, perc*	CoA
Kaufmann, A.	4 Pieces, op. 77. *cl, 2vn, vc, db, perc*	LDo
Krenek, E.	The "Alpbach Quintet." *fl, ob, cl, bsn, hn, perc*	UE
Lachenmann, H.	Introversion II (1964). *cl, tpt, db, hp, org, perc*	EdT
Lu, Y.	Piece for 7 Players (1967).	
	fl, cl, hn, tpt, vc, perc	See
Mellnäs, A.	Per Caso (1963). *asax, trb, vn, db, 2perc*	EdT
Miroglio, F.	Phases. *fl, vn, va, vc, pf, perc*	UE
Moffitt	Wham Doodle. *5cl, dr*	CF
Pablo, L. de	Prosodia (1962). *fl, cl, vib, 3perc*	EdT
Parris, R.	The Book of Imaginary Beings.	
	fl/pic, vn, vc, pf, 2perc	ACA
Petric, I.	Mosaics. *cl, trb, vc, hp, 2perc*	EdD
Plain, G.	Scenario. *fl, bsn, vn, vc, pf, mar*	AMC
Pleskow, R.	Crossplay (1963). *fl, cl, vn, vc, pf, vib*	See
Raxach, E.	Estrofas (1962). *fl, bcl, vn, vc, db, perc*	EdT
Rövenstrunck, B.	Kammerkonzert. *bcl, vn, va, vc, db, perc*	EMo
Schidlowsky, L.	Concerto. *cl, bcl, tpt, xyl, timp, pf*	SMP
Schwertsik, K.	Liebe sträume, op. 7.	
	asax, trb, db, harmonica, vib, mar	EMo
Sculthorpe, P.	Tabuh Tabuhan. *fl, ob, cl, bsn, hn, perc*	Fab
Seiber, M.	Jazzolettes. *2sax, tpt, trb, dr, pf*	Che
Stout, A.	Toccata. *asax, perc (5 players)*	CoF
Subotnick, M.	Serenade No. 1. *fl, cl, vc, vib, pf, mandolin*	M&M
Thilman, J.	Epigramme. *fl, vn, va, db, pf, perc*	BrH
Tippett, M.	Prelude-Summer. *2fl, tpt, vn, dr, pf*	S&C
Tomasi, H.	Recuerdos de las Baleaus. *ob, 3guit, pf, perc*	E-V

Six Instruments including Percussion

Villa-Lobos, H.	Sextuor Mystique (1917).	
	fl, ob, asax, guit, hp, cel	EME
Welin, K.	Warum Nicht? (1964). *fl, vn, vc, vib, 2perc*	STI

SIX INSTRUMENTS INCLUDING RECORDER

Huber, K.	Concerto per la Camerata. *rec, fl, ob, vn, vc, pf*	Hei
Telemann, G.-Hechler	Concerto a 6. *rec, bsn, 2vn, va, bc*	OHN
Prowo, P.-Ochs	Concerto a 6, C. *2rec, 2ob, 2vc, pf ad lib*	HMo
Prowo, P.-Hausswald	Concerto, d. *2rec, 2ob, 2bsn*	FrH

SIX INSTRUMENTS INCLUDING TAPE

Berio, L.	Differences. *fl, cl, va, vc, hp, tape*	UE
Bottje, W.	3 Etudes. *fl, ob, cl, hn, bsn, tape*	CoF
Burge, D.	Aeolian Music (1968). *fl, cl, va, vc, pf, tape*	Bow
Leeuw, T. de	Antiphonie (1960). *fl, ob, cl, bsn, hn, tape*	SD
Schwartz, E.	Interruptions (1965). *fl, ob, cl, bsn, hn, tape*	CF
Veyvoda, G.	Into the Artifice of Eternity.	
	fl, ob, cl, bsn, hn, tape	See

SEVEN INSTRUMENTS

SEVEN WOODWINDS (including horn)

	Believe Me If All Those Endearing Young Charms. *7sax, opt pf*	GFB
	Londonderry Air. *7sax, opt pf*	GFB
	The Last Rose of Summer. *7sax, opt pf*	GFB
Bach, C.P.E.-Simon	6 Marches. *2ob, 2cl, bsn, 2hn, perc ad lib*	EBM
Bach, J.C.-Raphael	Septett. *ob, 2cl, 2bsn, 2hn*	BrH
Baines, A.	9 Easy Pieces. *4fl(2fl, 2hn), 2ob(2cl), bsn(cl)*	OxU
Bolzoni, G.-Conn	Minuetto. *fl, ob, 2cl, acl, bsn, bcl*	CF
Busch, C.	An Ozark Reverie. *fl, ob, 2cl, bsn, 2hn*	Fit
Cavally, R.	8 Madrigals. *7fl*	SM
Dalley, O.	Serenade. *2fl, ob, 2cl, 2bsn*	War
Doppelbauer, J.	Divertimento. *fl, ob, ehn, cl, bcl, bsn, hn*	LDo
Driessler, J.	Aphorismen, op. 7a (1948).	
	fl, ob, ehn, cl, bcl, hn, bsn	B&N
Dvorak, A.	Songs My Mother Taught Me. *7sax, opt pf*	GFB
Frommel, G.	Bläser-Suite, op. 18. *fl, ob, 2cl, cbsn, 2hn*	B&N
Grieg, E.	Ase's Death (Peer Gynt). *7sax, opt pf*	GFB
Indy, V. d'	Chanson et danses, op. 50. *fl, ob, 2cl, 2bsn, hn*	Dur
Kesztler-Kovacs (arr)	Baroque Music for Woodwinds.	
	2fl, ob(fl), 2cl, bsn, hn	EMB
Koechlin, C.	Septuor. *fl, ob, cl, hn, asax, ehn, bsn*	EdL
Maury	Changes. *7fl*	Wes
Nelhybel, V.	Impromptus. *2fl, pic, ob, 2cl, bsn*	Gen
Pierné, G.	Preludio and Fughetta, op. 40/1.	
	2fl, ob, cl, 2bsn, hn	Int
Pierné, G.	Preludio et Fughetta, op. 40.	
	2fl, ob, cl, 2bsn, hn	Ham
Praag, H. van	3 Schetsen (1960). *fl, 2ob, 2cl, 2bsn*	SD
Rhené-Baton	Aubade, op. 53. *fl, ob, 2cl, 2bsn, hn*	Dur
Rosetti, A.	Parthia, B♭. *2ob, 2cl, bsn, 2hn*	B&B
Rosetti, A.	Parthia, F.	
	ob solo, 2ob, ehn, bsn, 2hn, db ad lib	B&B
Rosetti, F.-Kneusslin	Parthia No. 3, D. *2ob, 2cl, 2hn, bsn*	EK
Schumann, R.-Cavally	12 Selections (Album for the Young). *7fl*	SM
Searle, H.	Divertimento, op. 54. *7cl*	Fab
Zoncada, G.	Partita for Solo Oboe. *ob, 2cl, 2hn, 2bsn*	WIN

WOODWINDS, KEYBOARD

Francaix, J.	L'heure du berger. *ww sextet, pf*	SS
Hashagen, K.	Septalie. Studies for 7 players. *2 high instr,*	
	2 middle instr, 2 low instr, pf	B&N
Lesur, D.	Sextuor. *6cl, pf*	Amp
Williamson, M.	Concerto. *fl, ob, cl, bsn, hn, 2pf*	JoW

WOODWINDS, BRASS

Brugk, H.	Divertimento, op. 29. *fl, ob, cl, tpt, 2hn, bsn*	Sim
Emmert, A.	Harmonieen. *2cl, 2hn, 2bsn, tpt*	WIN
Gabrieli, A.-Shuman	Ricercare No. 2. *cl, 3tpt, 2trb, tu*	SMP
Hindemith, P.	Septet (1948). *fl, ob, cl, bcl, bsn, hn, tpt*	SS
Loucheur, R.	Concertino. *tpt solo, E♭ cl, 2cl, acl, bcl, cbcl*	EdS
Malzat, I.	Parthia. *pic, 2cl, 2hn, bsn, tpt*	WIN
Möckl, F.	Iphigenie in Delphi. *fl, ob, cl, bsn, hn, tpt, trb*	Hei
Pablo, L. de	Coral, op. 2. *fl, ob, cl, bsn, hn, tpt, trb*	EMo
Patzig, G. (ed)	Militärmärsche des 18. Jahrhunderts, Vol. 1.	
	2ob, 2cl, 2bsn, tpt	B&N
Pierné, G.	Pastorale Variée, op. 30.	
	fl, ob, cl, 2bsn, hn, tpt	Dur
Pluister, S.	Divertimento (1937). *2fl, ob, cl, bsn, tpt, trb*	SD
Thilman, J.	Bläserseptett, B♭, op. 68.	
	fl, ob, cl, hn, tpt, trb	FrH
Verrall, J.	Septet. *fl, ob, 2cl, 2bsn, hn*	CoF

WOODWINDS, STRINGS

Baaren, K. van	Settetto (1952). *fl, ob, cl, bsn, hn, vn, db*	SD
Beethoven, L. van	Septet, E♭, op. 20. *cl, bsn, hn, vn, va, vc, db*	BrH
Beethoven, L. van	Septet, E♭, op. 20. *cl, bsn, vn, va, vc, hn, db*	Int
Beethoven, L. van	Septet, op. 20. *cl, bsn, hn, vn, va, vc, db*	Pet
Berwald, F.	Stor Septett. *cl, bsn, hn, vn, va, vc, db*	CGM
Borris, S.	Kleine Suite, op. 31/3. *fl, ob, cl, bsn, vn, va, vc*	S-V
Brunswick, M.	Septet in Seven Movements.	
	fl, ob, cl, bsn, hn, va, vc	CoF
Davies, P.	Ricercar and Doubles. *fl, ob, cl, bsn, hn, va, vc*	S&C
Gluck, C.	Gavotte (Iphigenie en Aulide). *2ob, str quintet*	Dur
Crosse, G.	Villanelles. *fl, ob, cl, bsn, hn, vn, vc*	OxU
Handel, G.-Gevaert	Fragment du 5th concerto. *2ob, str quintet*	Dur
Hartwell, H.	Septet (1969). *3cl, hn, str trio*	Can
Haydn, F.-Janetzky	Divertimento, D. *2fl, 2hn, 2vn, vc*	PrM
Haydn, F.-Landon	Notturno No. 1 C, Hob. II: 25.	
	fl, ob, 2cl, 2vn, vc	LDo
Heppener, R.	Septet (1958). *fl, cl, bsn, 2vn, va, vc*	SD
Hespos, H.	druckspuren-geschattet.	
	fl/E♭ clar, asax, bsn, 2tpt, trb, db	EMo
Kenins, T.	Septuor (1949). *cl, bsn, hn, vn, va, vc, db*	Can
Koetsier, J.	Septett, op. 4 (1932). *cl, bsn, hn, vn, va, vc, db*	SD
Komma, K.	Septet. *cl, bsn, hn, vn, va, vc, db*	I-V
Kont, P.	Septet, op. 61/3. *fl, cl, bsn, vn, va, vc, db*	LDo
Kreutzer, C.	Grand Septuor, op. 62.	
	cl, bsn, hn, vn, va, vc, db	M&M
Kreutzer, C.-Redtenbacher	Septet, op. 62. *cl, bsn, hn, vn, va, vc, db*	LDo
Kreutzer, C.	Septet, op. 62. *cl, bsn, hn, vn, va, vc, db*	MR
Lacombe, P.	Serenade. *fl, ob, hn, 2vn, va, vc*	Ham
Martinu, B.	Serenata III (1932). *2vn, vc, ob, cl*	Art

Woodwinds, Strings

Milhaud, D.	Pastorale. *fl, ehn, bsn, vn, va, vc, db*	UE
Milhaud, D.	Serenade. *fl, cl, bsn, vn, va, vc, db*	UE
Mozart, W.	Idoménée, Marche. *2ob, str quintet*	Dur
Orgad, B.	Septet. *cl, bsn, hn, vn, va, vc, db*	Hei
Organn, R.	Waimea. *cl, bsn, hn, 2vn, va, vc*	Reb
Perry, J.	Pastoral. *fl, 2vn, 2va, 2vc*	SMP
Rosetti, A.-Paeuler	Partita, F. *3ob, bsn, 2hn, db*	Pet
Rossini, G.	Serenata per Piccolo Complesso.	
	fl, ob, ehn, 2vn, va, vc	M&M
Stearns, P.	Septet. *cl, tsax, hn, vn, va, vc, db*	CoF
Stevens, H.	Septet. *cl, bsn, hn, 2va, 2vc*	CoF
Tiessen, H.	Septet, G, op. 20. *fl, cl, hn, 2vn, va, vc*	R&E
Verrall, J.	Pastoral Elegy. *2fl, 2va, 3vc*	CoF
Villa-Lobos, H.	Choros No. 7. *fl, ob, cl, asax, bsn, vn, vc*	SS
Weber, B.	Concertino, op. 45. *fl, ob, cl, 2vn, va, vc*	CoF
Winter, P. von	Septet. *fl, cl, 2hn, vn, va, vc*	MR
Yun, I.	Musik (1959). *fl, ob, cl, bsn, hn, vn, vc*	B&B

WOODWINDS, BRASS, STRINGS

Cage, J.	6 Short Inventions (1933).	
	afl, cl, trb, vn, 2va, vc	Pet
Indy, V. d'	Suite en ré. *2fl, tpt, 2vn, va, vc*	Ham
Jones, C.	Septet. *fl, cl, bsn, tpt, trb, vn, db*	AMC
Köper, K.	Musik. *fl, cl, asax, hn, tpt, trb, db*	EMo
Neukomm, S. von	Septet. *fl, ob, cl, bsn, hn, tpt, db*	M&M
Weber, B.	Concerto, op. 32. *pf solo, vc, fl, ob, cl, bsn, hn*	ACA

WOODWINDS, BRASS, KEYBOARD

Mirouze, M.	Pièce en septuor. *fl, ob, cl, bsn, hn, tpt, pf*	ALe

WOODWINDS, STRINGS, KEYBOARD

Bach, C.P.E.-Dameck	Sonatine, C. *pf, 2fl, 2vn, va, vc*	B&B
Bach, J.C.F.-	Septet, C. *ob, 2hn, vn, va, vc, pf*	
Schünemann		Kis
Bach, J.S.-Pillney	Musikalisches Opfer, BWV 1079.	
	fl, 2vn, va, 2vc, pf	BrH
Cerha, F.	Fantasien nach Cardew's Herbst 60.	
	cl, bcl, tsax, vn, va, vc, pf	EMo
Gluck, C.-Barge	Melodie (Dance of the Blessed Spirits).	
	fl, 2vn, va, vc, db, pf	CF
Halffter, C.	Antiphonismoi. *fl, ob/ehn, cl, vn, va, vc, pf*	UE

228

Woodwinds, Strings, Keyboard

Heinichen, J.-	Weihnachts-Pastorale.	
Bachmair	2ob(fl), 2vn(ob), va, vc(bsn), pf	BrH
Homs, J.	Music for 7 Instruments (1960).	
	fl, 2vn, va, vc, db, pf	See
Hummel, J.	Septet, op. 74. fl, ob, hn, va, vc, db, pf	Pet
Imbrie, A.	Dandelion Wine. ob, cl, 2vn, va, vc, pf	Sha
Janácek, L.	Concertino. cl, bsn, hn, 2vn, va, pf	Int
Janácek, L.	Concertino. pf, cl, bsn, hn, 2vn, va	Art
Karlins, M.	Concerto Grosso No. 2.	
	fl/pic, cl, bsn, vn, va, vc, pf	CoF
Lewis, P.	Septet. fl, cl, bsn, vn, va, vc, pf	TP
Marx, K.	Kammermusik, op. 56.	
	fl, ob, va da gamba, pf, vn, va, vc	B&N
Mieg, P.	Musik (1954). fl, ob, vn, va, vc, db, hpcd	B&B
Moore, T.	Rhondallet. fl, ob, cl, 2vn, vc, pf	AMC
Moscheles, I.	Septet, op. 88. cl, hn, vn, va, vc, db, pf	MR
Natra, S.	Music (1964). fl, cl, 2va, vc, db, hpcd	Isr
Pijper, W.	Septet (1920).	
	fl/pic, ob/ehn, cl, bsn, hn, db, pf	SD
Poulenc, F.	Rhapsodie Nègre.	
	fl, cl, 2vn, va, vc, pf, voice ad lib	Che
Rea, J.	Anaphora (1970). fl, cl, bsn, vn, va, vc, pf	Can
Riotte, J.	Septet. cl, bsn, hn, vn, va, vc, pf	MR
Schoenberg, A.	Suite, op. 29. E♭ cl, cl, bcl, vn, va, vc, pf	UE
Stravinsky, I.	Septet. cl, bsn, hn, vn, va, vc, pf	B&H
Telemann, G.-Hechler	Concerto, a. 2fl, 2ob, 2vn, bc	SS
Telemann, G.-Töttcher	Concerto, B♭. 3ob, 3vn, bc	HSM
Telemann, G.-Kölbel	Concerto, D. 2fl, 2vn, va, bsn, bc	Hei
Telemann, G.-Kehr	Ouverture à 7, C. 3ob, 2vn, va, bc	SS
Vostrak, Z.	Afekty. fl, cl, bsn, vn, va, vc, pf	Art
Weber, B.	Concerto, op. 32. pf solo, vc, fl, ob, cl, bsn, hn	ACA
Wuorinen, C.	Tiento Sobre Cabezon.	
	fl, ob, vn, va, vc, hpcd, pf	CoF
Zender, H.	Kammerkonzert. fl, 2vn, va, vc, hp, hpcd	SS

WOODWINDS, BRASS, STRINGS, KEYBOARD

Betts, L.	Music for Theatre (1950).	
	ob, 2cl, hn, tpt, db, pf	Can
Hummel, J.	Military Septet, op. 114.	
	fl, cl, tpt, vn, vc, db, pf	MR
Hummel, J.	Septett militaire, op. 114.	
	fl, cl, tpt, vn, vc, db, pf	MRL
Martinu, B.	Rondi (1930). ob, cl, bsn, tpt, 2vn, pf	Art
Maselli, G.	Divertimento (1964).	
	fl, ob, tpt, trb, vn, db, hpcd	ESZ
Szathmary, Z.	Alpha. fl, cl, tpt, pf, vn, va, vc	HMo

SEVEN INSTRUMENTS INCLUDING HARP

Beecroft, N.	Ragas (1968). *fl, vn, va, vc, perc, hp, pf*	Can
Druckman, J.	Divertimento (1950). *cl, hn, hp, str trio*	MCA
Feldman, M.	The Straits of Magellan.	
	fl, hn, tpt, guit, hp, pf, db	Pet
Frid, G.	Nocturnes, op. 24 (1925). *fl, str quintet, hp*	SD
Genzmer, H.	Septet. *fl, cl, hn, vn, va, vc, hp*	SS
Hoddinott, A.	Variations. *fl, cl, hp, 2vn, va, vc*	OxU
Krol, B.	Harfen-Septett, op. 7.	PrM
	cl, bsn, hn, hp, vn, va, vc	
Mengelberg, K.	Ballade. *fl, cl, 2vn, va, vc, hp*	SD
Petric, I.	Croquis sonores.	
	hp solo, ob, bcl, hn, pf, db, perc	EdD
Petric, I.	7 Compositions. *ob, cl, hn, tpt, vn, vc, hp*	EdD
Pleskow, R.	Music for Seven Players (1965).	
	fl, cl, vn, vc, pf, perc, hp	See
Ravel, M.	Introduction and Allegro. *fl, cl, hp, 2vn, va, vc*	EdK
Read, G.	Sonoric Fantasia (1968). *5fl, hp, perc*	See
Suter, R.	Serenata. *fl, ob d'amore, bcl, hp, vn, va, vc*	Hei
Weber, B.	Chamber Fantasie, op. 51. *vn, 2cl, 3vc, hp*	CoF
Zagwijn, H.	Nocturne. *fl, ehn, cl, bsn, hn, hp, cel*	Pet
Zender, H.	Kammerkonzert. *fl, 2vn, va, vc, hp, hpcd*	SS

SEVEN INSTRUMENTS INCLUDING GUITAR

Cervetti, S.	6 Sequences for Dance.	
	fl, hn, vc, guit, cel, pf, perc	HMo
Feldman, M.	The Straits of Magellan.	
	fl, hn, tpt, guit, hp, pf, db	Pet
Schönberg, A.	Serenade, op. 24. *cl, bcl, mandolin,*	
	guit, vn, va, vc, voice ad lib	Che
Tanenbaum, E.	Consort. *fl, asax, hn, vc, db, guit, vib*	ACA

SEVEN INSTRUMENTS INCLUDING PERCUSSION

Ahlberg, G.	Aforismer (1965). *fl, afl, E♭ cl, cl, bcl, pf, perc*	STI
Amram, D.	Summernight's Dream.	
	ob, bsn, vn, vc, tpt, hpcd, perc	Pet
Avidom M.	Enigma (1962). *fl, ob, cl, bsn, hn, pf, perc*	Isr
Barati, G.	Hawaiian Forests. *fl, cl, hn, vn, va, vc, perc*	ACA
Beecroft, N.	Ragas (1968). *fl, vn, va, vc, perc, hp, pf*	Can
Berry, W.	Divertimento. *fl, ob, cl, bsn, hn, pf, perc*	E-V
Braun, R.	Bassoon Bug. *fl, ob, cl, 2bsn, hn, perc*	YM
Carmichael, H.-	Star Dust. *pic, 2fl, ob(fl), 2cl, bells*	
Klickman		B-M
Cervetti, S.	6 Sequences for Dance.	
	fl, hn, vc, cel, pf, perc, guit	HMo

Seven Instruments including Percussion

Chiaramello, G.	Concerto da Camera (1962).	
	fl, cl, bsn, vn, va, db, perc	ESZ
Chou, Wen-Chung	Yü Ko. *afl, ehn, bcl, vn, 2trb, perc*	Pet
Davies, P.	Antechrist. *pic, bcl, vn, vc, 3perc*	JB
Delp, R.	Dreams. *fl, cl, db, 4perc*	See
Dodge, C.	Folia. *pic, ehn, cl, tu, timp, vn, va*	CoF
Donatoni, F.	For Grilly (1960). *fl, cl, bcl, vn, va, vc, perc*	ESZ
Donovan, R.	Fantasia for Solo Bassoon.	
	bsn, timp, cel, vn, va, vc, db	CoF
Drew, J.	Polifonica II. *fl, ob, cl, va, vc, pf, perc*	CoF
Gerschefski, E.	"America" Variations for Winds, op. 45/10.	
	fl, ob, cl, bsn, tpt, trb, perc	CoF
Hambraeus, B.	Giuoco del Cambio.	
	fl, ehn, bcl, vib, hpcd, pf, perc	Nor
Hedwall, L.	Metamorfosi. *fl, cl, ehn, vn, vc, xyl, perc*	EMF
Heider, W.	Passatempo. *cl, bsn, tpt, trb, vn, vc, perc*	Pet
Helfritz, H.	Tanzsuite. *2fl, 3vn, vc, perc*	Pel
Hellermann, W.	Formata. *fl, cl, trb, pf, vib, 2perc*	ACA
Hespos, H.	passagen. *cl, asax, tpt, trb, va, db, perc*	EMo
Homs, J.	Heptandre (1969). *fl, ob, cl, vn, vc, pf, perc*	See
Homs, J.	Music for Seven (1966).	
	fl, ob, cl, bsn, vn, pf, perc	See
Kayn, R.	Kammerkonzert. *fl, ob, cl, hn, bsn, trb, perc*	HSM
Kersters, W.	Septet, op. 37 (1966). *4cl, perc, timp, pf*	CBD
Layton, B.	Divertimento, op. 6.	
	cl, bsn, vn, vc, trb, hpcd, perc	Sch
Linde, H.	Capriccio (1963). *3fl, vn, va, vc, dr*	AMP
Lu, Y.	Piece for Seven. *fl, cl, hn, tpt, vc, 2perc*	See
Ludwig, J.	Stenogramme. *fl, tsax, trb, db, perc, vib, hpcd*	EMo
Mamlok, U.	For Seven. *cl, bcl, tpt, vn, vc, db, perc*	CoF
Manzoni, G.	Musica Notturna (1966).	
	fl, 2cl, bsn, hn, pf, perc	ESZ
Marcelli, N.	Music Box Minuet. *pic, 2fl, ob(fl), 2cl, bells*	B-M
Martin, V.	Chamber Symphony.	
	fl, ob, cl, trb, db, pf, timp	AMC
Moss, L.	Exchanges (1968). *2fl, ob, 2tpt, trb, perc*	Fer
Motte, D. de la	Septet (1965). *cl, bsn, tpt, trb, vn, db, perc*	B&N
Mourant, W.	Ecstasy. *cl, 2vn, va, vc, pf, cel*	CoF
Mozart, W.-Kahn	Divertimento No. 5. *2cl, 3tpt, trb, timp*	EBM
Mozart, W.-Kahn	Divertimento No. 6. *2cl, 3tpt, trb, timp*	EBM
Nessler, R.	Motionen. *cl, bsn, tpt, vn, vc, pf, perc*	EMo
Nono, L.	Polifonica-Monodia-Ritmica.	
	fl, cl, bcl, asax, hn, pf, perc	S&C
Ohana, M.	Signes. *fl, pf, cithare, 4perc*	Amp
Parris, R.	Dirge for the New Sunrise.	
	fl, vn, vc, timp, 3perc	ACA
Pennisi, F.	Choralis cum Figuris (1968).	
	fl, ob, cl, bsn, vn, db, perc	ESZ
Persson, B.	Om Sommaren Skona II (1965).	
	fl, cl, trb, vc, vib, perc, tape	STI
Petric, I.	Croquis sonores.	
	hp solo, ob, bcl, hn, pf, db, perc	EdD

Seven Instruments including Percussion

Pleskow, R.	Music for 7 Players (1965).	
	fl, cl, vn, vc, pf, hp, perc	See
Razzi, F.	4 Invenzioni (1961). *fl, cl, trb, vn, va, vc, vib*	ESZ
Read, G.	Sonoric Fantasia (1968). *5fl, hp, perc*	See
Schat, P.	Septet. *fl, ob, bcl, hn, vc, pf, perc*	SD
Sculthorpe, P.	Tabuh Tabuhan (1968).	
	fl, ob, cl, bsn, hn, 2perc	Fab
Somer, A.	Concertino. *fl, cl, bsn,. va, vc, pf, perc*	AMC
Sternfeld, R.	To a Far Away Place. *fl, ob, cl, trb, 3perc*	See
Stout, Al	4 Antiphonies. *fl, trb, asax, org, perc, vn, va*	CoF
Stravinsky, I.	The History of A Soldier.	
	cl, bsn, tpt, trb, vn, db, perc	WH
Sydeman, W.	Homage to L'Histoire du Soldat (1962).	
	cl, bsn, vn, db, tpt, trb, perc	See
Takahasi, Y.	Chromamorphe I. *fl, vn, db, hn, tpt, trb, vib*	Pet
Tanenbaum, E.	Consort. *fl, asax, hn, vc, db, guit, vib*	ACA
Tippett, M.	Prelude-Autumn. *ob, 2vn, va, vc, perc, pf*	S&C
Toch, E.	Canzonetta, Caprice, Night Song.	
	fl, ob, cl, bsn, 2hn, dr	B-M
Toch, E.	Cavalcade. *fl, ob, cl, bsn, 2hn, dr*	B-M
Toch, E.	Roundelay. *fl, ob, cl, bsn, 2hn, dr*	B-M
Wolpe, S.	Piece for Two Instrumental Units.	
	fl, ob, vn, vc, db, pf, perc	M&M

SEVEN INSTRUMENTS INCLUDING TAPE

Persson, B.	Om Sommaren Skona II (1965).	
	fl, cl, trb, vc, vib, perc, tape	STI
Subotnik, M.	Play! *fl, ob, cl, bsn, hn, pf, tape*	AMC
Ward-Steinman, D.	Putney Three. *fl, ob, cl, bsn, hn, pf, tape*	EBM

EIGHT INSTRUMENTS

EIGHT WOODWINDS (including horn)

Composer	Title / Instrumentation	Publisher
Alpaerts, F.	Avondmusiek. *2fl, 2ob, 2cl, 2bsn*	EMe
Alpaerts, F.	Musique du Soir. *2fl, 2ob, 2cl, 2bsn*	EMe
Alpaerts, F.	Serenade. *2fl, 2ob, 2cl, 2bsn*	HeE
Andriessen, J.	Octuor (1948). *fl, 2ob, 2cl, bcl, 2bsn*	SD
Anonymous	Variations for Clarinet. *2ob, 2cl, 2hn, 2bsn*	WIN
Bach, W.F.	Parthie, E♭. *2ob, 2cl, 2hn, 2bsn*	WIN
Beethoven, L. van	Octet, E♭, op. 103. *2ob, 2cl, 2bsn, 2hn*	BB
Beethoven, L. van	Oktett, E♭, op. 103. *2ob, 2cl, 2bsn, 2hn*	BrH
Beethoven, L. van	Octet, op. 103. *2ob, 2cl, 2bsn, 2hn*	EdK
Beethoven, L. van	Octet, op. 103. *2ob, 2cl, 2bsn, 2hn*	MR
Beethoven, L. van	Rondino, E♭. *2ob(fl, ob), 2cl, 2bsn (bsn, bcl), 2hn*	TP
Beethoven, L. van	Rondino, E♭. *2ob, 2cl, 2bsn, 2hn*	BrH
Beethoven, L. van	Rondino, E♭. *2ob, 2cl, 2bsn, 2hn*	Int
Beethoven, L. van-May	Rondino. *2ob, 2cl, 2bsn, 2hn*	SS
Berger, A.	Canzon Octavi Modi. *4ob, 2ehn, 2bsn*	CP
Bialas, G.	Romanza e Danza. Oktett (J. Meyerbeer). *2ob, 2cl, 2hn, 2bsn*	B&N
Bradley, W.	Honeysuckle & Clover. *8ww*	AMC
Bradley, W.	The Deep Quarry. *8cl*	TP
Druschetzky, G.	French Zapfenstreich, March for the French Division of General Gudon. *2ob, 2cl, 2hn, 2bsn*	WIN
Druschetzky, G.	Motet. *2ob, 2cl, 2hn, 2bsn*	WIN
Druschetzky, G.- Weinmann	Partitas I-VI. *2ob, 2cl, 2bsn, 2hn* Published separately	
Druschetzky, G.	Variations on a March Theme by Count Szecheny. *2ob, 2cl, 2hn, 2bsn*	LDo WIN
Dubois, T.	2nd Suite. *2fl, ob, 2cl, 2bsn, hn*	ALe
Durand, P.	Let Us Take a Walk in the Woods. *2fl, 2ob, 2cl, bcl, bsn*	B-M
Ek, G.	Oktett (1970). *2fl, 2ob, 2cl, 2bsn*	STI
Erdmann, H.	Raumkomposition. *8fl*	JB
Fauré, G.	Nocturne. *fl, 2ob, 2cl, 2hn, bsn*	Ham
Fischer, J.	"Il Couraggio." *ob, ehn, 2cl, 2hn, 2bsn*	WIN
Gabrieli, A.-Ephross	Sonata Pian 'e Forte. *8fl*	TP
Garlick, A.	Piece. *8cl*	See
Handel, G.-Hindsley	Sarabanda. *8fl*	SM
Haydn, F.-Kahn	Allegro (Octet). *2ob, 2cl, 2bsn, 2hn*	EBM
Haydn, F.-Boudreau	Divertimento No. 1. *2ob, 2hn, 3bsn, cbsn(db)*	Pet
Haydn, F.-Geiringer	Divertimento, E♭. *2ob, 2cl, 2bsn, 2hn*	UE
Haydn, F.-May	Feldpartie. *2ob, 2cl, 2bsn, 2hn*	SS
Haydn, F.-Wollheim	Musik, F. *2fl(2ob), 2cl, 2bsn, 2hn*	B&B
Haydn, F.	Octet, F. *2ob, 2cl, 2bsn, 2hn*	Int
Henneberg, R.	Serenad. *fl, ob, 2cl, 2bsn, 2hn*	STI
Hoffmeister, F.	Serenade, E♭. *2ob(2fl), 2cl, 2bsn, 2hn*	EK
Horvath, J.	"Redundanz 1." *2ob, 2cl, 2hn, 2bsn*	LDo
Hummel, J.	Octet-Partita, E♭. *2ob, 2cl, 2hn, 2bsn, cbsn ad lib*	MR

233

Eight Woodwinds

Hummel, J.	Parthia, E♭. *2ob, 2cl, 2hn, 2bsn*	WIN
Jacob, G.	Divertimento, E♭. *2ob, 2cl, 2bsn, 2hn*	MR
Kreith, K.	Partita, C. *2ob, 2cl, 2hn, 2bsn*	WIN
Kramar-Krommer, F.	Octet, op. 79. *2ob, 2cl, 2bsn, 2hn*	MR
Krommer, F.	Octet-Partita, op. 57.	
	2ob, 2cl, 2hn, 2bsn, cbsn ad lib	MR
Krommer, F.	Octet-Partita, op. 69.	
	2ob, 2cl, 2hn, 2bsn, cbsn ad lib	MR
Krommer, F.	Octet-Partita, op. 67.	
	2ob, 2cl, 2hn, 2bsn, cbsn ad lib	MR
Krommer, F.	Partita, E♭. *2ob, 2cl, 2hn, 2bsn*	WIN
Lachner, F.	Octet, op. 156. *fl, ob, 2cl, 2hn, 2bsn*	MR
Laderman, E.	Octet in One Movement. *2ob, 2cl, 2hn, 2bsn*	OxU
Mills, C.	Concerto Sereno. *ww octet*	CoF
Mourant, W.	Evening Song. *8cl*	CoF
Mozart, W.-Giegling	Die Entfuhrung aus dem Serail.	
	2ob, 2ehn, 2bsn, 2hn	B&N
Mozart, W. (?)	Divertimento, E♭. *2ob, 2cl, 2hn, 2bsn*	WIN
Mozart, W.	Divertimento, E♭, K. 196E. *2ob, 2cl, 2hn, 2bsn*	MR
Mozart, W.	Divertimento, D. 166. *2ob, 2ehn, 2cl, 2bsn*	BrH
Mozart, W.-Einstein	Divertimento, E♭, K.V. 182.	
	2ob, 2cl, 2bsn, 2hn	Pet
Mozart, W.-Einstein	Divertimento, E♭, K.V. 227.	
	2ob, 2cl, 2bsn, 2hn	Pet
Mozart, W.-Einstein	Divertimento, E♭, K.V. 226.	
	2ob, 2cl, 2bsn, 2hn	Pet
Mozart, W.	Octet, K. 196e. *2ob, 2cl, 2bsn, 2hn*	M&M
Mozart, W.	Partita, F. *2ob, 2cl, 2hn, 2bsn*	WIN
Mozart, W.	Partita IV, K. 361. *2ob, 2cl, 2hn, 2bsn*	WIN
Mozart, W.	Partita III, E♭. *2ob, 2cl, 2hn, 2bsn*	WIN
Mozart, W.	Partita II, K. 361. *2ob, 2cl, 2hn, 2bsn*	WIN
Mozart, W.	Serenade, B♭, K.V. 196f. *2ob, 2cl, 2bsn, 2hn*	SS
Mozart, W.	Serenade, c, K. 388. *2ob, 2cl, 2bsn, 2hn*	BrH
Mozart, W.	Serenade, E♭, K. 375. *2ob, 2cl, 2bsn, 2hn*	BrH
Mozart, W.	Serenade, K. 182. *2ob, 2cl, 2bsn, 2hn*	M&M
Mozart, W.	Serenade No. 11, E♭, K. 375.	
	2ob, 2cl, 2bsn, 2hn	BB
Mozart, W.	Serenade No. 11, E♭, K. 375. *2ob, 2cl, 2hn, 2bsn*	MR
Mozart, W.	Serenade No. 12, c, K. 388. *2ob, 2cl, 2bsn, 2hn*	BB
Mozart, W.	Serenade No. 12, K. 388. *2ob, 2cl, 2hn, 2bsn*	MR
Mozart, W.-de Went	12 Stücke (Don Giovanni).*2ob, 2ehn, 2hn, 2bsn*	B&N
Myslivecek, J.-Racek-Schoenbaum	3 Octets. *2ob, 2cl, 2hn, 2bsn*	
		ES
Naibauer (Neubauer?)	Partita, G. *2ob, 2cl, 2hn, 2bsn*	WIN
Nilsson, B.	"Frequenzen."	
	fl, pic, ob, ehn, cl, bcl, tsax, bsn	UE
Nilsson, B.	"Zeiten im Umlauf."	
	pic, fl, ob, ehn, cl, bcl, tsax, bsn	UE
Novacek, R.	Sinfonietta, op. 48. *fl, ob, 2cl, 2bsn, 2hn*	M&M
Salieri, A.	Serenade No. 4. *2ob, 2cl, 2hn, 2bsn*	
Schneider, G.-	Harmonie-Musik, F. *2fl, 2cl, 2bsn, 2hn*	
Petyrek, F.	Divertimento. *2fl, ob, cl, 2bsn, 2hn*	UE

Eight Woodwinds

Poot, M.	Mosaique. *2fl, 2ob, 2cl, 2bsn*	UE
Rautavaara, E.	Wind Octet (1964). *8ww*	MT
Rychlik, J.	Serenade (Erinnerungen). *2ob, 2cl, 2bsn, 2hn*	CHF
Saint-Saens, C.-	Feuillet d'album, op. 81.	
Taffanel	*fl, ob, 2cl, 2bsn, 2hn*	Dur
Salieri, A.	Music for a Temple of the Night.	
	2ob, 2cl, 2hn, 2bsn	WIN
Salieri, A.	Serenades 1-3. *2fl, 2ob, 2hn, 2bsn*	
	Published separately	WIN
Salieri, A.	Serenade No. 4. *2ob, 2cl, 2hn, 2bsn*	
Schneider, G.-	Harmonie-Musik, F. *2fl, 2cl, 2bsn, 2hn*	
Wollheim		B&B
Schubert, F.-Kahn	Minuet. *2ob, 2cl, 2bsn, 2hn*	EBM
Schubert, F.	Menuet and Finale. *2ob, 2cl, 2bsn, 2hn*	M&M
Schubert, F.	Menuett und Finale (Octet, F).	
	2ob, 2cl, 2bsn, 2hn	BrH
Schubert, F.-Landon	7 Menuette, vol. 2(4-6). *fl, ob, 2cl, 2hn, 2bsn*	B&N
Starzer, J.	Le Matin et Soir. *2ob, 2cl, 2hn, 2bsn*	WIN
Stearns, P.	Octet. *pic, fl, ob, ehn, cl, bcl, bsn, cbsn*	CoF
Stieber, H.	Spielmusik (Octet) No. 3. *fl, 2ob, 2cl, hn, 2bsn*	FrH
Tansman, A.	4 Impressions. *2ob, 2cl, 2bsn, 2hn*	MCA
Triebensee, J.	Variations on a Theme from	
	"Der Champagner." *2ob, 2cl, 2hn, 2bsn*	WIN
Triebensee, J.	Variations on a Theme Haydn.	
	2ob, 2cl, 2hn, 2bsn	WIN
Triebensee, J.	Variations on a Theme of Mozart.	
	2ob, 2cl, 2hn, 2bsn	WIN
Triebensee, J.	Variations on an Andante Theme.	
	2ob, 2cl, 2hn, 2bsn	WIN
Triebensee, J.	Variations on an Original March.	
	2ob, 2cl, 2hn, 2bsn	WIN
Triebensee, J.	Variations on an Original Zapfenstreich.	
	2ob, 2cl, 2hn, 2bsn	WIN
Triebensee, J.	Variations on "O Du Lieber Augustin."	
	2ob, 2cl, 2hn, 2bsn	WIN
Uhl, A.	Eine vergnügliche Musik (Octet).	
	2ob, 2cl, 2bsn, 2hn	UE
Wagenseil, G.	Divertimento No. 1, F. *2ob, 2ehn, 2hn, 2bsn*	WIN
Wagenseil, G.	Divertimento, F, No. 2. *2ob, 2ehn, 2hn, 2bsn*	WIN
Wagenseil, G.	Partita, C. *2ob, 2ehn, 2hn, 2bsn*	WIN
Wendt, J.	Parthia, E♭. *2ob, 2cl, 2hn, 2bsn*	WIN
Winter, P. von	Partita. *2ob, 2cl, 2hn, 2bsn*	WIN

WOODWINDS, KEYBOARD

Tchaikovsky, P.	Scherzo (Symphony No. 1).	
	fl, 2ob, 2cl, 2bsn, pf	MR

WOODWINDS, BRASS

Angerer, P.	Quinta Tolen. *fl, ob, cl, bsn, hn, 2tpt, trb*	UE
Borris, S.	Bläser-Oktett, op. 55.	
	fl, ob, cl, bcl, bsn, 2hn, tpt	S-V
Brusselmans, M.	Prelude et Fugue. *fl, 2ob, 2cl, bsn, hn, tpt*	EdS
Fellegara, V.	Ottetto (1953). *fl, ob, cl, bsn, hn, 2tpt, trb*	ESZ
Gabrieli, G.-Shuman	Canzon Septimi Toni. *cl, 3tpt, 3trb, tu*	SMP
Haydn, F.-Landon	Märsche. *2cl, 2bsn, 2hn, tpt, tu*	LDo
Hermans, N.	Bagatellen (1964). *2fl, 2ob, 2cl, bsn, tpt*	SD
Homs, J.	Octet de Vent (1968).	
	fl, ob, cl, bcl, hn, tpt, trb, tu	See
Lazarof, H.	Oktett. *fl, ob, cl, bcl, bsn, hn, tpt, trb*	B&B
Lessard, J.	Octet. *fl, cl, bsn, 2hn, 2tpt, trb*	Gen
Pascal, C.	Octuor. *2fl, ob, cl, 2bsn, hn, tpt*	Dur
Pentland, B.	Octet for Winds (1948).	
	fl, ob, cl, bsn, tpt, 2hn, trb	Can
Rathburn, E.	Miniature (1949). *pic, ob, cl, bsn, 2tpt, hn, trb*	Can
Sallinen, A.	Serenade (1963). *ww quartet, br quartet*	MT
Stravinsky, I.	Octet. *fl, cl, 2tpt, 2trb, 2bsn*	B&H
Varèse, E.	Octandre. *fl, ob, cl, bsn, hn, tpt, trb, db*	Ric

WOODWINDS, STRINGS

Altmann, E.	Tanz-Suite. *fl, ob, 2cl, bsn, 2hn, db*	FrH
Arbatsky, Y.	Sinfonia Sacra Uticana. *ob, cl, bsn, 3vn, 2db*	M&M
Badings, H.	Octet (1952). *cl, bsn, hn, 2vn, va, vc, db*	SD
Bartolini, et al	3 Canzonas. *4ww, 4str*	Pet
Blacher, B.	Octet (1965). *cl, bsn, hn, 2vn, va, vc, db*	B&B
Boccherini, L.	Symphonie Concertante, op. 41.	
	ob(fl), bsn, hn, 2vn, va, 2vc	Int
Borris, S.	Oktett, op. 99/4. *cl, bsn, hn, 2vn, va, vc, db*	S-V
Eder, H.	Ottetto breve, op. 33. *fl, ob, cl, bsn, 2vn, va, vc*	LDo
Ferguson, H.	Octet. *cl, bsn, hn, str*	Boo
Frescobaldi-Guami-	2 Canzonas. *4ww, 4str*	
Moenkemeyer		Pet
Fricker, P.	Octet, op. 30. *fl, cl, bsn, hn, vn, va, vc, db*	S&C
Gabrieli, G.	Canzona No. 2 (1597). *4winds, 4str*	Pet
Gabrieli, G.	Sonata No. 13 (1615). *4winds, 4str*	Pet
Ganick, P.	Octet. *4cl, 2vn, va, vc*	See
Grainger, P.	My Robin is to the Greenwood Gone.	
	fl, ehn, vn, 2va, 2vc, db	S&C
Grillo, G.	Canzona No. 1. *4winds, 4str*	Pet
Grillo, G.-Winter	Canzone No. 2. *4winds, 4str*	Pet
Gussago	La Porcellaga (Sonata). *4winds, 4str*	Pet
Haydn, F.-Janetzky	Divertimento, F. *2ehn, 2bsn, 2vn, 2hn*	FrH
Henze, H.	4 fantasie (Adagio; Kammermusik).	
	cl, bsn, hn, str quintet	SS
Hindemith, P.	Octet (1957/58). *cl, bsn, hn, vn, 2va, vc, db*	SS
Josephs, W.	Octet, op. 43. *cl, hn, bsn, 2vn, va, vc, db*	Cha
Joubert, J.	Octet, op. 33. *cl, bsn, hn, 2vn, va, vc, db*	Nov
Kelterborn, R.	Oktett (1969). *cl, bsn, hn, 2vn, va, vc, db*	B&B
Krommer, F.	Concertante, op. 18. *fl, ob, 2hn, vn, 2va, db*	FrH

Woodwinds, Strings

Lappi, P.-Winter	La Negrona. *4winds, 4str*	Pet
Macudzinski, R.	Meditation and Dance, op. 40a.	
	vn solo, fl, ob, cl, bsn, hn, vc, db	SHF
Massaino, T.-Winter	Canzone. *4winds, 4str*	Pet
Maurer, L.	Variationen über ein russisches Thema,	
	op. 38. *fl, 2cl, 2bsn, 2hn, db*	FrH
Poot, M.	Octuor (1948). *cl, bsn, hn, str quintet*	CBD
Reicha, A.-Janetzky	Octet, op. 96. *ob, cl, bsn, hn, 2vn, va, vc*	MR
Schollum, R.	Octet, op. 63. *fl, ob, cl, bsn, vn, va, vc, db*	LDo
Schubert, F.	Oktett, F, op. 166. *cl, bsn, hn, 2vn, va, vc, db*	BrH
Schubert, F.	Octet, F, op. 166. *cl, bsn, hn, 2vn, va, vc, db*	Int
Schubert, F.	Octet, F, op. 166. *cl, bsn, hn, 2vn, va, vc, db*	Pet
Schubert, F.	Octet, op. 166. *ob, cl, bsn, hn, 2vn, va, vc*	Ric
Schwartz, P.	Wiener Barock. *cl, bsn, hn, str quintet*	CoF
Simons, N.	Time Groups No. 2. *cl, bsn, hn, 2vn, va, vc, db*	CoF
Skalkottas, N.	Octet. *fl, ob, cl, bsn, 2vn, va, vc*	UE
Spohr, L.-Uhlendorff	Octet, E, op. 32. *cl, 2hn, vn, 2va, vc, db*	B&N
Spohr, L.	Octet, E, op. 32. *cl, 2hn, vn, 2va, vc, db*	M&M
Spohr, L.	Octet, E, op. 32. *cl, 2hn, vn, 2va, vc, db*	MR
Spohr, L.	Octet, E, op. 32. *cl, 2hn, vn, 2va, vc, db*	MRL
Sydeman, W.	Divertimento (1957). *fl, cl, bsn, str quintet*	See
Sydeman, W.	7 Movements (1958).	
	ob, cl, bcl, bsn, 2vn, va, db	See
Taeggio, G.-Winter	La Porta. *4winds, 4str*	Pet
Thärichen, W.	Octet, op. 40. *cl, bsn, hn, 2vn, va, vc, db*	B&B
Vogel, E.	Octet (1970). *cl, bsn, hn, 2vn, va, vc, db*	LDo
Wellesz, E.	Octet, op. 67. *cl, bsn, hn, 5str*	LDo
Xenakis, I.	Anaktoria. *cl, bsn, hn, 2vn, va, vc, db*	EdS

WOODWINDS, BRASS, STRINGS

Indy, V. d'	Suite in Olden Style, op. 24.	
	2fl, bsn, tpt, 2vn, va, vc	Int

WOODWINDS, BRASS, KEYBOARD

Boehmer, K.	Zeitläufte (1962). *ehn, cl, bcl, bsn, 2pf, 2brass*	EdT

WOODWINDS, STRINGS, KEYBOARD

Balakirev, M.	Octet, op. 3. *fl, ob, hn, vn, va, vc, db, pf*	MR
Ciortea, T.	Din "Ispravile lui Pacala."	
	fl, ob/ehn, cl, bsn, hn, va, vc, pf	EMU
Dupont, J.	Octuor. *cl, bsn, hn, 2vn, va, vc, pf*	Ham
Eichner, E.	Concerto. *fl, 2hn, 2vn, va, db, pf*	FrH
Juon, P.	Octet, op. 27a. *ob, cl, bsn, hn, vn, va, vc, pf*	MRL
Louis Ferdinand	Octet, op. 10. *cl, 2hn, 2va, 2vc, pf*	MR
Metzler	Es ist ein Ros entsprungen.	
	2fl, 2vn, va, vc, db, org	Pet
Ries, F.	Octet, op. 128. *cl, bsn, hn, vn, va, vc, db, pf*	MR
Tippett, M.	Prelude - Spring. *2fl, cl, 2vn, va, vc, pf*	S&C

WOODWINDS, BRASS, STRINGS, KEYBOARD

Haieff, A.	Dance Suite. *fl, bsn, tpt, 2vn, 2vc, pf*	Be
Macero, T.	One-Three Quarters. *pic, fl, vn, vc, trb, tu, 2pf*	Pet
Viola, A.-Kastner	Concerto, F. *bsn, 2ob, 2tpt, 2vn, bc*	Hei
Wuorinen, C.	Octet. *ob, cl, hn, trb, vn, vc, db, pf*	M&M

EIGHT INSTRUMENTS INCLUDING HARP

Burkhard, W.	Serenade, op. 77.	
	fl, cl, bsn, hn, vn, va, db, hp	B&H
Delas, J. de	Eilanden. *cl, guit, 2vn, va, hp, pf, perc*	HG
Eichenwald, P.	Aspekte. *fl, bcl, vn, vc, hp, pf, 2perc*	EMo
Grandis, R. de	Instrumentalmusik ("Il Cieco di Hyuga").	
	fl, db, hp, cel, hpcd, 3perc	EdT
Koellreuter, H.	Constructio ad Synesin (1962).	
	pic, ehn, bcl, cbsn, vn, hp, pf, perc	EMo
Law, A.	Bouquet Chablis. *hp solo, 2fl, ob, 2cl, bcl, bsn*	ATL
Michaelides, S.	Suite Archaiique (1955).	
	fl, ob, hp, str quintet	See
Sibelius, J.-Stravinsky	Canzonetta, op. 62a. *cl, bcl, 4hn, hp, db*	BrH
Weber, B.	Chamber Fantasie, op. 51.	
	solo vn, 2cl, bcl, hp, 2vc, db	ACA

EIGHT INSTRUMENTS INCLUDING GUITAR

Andriessen, J.	Ars Antiqua Musicae.	
	fl, ob, 2hn, tpt, guit, perc, va	SD
Avshalomov, J.	Cues from the Little Clay Cart.	
	fl/pic, cl, va, vc, guit, 3perc	ACA
Delas, J. de	Eilanden. *cl, guit, 2vn, va, hp, pf, perc*	HG
Gerhard, R.	Concert for 8. *fl, cl, guit, perc, db, pf,*	
	mandolin, accordion	OxU
Grandert, J.	Kammarmusik (1961).	
	fl, cl, 2vn, va, vc, guit, perc	STI
Karkoff, M.	Kleine Suite. *rec, cl, tpt, guit, pf, vn, vc, hpcd*	WH
Olsen, P.	Patet per nove musici (1966).	
	fl, cl, vn, va, vc, guit, perc, vib	B&B

EIGHT INSTRUMENTS INCLUDING PERCUSSION

Albright, W.	Caroms. *fl/afl, bcl, tpt, db, pf, cel, 2perc*	Job
Alexander, J.	3 Pieces for Eight.	
	fl, cl, tpt, vn, vc, db, pf, perc	Gen
Amram, D.	Incidental Music to "After the Fall."	
	fl, tsax, hn, vn, va, db, pf, dr	Pet
Amy, G.	Invention I and II. *fl, pf, hp, vib, 4perc*	Heu
Andriessen, J.	Ars Antiqua Musicae.	
	fl, ob, 2hn, tpt, guit, perc, va	SD

Eight Instruments including Percussion

Antoniou, T.	Events III (1969).	
	fl, ob, cl, bsn, pf, tape, 2perc	B&N
Avshalomov, J.	Cues from the Little Clay Cart	
	fl/pic, cl, va, vc, guit, 3perc	ACA
Benguerel, X.	Joc. *fl, ob, cl, vn, va, vc, pf, perc*	HMo
Bjelik, M.	Oktett. *fl, cl, bcl, vn, va, vc, 2perc*	LDo
Cage, J.	16 Dances (1951). *fl, tpt, vn, vc, 4perc*	Pet
Cerha, F.	Enjambements. *fl/pic, tpt, trb, vn, db, 3perc*	UE
Chou Wen-Chung	Yün. *fl, cl, bsn, hn, tpt, trb, pf, perc*	Pet
Crawford, J.	3 Palindromes. *fl, bcl, hn, tpt, vn, va, db, perc*	CoF
Delas, J. de	Eilanden. *cl, 2vn, va, pf, hp, perc, guit*	HG
Dodge, C.	Folia. *fl, ehn, cl, vn, va, tu, pf, perc*	CoF
Eichenwald, P.	Aspekte. *fl, bcl, vn, vc, hp, pf, 2perc*	EMo
El-Dabh, H.	Octet. *fl, ob, cl, 2tpt, hn, 2perc*	Pet
Fellegara, V.	Serenata (1960).	
	fl, cl, bcl(bsn), vn, va, vc, pf, perc	ESZ
Gerhard, R.	Concert for 8. *fl, cl, guit, perc, db, pf,*	
	mandolin, accordion	OxU
Grandert, J.	Kammarmusik (1961).	
Grandis, R. de	Instrumentalmusik ("Il Ciero di Hyuga").	
	fl, cl, 2vn, va, vc, guit, perc	STI
Green, R.	3 Pieces for a Concert.	EdT
	fl, 2cl, 2tpt, trb, pf, perc	JB
Hodeir, A.	Flautando. *3fl, 2afl, db, pf, perc*	MJQ
Homs, J.	Music for Eight (1964).	
	fl, cl, vn, va, vc, tpt, pf, perc	See
Hounsell	Showcase for Saxes. *5sax, pf, db, perc*	Tem
Koellreuter, H.	Constructio ad Synesin (1962).	
	pic, ehn, bcl, cbsn, vn, hp, pf, perc	EMo
Korte, K.	Matrix. *fl, ob, cl, hn, bsn, asax, pf, perc*	ECS
Lully, J.	Le Carrousel du Roy, Lère partie.	
	2ob, ehn, bsn, 3tpt, timp	Heu
Lully, J.	Le Carrousel du Roy, 2ème partie.	
	2ob, ehn, bsn, 3tpt, timp	Heu
Martirano, S.	Octet (1963).	
	fl, cl, contra alto cl, mar, cel, vn, vc, db	Can
Matsushita, S.	Composizione da Camera.	
	fl, cl, tpt, trb, vn, vc, pf, perc	TP
Moss, L.	Remembrances. *fl, cl, hn, tpt, vn, vc, vib, perc*	AMC
Mozart, W.	Divertimento No. 5, C, K. 187. *2fl, 5tpt, timp*	BrH
Mozart, W.	Divertimento No. 6, C, K. 188. *2fl, 5tpt, timp*	BrH
Natanson, T.	3 Pictures (1960).	
	ob, bsn, asax, tpt, trb, vc, pf, perc	AP
Nilsson, B.	Scene I. *2fl, 2tpt, vib, hp, pf, perc*	UE
Olsen, P.	Patet per nove musici (1966).	
	fl, cl, vn, va, vc, guit, perc, vib	B&B
Rands, B.	Tableau. *fl, afl, cl, bcl, va, vc, pf/cel, perc*	UE
Rathburn, E.	Parade (1949). *fl, ob, cl, bsn, tpt, hn, trb, perc*	Can
Revueltas, S.	Toccata (Without a Fugue).	
	pic, 3cl, hn, tpt, vn, timp	SMP
Smith, W.	Elegy for Eric. *fl/asax, cl/bar sax,*	
	tpt, trb, vib, db, vn, perc	MJQ

Eight Instruments including Percussion

Sternfeld, R.	Return to Israel. *cl, hn, tpt, trb, db, 3perc*	See
Sternfeld, R.	Thoughts of C & C. *fl, cl, bcl, trb, 4perc*	See
Surinach, C.	Ritmo Jondo. *cl, tpt, 3perc, 3 hand clappers*	AMP
Suter, R.	Estampida. *fl, cl, tsax, hn, tpt, trb, db, perc*	EMo
Tailleferre, G.	Image. *fl, cl, pf, 2vn, va, vc, cel*	WH
Villa-Lobos, H.	Choros No. 7 (1924).	
	fl, ob, cl, bsn, sax, vn, vc, perc	EME
Vis, L.	Essay I. *fl, cl, bcl, vn, va, vc, xyl, mar*	SD
Wiszniewski, Z.	Tristia. *fl, cl, tpt, trb, va, db, pf, perc*	EMo

EIGHT INSTRUMENTS INCLUDING RECORDER

Karkoff, M.	Kleine Suite.	
	rec, cl, tpt, guit, pf, vn, vc, hpcd	WH
Telemann, G.-Brüggen	Concerto a 7. *2rec, 2ob, 2vn, vc, pf*	SS
Werdin, E.	Konzertante Musik. *rec, fl, ob, ehn, 2vn, va, vc*	Pet

EIGHT INSTRUMENTS INCLUDING TAPE

Antoniou, T.	Events III (1969).	
	fl, ob, cl, bsn, pf, tape, 2perc	B&N

NINE INSTRUMENTS

NINE WOODWINDS (including horn)

Bartos, J.	Divertimento I, op. 79. *fl, 2ob, 2cl, 2hn, 2bsn*	Pan
Beethoven, L. van-Hess	Adagio, F. (1799). *fl, 2ob, 2cl, 2hn, 2bsn*	BrH
Beethoven-Sedlak	Suite (Fidelio). *2ob, 2cl, 2hn, 2bsn, cbsn*	WIN
Bräutigam, H.	Kleine Jagdmusik, op. 11. *fl, 2ob, 2cl, 2hn, 2bsn*	BrH
Cole, H.	Serenade. *fl, ob, ob/fl, 2cl, cl/bsn, hn/cl/asax, 2bsn*	Nov
Donizetti, G.-Townsend	Sinfonia for Winds. *fl, 2ob, 2cl, 2bsn, 2hn*	AlB
Donizetti, G.-Päuler	Sinfonia. *fl, 2ob, 2cl, 2hn, 2bsn*	Eul
Gounod, C.	Petite Symphonie. *fl, 2ob, 2cl, 2hn, 2bsn*	Bil
Gounod, C.	Petite Symphony, op. 90. *fl, 2ob, 2cl, 2bsn, 2hn*	EdK
Hoffmeister, F.-Hess	Serenade, E♭. *2ob(2fl), 2cl, 2hn, 2bsn, cbsn(db)*	EK
Krommer, F.	Harmonie, B♭, op. 78. *2ob, 2cl, 2hn, 2bsn, cbsn*	WIN
Krommer, F.	Harmonie, C, op. 76. *2ob, 2cl, 2hn, 2bsn, cbsn*	WIN
Krommer, F.	Harmonie, E♭, op. 79. *2ob, 2cl, 2hn, 2bsn, cbsn*	WIN
Krommer, F.	Harmonie, F, op. 77. *2ob, 2cl, 2hn, 2bsn, cbsn*	WIN
Krommer, F.	Harmonie, F, op. 73. *2ob, 2cl, 2hn, 2bsn, cbsn*	WIN
Krommer, F.	Harmonie, op. 57. *2ob, 2cl, 2hn, 2bsn, cbsn*	WIN
Krommer, F.	Harmonie, op. 78. *2ob, 2cl, 2hn, 2bsn, cbsn*	FrH
Krommer, F.	Harmonie, op. 69. *2ob, 2cl, 2hn, 2bsn, cbsn*	WIN
Krommer, F.	Harmonie, op. 67. *2ob, 2cl, 2hn, 2bsn, cbsn*	WIN
Krommer, F.	Nonett, op. 79. *2ob, 2cl, 2hn, 2bsn, cbsn*	FrH
Krommer, F.	Partia, E♭, op. 71. *2ob, 2cl, 2hn, 2bsn, cbsn*	WIN
Mozart, W.-Pillney	Fantasie, f, K. 608. *fl, 2ob, 2cl, 2hn, 2bsn*	BrH
Nelhybel, V.	Ricercare. *E♭ cl, acl, bcl, cacl, cbcl, 2asax, tsax, bar sax*	Leb
Otten, L.	Divertimento No. 3 (1964). *fl, 2ob, 2cl, 2bsn, 2hn*	SD
Praag, H. van	Fantasie (1962). *2fl, 2ob, 2cl, 2hn, bsn*	SD
Ropartz, G.	Lamento. *ob solo, 2fl, ob, 2cl, 2bsn, hn*	EdS
Schreck, G.	Nonett, op. 40. *2fl, ob, 2cl, 2bsn, 2hn*	BrH
Sellner, J.	Variations, Nr. 2. *cl solo, cl, 2ob, 2hn, 2bsn, cbsn*	WIN
Triebensee, J.	"Echostucke." *2ob, 2cl, 2hn, 2bsn, cbsn*	WIN
Triebensee, J.	Partitta, E♭. *2ob, 2cl, 2hn, 2bsn, cbsn*	WIN

NINE INSTRUMENTS INCLUDING HARP

Arrigo, G.	Fluxus, op. 7 (1961). *fl, 2cl, bsn, tpt, va, vc, db, hp*	AlB

Nine Instruments including Harp

Balassa, S.	Xeniak - nonet.	
	fl, cl, bsn, vn, va, vc, pf, hp, perc	EMB
Bolcom, W.	Session IV. *cl, 2va, vc, trb, pf, hp, 2perc*	TP
Brown, E.	Pentathis. *fl, bcl, tpt, trb, hp, pf, vn, va, vc*	SS
Cerha, F.	Exercises for Nine, No. 1.	
	bcl, bar sax, bsn, tpt, trb, tu, vc, db, hp	UE
Fleming, R.	Maritime Suite (1962).	
	fl, ob, cl, bsn, hp, 2vn, va, vc	Can
Lebic, L.	kons (a). *fl, cl, hn, pf, hp, vn, va, vc, perc*	EdD
Lebic, L.	kons (b). *3bcl, 2vn, va, vc, hp, perc*	EdD
Magdic, J.	Apeiron. *hp solo, fl, cl, 2vn, va, vc, db, perc*	EdD
Milhaud, D.	Le Printemps. *pic, fl, ob, cl, 2vn, va, vc, hp*	UE
Paccagnini, A.	Musica da Camera.	
	pic, fl, bcl, hn, vn, vc, db, hp, vib	UE
Petric, I.	Petit concerto de chambre.	
	ob, cl, bcl, hn, vn, va, vc, db, hp	EdD
Ramovs, P.	Apel. *fl, cl, hn, 2vn, va, vc, db, hp*	EdD
Ramovs, P.	Enneaphonia.	
	fl, cl, bsn, vn, va, vc, pf, hp, perc	EdD
Vriend, J.	Paroesie. *fl, bsn, hn, tpt, vn, db, hp, pf, perc*	SD

NINE INSTRUMENTS INCLUDING GUITAR

Becker, G.	Game for Nine (1962).	
	fl, cl, bcl, perc, vib, guit, vn, va, vc	HG
Gorecki, H.	Concerto (1957), op. 11.	
	fl, cl, tpt, xyl, mandoline, 2vn, va, vc	AP
Schuller, G.	Abstraction. *asax, guit, perc, 2vn, va, vc, 2db*	MJQ
Soler, J.	Lachrimae (1967).	
	pic, fl, vn, va, vc, db, guit, 2perc	See

NINE INSTRUMENTS INCLUDING PERCUSSION

Balassa, S.	Xeniak - nonet.	
	fl, cl, bsn, vn, va, vc, pf, hp, perc	EMB
Bauer, M.	Pan & Syrinx. *fl, ob, cl, 2vn, va, vc, pf, perc*	ACA
Becker, G.	Game for Nine (1962).	
	fl, cl, bcl, perc, vib, guit, vn, va, vc	HG
Bentzon, N.	Chamber Concerto, op. 52.	
	cl, 2bsn, tpt, db, perc, 3pf	Che
Bolcom, W.	Session IV. *cl, 2va, vc, trb, pf, hp, 2perc*	TP
Bortz, D.	Kammarmusik (1964).	
	fl, cl/bcl, tpt, trb, vn, vc, 3perc	STI
Bozay, A.	Sorozat. *fl, ob, cl, vn, va, vc, db, pf/hpcd, perc*	EMB
Chemin-Petit, H.	Suite "Dr. Johannes Faust."	
	ob, cl, bsn, 2vn, va, vc, db, perc	MRL
Chou, Wen-Chung	Yun. *fl, cl, bsn, hn, tpt, trb, pf, 2perc*	Pet
Dodge, C.	Folia. *fl, ehn, cl, tu, vn, va, pf, 2perc*	ACA
Donovan, R.	Fantasia. *solo bsn, bsn*	
	vn, va, vc, db, cel, timp, perc	ACA

Feldman, M.	Numbers.	
	fl, vn, vc, db, hn, trb, tu, perc, pf/cel	Pet
Fellagara, V.	Serenata.	
	fl, cl, bcl(bsn), 2vn, va, vc, pf, perc	ESZ
Fribec, K.	Panta Rhei.	
	pic, fl, ehn, bcl, vn, db, pf, vib, perc	EMo
Gerhard, R.	Leo. *fl, cl, hn, tpt, trb, vn, vc, pf, perc*	OxU
Gorecki, H.	Concerto (1957), op. 11.	
	fl, cl, tpt, 2vn, va, vc, xyl, mandoline	AP
Grandert, J.	86 T. *fl, ehn, bcl, bar sax, cbsn, 2tpt, perc, pf*	STI
Gudmundsen-Holmgreen, P.	2 Improvisations, op. 9 (1961).	
	fl, cl, hn, tpt, trb, db, vib, pf, perc	SPD
Hambraeus, B.	Introduzione-Sequenze-Coda. *3fl, 6perc*	Che
Heussenstamm, G.	The Quiet Russian, op. 27.	
	fl, ob, cl, bsn, hn, vn, va, vc, perc	See
Hibbard, W.	4 Pieces. *fl, cl, hn, trb, vn, db, pf, vib, perc*	ACA
Hibbard, W.	Sensuous Extractions.	
	fl, cl, hn, trb, vn, db, pf, mar, perc	AMC
Hrusovsky, I.	Combinazioni Sonoriche (1963).	
	fl, ob, bcl, tpt, pf, vn, va, vc, vib	SHF
Jenni, D.	Cucumber Music.	
	pic, afl, va, pf, cel, vib, 3perc	ACA
Kroeger, K.	The Firebugs.	
	cl, bsn, tpt, 2trb, vn, db, pf, perc	CoF
Lebic, L.	kons (a). *fl, cl, hn, pf, hp, vn, va, vc, perc*	EdD
Lebic, L.	kons (b). *3bcl, 2vn, va, vc, hp, perc*	EdD
Legrand, M.	Porcelaine de Saxe. E^b *sop sax(E^b cl, cl), sop sax(cl), asax, tsax, bar sax, bass sax (bsn), db, trb, dr*	B-M
Machl, T.	3 Virtuoso Studies (1959).	
	2fl, ob, cl, bsn, hn, tpt, db, timp	AP
Magdic, J.	Apeiron. *hp solo, fl, cl, 2vn, va, vc, db, perc*	EdD
Naumann, S.	Cadenze (1964).	
	cl, vn, vc, 2tpt, hn, trb, fl, perc	STI
Paccagnini, A.	Musica da Camera.	
	pic, fl, bcl, hn, vn, vc, db, hp, vib	UE
Parris, R.	St. Winefred's Well. *fl, 2vc, pf, perc, 4timp*	ACA
Pleskow, R.	Movement for Nine Players (1967).	
	fl, cl, vn, vc, tpt, db, pf, perc, cel	See
Pospisil, J.	Nonet No. 2.	
	fl, ob, bcl, tpt, hn, vn, va, vc, pf, timp	SHF
Pospisil, J.	Trojversia, op. 22.	
	fl, bcl, hn, tpt, trb, vib, vn, va, vc	SHF
Ramovs, P.	Enneaphonia.	
	fl, cl, bsn, vn, va, vc, pf, hp, perc	EdD
Reynolds, R.	Wedge. *2fl/pic, 2tpt, 2trb, db, pf, perc*	Pet
Schuller, G.	Abstraction. *asax, guit, perc, 2vn, va, vc, 2db*	MJQ
Soler, J.	Lachrimae (1967).	
	pic, fl, vn, va, vc, db, guit, 2perc	See
Szabelski, B.	Aphorisms "9" (1962).	
	fl, ob, cl, tpt, trb, vn, va, vc, perc	AP

Nine Instruments including Percussion

Tremblay, G.	Epithalamium.	
	fl, ob, cl/sax, bsn, hn, tpt, trb, tu, perc	CoF
Tremblot de la Croix	Divertimento. *8ww, perc*	ALe
Vriend, J.	Paroesie. *fl, bsn, hn, tpt, vn, db, hp, pf, perc*	SD
Wolff, C.	Nine. *fl, cl, hn, tpt, trb, 2vc, pf, cel*	Pet

NINE INSTRUMENTS NOT INCLUDING
HARP, GUITAR, OR PERCUSSION

Adaskin, M.	Rondino (1961). *fl, ob, cl, bsn, hn, 2vn, va, vc*	Can
Angerer, P.	Cogitatio. *fl, ob, cl, bsn, hn, vn, va, vc, db*	LDo
Babusek, F.	Noneto. *fl, ob, cl, bsn, hn, vn, va, vc, db*	SHF
Bassett, L.	Nonet. *fl, ob, cl, bsn, hn, tpt, trb, tu, pf*	Pet
Bialas, G.	Pastorale und Rondo (Nonett) (1969).	
	ob, cl, hn, bsn, 2vn, va, vc, db	B&N
Bottje, W.	Serenade. *fl, ob, cl, bsn, hn, 2vn, va, vc*	CoF
Cazden, N.	6 Definitions. *cl, ehn, hn, tpt, 2vn, va, vc, db*	AMC
Chavez, C.	Energia. *pic, fl, bsn, tpt, hn, trb, va, vc, db*	B-M
Clementi, A.	Concertino in forma di variazioni (1956).	
	fl, ob, bsn, cbsn, hn, vn, vc, db, pf	ESZ
Custer, A.	Cycle. *fl, bcl, asax, hn, tpt, vn, va, vc, db*	Gen
David, T.	Konzert. *fl, ob, cl, bsn, hn, vn, va, vc, db*	LDo
Davidovsky, M.	Noneto. *fl, ob, cl, bsn, 2vn, va, vc, db*	EBM
Dubois, T.	Nonetto. *fl, ob, cl, bsn, 2vn, va, vc, db*	Heu
Eckhardt-Gramatte, S.	Nonet (1966). *fl, ob, cl, bsn, hn, vn, va, vc, db*	Can
Eisler, H.	Nonett No. 1. *fl, cl, bsn, hn, 2vn, va, vc, db*	Pet
Erbse, H.	Nonett, op. 28. *str & ww players*	HG
Feldman, M.	Projection 5. *3fl, 3vc, tpt, 2pf*	Pet
Fisher, S.	Music for Nine Instruments.	
	cl, bsn, hn, tpt, trb, tu, vn, vc, db	MJQ
Fröhlich, T.-Scherchen	Walzer. *fl, ob, 2cl, 2bsn, 2hn, trb*	SS
Geissler, F.	Ode an eine Nachtigall (1967/68).	
	fl, ob, cl, bsn, hn, 2vn, va, vc	B&N
Genzmer, H.	Nonett (Capriccio).	
	ob, cl, bsn, hn, 2vn, va, vc, db	Pet
Gilse, J. van	Nonet (1916). *ob, cl, bsn, hn, 2vn, va, vc, db*	SD
Goossens, E.	Fantasy. *fl, ob, 2cl, 2bsn, 2hn, tpt*	ALe
Grandert, J.	Nonett (1964).	
	fl, ob, cl, bsn, hn, tpt, trb, bar, vc	STI
Hába, A.	Erstes Nonett (1931), op. 40.	
	fl, ob, cl, bsn, hn, vn, va, vc, db	HG
Hauer, J.	Dance Suite No. 1, op. 70.	
	fl, ob, cl, bsn, 2vn, va, vc, pf	UE
Hauer, J.	Dance Suite No. 2, op. 71.	
	fl, ob, bcl, bsn, 2vn, va, vc, pf	UE
Haydn, F.-Landon	Concerto No. 5, F, Hob. VIIh: 5.	
	fl, ob, 2hn, 2vn, 2va, vc	LDo
Haydn, F.-Landon	Concerto No. 4, F, Hob. VIIh: 4.	
	fl, ob, 2hn, 2vn, 2va, vc	LDo

Nine Instruments not including
Harp, Guitar or Percussion

Haydn, F.-Landon	Concerto No. 1, C, Hob. VIIh: 1.	
	fl, ob, 2hn, 2vn, 2va, vc	LDo
Haydn, F.-Landon	Concerto No. 3, G, Hob. VIIh: 3.	
	fl, ob, 2hn, 2vn, 2va, vc	LDo
Haydn, F.-Landon	Concerto No. 2, G, Hob. VIIh: 2.	
	fl, ob, 2hn, 2vn, 2va, vc	LDo
Haydn, F.-Steppan	Divertimento, C, Hob. II: 17.	
	2cl, 2hn, 2vn, 2va, vc	LDo
Haydn, F.-Landon	Divertimento, F, Hob. II: 20.	
	2ob, 2hn, 2vn, 2va, db	LDo
Henkemans, H.	Primavera (1944). *fl, ob, 3vn, 2va, vc, db*	SD
Hlobil, E.	Nonetto, op. 27 (1946/47).	
	fl, ob, cl, hn, bsn, vn, va, vc, db	Art
Hovhaness, A.	Tower Music, op. 129.	
	fl, ob, cl, bsn, 2hn, tpt, trb, tu	BB
Jaroch, J.	Kindersuite. Nonett (1952).	
	fl, ob, cl, bsn, hn, vn, va, vc, db	Art
Karlins, M.	Concerto Grosso. *fl/pic, ob, cl, bsn, hn, trb,*	
	vn, va, vc	CoF
Kornauth, E.	Kammermusik, op. 31.	
	fl, ob, cl, hn, 2vn, va, vc, db	LDo
Kox, H.	Cyclophony VIII.	
	fl, ob, cl, bsn, hn, vn, va, vc, db	SD
Krol, B.	Konzertante Musik, op. 6.	
	va, 2ob, 2cl, 2bsn, 2hn	BrH
Krommer, F.	Harmonie, F, op. 83. *2ob, 2cl, 2hn, 2bsn, tpt*	WIN
Kubizek, A.	Sinfonia da camera, op. 26b.	
	fl, ob, cl, bsn, hn, vn, va, vc, db	LDo
Laderman, E.	Nonette. *fl, cl, bsn, tpt, hn, trb, vn, vc, pf*	OxU
Lully, J.-Schilling	Chaconne. *2ob(2fl), bsn, str quintet, pf*	BrH
Lutoslawski, W.	Dance Preludes (3rd version, 1959).	
	fl, ob, cl, bsn, hn, vn, va, vc, db	Che
Martinu, B.	Nonetto (1959).	
	fl, ob, cl, bsn, hn, vn, va, vc, db	B&N
Martinu, B.	Pastorals (1951). *5rec, cl, 2vn, vc*	B&N
Mestres-Quadreny, J.	Engidus (1967). *4fl, tpt, 4trb*	See
Milhaud, D.	Aspen Serenade.	
	fl, ob, cl, bsn, tpt, vn, va, vc, db	Heu
Mirk, V.	Nonet. *fl, ob, cl, bsn, hn, vn, va, vc, db*	EdD
Miroglio, F.	Espaces V. *fl, ob, cl, bsn, 2vn, va, vc, db*	ESZ
Mulder, E.	Fuga No. 4 (1940). *fl, ob, cl, hn, 2vn, va, vc, db*	SD
Musgrave, T.	Chamber Concerto.	
	ob, cl, bsn, hn, tpt, trb, vn, va, vc	Che
Novak, J.	Baletti a 9 (1955).	
	fl, ob, cl, bsn, hn, vn, va, vc, db	Art
Patzig, G. (ed)	Militärmärsche des 18. Jahrhunderts, Vol. 2.	
	2ob, 2cl, 2bsn, 2hn, tpt	B&N
Piston, W.	Divertimento. *fl, ob, cl, bsn, 2vn, va, vc, db*	AMP
Poulenc, F.	Mouvements Perpetuels.	
	fl, ob/ehn, cl, bsn, hn, vn, va, vc, db	Che

Nine Instruments not including
Harp, Guitar or Percussion

Rheinberger, J.	Nonet, op. 139. *fl, ob, cl, bsn, hn, vn, va, vc, db*	MR
Rudzinski, W.	Nonet (1947). *fl, ob, cl, bsn, hn, vn, va, vc, db*	AP
Schafer, R.	Concerto for Harpsichord (1954).	
	hpcd, 2fl, ob, 2cl, 2bsn, hn	Can
Schiske, K.	Divertimento, op. 49.	
	cl, bsn, tpt, trb, 2vn, va, vc, db	LDo
Schubert, F.	Eine Kleine Trauermusik.	
	2cl, 2bsn, cbsn, 2hn, 2trb	Ens
Schubert, F.	Eine Kleine Trauermusik.	
	2cl, 2bsn, cbsn, 2hn, 2trb	M&M
Schubert, F.-Landon	6 Menuette, Vol. 1 (1-3).	
	2ob, 2cl, 2hn, 2bsn, tpt	B&N
Schwantner, J.	Diaphonia Intervallum.	
	asax, fl, pf, str sextet	ACA
Searle, H.	Sinfonietta, op. 49 (1969).	
	fl/pic, ob, cl, bsn, hn, vn, va, vc, db	Fab
Smalley, R.	Missa Parodia II (1967).	
	fl/pic, ob, cl, hn, tpt, trb, vn, va, pf	Fab
Spohr, L.	Nonet, op. 31. *fl, ob, cl, bsn, hn, vn, va, vc, db*	M&M
Spohr, L.	Nonet, op. 31. *fl, ob, cl, bsn, hn, vn, va, vc, db*	Pet
Spohr, L.	Nonett, op. 31. *fl, ob, cl, bsn, hn, vn, va, vc, db*	MRL
Stewart, R.	Nonet. *fl, cl, bsn, hn, tpt, vn, va, vc, pf*	CoF
Stewart, R.	2 Ricercare. *fl, ob, cl, bsn, hn, 2vn, va, vc*	CoF
Takahashi, Y.	Bridges II. *2ob, 2cl, 2tpt, 3va*	Pet
Triebensee, J.	Concertino. *pf, 2ob, 2cl, 2hn, 2bsn*	WIN
Triebensee, J.	6 Marches. *2ob, 2cl, 2hn, 2bsn, tpt*	WIN
Triebensee, J.	Variations on a Theme of Gyrowetz.	
	2ob, 2cl, 2hn, 2bsn, tpt	WIN
Trimble, L.	Concerto. *fl, ob, cl, bsn, 2vn, va, vc, db*	Pet
Verrall, J.	Nonette. *fl, ob, cl, bsn, hn, 2vn, va, vc*	ACA
Webern, A.	Concerto, op. 24.	
	fl, ob, cl, hn, tpt, trb, vn, va, pf	UE
Welin, K.	Nr 3. *fl, ob, cl, bcl, hn, tpt, trb, vn, db*	Sim
Wolff, C.	Nine. *fl, cl, hn, tpt, trb, 2vc, cel, pf*	Pet
Zillig, W.	Serenade II (1929).	
	2cl, bcl, ct, tpt, trb, vn, va, vc	B&N

TEN INSTRUMENTS

TEN WOODWINDS (including horn)

Andriessen, J.	Concertino (1962). *2fl, 2ob, 2cl, 2bsn, 2hn*	SD
Andriessen, J.	Respiration-suite (1962).	
	2fl, 2ob, 2cl, 2bsn, 2hn .	SD
Ballou, E.	Suite for Winds. *2fl, 2ob, 2cl, 2bsn, 2hn*	CoF
Bernard, E.	Divertissement, op. 36. *2fl, 2ob, 2cl, 2bsn, 2hn*	Dur
Enesco, G.	Dixtuor. *2fl, 2ob, 2cl, 2bsn, 2hn*	M&M
Jacob, G.	Old Wine in New Bottles. *2fl, 2ob, 2cl, 2bsn,*	
	cbsn ad lib, 2hn, 2tpt ad lib	OxU
Lilien, I.	Sonatine apollinique (1939).	
	2fl, 2ob, 2cl, 2bsn, 2hn	SD
Lutyens, E.	Music for Wind. *2fl, 2ob, 2cl, 2hn, 2bsn*	S&C
Mengelberg, M.	Hello Windy Boys. *2fl, 2ob, 2cl, 2bsn, 2hn*	SD
Milhaud, D.	Petite Symphonie No. 5 (Dixtuor).	
	pic, fl, ob, ehn, cl, bcl, 2bsn, 2hn	UE
Mozart, W.	Divertimento No. 4, B♭, K. 186.	
	2ob, 2ehn, 2cl, 2hn, 2bsn	BrH
Mozart, W.	Divertimento No. 3, E♭, K. 166.	
	2ob, 2cl, 2ehn, 2hn, 2bsn	BrH
Nilsson, B.	"Zeitpunkte." *fl, afl, ob, ehn, cl, bcl,*	
	asax, tsax, bsn, cbsn	UE
Schibler, A.	Prologue. *2fl, 2ob, 2cl, bcl, 2bsn, cbsn*	A&S
Schibler, A.	Signal, Beschwörung.	
	2fl, 2ob, ehn, 2cl, bcl, 2bsn	A&S
Schmitt, F.	Lied et scherzo, op. 54.	
	2fl, 2ob, 2cl, 2bsn, solo hn, hn	Dur
Spino, P.	Prelude for Woodwinds. *2fl, opt ob, 3cl, bcl,*	
	opt bsn, 2asax, tsax, bar sax	StM
Sydeman, W.	Music. *10ww*	See
Taneyev, A.	Andante. *2fl, 2ob, 2cl, 2hn, 2bsn*	M&M

TEN INSTRUMENTS INCLUDING HARP

Birtwistle, H.	Tragoedia. *fl, ob, cl, bsn, hn, 2vn, va, vc, hp*	UE
Chou, Wen-chung	2 Miniatures from T'Ang.	
	2fl, cl, hn, vn, va, vc, hp, pf, perc	ACA
Custer, A.	Stream Music.	
	fl/pic, 2hn, 2tpt, 2trb, tu, hp, perc	Gen
Delas, J. de	"Imago" (1965).	
	fl, afl, cl, bcl, pf, hp, perc, vn, va, vc	HG
Frankel, B.	Bagatelles (5 Pezzi Notturni).	
	fl, ob, cl, bsn, 2vn, va, vc, db, hp	Nov
Heider, W.	Sonatina.	
	fl, cl, tsax, hn, trb, hp, vib, pf, db, perc	MJQ
Hovhaness, A.	Mountains and Rivers Without End.	
	fl, ob, cl, tpt, trb, tu, 3perc, hp	Pet
Miroglio, F.	Reseaux. *fl, cl, bsn, trb, 2vn, va, vc, hp, perc*	UE

Ten Instruments including Harp

Rydman, K.	Khoros 1 (1964).	
	3fl, ob, vn, va, vc, db, hp, perc	MT
Schaffer, B.	Permutationen.	
	fl, ob, cl, sax, tpt, trb, va, perc, hp, pf	A&S
Schuller, G.	Twelve by Eleven.	
	fl, cl, tsax, hn, trb, vib, pf, hp, db, perc	MJQ
Stockhausen, K.	"Kontra-Punkte" No. 1.	
	fl, cl, bcl, bsn, tpt, trb, vn, vc, pf, hp	UE

TEN INSTRUMENTS INCLUDING GUITAR

Lewis, J.	The Milanese Story	
	fl, tsax, guit, pf, db, perc, 2vn, va, vc	MJQ
Ruyneman, D.	Hieroglyphs.	
	3fl, hp, pf, 2mandoline, 2guit, perc	WH
Schwertsik, K.	Salotto Romano, op. 5. *bcl, bar sax, bsn, hn,*	
	trb, tu, perc, db, vc, guit	EMo

TEN INSTRUMENTS INCLUDING PERCUSSION

Adler, S.	Music for Eleven.	
	2fl, ob, cl, bcl, bsn, xyl, glock, timp, perc	OxU
Caturla, A.	Bembé. *fl, ob, cl, bsn, 2hn, tpt, trb, pf, perc*	EdS
Chavez, C.	Xochipilli. *pic, fl, E♭ cl, trb, 6perc*	B-M
Chou, Wen-chung	2 Miniatures from T'Ang.	
	2fl, cl, hn, vn, va, vc, hp, pf, perc	ACA
Custer, A.	Stream Music.	
	fl/pic, 2hn, 2tpt, 2trb, tu, hp, perc	Gen
Delas, J. de	"Imago" (1965).	
	fl, afl, bcl, cl, pf, hp, perc, vn, va, vc	HG
Ebenhöh, H.	4 Scenes for 10, op. 21/2.	
	fl, ob, bsn, 2vn, va, vc, db, 2perc	LDo
Ebenhöh, H.	4 Szenen, op. 21/1.	
	fl, ob, cl, bsn, 2vn, va, vc, db, perc	LDo
Etler, A.	Clarinet Concerto. *cl, 3tpt, 3trb, 3db, perc*	AMP
Ferrari, L.	Interrupteur. *ehn, cl, bcl, hn, tpt, vn, va, vc,*	
	2perc, 3 magneto-phone ad lib	HMo
Franco, J.	The Pilgrim's Progress.	
	fl/pic, ob/ehn, cl, bsn, 3tpt, trb, pf, perc	ACA
Giefer, W.	Pro-Kontra (1970).	
	fl, ob, cl, bsn, hn, vn, va, vc, db, perc	HG
Gudmundsen- Holmgreen, P.	2 Improvisations, op. 9 (1961).	
	fl, cl, hn, tpt, trb, db, vib, pf, 2perc	SPD
Handel, G.-Kahn	Firework Music II. *2ob, bsn, 3tpt, 3hn, timp*	EBM
Heider, W.	Sonatina.	
	fl, cl, tsax, hn, trb, hp, vib, pf, db, perc	MJQ
Heussenstamm, G.	Das Dreieck. *fl, ob, cl, bsn, hn, str trio, 2perc*	See

Ten Instruments including Percussion

Holmboe, V.	Chamber Concerto No. 2, op. 20.	
	fl, 3vn, va, vc, db, timp, dr, cel	SPD
Homs, J.	Impromptu for Ten (1970).	
	fl, ob, cl, tpt, pf, 2vn, va, vc, perc	See
Hovhaness, A.	Mountains and Rivers Without End.	
	fl, ob, cl, tpt, trb, tu, 3perc, hp	Pet
Huggler, J.	Music, op. 63.	
	fl, 2cl, 2tpt, timp, pf, vn, db, perc	Pet
Ives, C.-Cowell	Calcium Light Night.	
	pic, ob, cl, bsn, tpt, trb, 2pf, 2perc	TP
Lewis, J.	The Milanese Story.	
	fl, tsax, guit, pf, db, perc, 2vn, va, vc	MJQ
Ligeti, G.	Fragment.	
	cbsn, trb, tu, perc, hp, hpcd, pf, 3db	UE
Manzoni, G.	Parafrasi con Finale (1969).	
	fl, cl, bsn, hn, tpt, trb, hpcd, org, db, perc	ESZ
Matsudaira, Y.	Serenata (1963). *fl, ob, cl, 6vn, perc*	ESZ
Mestres-Quadreny, J.	Musica de Cambra II (1961).	
	3cl, ehn, vn, va, vc, tpt, trb, perc	See
Miroglio, F.	Reseaux. *fl, cl, bsn, trb, 2vn, va, vc, hp, perc*	UE
Paumgartner, B.	Divertimento. *pic, ehn, asax, bsn, hn, tpt,*	
	pf, va, vc, perc	UE
Ruyneman, D.	Hieroglyphs (1918).	
	3fl, cel, cupbells, pf, 2mandolins, 2guit	
Rydman, K.	Khoros 1 (1964).	
	3fl, ob, vn, va, vc, db, hp, perc	MT
Schaffer, B.	Permutationen.	
	fl, ob, cl, sax, tpt, trb, va, perc, hp, pf	A&S
Schuller, G.	Twelve by Eleven.	
	fl, cl, tsax, hn, trb, vib, pf, hp, db, perc	MJQ
Schwartz, E.	Concert Piece.	
	fl, ob, cl, bsn, hn, va, vc, db, 2perc	AlB
Schwertsik, K.	Salotto Romano, op. 5. *bcl, bar sax, bsn, hn,*	
	trb, tu, perc, db, vc, guit	EMo
Simons, N.	Variables (1967).	
	fl, cl, tpt, trb, vn, va, vc, db, pf, perc	CoF
Tremblay, G.	Champs III (Vers) (1969).	
	2fl, cl, tpt, hn, 3vn, db, perc	Can

TEN INSTRUMENTS NOT INCLUDING HARP, GUITAR, OR PERCUSSION

Aitken, H.	Serenade. *fl, ob, cl, bsn, hn, str quintet*	AMC
Andriessen, J.	Hommage à Milhaud.	
	fl, ob, cl, asax, bsn, tpt, trb, vn, va, vc	SD
Arnold, M.	Trevelyan Suite, op. 96 (1967).	
	3fl, 2ob, 2cl, vc, 2hn	Fab
Arrieu, C.	Dixtuor. *2fl, ob, 2cl, 2bsn, hn, tpt, trb*	Bil
Bialas, G.	Partita (1969). *fl, 2ob, 2cl, 2bsn, 2hn, db*	B&N

249

Ten Instruments not including
Harp, Guitar or Percussion

Bottenberg, W.	Variables (1969).	
	rec, fl, ob, cl, bsn, str quintet	Can
Cunningham, M.	Spring Sonnet. *fl, 2cl, asax, tsax, bcl, 3hn, db*	CoA
Dubois, T.	Dixtuor. *fl, ob, cl, hn, bsn, 2vn, va, vc, db*	
Dvorak, A.	March (Serenade).	
	2ob, 2cl, 2bsn, cbsn ad lib, 3hn, vc	EBM
Dvorak, A.	Serenade, op. 44. *2ob, 2cl, 2bsn, 2hn, vc, db*	EdK
Eisler, H.	Ouverture zu einem Lustspiel.	
	fl, cl, bsn, pf, 2vn, va, vc, db	Pet
Feldman, M.	Ixion. *3fl, cl, hn, tpt, trb, vc, db, pf*	Pet
Frid, G.	12 Metamorphoses, op. 54a.	
	2fl, 2ob, 2cl, 2bsn, hn, pf	SD
Friedlander, E.	Rhapsody for bassoon (1964).	
	bsn solo, ob, cl, bsn, hn, 2vn, va, vc, db	Can
Gabrieli, G.	Canzona No. 7 (1597). *5ww, 5str*	Pet
Gabrieli, G.-Winter	Canzone No. 10. *5ww, 5str*	Pet
Gruber, H.	Revue, op. 22. *fl, ob, cl, hn, bsn, 2vn, va, vc, db*	LDo
Guaccero, D.	" . . . Un Iter Segnato" (1960).	
	ob, cl, bsn, tpt, trb, str quintet	AlB
Harris, D.	Ludus. *fl, ob, cl, hn, bsn, 2vn, va, vc, db*	Job
Hartley, W.	Double Concerto.	
	asax, tu, fl, ob, cl, bsn, hn, 2tpt, trb	ArM
Hasquenoph, P.	Divertissement.	
	fl, ob, cl, bsn, hn, 2vn, va, vc, db	LDo
Haydn, F.-Landon	Cassatio, G. Hob. II: G 1.	
	2ob, 2hn, 2vn, 2va, vc, db	LDo
Hetu, J.	Cycle, op. 16 (1969).	
	fl, cl, bcl, bsn, hn, 2tpt, 2trb, pf	Can
Homs, J.	Polifonia (1965). *fl, ob, ehn, 2bsn, 2tpt, 3trb*	See
Hovhaness, A.	Tower Music. *fl, ob, cl, bsn, 2tpt, 2hn, trb, tu*	BB
Krommer, F.	Partita, op. 45/1.	
	2ob, 2cl, 2hn, 2bsn, cbsn, tpt	WIN
Kupferman, M.	Infinities Twelve.	
	pic, ob, ehn, cl, bcl, bsn, vn, vc, pf	Gen
Lutyens, E.	6 Tempi. *fl, ob, cl, bsn, hn, tpt, vn, va, vc, pf*	B-M
Malipiero, R.	Mosaico (1961).	
	fl, ob, cl, bsn, hn, 2vn, va, vc, db	ESZ
Malipiero, G.	Serenata Mattutina.	
	fl, ob, cl, 2bsn, 2hn, 2va, cel	UE
McCauley, W.	5 Miniatures (1968).	
	fl, ob, cl, bsn, 2hn, 2tpt, trb, tu	Can
Milhaud, D.	Concertino d'Automne. *fl, ob, 3hn, 2va, vc, 2pf*	Heu
Milhaud, D.	Concertino d'Eté.	
	fl, ob, cl, bsn, hn, tpt, va solo, 2vc, db	UE
Mills, C.	Chamber Concerto.	
	fl, ob, cl, bsn, 2hn, 2vn, va, vc	CoF
Moor, E.	Suite, op. 103.	
	fl, ob, cl, hn, bsn, 2vn, va, vc, db	EdS
Mozart, W.-Einstein	Galimathias Musicum (Quodlibet), K.V. 32.	
	2ob, 2hn, bsn, 2vn, va, vc, pf	Pet

Ten Instruments not including Harp, Guitar or Percussion

Nagel, R.	Divertimento. *fl, ob, cl, bsn, 2tpt, 2hn, trb, tu*	Men
Pedley, D. (arr)	3 English Tunes.	
	2fl, 2ob, 3cl, 2tpt(2hn), trb(bsn)	Cha
Persichetti, V.	Serenade No. 1.	
	fl, ob, cl, bsn, 2tpt, 2hn, trb, tu	E-V
Praag, H. van	Dixtuor (1949).	
	fl, ob, cl, bsn, hn, 2vn, va, vc, db	SD
Rawsthorne, A.	Concerto for Ten Instruments.	
	fl, ob, cl, bsn, hn, 2vn, va, vc, db	OxU
Razzi, F.	Musica (1968). *3ob, cl, 2bsn, 2tpt, 2trb*	ESZ
Schuller, G.	Double Quintet. *fl, ob, cl, bsn, 2hn,*	AMP
	2tpt, trb, tu	
Searle, H.	Variations and Finale, op. 34.	
	fl, ob, cl, bsn, hn, 2vn, va, vc, db	S&C
Stravinsky, I.	2 Sacred Songs (Spanisches Lieder Buch -	
	Wolf). *3cl, 2hn, 2vn, va, vc, db*	B&H
Triebensee, J.	Parthie, B♭. *2ob, 2cl, 2hn, 2bsn, cbsn, tpt*	WIN
Triebensee, J.	Variations on an Original Theme.	
	2ob, 2cl, 2hn, 2bsn, cbsn, tpt	WIN
Turner, R.	Variations and Toccata (1959).	
	fl, ob, cl, bsn, hn, str quintet	Can
Vranicky, P.	Jagermarsche. *2ob, 2cl, 2bsn, cbsn, 2hn, tpt*	B&N
Washburn, R.	Concertino. *fl, ob, cl, bsn, 2hn, 2tpt, trb, tu*	OxU

ELEVEN INSTRUMENTS

ELEVEN WOODWINDS (including horn)

Andriessen, J.	Concertino. *bsn solo, 2fl, 2ob, 2cl, 2bsn, 2hn*	SD
Brahms, J.	Herlich tut mich Verlangen, op. 122/10.	
	fl, afl, ob, ehn, bar ob, 2cl, bcl, 2bsn, cbsn	CP
Brant, H.	Angels and Devils. *3pic, 6fl, 2afl*	Pet
Gould (arr)	It Came Upon the Midnight Clear.	
	2fl, ob, 5cl, acl, bcl, bsn	Cha
Kroeger, K.	Suite. *2fl, 2ob, E♭ cl, 3cl, 2bcl, bsn*	CoF
Lewis, P.	Sestina. *2fl, 2ob, 2cl, bcl, 2bsn, 2hn*	CoF
Ponse, L.	Euterpe, op. 37 (1964).	
	2fl, 2ob, 3cl, 2bsn, 2hn	SD

ELEVEN INSTRUMENTS INCLUDING HARP

Boesmans, P.	Explosives. *fl, cl, 2vn, va, vc, db, pf, hp, 2perc*	Job
Gerschefski, E.	Prelude, op. 6/5.	
	pic, fl, ob, ehn, cl, bcl, hn, hp, 3perc	ACA
Hodeir, A.	Ambiquité I. *fl, E♭ cl, cl, bsn, hn, trb, hp, vib,*	
	pf, db, perc	MJQ
Maderna, B.	Serenata No. 2 (1957). *fl, cl, bcl, hn, tpt, vn,*	
	va, db, pf, perc, hp	ESZ
Maros, R.	Musica da camera.	
	fl, 2cl, 2vn, va, vc, db, hpcd, perc, hp	SMP
Mestres-Quadreny, J.	Conversa (1965).	
	fl, 2cl, tpt, pf, hp, perc, 2vn, va, vc	See
Rorem, N.	11 Studies for 11 Players.	
	fl, ob, cl, vn, va, vc, tpt, hp, 2perc, pf	JB

ELEVEN INSTRUMENTS INCLUDING GUITAR

Schuller, G.	Progression in Tempo. *fl, cl, 2vn, va, vc, db,*	
	pf, guit, vib, perc	MJQ

ELEVEN INSTRUMENTS INCLUDING PERCUSSION

Adler, S.	Music for 11.	
	2fl, ob, cl, bcl, bsn, timp, xyl, 3perc	OxU
Antoniou, T.	Concertino, op. 21 (1963).	
	fl, ob, 2cl, 2bsn, 2hn, tpt, perc, pf	B&N
Benvenuti, A.	3 Studies (1960-61).	
	fl, cl, bsn, hn, tpt, trb, vn, va, vc, pf, xyl	AlB
Boesmans, P.	Explosives. *fl, cl, 2vn, va, vc, db, pf, hp, 2perc*	Job
Bois, R. du	Cercle (1963).	
	fl, ob, 2cl, 2bsn, 2hn, tpt, perc, pf	SD

Eleven Instruments including Percussion

Bortolotti, M.	Studio per cummings No. 2 (1964).	
	ob, cl, E♭ cl/sax, bcl, hn, va, vc, db, 3perc	ESZ
Brun, H.	Gestures for Eleven. *fl/pic, ob/ehn, cl/bcl,*	
	bsn/cbsn, hn, tpt, trb, vn, va, db, perc/pf	WLP
Croley, R.	Concerto for Flute & Metal Orchestra.	
	fl, 4trb, tu, timp, pf, 3perc	JB
Davidovsky, M.	Inflexions.	
	2fl, cl, tpt, trb, perc, pf, vn, va, vc, db	EBM
Feldman, M.	Eleven Instruments. *fl, afl, hn, tpt, bass tpt,*	
	vn, vc, trb, tu, vib, pf	Pet
Gerschefski, E.	Prelude, op. 6/5.	
	pic, fl, ob, ehn, cl, bcl, hn, hp, 3perc	ACA
Hespos, H.	break. *ob, 3tpt, tsax, bar sax,*	
	vc, db, trb, pf, perc	EMo
Hodeir, A.	Ambiquité I. *fl, E♭ cl, cl, bsn, hn, trb, hp,*	
	vib, pf, db, perc	MJQ
Maderna, B.	Serenata No. 2 (1957).	
	fl, cl, bcl, hn, tpt, vn, va, db, pf, perc, hp	ESZ
Maros, R.	Musica da camera.	
	fl, 2cl, 2vn, va, vc, db, hpcd, perc, hp	SMP
Mayer, W.	Essay. *fl, ob, cl, bsn, 2hn, 2tpt, trb, tu, perc*	B&H
Mestral, P.	Alliages. *fl, cl, asax, 2trb, 2perc, pf, org,*	
	db, tpt solo	Job
Mestres-Quadreny, J.	Conversa (1965).	
	fl, 2cl, tpt, pf, hp, perc, 2vn, va, vc	See
Pablo, L. de	Modulos I (1964-65).	
	3cl, 2vn, va, vc, 2pf, 2perc	EdT
Pablo, L. de	Polar (1961). *bcl, sop sax, vn, 8perc*	EdT
Parris, R.	The Golden Net. *fl, ob, cl, bsn, hn, tpt, vn,*	
	va, vc, timp, perc	ACA
Rorem, N.	11 Studies for 11 Players.	
	fl, ob, cl, tpt, 2perc, hp, vn, va, vc, pf	JB

ELEVEN INSTRUMENTS NOT INCLUDING
HARP, GUITAR, OR PERCUSSION

Andriessen, J.	Hommage à Milhaud (1945). *fl, ob, cl, bsn,*	
	hn, tpt, trb, sax, vn, va, vc	SD
Bach, J.S.- Winschermann	Die Kunst der Fuge. *ob, ob d'amore, ehn, bsn,* *vn, 2va, vc, db, 2hpcd*	HSM
Bauer, M.	Patterns, op. 31/2. *2fl, 2ob, 2cl, 2bsn, 2hn, db*	CoF
Christiansen, C.	Leksaksasken, svit.	
	2fl, ob, 2cl, 2bsn, 2hn, tpt, trb	CGM
Crawford, J.	Lob der Musik.	
	fl, ob, cl, bsn, 2hn, 2vn, va, vc, db	CoF

Eleven Instruments not including Harp, Guitar or Percussion

Donatoni, F.	Movimento (1959).	
	3fl, 2cl, bsn, 2hn, tpt, hpcd, pf	ESZ
Donatoni, F.	Movimento (1950).	
	3fl, 2cl, bsn, 2hn, tpt, hpcd, pf	ESZ
Dvorak, A.	March (Serenade).	
	2ob, 2cl, 2bsn, cbsn ad lib, 3hn, vc, db	EBM
Frid, G.	12 Metamorphosen, op. 54a (1963).	
	2fl, 2ob, 2cl, 2bsn, 2hn, pf	SD
Godron, H.	Amabile-suite (1943). *cl, 4vn, 2va, 2vc, db, pf*	SD
Goeb, R.	Concertant IIIb. *va, 2fl, 2ob, 2cl, 2bsn, 2hn*	CoF
Malipiero, G.	Ricercari. *fl, ob, cl, bsn, hn, 4va, vc, db*	UE
Malipiero, G.	Ritrovari. *fl, ob, cl, bsn, hn, 4va, vc, db*	UE
Phillips, I.	Easy Arrangements. *2fl, 2ob, 3cl, 2hn, bsn, pf*	OxU
Purebel, J.	Concerto for E♭ Clarinet.	
	fl, 2E♭ cl, 2cl, 2hn, 2bsn, cbsn, tpt	WIN
Rayki, G.	Burleske. *fl, ob, 2cl, 2bsn, tpt, 3hn, trb*	UE
Sellner, J.	Variations, Nr. 1.	
	cl solo, cl, 2ob, 2hn, 2tpt, 2bsn, cbsn	WIN
Soler, J.	Movement for 11 (1966).	
	fl, 2cl, 2tpt, hn, trb, tu, vn, va, vc	See
Steiner, G.	Movements for Eleven.	
	fl/pic, 2cl, hn, 2tpt, trb, tu, vn, va, vc	CoF
Vern, A.	Nocturne en Harmonie.	
	fl, 2cl, 2hn, 2bsn, 2ob, tpt, trb	EdH

TWELVE INSTRUMENTS

TWELVE INSTRUMENTS (including horn)

Ganz, R.	Woody Scherzo.	
	pic, 2fl, 2ob, ehn, E♭ cl, 2cl, 2bsn, cbsn	B-M
Gould (arr)	Away In a Manger; O Little Town	
	of Bethlehem. 2fl, 2ob, 2cl, 2bsn, 4hn	Cha
Strauss, R.	Suite. 2fl, 2ob, 2cl, 2bsn, 4hn	M&M
Triebensee, J.	"Echo" Partita. 3ob, 3cl, 4hn, 2bsn	WIN

TWELVE INSTRUMENTS INCLUDING HARP

Birtwistle, H.	The World is Discovered. 2fl, ob, ehn, cl,	
	basset hn(bcl), 2bsn, 2hn, hp, guit	UE
Ketting, O.	2 Canzoni. fl, ob, 2cl, bsn, 2hn, tpt, trb, perc,	
	cel, hp	SD
Lewis, R.	Music for 12 Players. fl, cl, bsn, hn, tpt, trb,	
	vib, hp, vn, vc, db, pf	TP
Milhaud, D.	Stanford Serenade. ob solo, fl, cl, bsn, tpt,	
	2vn, va, vc, db, perc, hp	EME
Southers, L., Jr.	Concert Piece (1965). fl, ob, cl, bsn, hn, 2vn,	
	va, vc, db, hp, perc	Can
Wuorinen, C.	Canzona (to the memory of Igor Stravinsky).	
	fl, ob/ehn, cl/bcl, bsn, tpt, vn, va, vc, db,	
	hp, vib, pf	Pet

TWELVE INSTRUMENTS INCLUDING GUITAR

Birtwistle, H.	The World is Discovered. 2fl, ob, ehn, cl,	
	basset hn(bcl), 2bsn, 2hn, hp, guit	UE
Reck, D.	Number I for Twelve Performers.	
	fl, cl, tsax, hn, va, db, guit, vib, pf, 3perc	MJQ
Schuller, G.	Variants on a Theme of John Lewis (Django).	
	fl, asax/fl, vib, guit, pf,	
	2vn, va, vc, 2db, perc	MJQ

TWELVE INSTRUMENTS INCLUDING PERCUSSION

Edler, R.	Reflexions (1963).	
	cl, vn, va, vc, hn, trb, pf, vib, 4perc	EdT
Handel, G.-Kahn	Firework Music I. 3ob, 2bsn, 3tpt, 3hn, timp	EBM
Hiller, L.	Divertimento. pic, fl, ob, cl, bsn, hn, tpt, trb,	
	db, guit, 2perc	TP
Ketting, O.	2 Canzoni. fl, ob, 2cl, bsn, 2hn, tpt, trb,	
	perc, cel, hp	SD

Twelve Instruments including Percussion

Kurtz, E.	Conversations. *fl, ob, cl, hn, tpt, perc, pf, 2vn, va, vc, db*	Job
Lewis, A.	Pieces of Eight. *fl, 2ob, 3cl, bsn, 2tsax, hn, bar, perc*	CoA
Lewis, P.	Lament for Mrs. Bridge. *pic, fl, ob, cbsn, 2hn, tpt, trb, 3db, perc*	CoF
Lewis, R.	Music for 12 Players. *fl, cl, bsn, hn, tpt, trb, vib, hp, vn, vc, db, pf*	TP
Milhaud, D.	Stanford Serenade. *ob solo, fl, cl, bsn, tpt, 2vn, va, vc, db, perc, hp*	EME
Reck, D.	Number 1 for Twelve Performers. *fl, cl, tsax, hn, guit, vib, pf, va, db, 3perc*	MJQ
Schuller, G.	Variants on a Theme of John Lewis (Django). *fl, asax/fl, vib, guit, pf, 2vn, va, vc, 2db, perc*	MJQ
Southers, L., Jr.	Concert Piece (1965). *fl, ob, cl, bsn, hn, 2vn, va, vc, db, hp, perc*	Can
Tremblay, G.	Champs II (Souffles) (1968). *2fl, ob, cl, hn, 2tpt, 2trb, db, pf, perc*	Can
Wuorinen, C.	Canzona (to the memory of Igor Stravinsky). *fl, ob/ehn, cl/bcl, bsn, tpt, vn, va, vc, db, hp, vib, pf*	Pet

TWELVE INSTRUMENTS NOT INCLUDING HARP, GUITAR, OR PERCUSSION

Bauer, M.	Aguarelle, op. 39/2. *2fl, 2ob, 2cl, 2bsn, 2hn, 2db*	CoF
Dvorak, A.	Serenade, op. 44. *2ob, 2cl, 3bsn, 3hn, vc, db*	Int
Dvorak, A.	Serenade, d, op. 44. *2ob, 2cl, 2bsn, cbsn, 3hn, vc, db*	MR
Horvath, J.	"Redundanz 3." *wind octet, 2vn, va, vc*	LDo
Jadin, L.	Symphonie für Blasinstrumente. *2fl, 2cl, 2bsn, serpent(bsn), 2hn, 2tpt, trb*	FrH
Klusak, J.	Sonata (1963/65). *solo vn, fl, 2ob, 2cl, 2hn, 2bsn, tpt, trb*	EMo
Macchi, E.	Composizione 3 (1960). *fl, ob, cl, bsn, hn, tpt, trb, vn, 2va, vc, db*	AlB
Milhaud, D.	Stanford Serenade. *ob solo, fl, cl, bsn, tpt, 2vn, va, vc, db, perc, hp*	EME
Penderecki, K.	Capriccio. *ob, 11str*	JB
Rayki, G.	Burleske. *fl, ob, 2cl, 2bsn, 3hn, 2tpt, trb*	UE
Stachowiak, L.	3 Improvisations (1963). *3fl, 3cl, 2hn, 2vn, va, vc*	AP
Stravinsky, I.	Concertino. *fl, ob, ehn, cl, 2bsn, 2tpt, trb, bass trb, vn, vc*	Che
Vlad, R.	Serenata (1959). *fl, 2ob, 2cl, 2bsn, 2hn, 2va, cel*	ESZ

THIRTEEN INSTRUMENTS

THIRTEEN WOODWINDS (including horn)

Anderson, L.	Suite of Carols. *pic, 2fl, 2ob, ehn, 2cl, acl, bcl, 2bsn, cbsn*	B-M
Bach, J.S.-Christlieb	Ach Bleib bei uns Herr Jesu Christ. *pic, fl, ob, ob d'amore, ehn, bar ob, 2cl, bcl, 3bsn, cbsn*	CP
Brahms, J.	O Gott du frommer Gott, op. 122/7. *fl, afl, 2ob, ehn, bar ob, 2cl, bcl, 3bsn, cbsn*	CP
Mozart, W.	Serenade No. 10, B♭, K. 361. *2ob, 2cl, 2basset hn, 2bsn, cbsn, 4hn*	BrH
Mozart, W.	Serenade No. 10, B♭, K. 361. *2ob, 2cl, 2basset hn(2cl), 2bsn, cbsn(db), 4hn*	BB
Mozart, W.	Serenade No. 10, B♭, K. 361. *2ob, 2cl, 2basset hn(2cl), 2bsn, cbsn(db), 4hn*	MR
Spino, P.	Statement for Horn and Woodwinds. *solo hn, 2fl, ob, 3cl, bcl, bsn, 2asax, tsax, bar sax*	StM
Strauss, R.	Serenade, E♭, op. 7. *2fl, 2ob, 2cl, 2bsn, cbsn, 4hn*	UE
Strauss, R.	Serenade, op. 7, E♭. *2fl, 2ob, 2cl, 2bsn, cbsn, 4hn*	MR
Strauss, R.	Serenade, op. 7. *2fl, 2ob, 2cl, 2bsn, cbsn, 4hn*	EdK
Strauss, R.	Serenade, op. 7. *2fl, 2ob, 2cl, 2bsn, cbsn, 4hn*	Int

THIRTEEN INSTRUMENTS INCLUDING GUITAR

Hespos, H.	Keime und Male. *pic, fl, 2cl, asax, hn, guit, vn, va, db, 3perc*	Job
Schifrin, L.	Ritual of Sound. *fl, cl, bcl, hn, 2tpt, trb, tu, guit, vib, 2db, perc*	MJQ

THIRTEEN INSTRUMENTS INCLUDING PERCUSSION

Andriessen, J.	Rouw past Electra. *fl, 2ob, cl, 2bsn, hn, 2tpt, 2trb, timp, perc*	SD
Ferrari, L.	Flashes. *pic, ob, cl, bsn, hn, tpt, trb, 2vn, va, vc, db, perc*	EMT
Fields, F.	Chant Ritual No. 1. *12ww, timp*	SMP
Fritsch, J.	Modulation II. *fl/pic, ehn, bcl, tpt, 2trb, 2pf, perc, vn, va, vc, db*	Fab
Hespos, H.	Keime und Male. *pic, fl, 2cl, asax, hn, guit, vn, va, db, 3perc*	Job

Thirteen Instruments including Percussion

Reynolds, R.	Quick Are the Mouths of Earth.	
	3fl/pic, ob, 3vc, tpt, 2trb, 2perc, pf	Pet
Schiffrin, L.	Ritual of Sound. *fl, cl, bcl, hn, 2tpt, trb, tu,*	
	guit, vib, 2db, perc	MJQ
Soler, J.	The Vision of the Mystic Lamb (1968). *fl, ob,*	
	cl, hn, trb, tu, vib, cel, 4perc, pf solo	See
Tcherepnin, N.	Sonatine, op. 61.	
	2fl, 2ob, cl, 2bsn, hn, 2tpt, trb, timp, xyl	Be

THIRTEEN INSTRUMENTS NOT INCLUDING
HARP, GUITAR, OR PERCUSSION

Hedwall, L.	Partita (1961).	
	2fl, 2ob, 2cl, 2bsn, 2hn, 2tpt, trb	STI
Hemel, O. van	Divertimento No. 2 (1959).	
	2fl, 2ob, 2cl, 2bsn, 2hn, 2tpt, pf	SD
Huggler, J.	Music for 13 Instruments, op. 75.	
	2fl, ob, 2cl, bcl, bsn, cbsn, 2hn, tpt, trb, vc	ACA
Schwartz, E.	Texture for Strings, Winds, & Brass (1966).	
	13 players	BB
Spies	LXXXV. *5cl, 3vn, 3va, 2vc*	B&H

CHOIRS

FLUTE CHOIR

Organn, R.	Gentle Breezes	Reb
Organn, R.	Oriental Phantasy	Reb
Organn, R.	Summer Evening	Reb

CLARINET CHOIR

Bach, J.S.-Sacci	Air (Suite No. 3, D)	Ken
Bach, J.S.-Cailliet	Awake, Awake, A Voice Is Calling	Leb
Bach, J.S.-Underwood	Fantasia and Fugue, c	Ken
Bach, J.S.-Lang	Fuga XVI	Lan
Bach, J.S.-Ward	Gavotte	PrA
Bach, J.S.-Yates	Prelude in D	Ken
Bach, J.S.-Schmidt	Prelude, F	Wes
Bach, J.S.-Jennings	Prelude and Fugue, g	Ken
Bach, J.S.-Hite	Praeludium and Fugue, d	SM
Bach, J.S.-Fote	Praeludium XXII	Ken
Bach, J.S.-Howland	Sacred Head	Cre
Bach, J.S.-Fote	Sarabande (French Suite, d)	Ken
Bach, J.S.-Kikr	Siciliano and Minuet	SM
Bach, J.S.-Howland	Sinfonia (Christmas Oratorio)	Cre
Bach, J.S.-Howland	3 Baroque Dances	Reb
Bach, J.S.-Ross	2 Bach Preludes	Ken
Barat, J.-Roach	Piece in g minor	Leb
Barber, S.-Cailliet	Adagio for Strings	Sch
Bargiel, W.	Meditation	CF
Bartok, B.-Morris	Evening Walk (10 Easy Pieces)	PrA
Bartok, B.-Erickson	Folk Song Suite	Sch
Beethoven, L.-Sacci	Adagio Cantabile (Sonata Pathetique)	Ken
Bizet, G.-Cailliet	Adagietto (L'Arlesienne)	Leb
Bizet, G.-Feldsher	Allegro & Vivace (Symphony)	Tem
Bloch, E.-O'Reilly	Prelude and Processional	Sch
Boccherini, L.	Menuet	CF
Bolzoni, G.-McCathren-Pardee	Minuetto, B♭	Ken
Borodin, A.-Cabral	Nocturne (Quartet No. 4)	Ken
Borodin, A.-Nestico	Nocturne (String Quartet No. 4)	Ken
Brahms, J.-Fote	Chorale Prelude No. 8	Ken
Brahms, J.-Fote	Chorale Prelude No. 11	Ken
Brown, R.	Symphony for Clarinets	Wes
Cable, H.	Wind Song	Cha
Cacavas, J.	Barcarolle	ShB
Cacavas, J.	2 Miniatures	E-V
Cailliet, L.	Caprice Sentimental	Leb
Cailliet, L.	Carnaval	Leb
Cailliet, L.	Clarinet Poem	Leb
Cailliet, L.	Fantaisie	Leb

259

Clarinet Choir

Casteel-Boellmann	Suite Gothique	Leb
Chopin, F.-Underwood	Nocturne, op. 15/3	Ken
Clerisse, R.-Roach	Vielle Chanson	Leb
Corelli, A.-Thornton	Church Sonata, op. 1/2	SM
Corelli, A.-Morris	Folies d'Espagne	PrA
Debussy, C.-Howland	Ballet (Petite Suite)	Cre
Debussy, C.-Howland	Cortege (Petite Suite)	Cre
Debussy, C.-Howland	En Bateau (Petite Suite)	Cre
Debussy, C.-Howland	Minuet (Petite Suite)	Cre
Debussy, C.-Conley	Nuages	Ken
Debussy, C.-Barnes	Sarabande	Tem
Debussy, C.-Davis	Sarabande	Wes
DeJesu, J.	Largo Appassionata	Hal
DeJesu, J.	Prelude to Traviata	Hal
DeJesu, J.	To a Wild Rose	Hal
Dvorak, A.	Humoresque	CF
Fauré, G.-Lester	Pavane, op. 50	Wes
Findlay, F.	From Sweden	CF
Frackenpohl, A.	Prelude and Allegro	Sha
Franck, C.-Nyquist	Cantabile	Ken
Gabrielli, G.-Ayres	Canzona per Sonare No. 2	Bar
Frescobaldi, G.-Fote	Fugue	Ken
Frescobaldi, G.-Underwood	Ricercare	Ken
Galliard, J.-Howland	Pavane	Reb
Gates, E.	Seasonal Sketches	Leb
Handel, G.-Fote	Arioso	Ken
Handel, G.-Sacci	Larghetto	Ken
Handel, G.-Hite	Largo and Allegro (Concerto Grosso No. 2)	SM
Handel, G.	Largo and Gigue	YM
Handel, G.	Largo (Xerxes)	CF
Handel, G.-Wilcox	Overture to "Julius Caesar"	Sha
Handel, G.-Webb	Pastoral Symphony (The Messiah)	Ken
Handel, G.-Webb	Sarabande and Bourrée	Ken
Haydn, F.-Stouffer	Allegro	PrA
Haydn, F.-Hindsley	Divertimento No. 1	SM
Haydn, F.-Feldsher	Menuetto and Trio (Symphony No. 88)	Ken
Haydn, F.-Feldsher	Menuetto and Trio (Symphony No. 94)	Tem
Haydn, F.-Organn	Minuet (Quartet, op. 20/4)	Reb
Haydn, F.-Organn	Minuet (Quartet, op. 2/4)	Reb
Haydn, F.-Feldsher	Presto	PrA
Haydn, F.-Troxell	Rondo (Divertimento No. 1)	PrA
Jarcho-McCathren	Lady of Spain	SF
Karel, L.	Elegy and Danse	Leb
Kepner, F.	Playground. opt rhythm	SM
Klauss, N.-McCathren	Clarinetics	Ken
Klauss, N.	Girl with the White Dog	S-B
Klauss, N.	Jakarta. hn, cl choir	CoA
Klauss, N.-McCathren	Prayer from "Evangeline"	Ken
Klauss, N.	Song for Twilight	PrA

Clarinet Choir

Krenek, E.-Erickson	3 Short Pieces in Twelve-Tone Technique	Sch
Kroeger, K.	2 Pieces	CoF
Kuhlau, F.-Organn	Allegro (Sonatina, op. 20/1)	Reb
Kuhlau, F.-Organn	Rondo (Sonatina, op. 20/1)	Reb
Lang, R.	Grenadilla Rhapsody	Lan
Lang, R.	Opus in Ebony	Lan
Laube, P.	Alsatian Dance	CF
Logan, R.	Andante	Hal
Lotti, A.	Arietta	EdM
Loucheur, R.	En famille	B&V
MacDowell, E.-Ross	At An Old Trysting Place	Ken
Maganini, Q.	Shenandoah	EdM
Magnani, A.	Reverie	CF
Marie, G.	Berceuse	CF
Martini, P.	Plaisir d'Amour	EdM
Massenet, J.-Cailliet	Angelus	Leb
McCathren, D.-Reed	Clarinette Valsante	Ken
McCathren, D.-Klauss	Electronic Brain	Ken
McCathren, D.-Klauss	Lullaby for an E♭ Clarinet	Ken
Mendelssohn, F.-Feldsher	Allegro Vivace	PrA
Mendelssohn, F.-Howland	Saltarello (Symphony No. 4)	Cre
Mendelssohn, F.-Webb	Tarantella, op. 102/3	Ken
Mendelssohn, F.-Fote	Variation Serieuses, op. 54	Ken
Moross, J.	Sonatina	Cha
Mozart, W.-Howland	Adagio, K. 411	Reb
Mozart, W.-Sacci	Adagio (Quintet, g)	Ken
Mozart, W.-Fisher	Allegro (Quintet, K. 407). *hn, cl choir*	Ken
Mozart, W.-Ried	Andante (Divertimento No. 1)	Ken
Mozart, W.-Ried	Andante (Divertimento No. 1) K. 136)	Ken
Mozart, W.-Dominik	Divertimento No. 8	Reb
Mozart, W.-Johnson	Divertimento No. 6	Rub
Mozart, W.-Sacci	Eine Kleine Nachtmusik (1st movement)	Ken
Mozart, W.-Sacci	Eine Kleine Nachtmusik (4th movement)	Ken
Mozart, W.-Sacci	Eine Kleine Nachtmusik (2nd movement)	Ken
Mozart, W.-Sacci	Eine Kleine Nachtmusik (3rd movement)	Ken
Mozart, W.-Howland	Impresario Overture	Cre
Mozart, W.-Cailliet	Marriage of Figaro Overture	Leb
Mozart, W.-Sacci	Menuetto (Quintet, g)	Ken
Mozart, W.-Mutch	Minuet (Symphony No. 40)	Ken
Mozart, W.-Casteel-McCathren	Overture to Cosi Fan Tutte	Ken
Mozart, W.-Pillin	Rondo	Wes
Mozart, W.-Frackenpohl	Sinfonietta	Sha
Mozart, W.-Morris	Theme (Concerto No. 21)	PrA
Murray, L.	Clarinet Capriole	Wes
Nelhybel, V.	Chorale and Danza	Leb

Clarinet Choir

Nelhybel, V.	Ricercare. *cl & sax choirs*	Leb
Nelhybel, V.	Suite No. 1	ECK
Nestico, S.	A Study in Contrasts	Ken
Offenbach, J.	Beggars's Canon (The Brigands)	Sch
Oliver, R.	Lord Randall	EdM
Organn, R.	The Brook	Reb
Organn, R.	The Brook. *asax, cl choir*	Reb
Organn, R.	The Brook. *bsn, cl choir*	Reb
Organn, R.	Divertimento	Reb
Organn, R.	Maulawiyah	Reb
Organn, R.	Overture for Woodwinds	Reb
Organn, R.	Preghiera (Prayer)	Reb
Organn, R.	Suite Petite	Reb
Osterling, A.	A Study in Lavender	SM
Owen, H.	Fantasies on Mexican Tunes. *3tpt, cl choir*	Wes
Pachelbel, J.-Fote	Fuga	Ken
Palestrina, G.-Conley	Adoramus Te	Ken
Pezel, J.-Earle	3 Pieces	Ken
Pleyel, I.	Rondo	CF
Presser, W.	Choral Fantasy	Leb
Rarig, J.	Untitled Poem	Ken
Ravel, M.-Hite	Pavane	SM
Raymond, L.	Chorale in Gregorian Style	Wes
Rimsky-Korsakov, N.-Roach	Danse des Bouffons	Leb
Rimsky-Korsakov, N.-Cailliet	The Flight of the Bumble Bee. *asax, cl choir*	Leb
Roden, R.	Difference of Opinion	Leb
Roden, R.	2 Water Colors	SM
Roden, R.	Waltz and Beguine	SM
Saint-Saens, C.-Cailliet	Romance, F. *asax, cl choir*	Leb
Schaeffer, D.	The Clarinet Choir	PrA
Schein, J.	A Musical Banquet	EdM
Schinstine, W.	March	SM
Schmidt, W.	Vendor's Call. *pf, cl choir*	Wes
Schubert, F.	Rosamunde	CF
Schubert, F.-Sacci	Scherzo, op. 166	Ken
Schumann, R.-Fote	Opus 68, No. 30	Ken
Schumann, R.-Fote	Spring Song	Ken
Schwartz-Hite	Vienna Baroque	Lud
Snavely, J.	Motif and Variations	Ken
Stravinsky, I.-Lester	Ronde des Princesses	Wes
Tamiami, C.	4 Eary American Spirituals	Wes
Tartini, G.-Jacob	Concertino	B&H
Tchaikovsky, P.-Sacci	Andante Cantabile	Ken
Tchaikovsky, P.-Cailliet	Canzonetta (Violin Concerto). *asax, cl choir*	Leb
Tchaikovsky, P.-Casteel	Chanson Triste	Bar
Tchaikovsky, P.-Cailliet	Finale (Violin Concerto). *cl, cl choir*	Leb
Tchaikovsky, P.-Conley	Humoreske	Ken

Clarinet Choir

Tchaikovsky, P.-Sacci	Waltz	
	(Serenade for Strings, op. 48)	Ken
Telemann, G.-Johnson	Largo and Presto (Suite, a)	Rub
Telemann, G.-Johnson	Polonaise and Passepieds	
	(Suite, a)	Rub
Underwood, J. (arr)	Schumann Suite	Ken
Villa-Lobos, H.-Krance	Bachianas Brasileiras No. 5: Aria	AMP
Voxman, H.	Clarinet Choir Repertoire	Rub
Yoder, P. (arr)	Bach Suite	Leb
Zingarelli, N.-Joseph	Motet	Ken

MISCELLANEOUS CHOIR

Bach, J.S.-Gee	Bourree. *ww choir*	Sha
Chavez, C.	Xochipilli. *ww choir*	B-M
Klauss, N.	Night Song. *sax choir*	CoA
Marshall, J.	Goldrush Suite. *ww choir*	Sha
Organn, R.	Gentle Breezes. *fl choir*	Reb
Organn, R.	Oriental Phantasy. *fl choir*	Reb
Organn, R.	Summer Evening. *fl choir*	Reb
Schubert, F.-Hovey	Finale (Symphony No. 5).	
	ww choir	Sha
Schubert, F.-Hovey	Menuetto and Trio	
	(Symphony No. 5). *ww choir*	Sha
Verral, J.	Elegy. *ob, ww choir*	CoF

FLEXIBLE INSTRUMENTATION

Bantai, V. & I. Kovacs (ed)	Leichte Kammermusik.	
	1, 2, or 3fl, pf	Eul
Porcelijn, D.	Amoebe for X Flutes	SD

VOICE AND INSTRUMENTS

	4 Hungarian Folksongs. *S, fl, ob, cl, bsn, hn*	MR
-Maxwell	The Water of Tyne. *S, cl, pf*	S&C
Abbado, M.	Cantata (1948). *V, fl, cl, vn, va, vc, pf*	ESZ
Adam, A.-Schmidt	Bravour-Variationen. *V, fl, pf*	R&E
Adam, A.-Liebling	Bravura Variations. *V, fl, pf*	Sch
Ahlberg, G.	Mosaik. *S, 3 sax*	STI
Aitken, H.	Cantata No. 1. *T, ob, vn, vc*	OxU
Aitken, H.	Cantata No. 2. *T, fl, ob, vc, db*	OxU
Aitken, H.	Cantata No. 3. *T, ob, va*	AMC
Aitken, H.	Cantata No. 4. *S, fl, ob, vc, db*	OxU
Alabieff, A.-Dies	The Nightingale. *S, fl, pf*	Sch
Alabieff, A.-Liebling	The Russian Nightingale. *S, fl, pf*	Sch
Alain, J.	Messe modale en septuor. *S, A, fl, 2vn, va,*	
	vc(org)	LDo
Anders, E.	Flötenlieder, op. 109. *S, fl, pf*	WZ
Anhalt, I.	Chansons d'Aurore (1955). *S, fl, pf*	Can
Anonymous (18th	Menuet en Air. *S, fl, bc*	B&V
cent.)-Flothuis		
Antoniou, T.	Epilog nach Homers Odyssee. *MS, V, ob,*	
	hn, guit, pf, db, perc	B&N
Apostel, H.-Felmayr	5 Lieder, op. 22. *V, fl, cl, bsn*	UE
Arne, T.-Salkeld	A Wood Nymph. *S, fl, pf*	S&C
Arne, T.-Salkeld	The Morning. *S, fl, pf*	S&C
Arne, T.-Bergmann	Under the Greenwood Tree. *S, fl, pf*	S&C
Arrigo, G.	*S, 4 fl(one player)*	Heu
Avni, T.	Collage. *V, fl, perc, tape*	Isr
Babbitt, M.	2 Sonnets. *Bar, cl, va, vc*	AMP
Bach, J.S.	Aus Liebe will mein Heiland sterben. *S, fl,*	
	2 ob da caccia	B&H
Bach, J.S.-Dürr	Ensurientes (Magnificat). *A, 2 fl, pf, vc ad lib*	S&C
Bach, J.S.-Champion	Jesu Praise (Cantata No. 152). *MS, 2 fl, pf*	S&C
Bach, J.S.-Hunt	Sheep May Safely. *S, 2 fl, pf*	S&C
Bach, J.S.-Hunt	Stone Above All Others Treasured. *S, fl, vn, pf*	S&C
Bach, J.S.	Süsser Trost, mein Jesus kommt. *S, fl, bc*	B&H
Bach, J.S.-Champion	Yet Jesus Will the Righteous Keep. *A, 2 fl, ehn*	S&C
Baird, T.	Chansons des Trouveres. *MS, 2 fl, vc*	AP
Ballif, C.	Retrouver la parole, op. 33. *S, pic, fl, cl, bcl,*	
	pf, vn, va, vc	B&B
Barnes, M.	Nocturnes (1961). *S, fl*	Can
Barnes, M.	Poems for Voice and Flute - No. 2 "The New	
	Year" (1964). *V, fl*	Can
Bazlik, M.	5 Songs of Chinese Poetry (1960). *A, fl, vc, pf*	SHF
Beale, J.	Prayer, op. 35. *S, fl, pf*	CoF
Becker, G.	Moirologie. *S, E♭ cl, cl, bcl, hp*	WZ
Becker, G.	Rigolo (1967). *V, fl, cl, vn, vc, pf, tape*	HG
Beckwith, J.	The Great Lakes Suite (1949). *S, Bar, cl, vc, pf*	Can
Bedford, D.	Music for Albion Moonlight. *S, fl, cl, vn, vc,*	
	pf, harmonica	UE
Beecroft, N.	Elegy; Two Went to Sleep (1967). *S, fl, tape*	Can
Beekhuis, H.	Dans en pastorale. *V, fl, vn, pf*	B&V

Beekhuis, H.	Middeleeuws Kerstliedje. *V, fl, 3 vn, vc*	B&V
Bellini, V.-Liebling	It Was Here in Accents Tender. *S, fl, pf*	Sch
Bender, J.	From Heaven High, I Come to Earth. *SA or TB, vn, ob, vc, org*	Con
Benedict, J.	The Gipsy and the Bird. *V, fl, pf*	B&H
Benedict, Sir J.	The Wren. *S, fl, pf*	Sch
Benguerel, X.	Dos Canciones (1965). *MS, fl, pf*	See
Benhamou, M.	Mizmor 114 - Chir. *S, fl, hn, tpt, trb, vn, va, vc, db, vib, mar, perc*	Job
Bentzon, J.	Microphony, op. 44 (1939). *Bar, fl, vn, vc, pf*	SPD
Benvenuti, A.	Cantus Gemellus (1961). *S, fl*	AlB
Berger, A.	3 Poems of Yeats. *V, fl, cl, pf*	TP
Bergmann, W.	Pastorale. *A, fl*	S&C
Berio, L.	Chamber Music (1953). *V, cl, vc, hp*	ESZ
Berio, L.	O King. *MS, fl, cl, vn, vc, pf*	UE
Bettinelli, B.	La Terra. *S, cl, pf*	GZ
Betts, L.	Prelude for Spring (1951). *MS, Bar, fl, hp, 2 vn, va, vc*	Can
Birtwistle, H.	Entr'actes and Sappho Fragments. *S, fl, ob, vn, va, hn, perc*	UE
Birtwistle, H.	Monody for Corpus Christi. *S, fl, vn, hn*	UE
Birtwistle, H.	Ring a Dumb Carillon. *S, cl, perc*	UE
Bishop, Sir H.-Deis	Lo! Here the Gentle Lark. *S, fl, pf*	Sch
Bissell, K.	Overheard on a Saltmarsh. *MS, fl, pf*	ECK
Blacher, B.	5 Negro Spirituals (1962). *V, 3 cl, trb, db, perc*	B&B
Blacher, B.	Jazz-Koloraturen (1929). *S, asax, bsn*	B&B
Blacher, B.-Beyer	3 Psalmen (1943). *Bar, cl, bsn, vn, va, vc, org*	B&B
Blank, A.	Don't let that Horse eat that Violin. *S, bsn or S, vn, bsn*	See
Blank, A.	The Pennycandystore beyond the El. *S, bsn*	See
Bliss, A.	Madam Noy. *S, fl, cl, bsn, va, db, hp*	WH
Bliss, A.	2 Nursery Rhymes. *S, cl, pf*	WH
Blumenfeld, H.	Lovescapes. *S, fl, ob, cl, bsn, hn, str trio*	See
Boogaard, V. van	Synthetic Poeme. *MS, asax, bcl, pf*	SD
Bortolotti, M.	*V, cl, vn, db, trb, pf*	EdT
Bottenberg, W.	Those Passions . . . Which Yet Survive (1968) *B, fl, cl, vn, va, vc, perc*	Can
Boulez, P.	"Le Marteau sans Maitre". *V, fl, va, vib, guit, 2 perc*	UE
Bozay, A.	Slips of Paper (1962). *S, cl, vc*	EMB
Bresgen, C.	4 Gesange (1965). *Bar, cl, db, perc, pf*	HG
Breuer, H.	In memoriam Hans Arp (1968). *S, fl, tsax, tpt, pf/cel, db, perc*	B&N
Broder, T.	6 Rubaiyyat of Khayyam (1958). *S, fl, cl*	Isr
Brott, A.	Sept for Seven (1954). *nar, cl, asax, vn, va, vc, pf*	Can
Brugk, H.	Leuchgende Nacht, op. 18. *V, fl, pf*	Sim
Buczynski, W.	How Some Things Look (1967). *S, fl, cl, vc, pf*	Can

Voice and Instruments

Buczynski, W.	Milosc (Love) (1967). *S, fl, pf*	Can
Buczynski, W.	2 French Love Poems (1967). *S, fl, pf*	Can
Bujarski, Z.	Chamber Piece (1963). *V, fl, hp, pf, perc*	AP
Burkhart, F.	3 Adventlieder. *V, ob, guit*	LDo
Burkhart, F.	"Von guter Art". *V, ob, guit*	LDo
Canino	Cantata No. 2. *MS, fl, va, hp, perc*	Ric
Carol-Klause, G.	Wake, Nightingale, Awake. *SAB, fl*	Con
Carrillo, J.	Preludio a Colon. *S, fl, 2vn, va, vc, hp, guit*	Job
Casanova, A.	Divertimento. *MS, fl, ob, cl, bsn, vn, vc, pf*	Job
Cherney, B.	Mobile IV (1969). *S, fl/pic/afl, ob/ehn, cl/bcl, hn, vn, va, vc, hp, perc*	Can
Childs, B.	7 Epigrams (1955). *V, cl*	TP
Clementi, A.	Silben (1966). *V, cl, vn, 2 pf*	ESZ
Coleman, H.	Reality Sandwiches. *S, fl, ehn, vn, va, vc*	CoA
Cooke, A.	3 Songs of Innocence (1957). *S, cl, pf*	OxU
Cortese, L.	Salmo VIII (1943). *V, fl, vc, pf*	GSZ
Cortese, L.	2 Canti Persiani (1932). *MS, fl, pf*	ESZ
Couperin, F.	Adolescentulus sum. *S, 2 fl, vn, org*	EdL
Cowell, H.	Septet. *2S, A, T, B, cl, pf*	Pet
Croft, W.-Spiegl	Celladon. *S, ob, pf*	S&C
Crumb, G.	Ancient Voices of Children. *S, T, ob, hp, perc, mandolin, electric pf*	JB
Crumb, G.	Madrigals, Bk. II. *S, fl, perc*	B-M
Custer, A.	3 Love Lyrics. *T, fl, va, hp*	CoF
Dallapiccola, L.	Goethe Lieder (1953). *V, 3 cl*	ESZ
David, F.	Charmant Oiseau. *S, fl, pf*	S&C
David, G.	The Rose is Flaming (1966). *S, fl, va*	EMB
David, J.	Fröhlich wir nun all fangen an (1941). *V, ob, org*	BrH
Debussy, C.-Louys	Les Chansons de Bilitis. *2 fl, 2 hp, cel, narrator*	JB
Dekker, D.	Little John's Morning After. *V, fl, vc, pf*	SD
Delage, M.	7 Hai-Kai. *S, fl, ob, cl, 2 vn, va, vc, pf*	Job
Diepenbrock, A.	Come raggio di sol. *S, fl, ob, cl, bsn, hn*	Als
Dimov, B.	Incantationes I. *S, fl, tpt, va, hp*	EMo
Dimov, B.	Incantationes II. *S, fl, tpt, 2 va, hp, perc*	EMo
Dimov, B.	Incantationes III. *MS, fl, tpt, va, hp, perc*	EMo
Dionisi, R.	2 Canti Sacri. *V, cl, pf*	GZ
Dionisi, R.	2 Pezzi. *V, cl*	GZ
Döhl, F.	Fragment "Sybille" (1963). *Bar, fl, va, vc, pf*	HG
Döhl, F.	7 Haiku (1963). *S, fl, pf*	HG
Donizetti, G.-Liebling	The Mad Scene (Lucia di Lammermoor). *S, fl, pf*	Sch
Doppelbauer, J.-George	3 Gesänge. *S, fl, va, vc*	LDo
Druckman, J.	Laude (1952). *Bar, afl, va, vc* .	MCA
Duni, R.-Flothuis	Ariette (Le peintre amoureux de son modèlo). *S, fl, vn*	B&V
Durkó, Z.	Colloides (1969). *5A, pic, fl, bsn, 2 vn, va, vc*	EMB
Ehrlich, A.	The Writing of Hezekiah (1962). *S, vn, ob, bsn*	Isr
Eisler, H.	Palmström, op. 5. *V, fl/pic, cl, vn/va, vc*	UE

Voice and Instruments

Eisler, H.	3 Cantatas, op. 60, 62, 64. *A, 2 cl, va, vc*	UE
El-Dabh, H.	Tahmeela. *S, vn, fl, ob, cl, bsn, hn*	Pet
Elkus, J.	Triptych. *MS, 4 bsn*	M&M
Farkas, F.	Tibicinium. *V, fl*	EMB
Feldman, M.	Journey to the End of the Night. *S, fl, cl, bcl, bsn*	Pet
Feldman, M.	Rabbi Akiba. *S, fl, ehn, hn, tpt, trb, tu, perc, pf/cel, vc, db*	Pet
Feldman, M.	Vertical Thoughts 1. *S, fl, hn, tpt, trb, tu, pf/cel, vn, vc, db, 2 perc*	Pet
Ferritto, J.	4 Madrigali. *Bar, fl, cl*	CoF
Ferro	Suite agreste. *V, fl, ehn, cl, va, hp*	Ric
Flanagan, W.	Good-Bye, My Fancy. *S, fl, guit(pf)*	SMP
Flanagan, W.	The Weeping Pleiades. *Bar, fl, cl, vn, vc, pf*	PIC
Fortner, J.	Spring. *V, fl, asax, bsn, va, vc, db, vib, hp, pf*	Job
Freedman, H.	Toccata (1968). *S, fl*	Can
Freedman, H.	2 Vocalises (1954). *S, cl, pf*	Can
Fritsch, J.	Bestandteile des Vorüber (1962). *S, bcl, bsn, hn, 2 trb, tu, 3 db*	B&N
Fussan, W.	Die Chinesische Flöte. *S, fl, 2 vn, va, vc*	BrH
Fussel, K.	"Miorita". *S, fl/afl, cl/bcl, vn/va, pf*	UE
Gaburo, K.	Two. *MS, afl, db*	TP
Garant, S.	Anerca (1961; rev. 1963). *S, fl, cl, bsn, vn, va, vc, hp, perc*	Can
Garber, H.	Voce II. *A, afl, perc*	WLP
Gaslini, G.	Magnificat. *S, asax, pf, db*	UE
Gastyne, S. de	"Il Bacio," op. 45. *V, cl, pf*	Fer
Gastyne, S. de	2 Chansons Françaises. *S, fl, vib*	Fer
Gaveaux, P.-Flothuis	Aria (Le Trom per trompé). *S, cl, pf*	B&V
Gayfer, J.	Who Are You, Little I? (1963). *S, ob, cl, pf*	Can
Geissler, F.	5 Lieder nach Texten von J. Ringelnatz. *S, fl, ob, cl, bsn, hn*	Deu
Glaser, W.	6 Bittermandlar. *V, cl, fl, vc, guit, 2 perc*	STI
Gluck, C.-Flothuis	Aria (La Rencontre Imprévue). *T, fl, pf*	B&V
Gluck, C.-Buck	O Saviour, Hear Me. *S, fl, pf*	Sch
Goeyvaerts, K.	Goathemala (1966). *MS, fl*	CBD
Goldberg, T.	Samogonski-Trio, op. 8. *Bar, cl, vc, pf*	B&B
Gounod, C.	Tell Me, Beautiful Maiden. *V, fl, pf*	Sch
Grandert, J.	Aiakura (1966). *S, Bar, fl, va, db*	STI
Grandert, J.	Oktett (1966). *3 V, fl, va, db, trb*	STI
Gretry, A.	Recitativ et air. *V, fl, pf*	WZ
Gruenberg, L.	The Creation, op. 23. *S, fl, cl, bsn, hn, tpt, va, pf, perc*	UE
Gruenberg, L.	The Daniel Jazz, op. 21. *S, cl, tpt, pf, 2 vn, va, vc, perc*	UE
Hambraeus, B.	Gacelas y Casidas de Fed. G. Lorca. *T, fl, ehn, bcl, cel, vib, perc*	WH
Hambraeus, B.	Spectrogramm, op. 34. *S, fl, perc*	WH
Hammerschmidt, A.	O Beloved Shepherds. *SATB, fl(ob), cl(tpt), vc(trb)*	Con
Handel, G.	Aria (Berenice). *S, ob, bc*	B&V

Voice and Instruments

Handel, G.-Günther	Aria (Lamira). *V, ob, pf*	B&B
Handel, G.-Günther	Cara Sposa (Rinaldo). *V, ob, pf*	B&B
Handel, G.-Hunt	Hush Ye Pretty Warbling Quire. *S, fl, 2 vn, vc, pf*	S&C
Handel, G.-Günther	Liebliche Wälder (Almira). *S, ob, pf*	B&B
Handel, G.-Seydel	Nachtigallenarie (L'Allegro, il Pensieroso) *S, fl, pf*	Leu
Handel, G.-Behrend	Nell Dolce Dell'oblio. *S, fl, guit*	B&B
Handel, G.-Scheit	Nell Dolce Dell'oblio. *S, fl(ob), guit*	LDo
Handel, G.-Bergmann	Nell Dolce Dell'oblio. *S, fl, pf*	S&C
Handel, G.	Nell Dolce Dell'oblio. *V, fl, pf*	WZ
Handel, G.-Flothuis	Recitativ and Aria (The Triumph of Time and Truth). *S, ob, pf*	B&V
Handel, G.-Flothuis	Süsse Stille. *S, fl, pf*	B&V
Handel, G.-Wasner	Sweet Forgetting. *S, fl, pf*	Sch
Handel, G.-Scheit	2 Gesange aus den "Deutschen Arien" *S, fl, guit, vc ad lib*	LDo
Harrison, L.	Air (Rapunzel). *V, fl, vn, va, vc, hp, pf*	SMP
Hartig, H.	Der Trinker und die Spiegel. *Bar, fl, cl, tpt, va, db, pf, perc*	B&B
Hartley, W.	Psalm Cycle. *MS, fl, pf*	TP
Hartwell, H.	How to Play Winning Bridge (1969). *A, fl, va, perc*	Can
Haubiel, C.	Threnody for Love. *A, fl, cl, vn, vc, pf*	See
Hazzard, P.	Massage. *S, A, B, fl, cl, sax, fluegel hn, trb, 3 perc*	See
Heiss, H.	Galgenlieder nach Gedichten von C. Morgenstern. *S, fl*	WMS
Heiss, H.-Kästner	Zum Neuen Jahr (1954). *S, cl, pf*	BrH
Hennagin, M.	The Unknown (1967). *SSA, fl, pf, perc*	Can
Henze, H.	Kammermusik über die Hymne "In lieblicher Bläue". *T, guit, cl, hn, bsn, 2 vn, va, vc, db*	SS
Hillert, R.	And You, O Bethlehem. *SA or TB, fl, org*	Con
Hindemith, P.	Die Serenaden, op. 35. *S, ob, va, vc, pf*	SS
Hodkinson, S.	Arc (1969). *S, fl, pic, pf, perc*	Can
Hoffding, F.	Chamber Music (1927). *S, ob, pf*	SPD
Hook, J.-Bergmann	3 Songs. *S, cl, pf*	S&C
Hopkins, B.	2 Pomes. *S, bcl, tpt, va, hp*	UE
Horst, A.	3 Oud-Ned. Liederen, Serie 2. *V, fl, org(pf)*	Als
Hossein, A.	Chant de Chamelier. *V, fl, pf*	E&C
Huber, K.	"Askese". *fl, V, tape*	B&N
Huber, K.	Des Engels Anredung an die Seele. *T, fl, cl, hn, hp*	UE
Huber, K.	Psalm of Christ (1967). *Bar, cl, bcl, tpt, hn, vn, va, vc*	SS
Ivanov-Ippolitov	4 Poems. *V, fl, pf*	MR
Jacob, G.	3 Songs. *S, cl*	OxU
Jelinek, H.	Selbstbildnis des Marc Aurel. *V, fl, bcl, vc, pf*	EMo
Jenkins, J.	Czech Lullaby Carol (1959). *SSA, 3 cl, vc, db*	Can

Voice and Instruments

Jenkins, J.	Psalm 67 (1959). *SATB, fl, ob, hn, tpt, org*	Can
Jensen, J.	In Memorium: Dr. Martin Luther King, Jr.	
	S, fl, cl, bsn, tpt, trb, vn, vc	CoA
Jez, J.	Pastoral Songs. *2 V, fl, cl, vn, pf*	EdD
Jez, J.	3 Murn's Poems. *V, fl, va*	EdD
Jirasek, I.	Hudba. *S, fl, hp*	Art
Jolas, B.	Points d'aube. *A, 13 wind instr*	Heu
Jolivet, A.	Suite Liturgique. *V, ehn/ob, vc, hp*	Dur
Kadosa, P.	Volksliederkantate, op. 30. *V, cl, vn, vc*	EMB
Kapr, J.	The Dreambook. *V, fl, hp*	ES
Kapr, J.	Ubungen für Gydli. *S, fl, hp*	ES
Kelterborn, R.	Sestina (1957). *S, fl, vn, guit, tpt, pf, perc*	B&N
Kerr, H.	Notations on a Sensitized Plate. *S, cl, 2 vn,*	
	va, vc, pf	TP
Killmayer, W.	Blasons (1968). *S, cl, vn, vc, pf*	SS
Killmayer, W.	Le Petit Savoyard. *S, fl, pic, vn, vc, db,*	
	hpcd, 4 perc	EMo
Kim, E.	Dead Calm. *S, pic, ob, cl, perc, vn, vc*	EBM
Klebe, G.	Dramatische Szene. *S cl, pf*	B&B
Knad, R.	Melodie, die ich verloren hatte (1968).	
	S, fl, 2 vn, 2 vc	Deu
Koellreutter, H.	8 Haikai des Pedro Xisto. *B, fl, pf, guit, perc*	EMo
Koerppen, A.	Die Vagantenballade (1949). *B, fl, pf, perc*	BrH
Köhler, E.	Die Welle, op. 83. *V, fl, pf*	WZ
Kosteck, G.	Refrains and Canons (1965). *SSAA, 4 cl*	Can
Kounadis, A.	4 Pezzi. S, fl, vc, pf	Ton
Kounadis, A.	8 Nocturnes Nach Sappho. *S, fl, vn, va,*	
	vc, cel, vib	EMo
Kounadis, A.	2 Gedichte des Konstantinos Kavafis. *S, fl,*	
	cel, guit, vc, pf	Ton
Krauze, Z.	3 Malay Pantuns (1961). *MS, 3 fl*	AP
Krenek, E.	4 Songs, op. 53. *MS, fl, 3 cl, hn, tpt*	UE
Kröll, G.	Magnificat (1958). *S, ob, cl, asax, bcl, vn, db*	B&N
Kropfreiter, A.	Altdorfer-Passion. *A, Bar, fl/pic, ob/ehn,*	
	cl, hn, bsn, 2 vn, 2 vc, db, org	LDo
Kropfreiter, A.F.-Rilke	In Memoriam (1963). *S, fl, va, vc*	LDo
Kunz, A.	Love, Death and Fullmoonnights (1964).	
	Bar, ob(fl, cl), pf	Can
Kunz, A.	The Song of the Clarinet (1961). *nar, fl,*	
	ob, cl, bsn, str quintet	Can
Lachenmann, H.	temA. *V, fl, vc*	HG
LaForge, F.	Menuet Varie. *V, fl, pf*	Sch
Lampersberg, G.	3 Sacred Songs. *B, cl, hn, vn, db, hp, perc*	UE
Lang, I.	Chamber Cantata (1962). *S, cl, vc, pf, perc*	EMB
Lang, I.	Pezzi (1964). *S, fl, cl, va, 2 perc*	EMB
Lege, G.	Ubi caritas (1967). *T, Bar, B, fl, 4 vn*	B&N
Leichtling, A.	Canticle 1, op. 51. *S, fl*	See
Leichtling, A.	Rubayat Fragments, op. 55. *Bar, cl, hn, pf*	See
Leichtling, A.	Trial and Death of Socrates. *V, cl, fl, hp*	See
Leichtling, A.	2 Proverbs. *MS, 3 cl*	See

Voice and Instruments

Lewkovitch, B.	Cantata sacra. *T, fl, ehn, cl, bsn, trb, vc*	WH
Lidl, V.	Abends am Wasser. *S, fl, hp*	CHF
Lombardo, R.	2 Lyric Poems (1962). *SATB, cl*	Can
Lothar, M.	Oboen-Lieder, op. 47. *V, ob, pf*	R&E
Lutoslawski, W.	A Straw Chain (1951). *S, MS, fl, ob, 2 cl, bsn*	AP
Maderna, B.	Aria (Hyperion), 1964. *S, fl, O*	ESZ
Maderna, B.	Dimensioni III (1963). *S, fl, O*	ESZ
Maganini, Q.	3 Lyrics. *fl, S, dr*	EdM
Maklakiewicz, J.	Les Vierges aux Crepuscules (1927).	AP
	2 MS, fl, va, hp	AP
Malipiero, G.	4 Vecchie Canzoni (1940). *V, fl, ob, cl,*	
	bsn, hn, va, db	ESZ
Malipiero, R.	Sei Poesie di Dylan Thomas (1959).	
	S, fl, ob, bcl, 2 vn, va, vc, perc	ESZ
Mamangakis, N.	Kassandra. *S, fl, hn, tu, hp, perc*	EMo
Mamangakis, N.	Musik für vier Protagonisten. *S, A, T, B,*	
	fl, cl, bsn, vn, pf, perc	EMo
Mamangakis, N.	Paratasis. *V, fl, tape*	HG
Marietan, P.	Recit Suivi de Legende. *V, fl, hn, ehn, cl,*	
	pf, hp, va	Job
Massé, V.-Liebling	Song of the Nightingale. *S, fl, pf*	Sch
Martin, F.	4 Sonnets. *MS, fl, va, vc*	Hug
Martin, F.	3 Weihnachtslieder. *V, fl, pf*	UE
Martirano, S.	O, O, O, O, That Shakespeherian Rag (1960).	
	SATB, cl, asax, tpt, 2trb, db, pf, perc	AMP
Marv, J.	Pan Trauert um Syrinx. *V, fl, pf*	UE
Marx, K.	Die Unendliche Woge, op. 14. *T, cl, vc*	B&B
Mather, B.	Madrigal I (1967). *S, A, fl,*	
	mandolin, hp, vn, vc	Can
Mather, B.	Madrigal II. *S, A, fl, vn, va, vc, hp*	Job
Mather, B.	Venice (1957). *S, cl, vc, pf*	Can
Matuszczak, B.	A Chamber Drama. *Bar, A, bcl, vc, db,*	
	perc, tape	JB
Mayuzumi, T.	Sphenogrammes. *A, fl, asax, vn, vc, pf,*	
	marimba	Pet
McIntyre, P.	Out of the Cradle Endlessly Rocking (1966).	
	V, fl, va, vc, hpcd	Can
McPeek, B.	Crazy Jane (1957). *V, cl, perc, pf*	Can
Meyerbeer, G.	Hirtenlied. *S, cl, pf*	M&M
Mihaly, A.	3 Apocrypha (1962). *3 S, cl, perc*	EMB
Milhaud, D.	Machines Agricoles. *fl, cl, bsn, vn, va,*	
	vc, db, V	Heu
Monsigny, P.-Flothuis	Ariette (Le Maitre en Droit). *S, ob, pf*	B&V
Monteverdi, C.-Flothuis	Aria con Sinfonia "Ed è pur dunque vero".	
	S, vn(fl, ob), bc	B&V
Mortari, V.	2 Laude. *V, fl, vc, pf*	Car
Motte, D. de la	Die Niemandsrose. *Bar, fl, cl, bsn, vn, va,*	
	vc, hp	B&N
Mozart, W.-Flothuis	Aria (La Clemenza di Tito). *S, cl, pf*	B&V
Mozart, W.	Due Pupille, K. 439. *S, B, 3 basset hn(2cl, bcl)*	M&M
Mozart, W.	Ecco Quel Fiero Istante, K. 436. *2S, B, 3*	

	basset hn (2cl, bcl)	M&M
Mozart, W.-Deis	Faithful Heart Enraptured. *S, fl, pf*	Sch
Mozart, W.	Luci Care, Luci Belle, K. 346. *2S, B, 3*	
	basset hn(2cl, bcl)	M&M
Mozart, W.	Mi Lagnero Tacendo, K. 437. *2S, B, 2 cl,*	
	basset hn(bcl)	M&M
Mozart, W.	Parto! Ma tu ben mio! (Titus, K. 621).	
	cl, S, pf	BrH
Mozart, W.-Bergmann	Parto, Parto. *S, cl, pf*	S&C
Mozart, W.	Più Non Si Trovano, K. 549. *2S, B,*	
	3 basset hn(2cl, bcl)	M&M
Mozart, W.	Se Lontan, ben mio, tu sei, K. 438. *2S, B,*	
	2 cl, basset hn(bcl)	M&M
Myers, G.	A Mini-song Cycle. *S, fl*	EMC
Navarro, J.	Intemperances 1962. *V, fl, pic, bcl, tpt, trb,*	
	timp, perc	SMP
Naylor, B.	The Nymph Complaining for the Death of	
	Her Faun (1965). *MS, fl, ob, cl, bsn,*	
	2 vn, va, vc	Can
Nemiroff, I.	Solo Cantata. *S, fl, str*	M&M
Neilsen, S.	Duet. *S, A, fl, vc, vib, timp*	WH
Norgaard, H.	Serenade to Young Man with a Horn (1959).	
	V, cl, tpt, trb, vib, db	SPD
Novak, J.	Passer Catulli. *B, fl, ob, cl, bsn, hn, vn,*	
	va, vc, db	EMo
Oboussier, R.	3 Arien. *S, ob, hpcd*	B&N
Olah, T.	Equinoxe. *V, cl, pf*	EMU
Orgad, B.	Out of the Dust (1956). *MS, fl, bsn, va, vc*	Isr
Orland, H.	Love and Pity. *S, cl, va*	See
Pablo, L. de	Ein Wort (1965). *V, cl, vn, pf*	EdT
Mortari, V.	Canzone. *S, fl*	EDS
Pablo, L. de	Commentarios. *S, pic, db, vib*	EMo
Paisiello, G.-Flothuis	Aria (Il Barbiere di Siviglia). *S, fl, pf*	B&V
Paisiello, G.-Hunt	Rien ne Peut Calmer Ma Peine. *S, fl, pf*	S&C
Panni, M.	4 Melodie (1964). *S, ob, vc, mandoline*	ESZ
Papandopulo, B.	Concerto da Camera, op. 11. *S, pic, fl, ob,*	
	ehn, cl, bcl, bsn, pf	UE
Papineau-Couture, J.	Eglogues (1942). *A, fl, pf*	Can
Partos, O.	5 Israeli Songs (1960). *MS, ob, vc, pf*	Isr
Peacock, K.	Songs of the Cedar (1950). *MS, fl, vc, db, pf*	Can
Pelemans, W.	Ad Musicam. *MS, 4 cl*	Mau
Pepusch, J.-Wailes	Corydon. *S, fl, pf*	S&C
Perkowski, P.	3 Folk Songs (1952). *S, contralto choir,*	
	cl, vn, pf	AP
Petzold, J.	The Christmas Story. *SAB, fl(ob), org*	Con
Philidor, F.-Flothuis	Aria (Le Marèchal Ferrant). *S, ob, bc*	B&V
Philidor, F.-Flothuis	Aria (Sancho Panca). *S, ob, bc*	B&V
Piccolo, A.	Found in Machaut's Chamber. *T, fl, vc, guit*	CoA
Pillney, K.	In Dulci Jubilo. *V, fl, va, vc, pf*	BrH
Pisk, P.	Meadow Saffrons. *V, cl, bcl*	TP

Voice and Instruments

Porena, B.	4 Kanonische Lieder (1958). *S, cl*	ESZ
Pousseur, H.	Echoes II de Votre Faust. *MS, fl, vc, pf*	UE
Powell, R.	Of the Father's Love Begotten. *SATB, 2 fl, org*	Con
Purcell, H.-Tippett	Bid the Virtues. *S, ob, pf*	S&C
Purcell, H.-Bergmann	Hark, How the Songsters. *2S, 2fl, pf, vc ad lib*	S&C
Purcell, H.-Flothuis	One Charming Night (The Fairy Queen). *A, 2 fl, bc*	
Purcell, H.-Tippett	Strike the Viol. *A, 2 fl, pf, vc ad lib*	S&C
Purcell, H.-Bergmann	Why Should Men Quarrel. *S, 2 fl, pf, vc ad lib*	S&C
Rameau, J.	Arias, Vol 1. *S, fl, bc*	MR
Rameau, J.	5 Arias. *T, fl, bc*	MR
Rands, B.	Ballad I. *MS, fl, trb, db, pf, perc*	UE
Raphael, G.	Palmstrom-Sonate, op. 69. *T, cl, vn, pf, perc*	BrH
Rasmussen, K.	"Dieser Augenblick". *3 S, fl, perc*	WH
Ravel, M.	3 Poemes de Stéphane Mallarmé. *V, 2 fl, 2 cl, 2 vn, va, vc, pf*	Dur
Razzi, F.	Improvvisazione III (1967). *2 S, B, fl, db, hpcd, perc*	ESZ
Regt, H. de	Medea. *S, ob, hpcd*	SD
Reif, P.	Kaleidoscope (1966). *V, fl, ob, cl, bsn, hn*	See
Reimann, A.	3 Spanische Lieder (1958). *V, fl, hp, vc*	B&B
Riegger, W.	Music, op. 23. *V, fl(ob)*	AMP
Riley, D.	Cantata II (1966). *SATB, fl, pf, hp*	Can
Ringger, R.	4 Lieder auf Chinesische Texte. *S, fl, bcl, trb, vn, vc, db, hp, cel*	EMo
Ringger, R.	4 Lieder auf Japanische Lyrik. *S, cl, hn, vn, va, db, hp*	EMo
Rodrigo, J.	2 Poemas. *V, fl*	UME
Roetscher, K.	6 Lieder. *S, 4 fl*	B&B
Rohlig, H.	Behold, a Branch is Growing. *SATB, 2 fl, org*	Con
Rohlig, H.	O Holy Jesus. *SATB, fl, org*	Con
Ronnefeld, P.	2 Lieder zur Pauke. *A, fl, perc*	EMo
Ronnefeld, P.	4 Wiegenlieder. *S, fl*	EMo
Rontgen, J.	2 Lieder. *S, fl, va*	Als
Rorem, N.	Ariel. *S, cl, pf*	JB
Roxbury, R.	Motets for Vocal Improvisation and Ensembles. *V, fl, cl, vc, guit, perc*	Cap
Scarlatti, A.	Cantata. *S, fl, pf*	WZ
Schafer, R.	Minnelieder (1956). *S, fl, ob, cl, bsn, hn*	Can
Schafer, R.	Requiems for the Party-Girl (1966). *MS, fl, cl, hn, pf, hp, vn, va, vc, perc*	Can
Schafer, R.	5 Studies on Texts by Prudentius (1962). *S, 4 fl*	Can
Schalk, C.	In Adam We Have All Been One. *SATB, 2 ob, org*	Con
Scheel, J.	Dormi Jesu, op. 59. *V, ob, pf*	Hug
Schieckele, P.	On This Plain of Mist (1961). *S, A, cl, mar*	Can
Schmid, R.	10 Mädchenlieder. *S, ob, pf*	LDo
Schmit, C.	Psautier (1946). *V, cl, ob/ehn, bsn, pf*	CBD
Schoek, O.	Gaselen, op. 38. *Bar, fl, ob, bcl, tpt, pf, perc*	BrH

Voice and Instruments

Schoeck, O.	Wandersprüche, op. 42. *T(S), cl, hn, pf, perc*	BrH
Schoenberg, A.	Pierrot Lunaire, op. 21. *V, fl/pic, cl/bcl,*	
	vn/va, vc, pf	UE
Schoenberg, A.	Serenade, op. 24. *B, cl, basset hn, guit,*	
	mandolin, vn, va, vc	WH
Schramm, H.	Song of Tayumanavar. *S, fl*	TP
Schubert, F.	Ave Maria. *V, fl, pf*	Sch
Schubert, F.	Der Hirt auf dem Felsen, op. 129. *S, cl, pf*	BrH
Schubert, F.-Lancelot	Le Patre sur la Montagne. *S, 2 cl, pf*	Bil
Schubert, F.-Flothuis	Romance (Die Verschworenen). *S, cl, pf*	B&V
Schubert, F.-Ständchen	Serenade. *V, fl, pf*	Sch
Schubert, F.-Deis	The Shepherd on the Rock. *S, fl, pf*	Sch
Schubert, F.	Totus in Corde Lanqueo (Offertory, C).	
	S, cl, pf	LDo
Schubert, F.	Totus in Corde Lanqueo, op. 46. *V, cl, pf*	M&M
Schuster, G.	2 Dialogues and Recitative (1965). *V, fl(ob),*	
	pf	Isr
Schütz, H.	Father Abraham, Have Mercy on Me.	
	SSATB, 2 vn, 2 fl, vc	Con
Schwartz, E.	Variations. *S, bsn, perc*	Gen
Seiber, M.	3 Morgensternlieder. *V, cl*	UE
Seletsky, H.	Impressions (1966). *S, fl, cl, tpt, trb, vn,*	
	vc, db, perc	See
Serebrier, J.	Erotica. *V, fl, ob, cl, bsn, hn*	JB
Sheriff, N.	Ashrei (1961). *A, fl, 2 hp*	Isr
Sigtenhorst-Meyer, B.	Liederen van de Nijl, op. 44. *V, ob(fl)*	Als
Slowinski, W.	Makowski Fairy Tales (1961). *A, fl, ob, cl*	AP
Somers, H.	Kuyas (1967). *S, fl, perc*	Can
Souris, A.	L'Autre Voix (1947). *S, fl, cl, va, vc, pf*	CDB
Speare-Lutyens, S.	A Parody. *S, fl, vn, pf*	CoA
Spies, L.	5 Psalms. *S, T, fl, bsn, hn, va, vc, mandoline*	B&H
Spohr, L.-Leinert	6 Deutsche Lieder, op. 103. *S, cl, pf*	B&N
Steffani, A.-Wasner	Come, My Dear One. *S, fl, ob, vc, hpcd*	Sch
Steffani, A.-Wasner	O How Often. *V, 2 fl, vc, hpcd*	Sch
Steffens, W.	Neue Gleichnisse, op. 3b. *S, fl, cl, va*	BrH
Steffens, W.	Oboenlieder, op. 9. *V, ob*	BrH
Steiner, G.	Concert Piece No. 1. *S, fl, pf, vc, 2 perc*	See
Steiner, G.	Concert Piece No. 2. *S, fl, pf, db, 2 perc*	See
Sternberg, E.	Die Ferne Flöte. *A, fl*	Hei
Sternberg, E.	The Distant Flute. *A, fl*	Isr
Stout, A.	Canticum Canticorum, op. 66. *S, solo va, fl,*	
	ob, cl, bsn, hn	Pet
Stravinsky, I.	Berceuses du Chat. *A, 3 cl*	WH
Stravinsky, I.	Elegie for J.F.K. *MS(Bar), 3 cl*	B&H
Stravinsky, I.	4 Russian Lieder. *S, fl, hp, guit*	WH
Stravinsky, I.	4 Songs. *V, fl, hp, guit*	Che
Stravinsky, I.	4 Songs. *V, fl, hp, guit*	Sch
Stravinsky, I.	Pastorale. *S, ob, ehn, cl, bsn*	SS
Stuhec, I.	2 Fatal Songs. *S, fl, hp*	EdD
Suter, R.	"Heilige Leier Sprich, sei Meine Stimme"	
	S, fl, guit	Hei

273

Voice and Instruments

Suter, R.	Musikalisches Tagebuch Nr. 1. *A, ob, bsn, vn, va, vc, db*	EMo
Suter, R.	Musikalisches Tagebuch Nr. 2. *Bar, fl, cl, bcl, hn, vn, va, vc*	EMo
Sutermeister, H.	4 Lieder. *Bar, fl, ob, vn, bsn, hpcd*	SS
Szalonek, W.	Suite from Kurpie (1955). *A, fl, ob, cl, bsn, hn, vn, va, vc, pf*	AP
Szekely, E.	Maqamat. *S, cl, tpt, hpcd, 2 vn, va, vc*	EMB
Taubert, K.	Hausspruch. *V, fl, pf, guit ad lib*	R&E
Telemann, G.-Fock	Ew'ge Quelle, Milder Strom. *V, fl, bc*	B&N
Telemann, G.-Fock	Ihr Völker, hört. *V, fl, bc*	B&N
Telemann, G.-Bergmann	Tempt Me Then (Locket Nur). *S, fl, pf, vc ad lib*	S&C
Telemann, G.-Ermeler	"Tod und Moder dringt herein". *A, fl, pf, vc ad lib*	WZ
Togni, C.	6 Notturni (1965). *A, cl, vn, 2 pf*	ESZ
Trimble, L.	4 Fragments from The Canterbury Tales. *S, fl, cl, hpcd(pf)*	Pet
Trimble, L.	Petit Concert. *V, ob, vn, hpcd*	Pet
Turner, R.	Eclogue (1958). *S, ob(fl, cl), hpcd(pf)*	Can
Vandor, I.	Canzone di Addio (1967). *V, fl, va, perc, mandoline*	ESZ / ESZ
Vaughan Williams, R.	3 Vocalises (1958). *S, cl*	OxU
Veretti, A.	Elegie. *V, cl, vn, guit*	FrC
Villa-Lobos, H.	Nonet. *fl, ob, cl, asax, bsn, hp, pf, cel, perc, choir*	SS
Villa-Lobos, H.	Poêma da Criança e sua Mamâ (1923). *V, fl, cl, vc*	EME
Vlad, R.	Immer wieder. *S, ehn, cl, bsn, va, vc, vib, hp, pf, marimba*	UE
Vogel, W.	Dal Quaderno di Francine Settenne (1952). *S, fl, pf*	ESZ
Walacinski, A.	A Lyric Before Falling Asleep (1963). *S, fl, 2 pf*	AP
Washburn, R.	Scherzo for Spring (1960). *SSA, fl, cl, pf*	OxU
Weber, C. M. von-Liebling	Invitation to the Dance. *S, fl, pf*	Sch
Webern, A.-Rilke	2 Lieder, op. 8. *V, cl, hn, tpt, cel, hp, vn, va, vc*	UE
Webern, A.-Trakl	6 Lieder, op. 14. *S, cl, bcl, vn, vc*	UE
Webern, A.	5 Religious Songs, op. 15. *S, fl, cl, tpt, vn(va), hp*	UE / UE
Webern, A.	5 Canons, op. 16. *S, cl, bcl*	UE
Webern, A.	3 Volkstexte, op. 17. *V, cl, bcl, vn, va*	UE
Webern, A.	3 Lieder, op. 18. *V, E♭ cl, guit*	UE
Weill, K.	Frauentanz, op. 10. *S, fl, cl, bsn, hn, va*	UE
Wellesz, E.	The Leaden Echo and The Golden Echo. *V, cl, vc, pf*	S&C
Wernert, W.	Psalm 116. *S, fl, vib*	B&N
Wildgans, F.	An Den Knaben Elis. *S, cl, vn, vc*	LDo

Voice and Instruments

Wildgans, F.	Missa Minima. *S, cl, vn, vc*	LDo
Wildgans, F.	Rhénane d'Automne. *V, cl, pf*	UE
Wilkinson, M.	Voices. *A, fl, cl, bcl, vc*	UE
Wolpe, S.	Quintet with Voice. *Bar, cl, hn, vc, hp, pf*	M&M
Worst, J.	3 Biblical Chants. *Bar, fl, hn, vn, db*	Cap
Woytowicz, B.	Cradle Song (1931). *S, fl, cl, bsn, hp*	AP
Woytowicz, B.	Lamento (1960). *S, cl, pf*	AP
Zender, H.	3 Rondels nach Mallarmé. *S, fl, va*	B&B
Zender, H.	Les Sirènes Chantent Quand La Raison S'Endort (1966). *S, fl, cl, vc, pf, vib*	B&B
Zender, H.	3 Rondels Nach Mallarmé (1961). *A, fl, va*	B&B
Zur, M.	The Affairs. *S, fl, cl, tpt, trb, va*	See

KEY TO PUBLISHERS

Alphabetization of names of Publishers.
The sequence is given by the abbreviation of each publisher. To avoid duplicates (within a 3-letter system of abbreviations), a few arbitrary distinctions had to be made. For example, B&H is the abbreviation used for Boosey & Hawkes, yet B&H could well be the abbreviation also for Breitkopf & Härtel; thus the latter's abbreviation has been designated as BrH. One would logically conclude that the first name (Carl in Carl Fischer) should not be used in alphabetization, however, the entire trade uses CF for this name. We have followed that practice for comparable names. Many cross-references will assist the reader to locate the desired company name and its abbreviation.

American agents or distributors for foriegn firms are indicated in parentheses.

ABe	Anton J. Benjamin, 67 Belsize Lane, Hampstead, London NW3 5AX, England (AMP)
ABS	Anton Böhm & Sohn, Lange Gasse 26, 89 Augsburg 2, Germany
ACA	American Composers Alliance, 170 West 74th Street, New York, New York 10023
Acc	Accura Music, Box 887, Athens, Ohio 45701
AlB	Alexander Broude, Inc., 1619 Broadway, New York, New York 10019
ALe	Alphonse Leduc, 175, rue Saint-Honoré, Paris, France
Alf	Alfred Music Co., Inc., 75 Channel Drive; Port Washington, New York 11050
AlL	Alfred Lengnick & Co., Ltd., Purley Oaks Studios, 421a Brighton Road, South Croydon, Surrey, England (B-M)
Als	G. Alsbach & Co., Leidsegtacht 11, Amsterdam, Holland (Pet)
AMC	American Music Center, Inc., 2109 Broadway Suite 15-79, New York, New York 10023
AME	American Music Edition, 263 East 7th St., New York, New York 10009 (JB)
AMP	Associated Music Publishers, Inc., 866 Third Ave., New York, New York 10022
Amp	Amphion Editions Musicales, 9, rue d'Artois, Paris 8e, France (FrC)
AP	Ars Polona, Krakowskie Przedmieście 7, Warszaw, Poland
ArM	Artisan Music Press, P.O. Box 75, Cornwall, New York 12518
Art	Artia, Ve Smeckách 30, Praha 1, Czechoslovakia (B&N)
A&S	Ahn & Simrock, Mommsenstrasse 71, 1000 Berlin 12, Germany or
	Ahn & Simrock, Taunusstrasse 66, 6200 Wiesbaden, Germany
Ash	Ashley Dealers Service, Inc., 39 W. 60th St., New York, New York 10023
ATL	A.T.L. Publishing Co., 3105 S. Hughes Ave., Fresno, California 93706
Aug	Augsburg Publishing House, 426 S. Fifth St., Minneapolis, Minnesota 55415
Bar	C.L. Barnhouse Co., Oskaloosa, Iowa 52577
BB	Broude Brothers, 56 West 45th St., New York, New York 10036
B&B	Bote & Bock, Hardenbergstrasse 9a, 1 Berlin 12, Germany (AMP)
Be	M.P. Belaieff, Kronprinzeustrasse 26, Bonn, Germany (B&H)
	Belwin (See B-M)
B&H	Boosey & Hawkes, 30 W. 57th St., New York, New York 10019
Big	The Big 3 Music Corporation, 1350 Avenue of the Americas, New York, New York 10019
Bil	Billaudot Editions Musicales, 14, rue de l'Echiquier, Paris 10e, France (TP)
BM	Boston Music Company, 116 Boylston St., Boston, Massachusetts 02116
B-M	Belwin-Mills Publishing Corp., Melville, New York 11746
B&N	Bärenreiter & Neuwerk, Heinrich-Schütz-Allee 35, 35 Kassel-Wilhelmshöhe, Germany
Bos	Bosworth & Co., Ltd., 14/18, Heddon St., London, W. 1, England (B-M)
Bou	Bourne Co., 136 W. 52nd St., New York, New York 10019
Bow	Bowdoin College Music Press, Brunswick, Maine 04011
BPP	Berklee Press Publications, 1140 Boylston St., Boston, Massachusetts 02215
Bra	Branden Press, Inc., 36 Melrose St., Boston, Massachusetts
BrH	Breitkopf & Härtel, Walkmühlstrasse 52, D 6200 Wiesbaden 1, Germany (AMP)
Bro	Brodt Music Co., P.O. Box 1207, Charlotte, North Carolina 28201
B&V	Broekmans & Van Poppel, Van Baerlestraat 92-94, Amsterdam, Holland (Pet)
	B. Schott's Sohns (See SS)
BVC	Bregman, Vocco and Conn, Inc., 1619 Broadway, New York, New York 10019
Byr	Byron-Douglas Publications, P.O. Box 565, Phoenix, Arizona 85001
Cam	Camara Brass Quintet of San Francisco, 25 Elk St., San Francisco, California 94131
Can	Canadian Music Centre, 33 Edward St., Toronto 2, Canada
Car	Carisch S.p.A. 20124 - Via G. Fara, 39, Milan, Italy
CBD	Centre Belge de Documentation Musicale, Boulevard de l'Empereur 4, B-1000 Bruxelles, Belgium (HEl)
	C.L. Barnhouse (See Bar)
CBP	Claude Benny Press, Milton, Wisconsin 53564
CCo	Chas. Colin, 315 W. 53rd St., New York, New York
Cen	Century Music Publishing Co., Inc., 263 Veterans Blvd., Carlstadt, New Jersey 07072
CF	Carl Fischer, Inc., 62 Cooper Square, New York, New York 10003
	C.F. Peters (See Pet)
CFo	Charles Foley, Inc., 156 W. 44th St., New York, New York 10036
CFV	Chr. Friedrich Vieweg, Limonenstr. 10, 1 Berlin 45, Germany (Pet)
CGM	Carl Gehrmans Musikförlag, Vasagatan 46, Box 505, 101 26 Stockholm 1, Sweden (B&H)
Cha	Chappell & Co., Inc., 609 Fifth Ave., New York, New York 10017
Che	J. & W. Chester Ltd., Eagle Court, London EC1, England

CHF	Cesky Hudebni Fond, Ustredni archiv, Parizská 13, Praha 1, Czechoslovakia
ChM	Le Chant du Monde, 32 rue Beaujon, Paris 8e, France
	C.L. Barnhouse (See Bar)
CoA	Composers' Autograph Publications, P.O. Box 7103, Cleveland, Ohio 44128
CoF	Composers Facsimile Edition, 170 W. 74th St., New York, New York 10023
Col	M.M. Cole Publishing Co., 251 E. Grand Ave., Chicago, Illinois 60611
Con	Concordia Publishing House, 3558 S. Jefferson Ave., St. Louis, Missouri 63118
CoP	The Composers Press, Inc., 177 E. 87th St., ew York, New York 10028
Cor	Cor Publishing Co., 67 Bell Place, Massapequa, New York 11758
CP	Christlieb Products, 3311 Scadlock Lane, Sherman Oaks, California 91403
Cre	Crescendo Music Sales, Box 395, Naperville, Illinois 60540
Cur	J. Curwen & Sons Ltd., 29 Maiden Lane, London, W.C.2, England
	J. & W. Chester (See Che)
Deu	VEB Deutscher Verlag, Postfach 147, 701 Leipzig, Germany (AMP)
DGo	David Gornston, 117 W. 48th St., New York, New York
Dur	Editions Durand & Cie, 4, Place de la Madeleine, 4 Paris 8e, France (E-V)
EB	Edition Boileau, Post Box 6026, Barcelona, Spain
EBM	Edward B. Marks Music Corporation, 136 W. 52nd St., New York, New York 10019
E&C	Enoch & Cie, 27, Boulevard des Italiens, Paris 2e, France (AMP)
ECh	Editions Choudens, 38 rue jean Mermoz, Paris 8e, France (Pet)
ECK	E.C. Kerby, Ltd., 198 Davenport Road, Toronto 5, Ontario (JB)
ECM	Editions A. Cranz Musikverlag, Adelheidstrasse 68, 62 Wiesbaden, Germany (HEl)
ECS	E.C. Schirmer Music Co., 112 South St., Boston, Massachusetts 02111
EdB	Edizioni Bongiovanni, Via Rizzoli, 28/E, Bologna, Italy (FrC)
EdC	Editions Costallat, 60, Rue de la Chaussée-d'Antin, Paris 9e, France
EdD	Edicije Drustva slovenskih skladateljev, Trg francoske revolucije 6, 61000 Ljubljana, Yugoslavia
EdH	Edition Heuwekemeyer, Bredeweg, 21, Amsterdam, Netherlands (Hel)
Edi	Edizioni Curci, Galleria del Corso, 4, Milan, Italy
EdK	Edwin F. Kalmus, Opa Locka, Florida 33054
EdL	Editions de L'Oiseau-Lyre, Les Remparts, Monaco
EdM	Edition Musicus-New York, Inc., 333 W. 52nd St., New York, New York 10019
EdR	Editions Robert Martin, 106, Grande-rue de la Coupée, 71 Charnay-Les-Macon, France
EdS	Editions Salabert, 22, Rue Chauchat, Paris 93, France or 575 Madison ve., New York, New York 10022
EDS	Edizioni De Santis, Via Cassia, 13, Rome, Italy (FrC)
EdT	Edition Tonos, Ahastrasse 7-9, 6100 Darmstadt, Germany or P.O. Box 199, Coldwater, Michigan
EHe	Edition Helbling, 8604 Volketswil, Zurich, Switzerland
EK	Edition Kneusslin, Amselstrasse 43, Basel 24, Switzerland (Pet)
EMB	Editio Musica Budapest, Pf. 322, Budapest 5, Hungary (B&H)
EMb	Editions Musicales Brogneaux, 73, Avenue Paul Janson, Bruxelles, Belgium (HEl)
EME	Editions Max Eschig, 48, rue de Rome, Paris 8e, France (AMP)
EMe	Editions Metropolis, Frankrijklei 24, Antwerpen, Belgium (HeE)
EMG	Edition Marbot GmbH., Bornstrasse 12, Hamburg 13, Germany
EMo	Edition Modern, Franz Joseph Strasse 2, 8 Munich, Germany
EMP	Edition Maurice et Pierre Foetisch, 6 Rue de Bourg, Lausanne, Switzerland
EMT	Editions Musicales Transatlantiques, 14, Avenue Hoche, Paris 8e, France (TP)
EMU	Editura Muzicala, Compozitorilor Din R.P.R., Bucharest, Rumania
EPC	Editions Philippo-Combre, 24, Boulevard Poissonniere, Paris 9e, France (TP)
ES	Editio Supraphon, Palackeho 1, Praha 1, Czechoslovakia
ESu	Edition Suecia, Stockholm Sweden
ESZ	Edizioni Suvini Zerboni, Corso Europa 5/7, Milan, Italy
Ehr	Ehrling Musik AB, Stockholm, Sweden
Elk	Elkin and Co., Ltd., Borough Green - Sevenoaks, Kent, England (GaM)
EM	Edwin H. Morris & Co., Inc., 31 West 54th St., New York, New York 10019
EMC	Eastlane Music Corp., 623 Latona Ave., Trenton, New Jersey 08618
EMF	Eriks Musikhandel & Forlag AB, Karlavagen 40, Stockholm, Sweden
Ens	Ensemble Publications, Inc., Box 98, Bidwell Station, Buffalo, New York 14222
ERM	Emil Ruh Musikverlag, Zurichstrasse 33, Ch-8134 Adliswil, Zurich, Switzerland
Eul	Eulenburg GmbH., Grutstrasse 28, 8134 Adliswil-Zurich, Switzerland (Pet)
	Henri Elkan (See HeE)
E-V	Elkan-Vogel Co., Inc., c/o Theodore Presser, Presser Place, Bryn Mawr, Pennsylvania 19010
ExM	Experimental Music, 208 Ladbroke Grove, London W 10, England
Fab	Faber Music Ltd., 38 Russell Square, London WC1B 5DA, England
Fer	Fereol Publications, Box 6007, Alexandria, Virginia 22306
	F.E.C. Leuckart (See Leu)
Fit	H.T. FitzSimons Co., 615 N. LaSalle St., Chicago, Illinois 60610
	Carl Fischer (See CF)
	Charles Foley (See CFo)
	Sam Fox (See SF)
FrC	Franco Colombo Publications, Rockville Centre, Long Island, New York 11571
	Chr. Friedrich (See CFV)
FrH	Friedrich Hofmeister-Verlay, Ubierstrasse 20, 6238 Hofheim am Taunus, Germany (AMP)
	G. Alsbach (See Als)

Gal	Galliard Ltd., Queen Anne's Road, Great Yarmouth, Norfolk, England (GaM)
GaM	Galaxy Music Corporation, 2121 Broadway, New York, New York 10023
GD	Georges Delrieu & Cie, 45, Avenue de la Victoire, Nice, France (GaM)
Gen	General Music Publishing Co., Inc., P.O. Box 267, Hastings-on-Hudson, New York 10706
GFB	George F. Briegel, Inc., 4 Summit Court, Flushing, New York 11355
Gor	Gordon Music Co., 9601 Wilshire Boulevard, Beverly Hills, California 90210
	G. Ricordi (See Ric)
Gra	H.W. Gray Co., Inc., c/o Belwin-Mills, Melville, New York 11746
GrF	S.A.R.L. Gras Frères, 36, Rue Pape-Carpentier, 72 - La Flèche, France (MB)
	Ph. Grosch (See PG)
	G. Schirmer (See Sch)
GZ	G. Zanibon, Piazza Dei Signori 24/26, 35100 Padova, Italy (Pet)
Hal	Hal Leonard Music, Inc., 64 East 2nd St., Winona, Minnesota 55987
Ham	Hamelle & Cie, 24, Boulevard Malesherbes, Paris 8e, France
Har	T.B. Harms Co., 619 West 54th St., New York, New York 10019
HE	Hinrichsen Edition, Ltd., 10 Baches St., London, England (Pet)
HeE	Henri Elkan Music Publisher, 1316 Walnut St., Philadelphia, Pennsylvania 19107
Hei	Heinrichshofen Verlag, Liebigstrasse 4, Wilhelmshaven, Germany (Pet)
Heu	Heugel & Cie, 2 bis, Rue Vivienne, Paris, France (TP)
HG	Hans Gerig Musikverlage, Drususgasse 7-11, D-5, Cologne, Germany
HL	Harold Lyche & Co., Kongenst. 2, Oslo, Norway
HLe	Henry Lemoine & Cie, 17 rue Pigalle, Paris 9e, France (E-V)
HMo	Hermann Moeck Verlag, Postfach 143, D 31 Celle, Germany
HMP	Hargail Music Press, 28 West 38th St., New York, New York 10018
	H. Litolff's (See Lit)
Hoh	Hohner Verlag, 7218 Trossingen, Wurtemberg, Germany
HSM	Hans Sikorski Musikverlag, Johnsalle 23, 2 Hamburg 13, Germany (FrC)
HU	Harmonia-Uitgave, Roeltjesweg 23 - Postbus 126, Hilversum, Holland (Pet)
	H.T. FitzSimons (See Fit)
Hug	Hug & Co. Musikverlag, CH-8022 Zürich, Switzerland (Pet)
	H.W. Gray (See Gra)
InM	International Music Company Ltd., 16 Mortimer St., London W. 1, England (Sch)
Int	International Music Company, 511 Fifth Ave., New York, New York 10017
Isr	Israel Music Institute, P.O. Box 11253, Tel Aviv, Israel (B&H)
I-V	Ichthys Verlag GmbH., Postfach 834, 7000 Stuttgart 1, Germany
	J. Maurer (See Mau)
JB	Joseph Boonin, Inc., P.O. Box 2124, South Hackensack, New Jersey 07606
	Edwin F. Kalmus (See EdK)
JKM	Johann Kliment Musikverlag, Kolingasse 15, 1090 Vienna, Austria
JoA	Johann André Musikverlag, Postfach 141, 605 Offenbach am Main, Germany
Job	Jobert & Cie, 44, rue du Colisée, Paris 8e, France (E-V)
	J. Curwen (See Cur)
JoW	Josef Weinberger Musikverlag, Oederweg 26, Frankfurt, Germany (TP)
JS	J. Schuberth & Co., Zietopring 3, Wiesbaden, Germany
	J. & W. Chester (See Che)
Kaw	KaWe, Brederodestraat 90, Amsterdam 13, Holland
Ken	Kendor Music, Inc., Delevan, New York 14042
	E.C. Kerby (See ECK)
Kis	Kistner & Siegel & Co., Postfach 101, Cologne, Germany
KMV	Karl Merseburger Verlag, Alemannenstrasse 20, 1000 Berlin 38, Germany (Pet)
	Neil A. Kjos (See NK)
Kof	Koff Music Co., Box 1442, Studio City, California 91604
KPM	Keith Prowse Music Publishing Co., Ltd., 21 Denmark St., London WC2H 8NE, England
	E.C. Kerby (See ECK)
Lan	Lang Music Publications, P.O. Box 11021, Indianapolis, Indiana 46201
LDo	Ludwig Doblinger Verlag, Dorotheergasse 10, 1010 Vienna, Austria (AMP)
Leb	Leblanc Publications, Inc., 7019 30th Ave., Kenosha, Wisconsin 53141
Leu	F.E.C. Leuckart Verlag, Nibelungenstr. 48, Munich 19, Germany (AMP)
Lit	H. Litolff's Verlag, Forsthausstrasse 101, Frankfurt, Germany (Pet)
LK	Ludwig Krenn, Reindorfgasse 42, Vienna 15, Austria
LMP	Littlehall Music Publishers, 3315 Dellwood Drive, Parma, Ohio 44134
LP	Lariken Press, 2808 25th St., Lubbock, Texas 79410
Lud	Ludwig Music Publishing Co., 557-67 E. 140th St., Cleveland, Ohio 44110
MaM	Mannheimer Musikverlag GmbH., Mollstrasse 35, Mannheim 2, Germany
Mau	J. Maurer, Avenue de Verseau 7 Watermanlaan, Bruxelles 15, Belgium
MB	Maurice Baron Co., P.O. Box 149, Oyster Bay, Long Island, New York 11771
M-B	Magnamusic-Baton, Inc., 6394 Delmar Blvd., St. Louis, Missouri 63130
MCA	MCA Music, 445 Park Ave., New York, New York 10022
McK	McKinley Publishers, Inc., 797 8th Ave., New York, New York
Men	Mentor Music, Inc., Broadview Drive, Brookfield, Connecticut 06804
	Mills (See B-M)
Mit	Mitteldeutscher Verlag, Robert-Blum-Strasse 37, Halle/Salle, Germany
	M.M. Cole (See Col)
MJQ	MJQ Music, Inc., 200 West 57th St., New York, New York 10019
MM	Molenaar's muziekcentrale nv, Zuideinde 18, Wormerveer, Holland (HEl)

278

M&M	McGinnis & Marx, 201 West 86th St., New York, New York 10024
	M.P. Belaieff (See Be)
MR	Musica Rara, 2 Great Marlborough St., London, W. 1, England (Rub)
MRL	Musikverlag Robert Lienau, Lankwitzer Strasse 9, 1 Berlin 45, Germany (Pet)
MS	Music Sales Corporation, Bellvale Road, Chester, New York 10918
MT	Musiikin Tiedotuskeskus, Runeberginkatu 15 A 11, 00100 Helsinki 10, Finland
MV	Möseler Verlag, 3340 Wolfenbüttel, Germany
NK	Neil A. Kjos Music Co., 525 Busse Highway, Park Ridge, Illinois 60068
Nor	Nordiska Musikforlaget, Drottninggatan 37, 101 30 Stockholm 1, Sweden (AMP)
Nov	Novello & Co., Ltd., Borough Green, Sevenoaks, Kent, England (B-M)
NV	Nagels Verlag, Heinrich Schütz Allee 31, Kassel, Germany (AMP)
NVM	New Valley Music Press, Sage Hall, Smith College, Northampton, Massachusetts 01060
	N. Simrock (See Sim)
OHN	Otto Heinrich Noetzel, Liebigstrasse 4, Wilhelmshaven, Germany (Pet)
OJ	Otto Junne GmbH., Sendlinger-Tor-Platz 10, 8 Munich 2, Germany
OM	Omega Music Co., 1841 Broadway, New York, New York 10023
OxU	Oxford University Press, Inc., 200 Madison Ave., New York, New York 10016
Pan	Panton, Ricni 12, Prague, Czechoslovakia
Pat	Paterson's Publications Ltd., 38-40 Wigmore St., London WIHOEX, England (CF)
Pax	W. Paxton & Co., Ltd., 36-38 Dean St., Soho, WIV 6EP, London, England
PDS	Professional Drum Shop, Inc., 854 Vine St., Hollywood, California 90038
Pel	Pelikan Musikverlag, CH-8034 Zurich, Switzerland
Pet	C.F. Peters Corporation, 373 Park Ave. South, New York, New York 10016
PG	Ph. Grosch Musikverlag, 8000 Munich 8, Germany
PIC	Peer International Corporation, 1740 Broadway, New York, New York 10019
	P.J. Tonger (See Ton)
PMP	Providence Music Press, P.O. Box 2362, East Side Station, Providence, Rhode Island 02906
Pod	Podium Music, Inc., 4 Broadway, Valhalla, N.Y. 10595
	Theodore Presser (See TP)
Pr A	Pro Art Publications, Inc., 469 Union Ave., Westbury, New York 11590
Pr M	Pro Musica Verlag, Karl-Liebknecht-Strasse 12, 701 Leipzig 1, Germany
PWM	Polskie Wydawnictwo Muxyczne, See "AP"
Pyr	Pyraminx Publications, 358 Aldrich Road, Fairport, New York 14450
RBM	Richard Birnbach Musikverlag, Dürerstrasse 28, 1000 Berlin 45, Germany
R&E	Ries & Erler, Charlottenbrunner Strasse 42, Berlin 33 (Grunewald), Germany (Pet)
Reb	Rebo Music Publications, P.O. Box 9481, 425 East Alameda Ave., Denver, Colorado 80209
Reu	Reuter & Reuter, Stockholm, Sweden
Ric	G. Ricordi & Co., Via Salomone 77, Rome, Italy (FrC)
Roc	Rochester Music Publishers, Inc., 358 Aldrich Road, Fairport, New York 14450
Ron	Rongwen Music, Inc., 56 West 45th St., New York, New York 10036
RS	Richard Schauer, 67 Belsize Lane, Hampstead, London NW3 5AX, England
Rub	Rubank, Inc., 16215 N.W. 15th Ave., Miami, Florida 33169
RuE	Rud. Erdmann, Postfach 471, Wiesbaden, Germany
S-B	Summy-Birchard Co., 1834 Ridge Ave., Evanston, Illinois 60204
S&C	Schott & Co. Ltd., 48 Great Marlborough St., London W.1, England (AMP)
ScF	Schott, Frères, 30, Rue Saint-Jean, Bruxelles 1, Belgium (Pet)
Sch	G. Schirmer, Inc., 866 Third Ave., New York, New York 10022
	E.C. Schirmer (See ECS)
	J. Schuberth (See JS)
SD	Stichting Donemus, Jacob Obrechtstraat 51, Amsterdam, Holland (Pet)
See	Seesaw Music Corp. 177 East 87th St., New York, New York 10028
SF	Sam Fox Music Sales Corporation, 1540 Broadway, New York, New York 10036
	S.A.R.L. Gras Frères (See GrF)
Sha	Shawnee Press, Inc., Delaware Water Gap, Pennsylvania 18327
Sh B	Shapiro, Bernstein & Co. Inc., 666 Fifth Ave., New York, New York 10019
SHF	Slovenský Hudobný Fond, Gorkého 19, Bratislava, Czechoslovakia
SHM	Schmitt, Hall & McCreary Co., 527 Park Ave., Minneapolis, Minnesota 55415
Sid	Sidem Editions, 8 rue de Hesse, Geneva, Switzerland
Sim	N. Simrock, Werderstrasse 44, Hamburg 13, Germany (AMP)
SLP	Swing Lane Publications, Box 128, Beverly, New Jersey
SM	Southern Music Co., P.O. Box 329, San Antonio, Texas 78292
SMP	Southern Music Publishing Co., Inc., 1740 Broadway, New York, New York 10019
SPD	The Society for Publishing Danish Music, Graabrodretorv 7, 1154 Copenhagen, Denmark (Pet)
Spr	Spratt Music Publishers, 17 West 60th St., New York, New York 10023
SS	B Schott's Söhne, Weihergarten 1-9, 65 Mainz, Germany
Sta	Staff Music Publishing Co., Inc., 17 West 60th St., New York, New York 10023
STI	STIMS Informationscentral för Svensk Musik, Tegnérlunden 3, 111 85 Stockholm, Sweden
StM	Standard Music Publishing, Inc., P.O. Box 1043 - Whitman Square, Turnersville, New Jersey 08012
S-V	Sirius-Verlag, Wiclefstrasse 67, Berlin 21, Germany
	T.G. Harms (See Har)
Tem	Tempo Music Publications, Inc., P.O. Box 129, Chicago, Illinois 60690
Ten	Tenuto Publications, c/o Theodore Presser Co., Bryn Mawr, Pennsylvaina 19010
T-M	Tierolff-Muziekcentrale, Markt 90/92, Roosendaal, Netherlands (HE1)
Ton	P.J. Tonger Musikverlag, Bergstrasse 10, 5038 Rodenkirchen/Rhein, Germany (Pet)

TP   Theodore Presser Co., Bryn Mawr, Pennsylvania 19010
      T.P. Harms (See Har)
Tri   Tritone Press, c/o Theodore Presser Co., Bryn Mawr, Pennsylvania 19010
TRY   TRY Publications, 854 Vine St., Hollywood, California 90038
UE   Universal Edition, Karlsplatz 6, Wien 1, Austria .
UME   Union Musical Espanola, Carrera de San Jeronimo 26, y Arenal, 18 Madrid 14, Spain (AMP)
UMI   Universal Musical Instrument Co., 732 Broadway, New York, New York
Uni   University Music Press, P.O. Box 1267, Ann Arbor, Michigan 48103
Vol   Volkwein Bros., Inc., 117 Sandusky St., Pittsburgh, Pennsylvania 15212
      W. Paxton (See Pax)
War   Warner Bros. Music, 60 Metro Blvd., East Rutherford, New Jersey 07073
Wat   Waterloo Music Co. Ltd., 3 Regina St. N., Waterloo, Ontario, Canada
Wel   Weltmusik Edition International, Seilergasse 12, Wien 1/15, Austria
Wes   Western International Music, Inc., 2859 Holt Ave., Los Angeles, California 90034
WH   Wilhelm Hansen Musik-Forlag, Gothersgade 9-11, 1123 Copenhagen, Denmark (Sch)
WIN   W.I.N.D.S., Box 513, Northridge, California 91324
Wit   Witmark, 619 W. 54th St., New York, New York 10019 (War)
WLP   World Library Publications, 2145 Central Parkway, Cincinnati, Ohio 45214
WMS   Willy Müller - Süddeutscher Musikverlag, Marzgasse 5, Heidelberg, Germany (Pet)
WZ   Wilhelm Zimmermann Musikverlag, Zeppelinallee 21, 6000 Frankfurt, Germany (Pet)
YM   Ybarra Music, Box 665, Lemon Grove, California 92045
Za   Zalo Publications, P.O. Box 913, Bloomington, Indiana 47401
      G. Zanibon (See GZ)